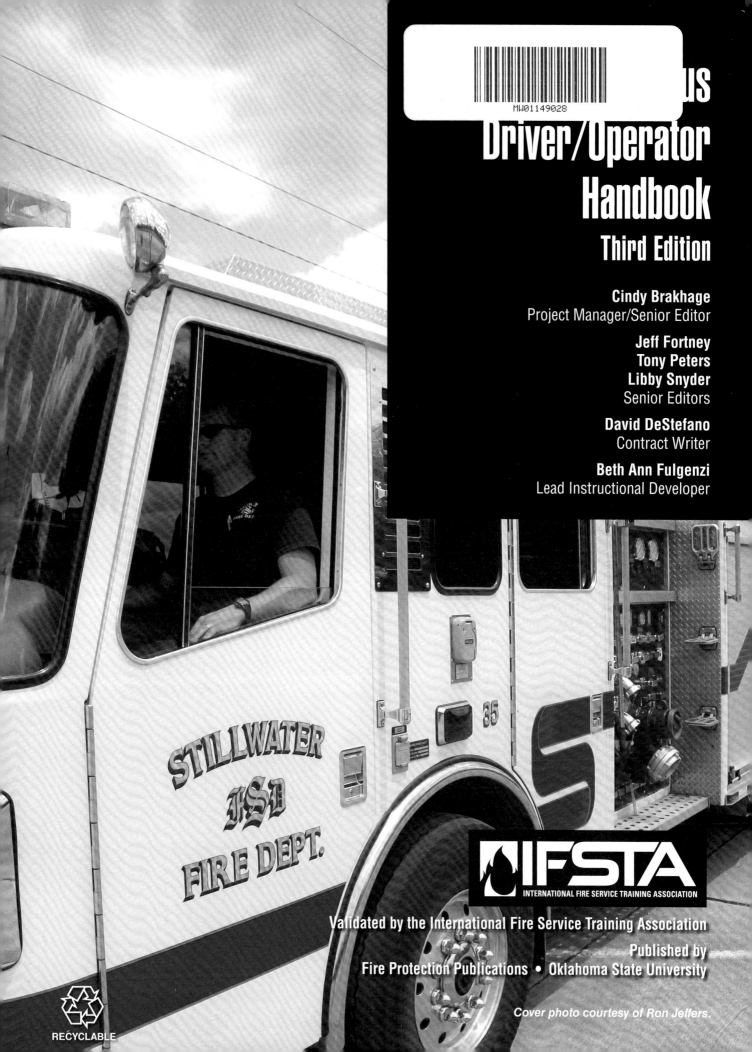

Pumping Apparatus Driver/Operator Handbook
Third Edition

Cindy Brakhage
Project Manager/Senior Editor

Jeff Fortney
Tony Peters
Libby Snyder
Senior Editors

David DeStefano
Contract Writer

Beth Ann Fulgenzi
Lead Instructional Developer

Validated by the International Fire Service Training Association

Published by
Fire Protection Publications • Oklahoma State University

Cover photo courtesy of Ron Jeffers.

RECYCLABLE

The International Fire Service Training Association (IFSTA) was established in 1934 as a *nonprofit educational association of fire fighting personnel who are dedicated to upgrading fire fighting techniques and safety through training.* To carry out the mission of IFSTA, Fire Protection Publications was established as an entity of Oklahoma State University. Fire Protection Publications' primary function is to publish and distribute training materials as proposed, developed, and validated by IFSTA. As a secondary function, Fire Protection Publications researches, acquires, produces, and markets high-quality learning and teaching aids consistent with IFSTA's mission.

IFSTA holds two meetings each year: the Winter Meeting in January and the Annual Validation Conference in July. During these meetings, committees of technical experts review draft materials and ensure that the professional qualifications of the National Fire Protection Association® standards are met. These conferences bring together individuals from several related and allied fields, such as:

- Key fire department executives, training officers, and personnel
- Educators from colleges and universities
- Representatives from governmental agencies
- Delegates of firefighter associations and industrial organizations

Committee members are not paid nor are they reimbursed for their expenses by IFSTA or Fire Protection Publications. They participate because of a commitment to the fire service and its future through training. Being on a committee is prestigious in the fire service community, and committee members are acknowledged leaders in their fields. This unique feature provides a close relationship between IFSTA and the fire service community.

IFSTA manuals have been adopted as the official teaching texts of many states and provinces of North America as well as numerous U.S. and Canadian government agencies. Besides the NFPA® requirements, IFSTA manuals are also written to meet the Fire and Emergency Services Higher Education (FESHE) course requirements. A number of the manuals have been translated into other languages to provide training for fire and emergency service personnel in Canada, Mexico, and outside of North America.

ISBN 978-0-87939-574-2   Library of Congress Control Number: 2014958246

Third Edition, First Printing, January 2015   *Printed in the United States of America*

10   9   8   7   6   5   4

If you need additional information concerning the International Fire Service Training Association (IFSTA) or Fire Protection Publications, contact:

Customer Service, Fire Protection Publications, Oklahoma State University

930 North Willis, Stillwater, OK 74078-8045

800-654-4055   Fax: 405-744-8204

For assistance with training materials, to recommend material for inclusion in an IFSTA manual, or to ask questions or comment on manual content, contact:

Editorial Department, Fire Protection Publications, Oklahoma State University

930 North Willis, Stillwater, OK 74078-8045

405-744-4111   Fax: 405-744-4112   E-mail: editors@osufpp.org

Chapter Summary

Table of Contents

List of Tables

Acknowledgements

The third edition of the IFSTA **Pumping Apparatus Driver/Operator Handbook** is designed to educate driver/operators who are responsible for operating apparatus equipped with fire pumps. The information in this manual aids the driver/operator in meeting the objectives found in Chapters 4, 5, and 10 of NFPA® 1002, *Standard for Fire Apparatus Driver/Operator Professional Qualifications* (2014 Edition).

Acknowledgement and special thanks are extended to the members of the IFSTA validating committee who contributed their time, wisdom, and knowledge to the development of this manual.

IFSTA Pumping Apparatus Driver/Operator Handbook
Third Edition Validation Committee

Chair
Robert H. Noll
Chief (Emeritus)
Yukon (OK) Fire Department
Yukon, OK

Vice Chair
Randal Klaybor, Retired
Captain
West Allis (WI) Fire Department
West Allis, WI

Secretary
David Bullard
Lieutenant
Columbia County (GA) Fire Rescue
Martinez, GA

Committee Members

Doug Allen
Fire Department Shift Command
Ames (IA) Fire Department
Ames, IA

Michael Boub
Apparatus Technician
Fairfax County Fire and Rescue
Fairfax, VA

Kris Cooper
Deputy Fire Marshal
Colorado Springs (CO) Fire Department
Colorado Springs, CO

Rommie L. Duckworth
Lieutenant
Ridgefield (CT) Fire Department
Ridgefield, CT

Tim Frankenberg
Deputy Chief
Washington (MO) Fire Department
Washington, MO

Jerry Hallbauer, Retired
Program Manager
Kansas Fire and Rescue Training Institute
Lawrence, KS

Michael Mallory
Chief of Physical Resources
City of Tulsa (OK) Fire Department
Tulsa, OK

Brent Meisenheimer
Lieutenant
Austin (TX) Fire Department
Austin, TX

Michael G. Miles
Deputy Chief
Division of Homeland Security and Emergency
    Services
Office of Fire Prevention and Control
Fire Operations and Training Branch
Guilford, NY

Brian Morrow
Assistant Chief, Operations
Orange County (FL) Fire Rescue
Winter Park, FL

Wayne Sandford
Professor of Fire Science
University of New Haven
West Haven, CT

Much appreciation is given to the following individuals and organizations for contributing information, photographs, and technical assistance instrumental in the development of this manual:

Alva (OK) Fire Department
    Bryan S. Miller

Ardmore (OK) Airpark Fire Department
    Ricky Prince

Ardmore (OK) Fire Department
    Brandon Spencer

Bethany (OK) Fire Department
    Josh Morgan

Bob Esposito

Chicago Fire Department

Chris Mickal

Cushing (OK) Fire Department
    Levi D. Collier
    Joseph Hale
    Mark Beitz

Deer Creek (OK) Fire Department
    Kory Hudelson

Edmond (OK) Fire Department
    Barry Garrett
    Bud Vandewalker
    Casey Stewart
    Jeremy Gary
    Ryan Gleghorn

El Reno (OK) Fire Department
    A.J. Hunter
    Brandon Faulk
    David Baker
    Nathan Plagg
    Slade Terry

FAMA

James Nilo

Las Vegas Fire and Rescue
    Bradley Iverson
    Corey Rice
    Craig Cooper
    Dale Branks
    Dennis Larkin
    Dustin Schelin
    Jason Williams
    June Egi
    Mark Zuniga

Robert Pitts
Stephen Hansen
Tim Burns
Tim Garrett
Timothy R. Szymanski
Travis Story

Midwest City (OK) Fire Department
    Nathan LeClaire

Mustang (OK) Fire Department
    Andrew Willrath
    Christopher Edwards

Mike Mallory

Monterey County Training Officers

Newcastle (OK) Fire Department
    Jeremy Walker

Norman (OK) Fire Department
    Aubrey Hale
    Chris Messner
    Joel Gerber

OSU Fire Service Training
    Courtney Powell

Perkins (OK) Fire Department
    John Konrad

Ron Jeffers

Shad Cooper/Wyoming State Fire Marshal's Office

Steve Lofton

Stillwater (OK) Fire Department
    Derek Baez
    Don Dominick
    Greg Connelly
    Rick Rogers
    Thomas Tharp

Tahlequah (OK) Fire Department
    Aaron Garrett

Tarrant County College
Fort Worth, Texas
    Allen Richards
    Frank Becerra
    Jacob Smith
    James Craft
    Kurt Howard

Robert Simmons
Steve Keller

Ted Boothroyd

Trident Emergency Products, LLC

Warr Acres (OK) Fire Department
Daniel Cota

Williams Fire and Hazard Control Inc.
Brent Gaspard
Yukon (OK) Fire Department
Brad Pappe
Jeremy Goodrich
Rudy Sanchez

Last, but certainly not least, gratitude is extended to the following members of the Fire Protection Publications staff whose excellent contributions made the final publication of this manual possible.

IFSTA Pumping Apparatus Driver/Operator Handbook
3rd Edition, Project Team

Project Manager
Cindy Brakhage, Senior Editor

Contract Writer
David DeStefano
Captain
North Providence (Rhode Island) Fire Department
North Providence, Rhode Island

Curriculum Manager
Lori Raborg

Editorial Manager
Clint Clausing

Production Coordinator
Ann Moffat

Editors
Jeff Fortney, Senior Editor
Libby Snyder, Senior Editor
Tony Peters, Senior Editor

Illustrators and Layout Designers
Ann Moffat, Production Coordinator
Errick Braggs, Senior Graphic Designer
Ben Brock, Senior Graphic Designer

Curriculum Development
Beth Ann Fulgenzi, Curriculum Developer
Lori Raborg, Curriculum Manager

Photographers
Clint Clausing, Editorial Manager
Jeff Fortney, Senior Editor
Leslie A. Miller, Senior Editor
Mike Wieder, Associate Director
Tony Peters, Senior Editor
Veronica Smith, Senior Editor

Technical Reviewer
Tracy Gray
Conferences and Special Projects Assistant
University of Missouri, Fire and Rescue Training
  Institute
Columbia, Missouri

Editorial Staff
Tara Gladden, Editorial Assistant

Indexer
Nancy Kopper

The IFSTA Executive Board at the time of validation of the IFSTA **Pumping Apparatus Driver/Operator Handbook** Third Edition was as follows:

IFSTA Executive Board

Executive Board Chair
Steve Ashbrock
Fire Chief
Madeira & Indian Hill Fire Department
Cincinnati, OH

Vice Chair
Bradd Clark
Fire Chief
Ocala Fire Department
Ocala, FL

Executive Director
Mike Wieder
Fire Protection Publications
Stillwater, Oklahoma

Board Members

Steve Austin
Past President
Cumberland Valley Volunteer FF Association
Newark, DE

Claude Beauchamp
Director
Institute of Emergency and Judicial Services
Ottawa, Canada

Roxanne Bercik
Deputy Chief of Training and Support Bureau
Los Angeles Fire Department
Los Angeles, CA

Mary Cameli
Assistant Chief
City of Mesa Fire Department
Mesa, AZ

Chief Dennis Compton
Chairman
National Fallen Firefighters Foundation
Mesa, AZ

John Cunningham
Executive Director
Nova Scotia Firefighter's School
Waverly, NS, Canada

John Hoglund
Director Emeritus
Maryland Fire & Rescue Institute
New Carrollton, MD

Wes Kitchel
Assistant Chief
Sonoma County Fire & Emergency Services
Cloverdale, CA

Brett Lacey
Fire Marshal
Colorado Springs Fire Department
Colorado Springs, CO

Lori Moore-Merrell
Assistant to the General President
International Association of Fire Fighters
Washington, DC

Jeff Morrissette
State Fire Administrator
State of Connecticut Commission on Fire Prevention and Control
Windsor Locks, CT

Josh Stefancic
Assistant Chief
City of Largo Fire Department
Largo, FL

Paul Valentine
Senior Engineer
Nexus Engineering
Oakbrook, IL

Steven Westermann
Fire Chief
Central Jackson County Fire Protection District
Blue Springs, MO

Introduction

Introduction Contents

Introduction

Driver/operators of pumping and aerial apparatus have vast responsibilities and include:

- Performing inspections and basic maintenance to ensure that the apparatus is working properly and safely

- Ensuring the safety of all personnel riding in the apparatus while it is in motion

- Driving the apparatus to and from the emergency scene safely

- Positioning the apparatus appropriately to maximize effectiveness when on the scene

- Operating apparatus equipment and components safely

Because of the many hazards involved with moving aerial devices, hydraulic pressures, nozzle reactions, and other forces involved, the driver/operator is also responsible for the safety of personnel who are operating near the apparatus. These responsibilities require driver/operators to complete an extensive training program to be capable of performing their duties.

Purpose and Scope

This 3rd Edition of the **Pumping Apparatus Driver/Operator Handbook** is designed to educate driver/operators who are responsible for operating apparatus equipped with fire pumps. The information in this manual aids the driver/operator in meeting the objectives found in Chapters 4, 5, and 10 of NFPA® 1002, *Standard for Fire Apparatus Driver/Operator Professional Qualifications* (2014 and 2017 Editions).

The purpose of this manual is to present general principles of pump operation, along with the application of those principles wherever feasible. It is also to guide the driver/operator in the proper operation and care of apparatus. This manual includes an overview of the qualities and skills needed by driver/operators, including safe driving techniques, types of pumping apparatus, positioning apparatus to maximize efficiency and water supply, fire pump theory and operation, hydraulic calculations, water shuttle procedures, foam systems operations, and apparatus maintenance and testing.

Information relevant to driver/operators of both pumping and aerial apparatus is contained in Chapters 1-3 of the **Pumping Apparatus Driver/Operator**

Handbook: Chapter 1, Types of Apparatus Equipped with a Pump; Chapter 2, Apparatus Inspection and Maintenance; and Chapter 3, Apparatus Safety and Operating Emergency Vehicles.

The extended version of this manual, **Pumping and Aerial Apparatus Driver/ Operator Handbook**, includes aerial-specific information in chapters 16-20 written for aerial apparatus driver/operators. The additional chapters are designed to educate driver/operators responsible for operating fire apparatus equipped with aerial devices, which include aerial ladders, aerial ladder platforms, articulating elevating platforms, telescoping elevating platforms, and water towers.

Pumping and Aerial Apparatus Driver/Operator 3rd Edition includes all the information necessary to meet the job performance requirements contained in NFPA® 1002, *Standard for Fire Apparatus Driver/Operator Professional Qualifications* (2014 and 2017 Editions), Chapters 4, 6, and 7. The additional chapters provide an overview of the qualities and skills needed by the driver/ operator, safe driving techniques, types of aerial apparatus, positioning of the aerial apparatus, vehicle stabilization, the operation of telescoping and articulating aerial devices, fire fighting tactics as they apply to the use of aerial devices, and apparatus maintenance and testing.

The Chapter Addendum covers material added to NFPA® 1002 in the 2017 Edition. Each Edition of the book includes the Chapter Addendum. The Addendum has a unique page numbering system. Regular page numbering resumes in the book following the Chapter Addendum.

Book Organization

Each chapter begins with a list of Chapter Contents, Key Terms with page numbers, NFPA® Job Performance Requirements, and Chapter Objectives. Each chapter contains a case history, key terms with definitions, chapter summary, and review questions. Skill Sheet steps are referenced in the chapter text and provided in full at the end of the chapter. Also included in each manual is Appendix A, which is the NFPA® Job Performance Requirements (JPRs) with Chapter and Page References. A Glossary and an Index are the final parts of the manual.

Terminology

This manual is written with a global, international audience in mind. For this reason, it often uses general descriptive language in place of regional- or agency-specific terminology (often referred to as *jargon*). Additionally, in order to keep sentences uncluttered and easy to read, the word *state* is used to represent both state and provincial level governments (and their equivalent). This usage is applied to this manual for the purposes of brevity and is not intended to address or show preference for only one nation's method of identifying regional governments within its borders.

The glossary at the end of the manual will assist the reader in understanding words that may not have their roots in the fire and emergency services. The source for the definitions of fire-and-emergency-services-related terms is the IFSTA **Fire Service Orientation and Terminology** manual.

Resources

Additional educational resources to supplement this manual are available from IFSTA and Fire Protection Publications (FPP). The operation of aircraft and rescue fire fighting (ARFF) apparatus (NFPA® 1002, Chapter 9) is covered in the IFSTA **Aircraft Rescue and Fire Fighting** manual. Operation of apparatus equipped with aerial devices is covered in the IFSTA **Pumping and Aerial Apparatus Driver/Operator** manual. Support products are available for both manuals..

Key Information

Various types of information in this book are given in shaded boxes marked by symbols or icons. See the following definitions:

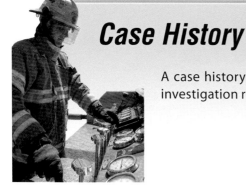

Case History

A case history analyzes an event. It can describe its development, action taken, investigation results, and lessons learned.

Safety Alert

Safety alert boxes are used to highlight information that is important for safety reasons. (In the text, the title of safety alerts will change to reflect the content.)

Parked Regeneration Hazards

Parked regeneration causes high exhaust gas temperatures at zero vehicle speed. Keep personnel away from exhaust outlet to avoid serious burns and injury. Do not perform parked regeneration while connected to an exhaust extraction system. Damage to the exhaust extraction system may result.

Information

Information boxes give facts that are complete in themselves but belong with the text discussion. It is information that needs more emphasis or separation. (In the text, the title of information boxes will change to reflect the content.)

Right-of-Way

Emergency vehicles on response have the right-of-way; however, this is not an excuse for a driver/operator getting into a collision. Proper situational awareness involves allowing the right-of-way if doing so decreases the chance of a collision.

It is best to anticipate unpredictable behavior from other drivers during emergency response. Emergency lights, sirens, and horns are a request for other drivers to yield to the emergency vehicle. Driver/operators must recognize that some motorists may not grant the right-of-way.

What This Means to You

These boxes take information presented in the text and synthesize it into an example of how the information is relevant to (or will be applied by) the intended audience, essentially answering the question, "What does this mean to you?"

What This Means to You

The ultimate mission of any emergency response vehicle is to safeguard the health and welfare of the people it is meant to protect. This mission fails if the emergency responders themselves do not arrive safely. It is therefore essential that you drive the apparatus in a safe manner and that all occupants are seated and belted while the vehicle is in motion. During emergency responses, personnel may be inclined to take more risks than usual and to skip basic vehicle safety precautions. Resist this inclination. For example, it is important to don gear in the station before getting into the apparatus so that there is no need or temptation to unbuckle the seat belt. If a vehicle is in a crash, anyone who is unbelted becomes a hazard to anyone else in the vehicle. An unbelted occupant will become a lethal projectile with the potential to injure or kill those around them.

Key Term

A **key term** is designed to emphasize key concepts, technical terms, or ideas that the driver/operator needs to know. Key terms are listed at the beginning of each chapter and the definition is placed in the margin for easy reference.

Overthrottling — Process of injecting or supplying the diesel engine with more fuel than can be burned.

Signal Words

Three key signal words are found in the book: **WARNING**, **CAUTION**, and **NOTE**. Definitions and examples of each are as follows:

- **WARNING** indicates information that could result in death or serious injury to the driver/operator. See the following example:

WARNING!
Firefighters must never ride on the outside of a moving apparatus for any reason. Serious injury or death could occur if the apparatus is involved in a collision or rollover or if the firefighter falls from the moving apparatus.

- **CAUTION** indicates important information or data that the driver/operator needs to be aware of in order to perform his or her duties safely. See the following example:

CAUTION
On high-speed roadways, apparatus should not be driven against the normal flow of traffic unless the road has been cleared by law enforcement officials for that purpose.

- **NOTE** indicates important operational information that helps explain why a particular recommendation is given or describes optional methods for certain procedures. See the following example:

NOTE: It is recommended that aerial apparatus carry voltage detectors.

FAMA Safety Signage

In appropriate locations, this book provides examples of Fire Apparatus Manufacturers Association (FAMA) safety signage to be used on newly manufactured pumping and aerial apparatus. Driver/operators may see these signs on their apparatus as well as in the manual:

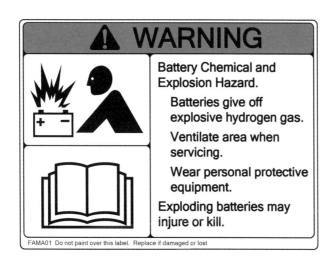

Pumping Formula Examples, Tables, Figures, and Conversions

Driver/operators must consider the effects of friction loss on hose layouts. Identifying variables such as pressure loss due to elevation, appliances, and other factors is a necessary part of the driver/operator's duties.

The theoretical calculations contained in Chapter 7, Theoretical Pressure Calculations, are rarely performed by driver/operators on the fireground. The methods explained in Chapter 9, Fire Pump Theory, are more likely to be used due to the dynamic nature of fire fighting. However, driver/operators should have the ability to calculate theoretical friction loss because understanding the factors that influence flow rates gives driver/operators the following advantages:

- Provides a better understanding of the basis for the methods used in Chapter 9.
- Allows driver/operators to predetermine approximate pump discharge pressures for pre-connected hoselines and common hose lays for the apparatus and district to which they are assigned.
- Provides the ability to conduct preincident planning of hose deployment at target hazards, or unusual occupancies in the jurisdiction.

For safe and efficient operations on the fireground, driver/operators must be able to develop proper pump discharge pressure for specific fire streams. This manual provides foundational knowledge for a driver/operator to consider friction loss when calculating pump discharge pressure.

Metric Conversions

All metrics in IFSTA publications follow a document titled "Training Guidelines for the Metric Conversion of Fire Departments in Canada." The NFPA® does not follow these guidelines. This may result in some differences in what a particular size hose is called in metric terms.

Throughout this manual, U.S. units of measure are converted to metric units for the convenience of our international readers. Be advised that we use the Canadian metric system. It is very similar to the Standard International system, but may have some variation.

We adhere to the following guidelines for metric conversions in this manual:

- Metric conversions are approximated unless the number is used in mathematical equations.
- Centimeters are not used because they are not part of the Canadian metric standard.
- Exact conversions are used when an exact number is necessary such as in construction measurements or hydraulic calculations.
- Set values such as hose diameter, ladder length, and nozzle size use their Canadian counterpart naming conventions and are not mathematically calculated. For example, 1 ½ inch hose is referred to as 38 mm hose.

The following two tables provide detailed information on IFSTA's conversion conventions. The first table includes examples of our conversion factors for a number of measurements used in the fire service. The second shows examples of exact conversions beside the approximated measurements you will see in this manual.

U.S. to Canadian Measurement Conversion

Measurements	Customary (U.S.)	Metric (Canada)	Conversion Factor
Length/Distance	Inch (in) Foot (ft) [3 or less feet] Foot (ft) [3 or more feet] Mile (mi)	Millimeter (mm) Millimeter (mm) Meter (m) Kilometer (km)	1 in = 25 mm 1 ft = 300 mm 1 ft = 0.3 m 1 mi = 1.6 km
Area	Square Foot (ft^2) Square Mile (mi^2)	Square Meter (m^2) Square Kilometer (km^2)	1 ft^2 = 0.09 m^2 1 mi^2 = 2.6 km^2
Mass/Weight	Dry Ounce (oz) Pound (lb) Ton (T)	gram Kilogram (kg) Ton (T)	1 oz = 28 g 1 lb = 0.5 kg 1 T = 0.9 T
Volume	Cubic Foot (ft^3) Fluid Ounce (fl oz) Quart (qt) Gallon (gal)	Cubic Meter (m^3) Milliliter (mL) Liter (L) Liter (L)	1 ft^3 = 0.03 m^3 1 fl oz = 30 mL 1 qt = 1 L 1 gal = 4 L
Flow	Gallons per Minute (gpm) Cubic Foot per Minute (ft^3/min)	Liters per Minute (L/min) Cubic Meter per Minute (m^3/min)	1 gpm = 4 L/min 1 ft^3/min = 0.03 m^3/min
Flow per Area	Gallons per Minute per Square Foot (gpm/ft^2)	Liters per Square Meters Minute (L/(m^2.min))	1 gpm/ft^2 = 40 L/(m^2.min)
Pressure	Pounds per Square Inch (psi) Pounds per Square Foot (psf) Inches of Mercury (in Hg)	Kilopascal (kPa) Kilopascal (kPa) Kilopascal (kPa)	1 psi = 7 kPa 1 psf = .05 kPa 1 in Hg = 3.4 kPa
Speed/Velocity	Miles per Hour (mph) Feet per Second (ft/sec)	Kilometers per Hour (km/h) Meter per Second (m/s)	1 mph = 1.6 km/h 1 ft/sec = 0.3 m/s
Heat	British Thermal Unit (Btu)	Kilojoule (kJ)	1 Btu = 1 kJ
Heat Flow	British Thermal Unit per Minute (BTU/min)	watt (W)	1 Btu/min = 18 W
Density	Pound per Cubic Foot (lb/ft^3)	Kilogram per Cubic Meter (kg/m^3)	1 lb/ft^3 = 16 kg/m^3
Force	Pound-Force (lbf)	Newton (N)	1 lbf = 0.5 N
Torque	Pound-Force Foot (lbf ft)	Newton Meter (N.m)	1 lbf ft = 1.4 N.m
Dynamic Viscosity	Pound per Foot-Second (lb/ft.s)	Pascal Second (Pa.s)	1 lb/ft.s = 1.5 Pa.s
Surface Tension	Pound per Foot (lb/ft)	Newton per Meter (N/m)	1 lb/ft = 15 N/m

Conversion and Approximation Examples

Measurement	U.S. Unit	Conversion Factor	Exact S.I. Unit	Rounded S.I. Unit
Length/Distance	10 in 25 in 2 ft 17 ft 3 mi 10 mi	1 in = 25 mm 1 in = 25 mm 1 in = 25 mm 1 ft = 0.3 m 1 mi = 1.6 km 1 mi = 1.6 km	250 mm 625 mm 600 mm 5.1 m 4.8 km 16 km	250 mm 625 mm 600 mm 5 m 5 km 16 km
Area	36 ft^2 300 ft^2 5 mi^2 14 mi^2	1 ft^2 = 0.09 m^2 1 ft^2 = 0.09 m^2 1 mi^2 = 2.6 km^2 1 mi^2 = 2.6 km^2	3.24 m^2 27 m^2 13 km^2 36.4 km^2	3 m^2 30 m^2 13 km^2 35 km^2
Mass/Weight	16 oz 20 oz 3.75 lb 2,000 lb 1 T 2.5 T	1 oz = 28 g 1 oz = 28 g 1 lb = 0.5 kg 1 lb = 0.5 kg 1 T = 0.9 T 1 T = 0.9 T	448 g 560 g 1.875 kg 1 000 kg 900 kg 2.25 T	450 g 560 g 2 kg 1 000 kg 900 kg 2 T
Volume	55 ft^3 2,000 ft^3 8 fl oz 20 fl oz 10 qt 22 gal 500 gal	1 ft^3 = 0.03 m^3 1 ft^3 = 0.03 m^3 1 fl oz = 30 mL 1 fl oz = 30 mL 1 qt = 1 L 1 gal = 4 L 1 gal = 4 L	1.65 m^3 60 m^3 240 mL 600 mL 10 L 88 L 2 000 L	1.5 m^3 60 m^3 240 mL 600 mL 10 L 90 L 2 000 L
Flow	100 gpm 500 gpm 16 ft^3/min 200 ft^3/min	1 gpm = 4 L/min 1 gpm = 4 L/min 1 ft^3/min = 0.03 m^3/min 1 ft^3/min = 0.03 m^3/min	400 L/min 2 000 L/min 0.48 m^3/min 6 m^3/min	400 L/min 2 000 L/min 0.5 m^3/min 6 m^3/min
Flow per Area	50 gpm/ft^2 326 gpm/ft^2	1 gpm/ft^2 = 40 L/(m^2.min) 1 gpm/ft^2 = 40 L/(m^2.min)	2 000 L/(m^2.min) 13 040 L/(m^2.min)	2 000 L/(m^2.min) 13 000L/(m^2.min)
Pressure	100 psi 175 psi 526 psf 12,000 psf 5 psi in Hg 20 psi in Hg	1 psi = 7 kPa 1 psi = 7 kPa 1 psf = 0.05 kPa 1 psf = 0.05 kPa 1 psi = 3.4 kPa 1 psi = 3.4 kPa	700 kPa 1225 kPa 26.3 kPa 600 kPa 17 kPa 68 kPa	700 kPa 1 200 kPa 25 kPa 600 kPa 17 kPa 70 kPa
Speed/Velocity	20 mph 35 mph 10 ft/sec 50 ft/sec	1 mph = 1.6 km/h 1 mph = 1.6 km/h 1 ft/sec = 0.3 m/s 1 ft/sec = 0.3 m/s	32 km/h 56 km/h 3 m/s 15 m/s	30 km/h 55 km/h 3 m/s 15 m/s
Heat	1200 Btu	1 Btu = 1 kJ	1 200 kJ	1 200 kJ
Heat Flow	5 BTU/min 400 BTU/min	1 Btu/min = 18 W 1 Btu/min = 18 W	90 W 7 200 W	90 W 7 200 W
Density	5 lb/ft^3 48 lb/ft^3	1 lb/ft^3 = 16 kg/m^3 1 lb/ft^3 = 16 kg/m^3	80 kg/m^3 768 kg/m^3	80 kg/m^3 770 kg/m^3
Force	10 lbf 1,500 lbf	1 lbf = 0.5 N 1 lbf = 0.5 N	5 N 750 N	5 N 750 N
Torque	100 500	1 lbf ft = 1.4 N.m 1 lbf ft = 1.4 N.m	140 N.m 700 N.m	140 N.m 700 N.m
Dynamic Viscosity	20 lb/ft.s 35 lb/ft.s	1 lb/ft.s = 1.5 Pa.s 1 lb/ft.s = 1.5 Pa.s	30 Pa.s 52.5 Pa.s	30 Pa.s 50 Pa.s
Surface Tension	6.5 lb/ft 10 lb/ft	1 lb/ft = 15 N/m 1 lb/ft = 15 N/m	97.5 N/m 150 N/m	100 N/m 150 N/m

Types of Apparatus Equipped with a Pump

Courtesy of Ron Jeffers.

Chapter Contents

chapter 1

Key Terms

Learning Objectives

After reading this chapter, students will be able to:

1. Describe fire department pumpers.

2. Describe initial attack fire apparatus.

3. Describe mobile water supply apparatus.

4. Distinguish among specialty fire apparatus.

5. Identify apparatus-mounted special systems.

Chapter 1
Types of Apparatus
Equipped with a Pump

Case History

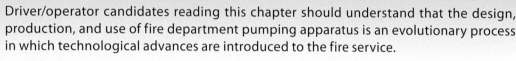

Driver/operator candidates reading this chapter should understand that the design, production, and use of fire department pumping apparatus is an evolutionary process in which technological advances are introduced to the fire service.

With the invention of the siphon pump used during Roman times to the advent of the first pieces of sewn leather fire hose in Holland during the late 1600s, fire fighting capabilities have advanced as better equipment and tactics have developed. Hand tub apparatus like the Newsham engine gave way to the horse drawn steam engine and finally motorized fire apparatus.

While pumpers of a generation ago may have carried hose, a few nozzles, and ground ladders, the many configurations, special applications, and wide variety of equipment carried on modern pumpers are a direct result of adapting evolving technology to the expanding mission of the fire service.

Pumping apparatus capable of supporting extrication or technical rescue incidents as well as providing scene lighting and electrical power are now commonly found in many jurisdictions. The driver/operator must often be proficient in the operation of many types of specialized equipment as well as safely driving the apparatus and operating the fire pump.

Fire apparatus are classified according to the primary function for which they are designed. This chapter describes various types of apparatus that are equipped with a fire pump. Some of these vehicles feature additional systems such as aerial devices or rescue tool systems. The fire department pumper is the core unit of the fire service and is sometimes expected to fill several roles such as rescue, hazardous materials (haz mat), or medical responses.

Fire Department Pumpers

The main purpose of a fire department pumper is to provide adequate water pressure for effective fire streams. The water source may be the apparatus internal water tank, a fire hydrant, or a static water source such as a lake or portable water tank **(Figure 1.1)**.

Figure 1.1 The pumper's water source is this fire hydrant. *Courtesy of Ron Jeffers.*

Common Pumper Requirements and Equipment

NFPA® 1901, *Standard for Automotive Fire Apparatus*, contains the requirements of pumper design. The standard specifies a minimum pump capacity of 750 gpm (3 000 L/min) and a water tank with a capacity of at least 300 gallons (1 200 L). Pump capacities larger than 750 gpm (3 000 L/min) increase in increments of 250 gpm (1 000 L/min) with most municipal fire departments operating pumpers of 2,000 gpm (8 000 L/min) or less. There are, however, many pumpers in service with industrial fire departments that exceed 2,000 gpm (8 000 L/min).

In addition to a fire pump, the apparatus must be equipped with intake and discharge pump connections, pump controls and gauges, as well as a variety of hose sizes and types. These hoses include intake, supply, and attack hose. The apparatus will also feature various nozzles and appliances based on local requirements.

Modern fire department pumpers carry a wide variety of portable equipment in addition to that associated with its water supply function (**Figure 1.2**). NFPA® 1901 specifies the minimum portable equipment that must be carried on all fire department pumpers. Each jurisdiction may supplement this equipment based on local practices and conditions. The following list contains equipment commonly found on pumpers:

- Ground ladders
- Self-contained breathing apparatus (SCBA)
- Forcible entry tools
- Salvage tools and equipment
- Portable water tank
- Emergency medical equipment

Rescue Pumper — Specially designed apparatus that combines the functions of both a rescue vehicle and a fire department pumper.

Fire departments may combine some of the functions of a rescue company with a fire department pumper. The apparatus typically used are referred to as **rescue pumpers (Figure 1.3)**. These vehicles are designed with more compartment space than a standard fire department pumper. In addition to standard engine company equipment, rescue pumpers carry medical, rescue, and extrication equipment.

Figure 1.2 A modern fire department pumper carries a variety of portable equipment. *Courtesy of Ron Jeffers.*

Figure 1.3 A rescue pumper combines the functions of both a rescue vehicle and a pumping apparatus. Rescue pumpers carry medical, rescue, and extrication equipment.

Foam Capability

Many fire departments including municipal, airport, wildland, and those serving industrial facilities operate pumpers capable of discharging foam on Class A (ordinary combustible) and/or Class B (flammable and combustible liquid and gas) fires. Many industrial pumpers, while capable of flowing plain water on Class A fires, are also large capacity foam pumpers. These types of apparatus, built based upon the requirements in Chapters 11, 16, and 20 of NFPA® 1901, are operated by members of the facility's industrial fire brigade or department. Some industrial fire brigades and airport fire departments also operate mini-pumpers that have smaller pumping and tank capacity of the full-sized apparatus.

Both municipal and industrial foam pumpers may be equipped with any of the following:

- Around-the-pump, direct injection, balanced pressure foam proportioning systems
- **Compressed air foam systems (CAFS)** (combined with or in addition to another proportioning system)
- Balanced pressure proportioning system (provide reliability of foam proportioning at larger flows)
- Fire pumps ranging in capacity from 750 to 3,000 gpm (3 000 L/min to 12 000 L/min) or greater
- Large onboard tank of foam concentrate (usually found on industrial pumpers) **(Figure 1.4, p. 16)** often contain 500 gallons (2 000 L) or more of foam concentrate
- Large fixed foam/water turret capable of flowing the entire capacity of the fire pump

NOTE: Some apparatus may have foam proportioning systems that exceed the capacity of the apparatus and may be supported by other pumpers.

Compressed Air Foam Systems (CAFS) — Generic term used to describe a high-energy foam-generation system consisting of a water pump, a foam proportioning system, and an air compressor (or other air source) that injects air into the foam solution before it enters a hoseline.

Figure 1.4 This foam unit may contain 500 gallons (2 000 L) or more of foam concentrate. *Courtesy of Ron Jeffers.*

Class A foam systems commonly installed on municipal fire pumpers may be the CAFS types discussed in Chapter 14 of this manual. Often, regardless of the type of foam system installed, only a few discharge outlets are capable of flowing foam solution.

The foam proportioning systems commonly found on municipal fire pumpers are scaled down versions of those used for industrial fire pumpers. Likewise, the foam tanks are correspondingly smaller, usually ranging from 20 to 100 gallons (80 L to 400 L). These tanks are often designed to be refilled directly from 5 gallon (20 L) containers.

NOTE: More detailed information on foam systems may be found in Chapter 14 of this manual.

Elevating Water Devices

Some fire departments operate pumpers equipped with various types of elevating devices to apply fire streams. The articulating or telescoping devices most commonly combined with pumpers generally range in height from 50 to 75 feet (15 to 23 m).

NOTE: More information on the operation of elevating water devices may be found in the expanded version of the **Pumping and Aerial Apparatus Driver/Operator Handbook**.

Initial Attack Fire Apparatus

Many fire departments use scaled-down versions of full-size pumpers, which are called *initial attack fire apparatus*. The specific requirements for the design of initial attack apparatus are detailed in Chapter 6 of NFPA® 1901.

In some regions, the terms **mini-pumper** or **midi-pumper** have come to define pumping apparatus smaller than a full-size pumper. Although these terms are not specifically referenced in NFPA® 1901, some apparatus manufacturers use them to define pumpers with smaller chassis, pump, and agent tank sizes **(Figure 1.5)**. Highly maneuverable apparatus are often used to respond to incidents where access is limited.

Initial Attack Fire Apparatus — Fire apparatus whose primary purpose is to initiate a fire attack on structural and wildland fires and support associated fire department actions. *Also known as* Midi-Pumper or Mini-Pumper.

Mini-Pumper — Small fire apparatus mounted on a pickup-truck-sized chassis, usually with a pump having a rated capacity less than 500 gpm (2 000 L/min). Its primary advantage is speed and mobility, which enables it to respond to fires more rapidly than larger apparatus.

Midi-Pumper — Apparatus sized between a mini-pumper and a full-sized fire department pumper, usually with a gross vehicle weight of 12,000 pounds (6 000 kg) or greater. The midi-pumper has a fire pump with a rated capacity generally not greater than 1,000 gpm (4 000 L/min).

Figure 1.5 A mini-pumper is smaller than a full-size pumping apparatus. *Courtesy of Ron Jeffers.*

Apparatus Typing

The Incident Command System (ICS), as defined by the National Incident Management System (NIMS), categorizes pumping apparatus and mobile water supply apparatus based on capability. This system, called *apparatus typing*, is intended to make it easier for Incident Commanders to call for exactly the types of resources they need to manage an incident. Various agencies, including the Federal Emergency Management Agency and the National Wildfire Coordinating Group, use similar terms. Other terms for apparatus typing may be used in other states or local jurisdictions.

Mobile Water Supply Apparatus

Mobile water supply apparatus, locally known as *water tenders* or *tankers*, are used to transport water to areas where a water system is nonexistent or inadequate **(Figure 1.6, p. 18)**. Although attack pumpers carry an onboard water tank, it is usually insufficient to sustain an extended fire attack. The capacity of mobile water supply apparatus operating in a particular jurisdiction is based on a variety of factors including:

- **Terrain** — Apparatus must be capable of traversing roads in the area, including hills and winding, narrow roads **(Figure 1.7, p. 18)**.

- **Bridge and weight limits** — Bridges in a response area must be capable of supporting the weight of water supply apparatus. If the apparatus is overweight for some older bridges, alternate routes should be preplanned.

- **Monetary constraints** — Local jurisdictions may not have enough funding to purchase and operate a large mobile water supply apparatus.

- **Interoperability** — The capability of nearby jurisdictions should be considered before making a purchase. Water shuttles may operate more efficiently with apparatus of similar capacity.

Mobile water supply apparatus, as stated in NFPA® 1901, Chapter 7, are equipped with a tank capacity of at least 1,000 gallons (4 000 L). State, federal, and gross vehicle weight limits may regulate weight distribution and load requirements of the chassis. In order to accommodate greater capacities, tandem rear axles, tri-axles, or a tractor-trailer design should be considered. These apparatus will require additional driver training.

Figure 1.6 A mobile water supply apparatus. *Courtesy of Ron Jeffers.*

Figure 1.7 Water supply apparatus must be able to traverse winding, narrow roads. *Courtesy of Bob Esposito.*

The design and construction process of mobile water supply apparatus should meet certain safety and efficiency requirements including some of the following:

- Adequate but reasonable water capacity
- Efficient fill and dump time
- Suspension and steering matched to terrain requirements
- Properly sized chassis
- Adequately sized engine for vehicle size and terrain
- Sufficient braking ability for vehicle and terrain
- Proper tank mounting and baffling
- Adequate tank venting system
- Ability to dump water from either side or rear of apparatus

Mobile water supply apparatus have two basic functions on the fireground. The water tender may be used in a mobile shuttle operation. In this operation, the water tender arrives at the designated dump site and either pumps off or uses the quick dump valve to off-load its water supply into folding portable water tanks **(Figure 1.8)**. Once it is off-loaded, the water tender returns to the fill site to reload and the process is repeated. The apparatus may also be used as a stationary reservoir or "nurse tender," which can be useful in certain situations. In this operation, the apparatus is parked in close proximity to the fire scene. The pumpers connect to the water tender and use its supply during suppression operations. Knowing the limitations of your apparatus, water

Figure 1.8 A water tender dumped its water supply into a folding portable water tank. *Courtesy of Bob Esposito.*

tank capacity, training and preplanning of your response area is paramount for this operation to function correctly.

Specialty Fire Apparatus

A wide variety of apparatus are designed for fire fighting and rescue operations in specific situations or environments. These apparatus include wildland fire apparatus, aircraft rescue and fire fighting apparatus, fireboats, aerial apparatus equipped with fire pumps, rescue apparatus equipped with fire pumps, and trailer-mounted fire pumps.

Wildland Fire Apparatus

Combating wildland fires requires an apparatus design that is lightweight, highly maneuverable, and all-terrain. Specially designed wildland apparatus are often mounted on one-ton or larger chassis, usually featuring all-wheel drive. Commonly known as *brush trucks*, *brush breakers*, or *booster apparatus*, these vehicles often have pump capacities and water tanks of 500 gallons (2 000 L) or less **(Figure 1.9)**. However, some jurisdictions operate larger apparatus with pumps up to 1,000 gpm (4 000 L/min) and water tanks of 1,000 gallons (4 000 L) or larger.

A pump and roll system that allows the apparatus to be driven while discharging water is an advantage when combating wildland fires. Vehicles with this feature use a separate motor or a power take off (PTO) to power the fire pump. Some wildland vehicles may be designed for firefighters to ride on the outside of the apparatus to discharge water. This is a dangerous practice. IFSTA does not recommend riding on the outside of the apparatus, and this practice is prohibited by NFPA® 1500 *Standard on Fire Department Occupational Safety and Health Program.*

Figure 1.9 Brush trucks are wildland fire apparatus with pumping capabilities. *Courtesy of Steve Lofton.*

WARNING!
Riding on the outside of the apparatus may result in death or severe injury.

Most wildland apparatus carry booster hose, forestry hose, and/or small diameter attack hose. In addition to remote-controlled nozzles for fire suppression, some vehicles may be equipped with ground sweep nozzles intended to extinguish small fires and hot spots as the vehicle advances through short vegetation **(Figure 1.10)**.

Many wildland fire apparatus are now equipped with CAFS or other types of Class A foam systems. Class A foam agents are extremely effective in attacking wildland fires and protecting exposures. Additional information concerning foam systems may be found in Chapter 14.

NOTE: Additional details on wildland fire fighting may be found in the IFSTA **Wildland Fire Fighting for Structural Firefighters** manual. Consult NFPA® 1906, *Standard for Wildland Fire Apparatus,* for specific requirements concerning the design of wildland apparatus.

Figure 1.10 Vehicles equipped with ground sweep nozzles can extinguish small fires and hot spots as the vehicle advances.

Aircraft Rescue and Fire Fighting Apparatus

Aircraft rescue and fire fighting (ARFF) apparatus are used to provide immediate suppression of flammable liquid fires and suppression of vapors from fuel spills. Airport apparatus sometimes respond off of airport property to assist municipal fire departments with large scale flammable liquid incidents.

Requirements for ARFF apparatus are found in NFPA® 414, *Standard for Aircraft Rescue and Fire-Fighting Vehicles.* While this standard classifies apparatus by the type of suppression agent(s) carried, agent capacity, or numbers of drive wheels, many local jurisdictions divide their apparatus into three general categories:

● Major fire fighting vehicles **(Figure 1.11)**

● Rapid intervention vehicles **(Figure 1.12)**

● Combined agent vehicles

NOTE: Detailed information on the design and operation of ARFF vehicles is found in the IFSTA **Aircraft Rescue and Fire Fighting** manual.

Figure 1.11 A major ARFF apparatus. *Courtesy of James Nilo.*

Figure 1.12 A rapid intervention vehicle. *Courtesy of James Nilo.*

Figure 1.13 A fireboat may operate in areas containing boat or ship traffic. *Courtesy of Ron Jeffers.*

Fireboats

Jurisdictions may use **fireboats** to protect hazards on and adjacent to waterways. Fireboats commonly operate in areas containing boat or ship traffic as well as harbors with wharves, piers, and docks **(Figure 1.13)**. These vessels vary in size from small, high speed, shallow draft boats to larger craft that may operate outside of sheltered waterways.

Functions of modern fireboats include ice and water rescue, emergency medical services, fire fighting, and relay pumping to land-based apparatus. Some fireboats have capacities as high as 50,000 gpm (200 000 L/min). Individual master stream devices on these vessels may discharge large volumes of water sometimes in excess of 10,000 gpm (40 000 L/min).

Fireboat — Vessel or watercraft designed and constructed for the purpose of fighting fires; provides a specified level of pumping capacity and personnel for the extinguishment of fires in the marine environment. *Also known as* Marine Unit.

Aerial Apparatus Equipped with Fire Pumps

Aerial apparatus equipped with a fire pump have additional benefits on the fireground including the ability to supply its own master streams and extinguish small fires when an engine company is not available. Depending on the tactical requirements of a given incident, the apparatus may function with the capabilities of an engine or a ladder company. This flexibility may provide more options for Incident Commanders. These apparatus should always be positioned with consideration of the reach of the aerial device. Hoselines may be lengthened and stretched around corners, but the aerial device is limited in its reach.

A **quint** is an apparatus equipped with a fire pump, water tank, and hose, in addition to an aerial device and ground ladders. According to the NFPA® 1901, *Standard for Automotive Fire Apparatus*, the vehicle must be equipped with a pump rated at a minimum of 1,000 gpm (4 000 L/min) and a water tank of at least 300 gallons (1 200 L). Some jurisdictions operate aerial apparatus equipped with smaller pumps that are only expected to extinguish small fires when an engine company is not available.

NOTE: For additional information concerning the operation of aerial apparatus, the reader may refer to chapters 16-20 in the IFSTA **Pumping and Aerial Apparatus Driver/Operator Handbook**.

Rescue Apparatus Equipped with Fire Pumps

Rescue vehicles in some jurisdictions may be equipped with small fire pumps and tanks in order to extinguish small fires and provide protective hoselines at extrication and other incidents. Some of these vehicles may feature foam proportioning equipment and a tank for foam concentrate. These units are often designed with the pump panel and one or more preconnected hoselines housed in a compartment. Another common location for preconnects is the front bumper of the apparatus. These vehicles should not be confused with rescue pumpers discussed earlier in this chapter as they do not have the fire fighting capabilities of a full-sized fire department pumper.

Along similar lines, some departments may operate ambulances equipped with small fire pumps. These pumps are normally housed in a manner similar to those on rescue apparatus. The extra space required and additional weight of this equipment usually means the ambulance must be constructed on a chassis larger than the standard one-ton vehicle chassis used for most ambulances.

Trailer-Mounted Fire Pumps

Although not common in most municipal fire departments, trailer-mounted fire pumps may serve certain fire service applications. Long-term pumping operations, such as those involving fires at petroleum storage facilities or landfills, may be suitable for the deployment of trailer-mounted pumps in order to release standard fire department pumpers for response to other incidents **(Figure 1.14)**.

Figure 1.14 A trailer-mounted fire pump.

Apparatus-Mounted Special Systems

A wide variety of specialized equipment is commonly mounted on fire department pumping apparatus. In many jurisdictions, the driver/operator is responsible for the operation of this equipment as well as the fire pump. Although the exact procedure for operation will vary based on the manufacturer and design of the system, as well as jurisdictional policy, some of the more common systems are explained briefly in the following sections.

Electric Power Generators

Fire apparatus, including pumpers, are often equipped with electric power generation equipment. The generators are used to power electrical equipment used at scenes.

When a small amount of electric power is needed, a step-up transformer called an **inverter** can be used to convert a vehicle's 12- or 24-volt DC current into 110- or 220-volt AC current. These inverters have the advantage of fuel efficiency as well as nearly noiseless operation. However, they can be moved only a short distance away from the vehicle and have relatively small power supply capacities. Inverters are typically used to power vehicle-mounted floodlights.

Generators are the most common power source used for emergency services. They may be portable units or fixed to an apparatus **(Figure 1.15)**. Portable generators powered by small gasoline or diesel engines generally have 110 and/or 220 volt capability. These units may be operated in the compartment of an apparatus or carried to a remote location. Portable generators are highly useful when electric power is needed remote from the position of a fire apparatus. Portable generators are available with a variety of power capacities; 5,000 watts is typically the largest capacity.

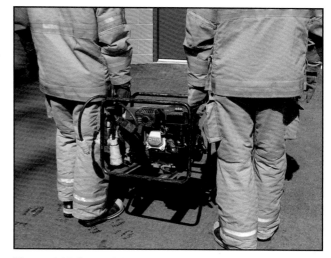

Figure 1.15 A portable generator.

Typically, vehicle-mounted generators have a larger capacity than portable units. In many systems, the vehicle-mounted generator provides power for the apparatus floodlights as well as any portable electrically operated equipment. These generators may be equipped as follows:

- Powered by gasoline, diesel, power-take-off, or hydraulic systems
- Have 110 and 220 volt capabilities
- Have capacities up to 12,000 watts

Rescue apparatus or other specialized units may feature fixed generator systems with capacities of 50,000 watts or greater. Apparatus-mounted generators with separate engines may create noisy work environments near the apparatus making radio and face-to-face communication difficult.

Scene Lighting

Most fire department pumpers are equipped with some amount of scene lighting and electric power distribution equipment to utilize various tools at incident scenes. The driver/operator must be proficient in the setup and operation of this equipment as well as have an awareness of the capabilities and limitations of these systems.

The lighting equipment carried on pumping apparatus may be portable or fixed. Ranging from 300 to 1,000 watts, portable lights are advantageous during incidents where illumination is needed some distance away from a

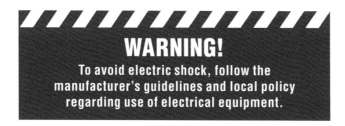

WARNING!
To avoid electric shock, follow the manufacturer's guidelines and local policy regarding use of electrical equipment.

piece of apparatus, or where additional lights are required. Some portable lights feature telescoping stands that allow a scene to be illuminated from an elevated position.

The fixed lights mounted on a vehicle provide general lighting around the apparatus and nearby scene. Often these lights are mounted so that they may be raised, lowered, or turned to provide the best possible lighting. Some apparatus are equipped with banks of lights mounted on booms that are powered by electric, pneumatic, or hydraulic systems. These installations generally have a capacity of 500 to 1,500 watts per light. Lighting should be connected only to power generators that can handle the additional wattage load. Overtaxing the electrical supply will result in poor lighting quality, damage to the lighting and generator equipment, and restriction of other tools operated with the same power source.

Figure 1.16 Junction boxes supply power to several connections from one supply source.

Electrical Power Distribution Equipment

The use of extension cords during incident operations is a common occurrence. Electrical cords may be stored on apparatus in coils, portable reels, or fixed automatic rewind reels. Some jurisdictions may specify 12-gauge, 3-wire cords with 600-volt insulation and twist-lock receptacles to provide secure connections. These heavy duty cords provide greater abrasion protection on the fireground. Junction boxes are used to supply power to several connections from one supply source **(Figure 1.16)**. Adapters should also be carried on the apparatus to allow rescuers to plug their equipment into standard electrical outlets or electrical equipment from other agencies that use different types of connections. In areas where departments routinely provide mutual aid, jurisdictions should work together to ensure compatibility of equipment, including electrical supply cords.

Rescue Tools

As discussed earlier in this chapter, some fire department pumping apparatus are also equipped with a variety of extrication equipment to perform some of the duties of rescue apparatus. The most common rescue tools found on pumping apparatus include the following:

• Extrication equipment such as spreaders and shears

• Combination spread and shear tools

• Extension rams

These tools are powered by either:

— Hydraulic pressure

— Compressed air or apparatus power take-off system

Depending on the design, these power systems may be portable or apparatus mounted. In all cases, the driver/operator must know the capabilities and limitations of the system as well as the proper method for engaging the equipment.

NOTE: For detailed information regarding the operation of hydraulic and electric extrication equipment, refer to the IFSTA **Principles of Vehicle Extrication** manual.

Chapter Summary

Fire apparatus are classified according to the function for which they are designed. Specifications for most pumping apparatus are contained in NFPA® 1901, *Standard for Automotive Fire Apparatus.* Within the category of pumping apparatus, a wide variety of designs and capabilities are built to serve specific needs within the fire service and the jurisdictions where particular apparatus are used. Fire apparatus with pumping capability may include small vehicles used for initial attack and wildland fire fighting to standard municipal fire pumpers and large tandem axle mobile water supply apparatus with pumping capability. Modern pumping apparatus operated by some fire departments may also feature aerial devices as well as foam making systems or specialized equipment for use at rescue or emergency medical incidents.

Review Questions

1. What are common requirements for fire department pumpers? (p. 14)

2. What are some characteristics of initial attack fire apparatus? (p. 16)

3. What are the two basic functions of mobile water supply apparatus on the fireground? (p. 18)

4. What are some types of specialty fire apparatus and their uses? (pp. 19-22)

5. What are the two types of electric power generators used in emergency services operations? (p. 23)

Apparatus Inspection and Maintenance

Chapter Contents

chapter 2

Key Terms

NFPA® Job Performance Requirements

This chapter provides information that addresses the following job performance requirements of NFPA 1002, *Standard for Fire Apparatus Driver/Operator Professional Qualifications (2014)*.

4.2.1, 4.2.2, 4.3.7, 5.1.1, 10.1.1

This chapter provides information that addresses the following job performance requirements of NFPA 1002, *Standard for Fire Apparatus Driver/Operator Professional Qualifications (2017)*.

4.2.1, 4.2.2, 4.3.7, 5.1.2, 10.1.1

Apparatus Inspection and Maintenance

Learning Objectives

After reading this chapter, students will be able to:

1. Explain a systematic maintenance program. (*NFPA 1002, 2014:* 4.2.1, 4.2.2, 4.3.7, 5.1.1 & *NFPA 1002, 2017:* 4.2.1, 4.2.2, 4.3.7, 5.1.2)

2. Explain the importance of accurate documentation, reporting, and follow-up for apparatus inspections. (*NFPA 1002, 2014:* 4.2.1, 4.2.2, 4.3.7, 5.1.1 & *NFPA 1002, 2017:* 4.2.1, 4.2.2, 4.3.7, 5.1.2)

3. Describe actions taken to ensure vehicle cleanliness.

4. Summarize considerations for conducting an apparatus inspection. (*NFPA 1002, 2014:* 4.2.1, 4.2.2, 4.3.7, 5.1.1, 10.1.1 & *NFPA 1002, 2017:* 4.2.1, 4.2.2, 4.3.7, 5.1.2, 10.1.1)

5. Describe actions taken to ensure batteries are operable. (*NFPA 1002, 2014 and 2017:* 4.2.1, 4.3.7)

6. Describe general fire suppression equipment maintenance procedures. (*NFPA 1002, 2014:* 4.2.1, 4.2.2, 4.3.7, 5.1.1 & *NFPA 1002, 2017:* 4.2.1, 4.2.2, 4.3.7, 5.1.2)

7. Clean the interior and wash and wax the exterior of a fire department apparatus. (Skill Sheet 2-1)

8. Perform a walk-around routine maintenance inspection. (*NFPA 1002, 2014 and 2017:* 4.2.1, 4.2.2, Skill Sheet 2-2)

9. Perform an in-cab operational inspection. (*NFPA 1002, 2014 and 2017:* 4.2.1, 4.2.2, 4.3.7, Skill Sheet 2-3)

10. Test apparatus road and parking brakes. (*NFPA 1002, 2014 and 2017:* 4.2.1, Skill Sheet 2-4)

11. Perform engine compartment inspection and routine preventive maintenance. (*NFPA 1002, 2014 and 2017:* 4.2.1, 4.2.2, Skill Sheet 2-5)

12. Charge an apparatus battery. (*NFPA 1002, 2014 and 2017:* 4.2.1, Skill Sheet 2-6)

13. Perform daily inspections for apparatus equipped with a fire pump. (*NFPA 1002, 2014:* 4.2.1, 4.2.2, 5.1.1, Skill Sheet 2-7 & *NFPA 1002, 2017:* 4.2.1, 4.2.2, 5.1.2, Skill Sheet 2-7)

14. Perform weekly inspections for apparatus equipped with a fire pump. (*NFPA 1002, 2014:* 4.2.1, 4.2.2, 5.1.1, Skill Sheet 2-8 & *NFPA 1002, 2017:* 4.2.1, 4.2.2, 5.1.2, Skill Sheet 2-8)

15. Perform a hard intake hose service test. (*NFPA 1002, 2014:* 4.2.2, 5.1.1, Skill Sheet 2-9 & *NFPA 1002, 2017:* 4.2.2, 5.1.2, Skill Sheet 2-9)

Chapter 2
Apparatus Inspection and Maintenance

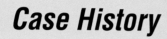

Case History

A volunteer fire captain was pinned against the wall of the fire station when he walked in front of a brush truck undergoing maintenance. A mechanic working on the steering column of the vehicle turned the ignition key to unlock the steering wheel. The ignition activated, and the brush truck lurched forward, pinning the captain. The captain died from injuries sustained in the accident.

Policies should be developed, implemented, and enforced that mandate chocking wheels or otherwise preventing the unintentional movement of apparatus undergoing repair or maintenance. All personnel should be aware of the operating features of vehicles they drive or service. Personnel not engaged in maintenance or repair activities should be excluded from the work area.

Source- NIOSH # F2010-37

Regardless of the number of incidents a fire apparatus responds to during the course of a day, it must be ready to respond and capable of performing its intended function with peak efficiency at all times. Preventive maintenance programs and routine maintenance checks are proactive measures that can ensure that a piece of fire apparatus is maintained in the highest state of readiness and will operate safely and efficiently at emergency scenes. Driver/operators in many jurisdictions are required to perform these routine maintenance checks and functions. NFPA® 1002 also requires that driver/operators be skilled in the performance of certain maintenance tasks.

The terms *maintenance* and *repair* are often used interchangeably in the fire service. However, they have different definitions and should be applied appropriately when discussing the serviceability of apparatus. Maintenance refers to keeping apparatus in a state of usefulness or readiness while repair means to restore that which has become inoperable. Vehicles or equipment that is in a good state of repair has likely been well maintained. Preventive maintenance helps to ensure reliability, reduce the frequency and cost of repairs, and reduces out-of-service time. The goal of preventive maintenance is to eliminate unexpected and catastrophic failures that may endanger firefighters and the general public.

Some basic preventive maintenance tasks may be performed by the driver/operator, while others are normally carried out by apparatus mechanics. NFPA® 1071, *Standard for Emergency Vehicle Technician Professional Qualifications*, provides a basis to train and certify fire apparatus mechanics and fire department maintenance officers. Driver/operators must not attempt to perform work beyond the scope of their knowledge and training, leaving repairs to qualified personnel.

In order to ensure operational status of the vehicle, NFPA® 1002 requires driver/operators to be able to perform routine tests, inspections, and servicing of the following systems:

- Batteries
- Braking systems
- Coolant system
- Electrical system
- Fuel system
- Hydraulic fluids

- Oil
- Tires
- Steering system
- Belts
- Tools, appliances, and equipment

Systematic Maintenance Program

Maintenance — Keeping equipment or apparatus in a state of usefulness or readiness.

Repair — To restore or put together something that has become inoperable or out of place.

Every fire department should develop standard operating procedures (SOPs) that provide for a systematic apparatus maintenance program that complies with applicable NFPA® standards. These procedures should specify maintenance procedures, when they are performed, and who is responsible for conducting the maintenance. The procedures should also specify a method for reporting, correcting, and documenting all activities.

The procedures should be clearly established within the level of responsibility for the driver/operator. Specific items that driver/operators must check and those that they are able to remedy should be identified and understood by all personnel. The **maintenance/repair** responsibilities of the driver/operator vary by jurisdiction; however, minor deficiencies such as low fluid levels or burned out bulbs are often corrected as part of the maintenance function of the driver/operator **(Figure 2.1)**. Repair work that involves complex tools, parts, or in-depth mechanical knowledge is left to a certified mechanic. Larger jurisdictions operate their own repair facilities with mechanics who can perform work at the shop or respond to a fire house or incident scene to perform repairs **(Figure 2.2)**. Some fire departments contract out repair work to local repair services.

NOTE: The AHJ will determine the assignment of maintenance and repair in each department.

The schedule for performing routine maintenance checks varies by jurisdiction and may differ based on how a department is staffed. Some fire departments require the driver/operator to perform an apparatus inspection and maintenance check at the beginning of each tour of duty. A more detailed inspection list may be completed on a weekly or monthly basis. Based on staffing, other fire departments establish a standard procedure to ensure that apparatus are inspected and maintained on a weekly schedule.

Documentation, Reporting, and Follow-Up

Each jurisdiction should establish an inspection and maintenance policy that details how the results of an inspection are documented and transmitted to the appropriate person in the administrative system. Standardized written forms or computer programs are often used for this purpose. In addition to proper completion and routing of the information, a filing system that allows for storage and retrieval of data should be in place in order to facilitate review

Figure 2.1 Check fluid levels during maintenance.

of records. An inspection checklist designed by the AHJ for specific apparatus will ensure that each driver/operator conducts a uniform and complete inspection by using the checklist as a guide. See **Appendix B** for a sample fire department vehicle inspection form.

Whenever the apparatus or a piece of equipment onboard is found broken, defective, or in need of any type of repair, the driver/operator should follow the established policy of the AHJ for documenting, reporting, and following up on the status of the repair. Depending on the jurisdiction, follow up may be done by the original reporting driver/operator, an immediate superior, or a staff officer with oversight responsibilities for repair functions. A guideline for these actions follows:

Figure 2.2 Larger fire departments have their own apparatus maintenance shops.

- Inspection of apparatus results in finding a system in need of repair.

- The driver/operator documents the defective system as per local policy such as written or computerized document.

- The driver/operator notifies their immediate supervisor of the defect and documentation.

- The status of the repair is followed up in a reasonable amount of time based on the nature of the problem. For serious issues or items meeting the NFPA® 1911 "Out-of-Service" criteria, immediate action must be taken.

Apparatus maintenance and inspection records are important documents that may serve several functions. In a warranty claim, these records may be needed to document that required maintenance was performed. In the event of an accident, maintenance records are among those likely to be scrutinized by investigators. A completely documented history of recurrent repairs may also assist in deciding whether to purchase a new apparatus as opposed to continuing to repair an older vehicle. Driver/operators must be trained in the recording system in use by their department and understand the importance of accurate and timely record keeping.

Vehicle Cleanliness

The cleanliness of apparatus and the equipment carried onboard is an important aspect of any inspection and maintenance program. Many firefighters are aware that keeping vehicles and equipment clean at all times is part of a long-standing fire service tradition. They also understand that local taxpayers have a significant capital investment in a piece of fire apparatus and that taxpayers expect vehicles to be well cared for and maintained. See **Skill Sheet 2-1** for steps on cleaning apparatus.

Keeping the apparatus body clean also helps promote a longer vehicle life. In cold weather climates where road salt is used during inclement weather, a corrosive effect on steel body components may occur. Frequent washing to remove these chemicals will reduce the likelihood of body and component damage.

Proper inspection of apparatus and equipment components is made much easier when parts are free of dirt and grime. A clean engine permits proper inspection for leaks and their source. For example, if hoses or wires are covered in oil and dust, it will be difficult to determine if they are cracked or frayed as the true condition of the rubber or insulation cannot be seen. Diesel fuel residue is problematic because it sticks to anything that it touches, leaving a gummy residue. Some of the most vulnerable areas are in the engine compartment where linkages, fuel injectors, or other controls may become inoperable due to collection of dirt. Firefighters should check the side of the engine where the fuel lines and fuel filter are located.

NOTE: While fuel injectors do not have external moving parts, they are still a source of collected dirt and oil. This area should be checked and cleaned.

Fire apparatus should be kept clean underneath as well as on top. Oil, moisture, dirt, and grime should not be permitted to collect on the undercarriage so that mechanical defects are more obvious. Several components that may be visualized more easily include suspension and brake parts as well as spring shackles, driveline, and steering mechanisms.

Road Treatments for Cold Weather Climates

Highway maintenance crews in many cold weather climates use a salt or brine solution to pre-treat roadways when a snow event is expected. This pre-treatment may occur hours or days before inclement conditions are forecast to begin. The liquid solution applied to the roadway dries and forms a fine dust. The dust is then picked up by passing fire apparatus, sticking to the undercarriage and finding its way into electrical connections causing corrosion. When sprayed with water in an attempt to wash the dust off, the salt moistens and remains active. Jurisdictions where these chemicals are used should consult their highway maintenance authorities to determine a way to neutralize the solution. In addition, the apparatus manufacturer may be of assistance with this issue.

There are adverse effects to overcleaning fire apparatus. Steam cleaning or high pressure water spray may remove lubrication from the chassis, engine, pump and underbody. This effect could be magnified by using degreasers or detergents. Care should be taken not to strip away necessary lubricants when washing the vehicle body and components. Modern apparatus also have a complex network of wiring and connections. Use caution when employing high pressure cleaning equipment around wiring harnesses and connections. After a heavy cleaning, it may be necessary to perform a routine lubrication to ensure that all components are properly protected from excessive wear.

Washing

Most apparatus manufacturers provide fire departments with specific instructions on how to best clean their apparatus. The following sections offer general guidance for apparatus cleaning if specific instructions are not available from the manufacturer.

Washing the exterior of the apparatus is one of the most commonly performed maintenance functions. Many vehicle manufacturers recommend slightly different procedures based on the age of the vehicle. Newer apparatus may require gentler cleaning in order to avoid damaging new paint, detailing, or clear-coat protection.

During the first six months after an apparatus is received, while the paint and protective coating are new and unseasoned, the vehicle should be washed frequently using cold water to harden the paint and keep it from spotting. To ensure the best overall appearance of the apparatus in the future and reduce the chance of damaging new paint and protective coatings, the following washing instructions are recommended:

- Use a garden hose without a nozzle to apply water to the apparatus. High pressures can drive dirt and debris into the finish **(Figure 2.3)**.

- Rinse as much loose dirt as possible from the vehicle before applying soap. This will lessen the amount of grit that may be scratched into the finish. Never remove dirt by dry rubbing.

Figure 2.3 Use a garden hose without a nozzle to wash a new vehicle. This reduces the chance of damaging new paint and protective coatings.

- Wash the apparatus before dirt, grit, and road salt can dry on the surface. Use only cleaning products that have been specifically designed for use on automotive paint.

- Do not wash with extremely hot water or while the surface of the vehicle is hot.

- Begin washing from the top of the vehicle and work downward.

- Dry the apparatus with a clean chamois that is rinsed frequently in clean water, or use a rubber squeegee. Failure to dry the vehicle thoroughly may encourage corrosion.

Once a new vehicle's finish is properly cured in accordance with the manufacturer's recommendations, either a garden hose with a nozzle or a pressure washer may be used for speed cleaning of the apparatus **(Figure 2.4)**. However, soapy water and hand washing on a regular basis are still required to ensure proper cleanliness.

Glass Care

To clean automotive glass, use warm soapy water or commercial glass cleaner. These liquids may be used in conjunction with paper towels or clean cloth rags **(Figure 2.5)**. Shop towels are generally not acceptable because even after being laundered, they may have metal shavings embedded in the cloth. Avoid using dry towels or cloths because they may grind grit or dirt into the glass surface. Do not use putty knives, steel wool, or any abrasive tool to remove deposits from the glass.

Figure 2.5 To clean automotive glass, use a soft cloth and commercial glass cleaner.

Figure 2.4 Use a hose with a nozzle for speed cleaning of the apparatus.

Interior Cleaning

Keep seat upholstery, dashboard and engine compartment coverings, and floor surfaces clean because an accumulation of dirt and debris may cause deterioration of these finishes. Modern apparatus have sensitive electronic equipment that can be damaged or destroyed by water or cleaning fluids. Follow manufacturer's instructions for cleaning apparatus interiors. Use the following steps to clean the interior:

- Sweep or vacuum large, loose dirt particles **(Figure 2.6)**.

- Use warm soapy water or commercial cleaning products to clean surfaces. Take care to use only products specified by the apparatus manufacturer to avoid possible damage to interior surfaces.

- Avoid using solvents such as lacquer thinner, acetone, laundry soap, bleach, and naphtha.

- Ventilate the cab or crew riding area when using cleaning agents.

- Take care when using any liquids around the vehicle's electrical system.

- Keep compartments, hinges, slide tracks, and seals clean and free of debris. Lubricate according to the manufacturer's specifications.

Waxing

Fire departments should follow the apparatus manufacturer's instructions regarding the application of wax or polishes to the exterior of apparatus, to include the following:

- Review instructions before applying products on newer apparatus. The application of some products may no longer be necessary and, in fact, may damage some clear-coat protective seal finishes that are applied over paints.

- Reference the manufacturer's manual before using any wax or polishes.

- Wait until the apparatus is six months old to apply these products, if necessary.

- Wash and dry the vehicle thoroughly and apply the wax or polish according to product instructions. Polish out the vehicle with a soft cloth or mechanical buffer **(Figure 2.7)**.

Figure 2.6 A firefighter cleans the interior of the apparatus by sweeping out dirt and other debris.

Figure 2.7 A firefighter uses a soft cloth to polish the apparatus.

Apparatus Inspection

In departments where driver/operators relieve each other at a specified shift change, the incoming driver/operator should consult the person being relieved for any pertinent information regarding incident activity, equipment usage, or problems. Driver/operators should follow a systematic procedure based on department SOPs, NFPA® standards, and manufacturer recommendations for inspecting apparatus. Taking a systematic approach helps ensure that all required items are checked each time an inspection is completed. The information in the following section is based on the requirements of NFPA® 1002 and the government pretrip inspection requirements for obtaining a **commercial drivers' license (CDL)** in the United States. Not all jurisdictions require their driver/operators to obtain a CDL. However, these inspection procedures provide a sound basis for the type of inspection that all driver/operators should be able to perform at the beginning of each tour of duty in a career department and on a weekly basis as well as after each run in a volunteer department.

Walk-Around Method

A particular method of performing an apparatus inspection is referred to as the **circle or walk-around method**. Two types of inspections are actually conducted during a walk-around inspection: the **operational readiness inspection** (required by NFPA® standards and the authority having jurisdiction) and the vehicle **pretrip road worthiness inspection**.

NOTE: IFSTA recognizes these descriptions as important minimum inspection points. The driver/operator is responsible to follow all jurisdictional laws, codes, and policies.

The driver/operator begins the walk-around inspection at the driver's door on the cab and works around the apparatus in a clockwise pattern **(Figure 2.8)**. Check each important area as you circle the vehicle. Get in the cab, start the apparatus, and perform a **functional check** on apparatus systems. (Exact procedures may vary by department policy as well as the design of the apparatus.) **Skill Sheet 2-2** provides instructions for performing a walk-around routine maintenance inspection.

If records from previous inspections or apparatus usage are available, the driver/operator may find it helpful to review them to see if any problems were previously reported. This prior knowledge will allow you to pay special attention to those areas for possible reoccurrence of the problem. You may also benefit from talking to the last person who drove the apparatus to get his or her impression of its overall condition.

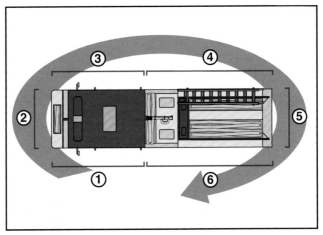

Figure 2.8 Driver/operators should use a systematic approach when performing an apparatus inspection.

Approaching the Vehicle

When approaching a vehicle to be inspected, driver/operators should observe:

- Any problems that may be readily apparent from a distance such as body damage or a severe lean to one side.

- The terrain on which the vehicle is parking. Fire station apparatus floors, driveways, or parking areas may have sloped surfaces.

- Vehicle fluid leaks, such as water, coolant, oil, hydraulic fluid, or transmission fluid, which may indicate a serious mechanical problem **(Figure 2.9)**.

When approaching a vehicle to be inspected indoors, be sure that the area is properly ventilated before conducting the inspection. Weather permitting; the apparatus should be parked outside for functional tests. Whenever the apparatus is parked, be sure to chock its wheels **(Figure 2.10)**.

CAUTION

Diesel exhaust may contain up to 100 harmful chemicals and compounds. Do not run these engines in unvented areas for any period of time.

Figure 2.9 The driver/operator should check for fluid leaks.

Figure 2.10 Always chock the apparatus' wheels when it is parked.

Left and Right Orientation

The sides of an apparatus may be identified by different names in various departments. Driver/operators should use the terms commonly accepted in their departments. (Some jurisdictions use street side/curb side, others driver side/officer side.)

Exterior Inspection

Driver/operators should begin their walk-around inspection at the driver's side of the cab making a general observation of the vehicle for any damage not previously noted. The same should be noted for the officer's side. This visual inspection involves checking items for condition, cleanliness, damage, defects, functionality, leaks, and presence of or missing items **(Figure 2.11)**. **Skill Sheet 2-2** includes steps to check all of the exterior lights on the apparatus, audible warning devices, and hose/equipment.

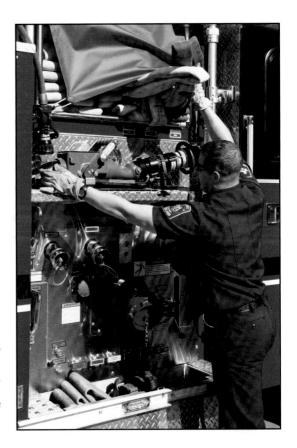

Figure 2.11 During the exterior inspection, the driver/operator observes any damage not previously noted.

Tire Types, Condition, and Inflation

A number of items should be checked relative to the tires. Most importantly, the driver/operator should check the tire type, condition, and inflation.

Tire Types and Condition

Driver/operators should make certain that tire types match. It is never acceptable to mix radial tires with bias-ply tires. In addition, all tires should be the same size and weight ratings according to appropriate manufacturer specifications.

The correct tire for any commercial vehicle is determined after the vehicle's specifications are final. Tire selections for fire apparatus are based on **gross axle weight ratings** for the apparatus. Too much or too little pressure will damage tires and cause poor road-handling characteristics, as well as excessive fuel consumption. The maximum mph (km/h) rating on the tire is not

Gross Axle Weight Rating — The maximum amount of weight that an axle system can safely carry.

an invitation to continually operate at that speed; it is the rated upper limit of the tire's performance level. Driver/operators must adhere to the specified limitations of the tires on every assigned apparatus.

When examining tire condition, driver/operators should check for proper tread depth (varies according to state or provincial inspection requirements), tread separation, cupping, excessive wear on the sidewalls, cuts, dry rotting, cracking tires, or objects impaled in the tire per department policy **(Figure 2.12)**.

NOTE: The valve stem should not be cut, cracked, or loose. Valve stem caps should be in place.

NFPA® 1911 requires that all tires be replaced every seven years, regardless of their condition. Old tires with generous tread depth have been the cause of blowouts that have led to serious accidents and death. This is of particular concern where the apparatus may log very few miles (kilometers) every year.

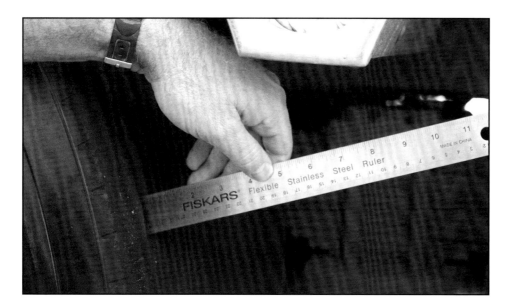

Figure 2.12 A driver/operator checks for proper tread depth.

Tire Inflation

The driver/operator should understand all the information imprinted on the sidewall of a truck tire. Check that apparatus tires are inflated to the apparatus manufacturer's recommended tire pressure, according to NFPA® 1911. Always follow department tire inflation SOPs.

Tire Pressure

The maximum tire pressure imprinted on the exterior of each tire is not the recommended operating tire pressure. Set and maintain the tire pressure at the tire manufacturer's pressure recommendations for the correct tire size, type, load range (ply rating), and measured in-service axle loads. Each tire manufacturer will have published charts so you can customize the pressures to the actual axle weights.

⚠ WARNING

Crash Hazard

Tires subject to fire-service ratings.

Tire may fail if driven continuously at highway speeds.

Keep tires properly inflated.

See Operator's Manual for instructions.

Crash by failed tire may injure or kill.

FAMA12   Do not paint over this label. Replace if damaged or lost.

Interior Inspection

Once the exterior of the apparatus has been checked, the driver/operator may enter the cab to begin inspecting the cab interior **(Figure 2.13)**. Adjust mirrors, seats, and seat belts; start the engine; and check all dashboard instruments for correct readings. Check any miscellaneous equipment stored in the cab at this time. This equipment may include items such as a breakdown kit containing reflective triangles or paperwork required by the jurisdiction where the apparatus is operated. See **Skill Sheet 2-3** for performing an in-cab operational inspection.

Electrical Load Management System

Newer apparatus may be equipped with electrical **load management systems** that are intended to prevent an overload of a vehicle's electrical generation system. **Overload** may be a problem due to the large amount of electrical equipment added to modern fire apparatus **(Figure 2.14)**. In general, load management systems sometimes incorporate a **load sequencer** and **load monitor** into the same device. The load sequencer turns on various lights at specified intervals so that the startup electrical load for all the devices does not occur at the same time. The load monitor "watches" the system for any added electrical loads that threaten to overload the system. If an overload condition occurs, the load monitor will shut down less important electrical equipment in order to prevent the overload. This is referred to as **load shedding**. For example, if an inverter is activated to supply power to two 500-watt flood lights, the load monitor may

Load Management System — An electrical monitoring system that will shed electrical load in a predetermined order if the chassis voltage begins to drop below a predetermined level.

Overload — Operation of equipment or a conductor in excess of its rated ampacity; continuous overload may result in overheating that damages the equipment.

Load Sequencer — Device in an electrical system that turns lights on at specified intervals, so that the start-up load for all of the devices does not occur at the same time.

Load Monitor — Device that "watches" an electrical system for added loads that may threaten to overload the system.

Load Shedding — When an overload condition occurs, the load monitor will shut down less important electrical equipment to prevent the overload.

Figure 2.13 The driver/operator conducts an interior inspection.

Figure 2.14 A large amount of electrical equipment added to an apparatus may cause overload.

shut down the air conditioning system in the cab or the compartment lights. Driver/operators must understand the design of the electrical load management system on their apparatus so that they can determine if it is operating properly. They must also be able to distinguish between load shedding and an electrical system malfunction.

Manual Shift Transmissions

If the apparatus is equipped with a **manual shift transmission**, check the adjustment of the clutch pedal. The pedal should not have insufficient or excessive **free play** (also called free travel). Free play is the distance that the pedal must be pushed before the **throw-out bearing** actually contacts the clutch release fingers. Insufficient free play will cause the clutch to slip, overheat, and wear out sooner than necessary. The throw-out bearing will also have a shorter life. Excessive free play may result in the clutch not releasing completely. This can cause harsh shifting, gear clashing, and damage to gear teeth. Driver/operators should be familiar with the normal amount of free play in vehicles they are assigned to drive. A certified mechanic should check and adjust any clutch that does not appear to have the proper amount of free play.

Steering System

The driver/operator should inspect the steering system for proper adjustment and reaction. Check the steering wheel for excess play that does not result in the actual movement of the vehicle's front wheels. In general, **steering wheel play** should be no more than approximately 10 degrees in either direction **(Figure 2.15)**. On a 20-inch (500 mm) diameter steering

Figure 2.15 A driver/operator inspecting for steering wheel play.

wheel, the play may be about 2 inches (50 mm) in either direction. Play that exceeds these parameters could indicate a serious problem that may result in loss of vehicle control during routine and emergency driving conditions.

Gross Vehicle Weight

Every vehicle is placarded with a Gross Vehicle Weight Rating (GVWR). Every driver/operator should be familiar with this placard and maintain the vehicle accordingly. Commercial vehicles are required to have this placard in plain view. Often Gross Vehicle Weight Rating is confused with curb weight. Curb weight is the weight of an empty fire apparatus fresh off the assembly line with no tools, water, equipment, or passengers. The manufacturer determines the GVWR as the maximum weight at which a vehicle can be safely operated on roadways in ideal conditions. The GVWR placard may also indicate the maximum weight for each axle on the apparatus, along with tire pressure recommendations.

Manual Shift Transmission — A component of the power train that receives torque from the engine and converts it to rotation to the wheels. A clutch is used to disengage the transmission from the engine to allow the apparatus to start, stop, or change gears to maximize engine performance.

Free Play — Amount of travel the clutch has before it begins to disengage the engine from the transmission.

Throw-Out Bearing — The component used to push on the internal clutch fingers connected to the clutch pedal and when activated, disengages the clutch from the engine.

Steering Wheel Play — In a steering system, the amount of travel between turning the wheel and when the steering system moves.

Before placing any apparatus in service, load all compartments with the intended in-service equipment, hose, water, and crew. Weigh each axle and compare the results to the Gross Axle Weight Ratings (GAWR) placard. If the measured weights are higher than the GAWRs, remove or redistribute equipment until a safe loading is achieved.

Driver/operators should be aware of vehicles around them that are "over-grossed." Vehicles that sway from side to side and vehicles that seem to be resting on their axles (motor homes, trailers, pickup trucks, etc.) are seen every day on roadways. Per NFPA® 1901 and 1911, a side-to-side variance in weight should not exceed seven percent.

In Cab Fire/Rescue Equipment

Many jurisdictions store fire and rescue equipment in the front and/or rear of the crew cab. Although inspection of this equipment is not required to determine road worthiness of the vehicle, it is a vital part of maintaining readiness for emergency incidents. The equipment should be in good order and securely stowed. IFSTA's **Essentials of Fire Fighting** manual offers additional information on inspecting fire and rescue equipment for serviceability.

Brake Inspection and Tests

Ensuring that the vehicle's brakes are in proper working order is an extremely important part of the inspection process. Many serious fire apparatus collisions have been caused by faulty brakes **(Figure 2.16)**. A number of tests may be used to check the function of the service

Figure 2.16 This accident was caused by faulty brakes.

brakes. Federal, state, and provincial laws may dictate how and when brakes are tested. The following section highlights some of the more commonly recognized brake tests. See **Skill Sheet 2-4** for information on testing apparatus road and parking brakes.

Smaller apparatus, as well as some older vehicles, may be equipped with **hydraulic braking systems**. Most commercial and private vehicles built since 1990 are equipped with **antilock braking systems**.

Air Brakes

Most large, modern fire department pumping apparatus are equipped with **air-actuated braking systems** (air brakes). The NFPA® and other sources have developed recommendations for air brake use. On apparatus equipped with air brakes, the air pressures must build up to a sufficient level within a defined period of time after starting the engine.

Hydraulic Braking Systems — A braking system that uses a fluid in a closed system to pressurize wheel cylinders when activated.

Antilock Braking Systems — An electronic system that monitors wheel spin. When braking and a wheel are sensed to begin locking up, the brake on that wheel is temporarily released to prevent skidding.

Air-Actuated Braking Systems — A braking system that uses compressed air to hold off a spring brake (parking brake) and applies air pressure to a service brake for vehicle stopping.

If the engine must be run longer than the specified period of time to build sufficient air pressure, the apparatus should be inspected and repaired by a certified mechanic. It may be necessary to add an electric air compressor, or connect the apparatus to a fire station compressed air system to maintain adequate air pressure when the apparatus is not in use. These measures may prevent delays in responding to emergencies.

Apparatus with air brakes are to be equipped with an air pressure protection valve that prevents air horns or other nonessential devices from being operated when the pressure in the air reservoir drops below 80 psi (560 kPa). Any deficiencies in this system must be reported and repaired by a certified mechanic.

Compressed Air Tanks

Compressed air tanks will develop moisture that can cause rusting inside the tank. This moisture may freeze during cold weather and cause a malfunction of any air-operated devices. Frequent draining will minimize or eliminate rust and freezing. While newer apparatus will be equipped with automatic air drain systems, the air tanks will still need to be manually drained in accordance with the AHJ's maintenance schedule. During inspection, if water is found in the air tanks or reservoirs, it should be immediately reported for service maintenance.

ABS Brake Systems

Antilock braking systems (ABS) reduce the possibility of an apparatus going into a slide, jackknife, or spin during heavy braking. ABS brakes also assist the driver/operator in keeping the apparatus in a straight trajectory during heavy or emergency braking. ABS technology does not necessarily provide a faster stop, but it greatly enhances a controlled stop. Driver/operators must know the type of braking system used on their apparatus and be familiar with its operation. Procedures for using different types of braking systems are discussed in Chapter 3 of this manual.

Brake Tests

Apparatus brakes should be thoroughly tested at least annually using the methods outlined in NFPA® 1911, *Standard for the Inspection, Maintenance, Testing, and Retirement of In-Service Automotive Fire Apparatus*. These tests determine the braking ability of apparatus while in motion and evaluate the parking brake while the vehicle is stopped. The driver/operator should conduct an **air brake test** (required by many states and provinces before road operation of a commercial vehicle) as defined by the AHJ inspection and maintenance schedule.

Driver/operators are normally not expected to make repairs or adjustments to compensate for brake problems. Apparatus with too much brake slack can be difficult to stop. If the **slack adjusters** are not operating within manufacturer's specifications, the vehicle should not be driven until a certified mechanic has made repairs.

Air Brake Test — A series of tests used to ensure the serviceability of an air braking system. Tests include air loss, air compressor buildup, air warning, and emergency parking brake activation.

Slack Adjusters — Devices used in an air brake system that connect between the activation pads and the brake pads that compensate for brake pad wear.

Automatic Slack Adjusters

Automatic slack adjusters are made by many different manufacturers and do not all operate the same. Always consult the apparatus manufacturer's operator's manual or laws affecting states and provinces for more detailed information on braking systems and brake tests.

The apparatus should be taken out of service and repaired if any tests indicate the brakes do not perform in accordance with applicable state or provincial requirements. The driver/operator should refer to NFPA® 1911 for additional guidelines.

The air brake test is designed to provide the driver/operator with safety information that may not have otherwise been evident. The aforementioned procedures may vary by state and province. It is the responsibility of the driver/operator to be familiar with all laws, policies, and manufacturer's recommendations in the operator's manual.

NOTE: IFSTA considers the air brake testing procedures outlined in this manual to be the minimum acceptable daily air brake test; other laws or departmental policies may prevail as more restrictive.

Engine Compartment Inspection

Once the entire exterior of the apparatus has been inspected, the in-cab checks have been completed, and the air brake testing is complete, the driver/operator should shut off the engine and prepare to perform checks and routine preventive maintenance in the engine compartment. Depending on department policy or driver/operator preference, these checks may be conducted before the apparatus has been started. If this is the preferred practice, the readings of some fluid levels (crankcase oil, transmission fluid) must be considered due to the cold engine. While it is acceptable to perform these checks either before or after the engine has been run, most checks (with the exception of the transmission fluid level) should not be conducted while the vehicle is running. The driver/operator should never rely solely on warning lights or gauges; all fluid levels should be inspected. For inspection of vehicles equipped with a **tilt cab**, ensure that the control operates freely without binding and that the hold-open device is latched **(Figure 2.17)**. In addition, check cab latches for security of mounting, lubrication, and accumulation of metal fillings in the mechanism.

Tilt Cab — A truck that uses a cab that lowers over the power train.

CAUTION

Before lifting the cab, be sure that there is adequate vertical clearance and secure all loose equipment in the cab.

⚠ **WARNING**

Crush Hazard.

Stay clear of raised cab.

Before working under cab engage prop support.

Falling cab may injure or kill.

FAMA41 Do not paint over this label. Replace if damaged or lost

NOTE: Many tilt cabs have inspection doors that allow a check of engine oil, coolant, and other fluids. However, the cab should still be lifted on a weekly basis for a thorough inspection of the engine compartment.

There is no established order in which to check items in the engine compartment. The driver/operator may wish to proceed in the order that is listed on the apparatus inspection form to ensure that no check is overlooked. In all cases, consult operator manuals to determine proper procedures and accepted fluids for each vehicle. See **Skill Sheet 2-5** for steps on performing an engine compartment inspection.

Exhaust Emissions

Exhaust systems on newer apparatus, depending on their date of manufacture, may be equipped with systems to provide for cleaner emissions from diesel engines. **Diesel particulate filters (DPF)** trap much of the particulate matter in exhaust emissions. However, these systems must periodically conduct a process of regeneration in which the exhaust temperature is raised in order to burn off particulate matter accumulated in the filter. In automatic regeneration mode, the vehicle may be operated normally. If the vehicle is driven without automatic regeneration and the filter becomes too contaminated, the vehicle will experience reduced power and driving capability until a regeneration cycle is complete. This condition will prevent use for emergency response.

Figure 2.17 An apparatus tilt cab provides access to the engine compartment.

In addition to a DPF system, engines produced after January 1, 2010, may be equipped with an exhaust after-treatment system called Selective Catalyst Reductant (SCR). An SCR system uses Diesel Exhaust Fluid (DEF) to help further reduce emissions. DEF is stored in a tank downstream of the DPF and is injected into the gas in order to reduce the nitrogen oxide (NOx) emissions from diesel engines. The DEF levels in the DEF tank on apparatus that use this system should be checked during apparatus inspections.

Periodically inspect the exhaust system and look for signs of cracks or leaks. Ensure that exhaust pipe wrap or insulation is intact and undamaged. Pay close attention to joints and flex-pipes. While this is important on any apparatus, it is extremely important on 2007 and later engines equipped with DPFs. The exhaust gas can reach extremely high temperatures during the regeneration process and exhaust leaks can damage surrounding components or set them on fire. These high temperatures are present in the pipe sections behind the DPF and may be present in certain engines in front of the DPF as well.

Chassis Lubrication

Some fire departments require driver/operators to perform routine **chassis lubrication**. Proper lubrication helps prevent costly repairs and may reduce out-of-service time. Effective lubrication depends on use of the proper grade lubricant, the frequency of lubrication, the amount used, and the method

Diesel Particulate Filter (DPF) — A device designed to remove diesel particulate matter or soot from the exhaust gas of a diesel engine.

Chassis Lubrication — Applying grease and other lubricants to specific parts of a chassis to reduce wear, noise, and binding.

of lubrication. To select the proper lubricant, consider the requirements of the unit, the characteristics of the lubricant, and the manufacturer's recommendations.

The manufacturer's manual will recommend the Society of Automotive Engineers (SAE) numbers for engine oil. The SAE number indicates only the viscosity of the oil. Some other essential characteristics of oil are corrosion protection, foaming, sludging, and carbon accumulation. These characteristics may be controlled by the refiner. Driver/operators should consult the operator's manual for the type of oil and location of fill ports and grease fittings.

CAUTION
Use the proper oil for the engine as per manufacturer's recommendation. Failure to use the proper engine oil can lead to costly engine and emission system damage.

If chassis lubrication is within the responsibilities of the driver/operator, take the following steps to complete these duties:

- Be familiar with all the lubrication fill points. Most apparatus owner's manuals will include a diagram of lubrication fittings.
- Wipe the fitting clean with a shop rag.
- Press the end of the lubrication gun fill hose onto the fitting.
- Operate the pump handle on the lubrication gun until resistance is felt.

   NOTE: Continuing to pump after resistance is felt causes excessive pressure and may damage rubber grease seals.

- Continue this process around the vehicle until all lubrication points have been filled.

Newer apparatus may be equipped with an automatic lubrication system. If the apparatus is so equipped, follow the manufacturer's guidelines for operating the system. Not all vehicle fittings may be serviced by an automatic system. The driver/operator should consult the owner's manual to identify fittings that must be manually lubricated.

In addition to the parts of the engine and apparatus mentioned in the previous sections, the driver/operator may be required to check additional equipment based on department policy. Properly document each item checked according to local requirements.

Vehicle Batteries

Most modern truck batteries are maintenance free. Driver/operators should check that the cable connections are tight and protected with a film of grease, petroleum jelly, or battery terminal protection product **(Figure 2.18)**. Older apparatus may still have batteries that required the addition of distilled water to replenish the cell's fluid as it evaporates over time. Keep the cells of this type of battery topped off, or replace them with maintenance free batteries. Keep batteries clean.

Look for signs of cracks or leaks. Most automotive batteries contain lead and sulfuric acid. Leaking acid is highly corrosive and hazardous if it gets on your skin or eyes. Batteries can also give off hydrogen gas, which is highly explosive and a mere spark can ignite it. Some automotive batteries contain vents to allow the gas to escape, so any ignition source or even a cigarette near the battery may cause an explosion or fire. A battery detonation will likely throw caustic acid into your eyes or skin.

Figure 2.18 Driver/operators should check battery terminals for corrosion and tightness.

WARNING!
Batteries give off explosive hydrogen gas. Ventilate area when servicing. Wear safety goggles and acid resistant gloves. Exploding batteries can injure or kill.

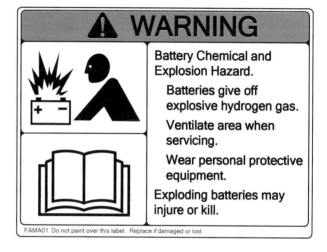

In some jurisdictions, driver/operators may be responsible for charging vehicle batteries. Apparatus batteries may require charging or jump-starting because of long periods of inactivity or improper drains on the electrical system. Report to the department mechanic any apparatus that regularly require charging or jump-starting so that corrective measures may be taken.

In the fire station, charging is generally performed with a battery charger. Driver/operators should be proficient in their operation as they may need to be used rapidly in order to start a vehicle for an emergency response. Because batteries produce explosive hydrogen gas when being charged, it is important that personnel responsible for this activity follow proper instructions and safety procedures, including the use of safety eye protection whenever performing battery charging. **Skill Sheet 2-6** lists the procedure for charging a vehicle's battery or batteries.

NOTE: Newer apparatus may be equipped with an onboard charging system or jumper studs to facilitate jump-starting without directly accessing the battery.

If the vehicle needs to be jump-started when away from the fire station, it may be necessary to connect it to another vehicle with jumper cables. Before attempting to jump-start a vehicle, the driver/operator must be aware of several important considerations:

- Ensure that the vehicle being used as the power source has the same voltage electrical system as the apparatus being jump-started. This will prevent damage from occurring to either system.

- Check the manufacturer's operations manual before jumping or charging the system. The operations manual should specify to which battery the cables should be connected. Most fire apparatus have more than one battery connected to the apparatus.

- Make sure that the jumper cables are connected to the specified battery in the recommended manner. Be sure that all personnel in the area are wearing appropriate protective clothing including eye protection.

Posttrip Inspections

All the functions described up to this point in the chapter are intended to be performed before the operation of the vehicle. It is prudent to perform some of the inspections after the apparatus has been operated for an extended period of time at a fire or other emergency scene or when the vehicle has completed a long road trip. Each jurisdiction may adopt its own procedure for posttrip inspections. However, IFSTA recommends use of the same procedures used for pretrip inspections.

General Fire Suppression Equipment Maintenance

Fire pumps are tested at regularly scheduled intervals to compare actual performance to specific standards. In addition to this testing, fire departments should require regular inspections to detect deficiencies or failure of the fire pump and other fire suppression equipment. Some jurisdictions require driver/operators to perform this function while others assign this work to mechanics. Some items should be checked daily while other checks may be performed as a weekly routine. **Skill Sheet 2-7** identifies the steps for performing daily inspections; **Skill Sheet 2-8** identifies the steps for performing weekly inspections.

Some apparatus checks may also be performed on an "as needed" basis. For example, anytime a pump has been operated at draft from a static supply, such as a saltwater source, lake, or pond, or in areas served by old water mains, the pump and piping should be thoroughly flushed before the apparatus is placed back in service **(Figure 2.19)**. For more information concerning fire pump testing, the reader may consult Chapter 15, Apparatus Testing.

NOTE: Skill Sheet 2-9 shows the steps for performing a hard intake hose service test.

In addition, the driver/operator should perform **post-maintenance/repair inspection** to ensure that all work has been properly completed in accordance with the manufacturer's guidelines and AHJ.

Post-Maintenance/Repair Inspection — A specific inspection to an area of a chassis or apparatus to ensure that the unit is operating properly in accordance with the manufacturer's initial design.

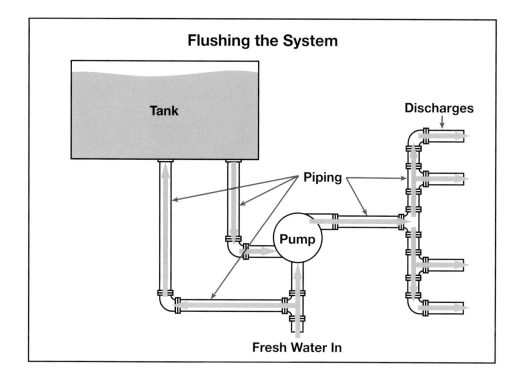

Figure 2.19 Flush the pump system if the pump has been operated at draft from a static water supply.

Chapter Summary

To ensure that the pumping apparatus is always ready to respond to and perform effectively at emergencies, the driver/operator must regularly inspect the vehicle for safety and serviceability. Based on department policy and the qualifications of the driver/operator, the appropriate maintenance should be performed or defects reported for repair. Using a standardized checklist and systematic approach to vehicle inspection will ensure that the apparatus is checked the same way each time and no components are overlooked.

Review Questions

1. What should systematic maintenance procedures specify? (p. 30)

2. What are the functions of apparatus maintenance and inspections records? (pp. 31-32)

3. Why is inspection of apparatus easier if the apparatus is clean? (p.32)

4. When approaching a vehicle to be inspected, what should driver/operators observe? (p. 37)

5. Why should fire pumps be tested at regularly scheduled intervals? (p. 48)

Preparation

Step 1: Park the apparatus in an appropriate location; starting, driving, and braking according to local SOPs.

Step 2: Chock the apparatus wheels.

Step 3: Gather equipment and set up work area.

Interior Cleaning

Step 4: Sweep or vacuum large, loose dirt particles.

Step 5: Clean the interior surfaces, using warm soapy water or other manufacturer-approved products.

NOTE: Take care when using any liquids around the vehicle's electrical system. Use of a water hose to flush out the interior floor area can result in electrical/electronic failures.

Step 6: Clean any debris from compartments, hinges, slide tracks, and seals. Lubricate according to manufacturer's specifications.

Step 7: Clean interior glass using warm soapy water or glass cleaner in conjunction with paper towels or clean cloth rags.

NOTE: Do not use anything abrasive on window glass.

Washing the Exterior

Step 8: Apply water to the apparatus from top to bottom using a garden hose without a nozzle. Rinse as much loose dirt as possible from the vehicle before applying cleaning agent.

NOTE: Do not wash with extremely hot water or while the surface of the vehicle is hot.

Step 9: Wash the apparatus from top to bottom using appropriate automotive cleaning products.

2-1

Clean the interior and wash and wax the exterior of a fire department apparatus.

SKILL SHEETS

Step 10: Dry the apparatus exterior completely using a clean chamois or rubber squeegee.

Step 11: Clean exterior glass using warm soapy water or glass cleaner in conjunction with paper towels or clean cloth rags.

NOTE: Do not use anything abrasive on window glass.

Wax or Protective Finish

Step 12: Apply wax or protective finish following manufacturer's recommendations

Begin Inspection

Step 1: Set up the inspection area. Park the apparatus outdoors, if weather permits. If indoors, be sure that proper ventilation equipment is in place or doors are open to vent vehicle exhaust.

CAUTION: Diesel exhaust may contain up to 100 harmful chemicals and compounds. Do not run these engines in unvented areas for any period of time.

Step 2: Chock the vehicle's wheels.

Step 3: Begin inspection when approaching the vehicle.

    a. Look for readily apparent damage.

    b. Look beneath the vehicle for spots that indicate leakage.

    c. Look for unusual leaning that indicates chassis defects.

Front Left- and Right-Side Inspection

Step 4: Check the left (driver's) side of the cab and mirrors for any damage.

Step 5: Check the right (passenger's or officer's) side of the cab and mirrors for any damage.

Step 6: Check the cab doors to ensure that they are in proper working order.

    a. Ensure that the doors close tightly.

    b. Ensure that the latch works as it was designed and that it operates with little or no play.

    c. Check that all doors and window glass are intact and clean.

f. Check that there are no trails of fluid on the wheel or tire indicating axle gear oil leaks.

NOTE: Seals that retain axle gear oil may show slight seepage and still be serviceable, but trails of fluid on the wheel, brake components, or tire are unacceptable.

Step 11: Visually inspect the suspension components found behind the front left and right wheels.

    a. Look for defects involving the torsion bars, springs, spring hangars, shackles, U-bolts, shock absorbers, or mounting hardware.

    b. Check for springs with cracked, otherwise broken, or missing leaves.

    c. Check that there is no spring deflection when the vehicle is on a level surface.

Step 7: Check that all steps, platforms, handrails, and mirrors are securely mounted and not deformed.

Step 8: Check the saddle fuel tanks beneath the door opening, if the vehicle is so equipped.

    a. Check for leaks or other problems.

    b. Check the fuel tank straps for corrosion.

Step 9: Check that the equipment in the rear portion of the cab is all onboard and complete, in proper working order, and securely stowed.

Tires and Wheels

Step 10: Check the condition of the tire/wheel assembly on the front left and right sides of the vehicle.

    a. Check for bent or broken studs, lugs, or clamps. Ensure that parts are not missing from the tire/wheel assembly.

    b. Ensure that lug nuts are tight.

    c. Check that there are no cracks or damage that would prevent the sealing of the tire to the rim.

    d. Check to see that front splash guards (mud flaps) are in place and secure.

    e. Check for unusual accumulations of brake dust, metal flake, and/or corroded metal flake accumulations or trails on the wheel or adjacent areas.

Step 12: Check that the front tires are properly inflated using a pressure gauge. Check this reading against the pressure recommended by the apparatus manufacturer on the federally required apparatus GVWR sticker.

Step 13: Check the front tire valve stems and valve stem caps for cracks or looseness.

Step 14: Check the front tires.

    a. Check for proper tire type as listed on the sidewall of the tire and federally required GVWR sticker.

    b. Ensure the proper tread depth with the tread depth gauge (proper tread depth varies according to state or provincial inspection requirements).

    c. Check that there is no tread separation or excessive sidewall wear.

    d. Be sure that there are no cuts or objects impaled in the tire.

    e. Check for bulges greater than 3/8 of an inch (9 mm) per NFPA® 1911 (2012).

    f. Check retread tires for tread separation.

    g. Make sure that the splash guards are in place, properly attached, and in good condition.

    h. Ensure that tires are less than seven years old.

Front Inspection

Step 15: Approach the front of the vehicle noting any body damage not present in previous inspections.

Step 16: Look beneath the vehicle noting any obvious damage to brakes, front axle, steering system, or pump piping (if present). Note any loose, bent, worn, damaged, or missing parts.

Step 17: Check that the windshield is free of defects and is clean.

Step 18: Check that the wiper blades are held appropriately against the windshield, are intact, and in good condition.

Step 19: Start the apparatus engine, or hook the apparatus to the electrical charging system.

Step 20: Second Firefighter: Operate all front running and emergency light switches in the cab one at a time, calling out switch type to inspecting firefighter.

Step 21: Check all front running and emergency lights as they are activated, ensuring that they are functioning properly, all bulbs are working, and that lenses are in place and not cracked or broken.

Step 22: Visually inspect any audible warning devices on the front of the vehicle (electric siren speakers, mechanical sirens, and air horns).

CAUTION: Do not test the operation of audible warning devices inside of the building or with someone standing in front of the vehicle. This can cause hearing damage to that person.

Emergency Equipment on Front Bumper Area

Step 23: Check the pump intakes and discharges.

    a. Check that the intake cap is tight enough to prevent air leaks but not too tight for easy removal.

    b. Ensure that the preconnected intake hose (if so equipped) is firmly attached and has a gasket that will seal to a source.

    c. Make sure that the intake valve is fully closed and that the intake hose is in good physical condition and properly stowed.

Step 24: Check that any front-loaded hose is properly loaded and secure for road travel. Check that nozzles are clean and in place.

Step 25: Check the front-mounted winch, if the apparatus is so equipped. Make sure that it operates properly and that there is no damage to the winch components.

Step 26: Check that all front-mounted hydraulic rescue tool systems operate properly and are clean and undamaged.

Step 27: Check that the front-mounted fire pump operates properly, if the apparatus is so equipped.

Step 28: Unreel the electrical cord reels and inspect them as they are wiped down with a damp cloth. Check all electrical connections for tightness and condition.

Step 29: Unreel reel-mounted air hoses and inspect for cuts or other damage to the outer covering.

Left- and Right-Rear Side Inspection

NOTE: This part of the inspection should cover everything from the rear of the cab to the tailboard on each side of the apparatus.

Step 30: Note any obvious body damage that has occurred since the previous inspection.

Tires and Wheels

Step 31: Check the condition of the tire/wheel assembly on the back left and right sides of the apparatus.

    a. Check for bent or broken studs, lugs, or clamps. Ensure that parts are not missing from the tire/wheel assembly.

    b. Check by hand the tightness of the lug nuts.

    c. Make sure that there are no cracks or damage that would prevent sealing of the tire to the rim.

    d. Check for unusual accumulations of brake dust, metal flake, and/or corroded metal flake accumulations or trails on the wheel or adjacent areas.

    e. Ensure that there are no trails of fluid on the wheel, tire or brake components, or tire indicating axle gear oil leaks.

NOTE: Seals that retain axle gear oil may show slight seepage and still be serviceable, but trails of fluid on the wheel or tire are unacceptable.

Step 32: Make a quick visual inspection of the suspension components found behind the back left and right wheels.

    a. Check for proper tire type as listed on the sidewall of the tire and on the federally required GVWR sticker.

    b. Check for proper tread depth with tread depth gauge.

    c. Check for tire defects (separation, bubbles, etc.).

    d. Check that there is no excessive sidewall wear.

Step 33: Check that the rear tires are properly inflated by using a pressure gauge, and check the reading against the pressure recommended by the apparatus manufacturer on the federally required apparatus GVWR sticker. Ensure both valve stems are accessible on duals.

Step 34: Check that the rear tire valve stems and valve stem caps have no cracks or looseness.

Step 35: Check the rear tires.

    a. Check for proper tire type as listed on the sidewall of the tire and on the federally required GVWR sticker.

    b. Ensure the proper tread depth with tread depth gauge (proper tread depth varies according to state or provincial inspection requirements).

    c. Check that there is no tread separation or excessive sidewall wear.

    d. Be sure that there are no cuts or objects impaled in the tire.

    e. Check for bulges greater than 3/8 of an inch (9 mm) per NFPA® 1911 (2012).

    f. Check that dual tires are not in contact with each other or other parts of the apparatus, and ensure that there is no debris between the duals.

    g. Check retread tires for tread separation.

    h. Make sure that the splash guards are in place, properly attached, and in good condition.

    i. Ensure that tires are less than seven years old.

Step 36: Inspect the automatic snow chains, if the apparatus is so equipped. Make sure that all chains are present and in good working order.

Equipment Compartments

Step 37: Check all equipment compartments.

    a. Check that all equipment required to be in each compartment is there and that it is properly stowed and in operating condition.

    b. Check that compartment lights are operating.

    c. Ensure that compartment and equipment it contains are neat and clean.

    d. Make sure that each compartment door opens, closes properly, and latches tightly.

NOTE: You may perform equipment inspections at this time, or wait until you are performing your operational inspection.

Hose

Step 38: Examine any hose stored midship or on the side of the vehicle. Ensure that the hose is secure and properly stowed.

NOTE: This inspection should include preconnected attack lines that traverse the midship area of the apparatus or on top of the fender compartments.

Step 39: Check that the top-mounted booster hose and reels are securely and properly stowed.

Step 40: Check the water level in the booster tank through the top vent opening or sight glass; note low water level and replenish if necessary after the visual inspection.

Exterior Equipment and Condition

Step 41: Check that any equipment stored on the exterior of the vehicle is in good physical condition and properly stowed.

NOTE: This equipment includes ladders, hose, forcible entry tools, SCBA and/or spare cylinders, hand lights, floodlights, cord reels, portable water tanks, portable fire extinguishers, and other portable equipment.

Step 42: Check that equipment stored above the pump panel is in good physical condition and properly stored.

Step 43: Ensure that the reflective striping on the side of the apparatus is in good condition.

Step 44: Second Firefighter: Operate the side warning light switch in the cab, calling out to the inspecting firefighter when activated.

Step 45: Check the side-mounted warning lights. Make sure that warning lights are functioning properly, all bulbs are working, and lenses are in place and not cracked or broken.

Rear Inspection

Step 46: Check the rear bumper or tailboard for any new damage.

Step 47: Second Firefighter: Operate all rear running and emergency light switches in the cab one at a time, calling out switch type to inspecting firefighter.

Step 48: Check all running and emergency lights as they are activated. Be sure that they are functioning properly, all bulbs are working, and lenses are in place and not cracked or broken. Check brake lights and reverse lights.

Step 49: Be sure that any equipment contained in the rear compartment is present, clean, operable, and properly stowed.

Step 50: Check that the rear compartment doors open and close properly.

Step 51: Check that any equipment stored on the outside of the rear of the apparatus is in proper working order and securely stowed.

NOTE: This equipment includes portable fire extinguishers, spanner wrenches, hydrant wrenches, hydrant valves, portable master stream devices, etc.

Step 52: Ensure that any towing attachments are free of defects.

Step 53: Inspect the hose loads and cover in the main hose bed. Make sure that there is an adequate amount of hose, the hose is loaded and finished correctly, and the cover is in good condition.

Step 54: Check that the solid hose bed doors stay open, when necessary, if the apparatus is so equipped.

Step 55: Be sure that any other equipment stored in the hose bed area is in working condition and is properly stowed.

NOTE: This equipment includes ground ladders, portable water tanks, intake hose, and pike poles.

Step 56: Test and inspect all on-board hydraulic, pneumatic, and electric racks or devices for proper operation.

Documentation

Step 57: Document the inspection, record any maintenance actions, and report any deficiencies per local policy.

Cab

Step 1: Park the apparatus outdoors, if weather permits.

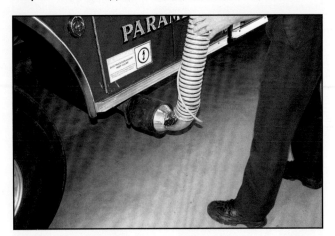

Step 2: Set up the inspection area. If indoors, be sure that proper ventilation equipment is in place, or doors are open to vent vehicle exhaust.

CAUTION: Diesel exhaust may contain up to 100 harmful chemicals and compounds. Do not run these engines in unvented areas for any period of time.

Step 3: Chock the vehicle's wheels.

Step 4: Mount the vehicle cab safely.

Step 5: Check the seat belts/restraints.
  a. Be sure that they are securely mounted and operate freely without binding.
  b. Make certain that the webbing is not damaged, cut, or frayed.
  c. Check that the buckles open and close freely.

Step 6: Check that the mirrors are not missing or broken.

Step 7: Make sure that the tilt/telescopic steering wheel is in a suitable position and is functioning correctly.

Step 8: Adjust the seat and mirrors.

Step 9: Turn off all accessory electrical switches.

Step 10: Start the vehicle.

Step 11: Run the engine at low idle per local SOPs until it has warmed to its operating temperature.

Dashboard Gauges

Step 12: Make sure that the following gauges are functioning in the normal operating range:
  a. Speedometer/odometer
  b. Tachometer
  c. Oil pressure
  d. Fuel gauge
  e. Ammeter and/or voltmeter
  f. Air pressure
  g. Coolant temperature

h. Vacuum gauge

i. Hydraulic pressure gauge

j. Transmission oil temperature gauge

k. Engine/pump hour gauge

l. DEF tank full (2010 and newer SCR equipped diesel engines)

m. DPF indicator lamp OFF (2007 and newer diesel engines)

Step 13: Check that the speedometer is at or very near zero with the apparatus parked.

NOTE: If the speedometer shows anything above zero, the gauge is defective or the apparatus is in pump gear.

Step 14: Make sure that the fuel gauge reads at least three-quarters full.

Step 15: Check that all other gauges register within limits specified in the operator's manual.

NOTE: These limits are typically graphically noted directly on the face of the gauge.

Control Operation

Step 16: Briefly operate all controls in the cab, checking each system below:

a. Electrical equipment switches

b. Turn signal switches

c. High beam headlight switches

d. Heating and air-conditioning controls

e. Radio controls

f. Public address systems (if so equipped)

g. Audible warning device controls (sirens, auto warning horns, air horns, backup alarms, etc.)

CAUTION: Before testing audible warning devices, don appropriate hearing protection. Do not test the operation of audible warning devices indoors or if anyone is standing in front of or near the apparatus. The loud noise can cause hearing damage to that person. Test these devices when no one else is in a position to be harmed.

h. Controls for any computer equipment in the cab (mobile data terminal [MDT], mobile computer terminal [MCT], etc.)

i. Windshield wiper controls

j. Window defroster controls

k. Automatic snow chain control (if applicable)

l. Load management system

Manual Transmission Clutch

Step 17: Check clutch pedal free play, noting in apparatus log or on inspection form insufficient or excessive free play. Schedule repair with a certified mechanic if there is inappropriate free play.

Steering Wheel

Step 18: Check steering wheel free play, noting in apparatus log or on inspection form insufficient or excessive free play. Schedule repair with a certified mechanic if there is inappropriate free play (excess play that does not result in the actual movement of the vehicle's front tires).

NOTE: If the apparatus is equipped with power steering, the engine must be running for the 'freeplay' inspection.

Air Brake System

Step 19: Press the brake pedal to floor when the engine is off, wheels are chocked, transmission is in neutral, air tanks are full, and parking brake is released.

NOTE: If the apparatus is in service, it may need a shoreline in case an alarm comes in during the test. Keep in mind the amount of time for air pressure buildup from above.

Step 20: Note any sounds of air leaking, position of needles. After one minute, air pressure should not drop more than 3 psi (20 kPa) for straight-chassis vehicles or 4 psi (30 kPa) for tractor-drawn aerial apparatus.

Step 21: With engine off and master switch on, pump brake pedal continually lowers air tank pressure. Warning light and buzzer should activate before 60 psi (420 kPa).

Step 22: After step 21 is complete, with parking brake released, continue to pump brake pedal until air brake control sets automatically by the button popping out.

NOTE: The button should pop out between 20 and 40 psi (140 and 280 kPa).

Step 23: Start engine and let air pressure build up to normal.

NOTE: Air pressure should build to 85-100 psi (595-700 kPa) in 45 sec at full engine RPM.

Step 24: When the needle stops climbing, the air compressor has cut out.

NOTE: The needle should stop climbing between 120 and 130 psi (840-910 kPa).

Step 25: Apply the brake pedal, lowering the pressure in the tanks by 5 to 10 psi (35-70 kPa) increments stopping at 85 psi (595 kPa). Ensure that the air gauge needle begins to indicate a pressure increase following the test.

Documentation

Step 26: Document the inspection, record any maintenance actions, and report any deficiencies per local policy.

Road Brakes

Step 1: Mount the vehicle cab safely.

Step 2: Fasten all safety restraints.

Step 3: Adjust the mirrors, steering wheel, and seat.

Step 4: Start the vehicle per vehicle manufacturer's recommendations.

Step 5: Drive the vehicle to the flat section of the test area. Observe all traffic rules and regulations if the test must be done on a public road.

Step 6: Begin at the testing area by slowly and smoothly moving the apparatus forward.

Step 7: Check brakes. Step on the brake pedal firmly when the apparatus is moving at about 5 mph (10 km/h).

Step 8: Judge or measure the distance it takes for the apparatus to come to a complete stop.

    a. Evaluate if there is any indication of pulling to one side or delayed stopping action, or unusual noise.

    b. Park apparatus safely.

    c. Dismount safely.

    d. Use caution if on a public road.

NOTE: If on a marked course, remain in the cab and read the distance.

Step 9: Determine if brakes meet necessary criteria.

    a. As a daily check, if the apparatus does not meet any of the following criteria, have the apparatus road-braking system checked by a certified mechanic.

      1. The apparatus should come to a complete stop within about 20 feet (6 m).

      2. The apparatus should stop in a straight line (not pull to the side) when the brakes are applied.

      3. The brake pedal should feel normal (no mushy or otherwise unusual feel) when the brakes are applied.

Step 10: Perform a parking brake test.

    a. Perform a daily parking brake test by repeating steps 7 through 9 but operating the parking brake instead of the service brake.

Step 11: Perform an air-brake equipped apparatus air pressure buildup test. Run pressure down by pressing on brake while the engine is off. Restart the truck and verify sufficient air pressure builds within 60 seconds or less to allow vehicle operations (90 psi [630 kPa]).

   a. Air pressure protection valve, if equipped, should prevent air horns from being operated when the pressure in the air reservoir drops below 80 psi (560 kPa).

Step 12: Document the test and any maintenance actions, and report any deficiencies per local policy.

Step 13: On air tanks not equipped with automatic drains, drain any accumulated condensation. If the wet tank has excessive amounts of water, the air dryer desiccant may need to be replaced and/or the system needs to be serviced by an AHJ approved EVT.

Air Brake System

Step 14: Press the brake pedal to floor when the engine is off, wheels are chocked, transmission is in neutral, air tanks are full, and parking brake is released.

NOTE: If the apparatus is in service, it may need a shoreline in case an alarm comes in during the test. Keep in mind the amount of time for air pressure (buildup) from above.

Step 15: Note any sounds of air leaking and position of needles. After one minute, air pressure should not drop more than 3 psi (20 kPa) for straight-chassis vehicles or 4 psi (30 kPa) for tractor-drawn aerial apparatus.

Step 16: With engine off and master switch on, pump brake pedal continually lowers air tank pressure. Warning light and buzzer should activate before 60 psi (420 kPa).

Step 17: After Step 16 is complete, with parking brake released, continue to pump brake pedal until air brake control sets automatically by the button popping out.

NOTE: The button should pop out between 20 and 40 psi (140 and 280 kPa).

Step 18: Start the engine and let the air pressure build up to normal.

NOTE: Air pressure should build to 85-100 psi (595-700 kPa) in 45 seconds at full engine RPM.

Step 19: When the needle stops climbing, the air compressor has cut out.

NOTE: The needle should stop climbing between 120 and 130 psi (840 and 910 kPa).

Step 20: Apply the brake pedal, lowering the pressure in the tanks by 5 to 10 psi (35 to 70 kPa) increments stopping at 85 psi (595 kPa). Ensure that the air gauge needle begins to indicate a pressure increase following the test.

Documentation

Step 21: Document the test, record any maintenance actions, and report any deficiencies per local policy.

Prepare for Inspection

NOTE: Check the apparatus operator's manual to determine whether the transmission and power steering fluid levels must be checked while the vehicle is running at normal operating temperature. If this is the case, perform these checks now (directly after the in-cab inspection) before shutting off the apparatus.

Step 1: Shut down the apparatus. Chock wheels, if necessary.

Step 2: Tilt-Cab Apparatus: Check that the level and/or control mechanism operates freely without binding and that the hold-open device is latched.

CAUTION: Before lifting the cab, be sure that there is adequate vertical clearance and secure all loose equipment in the cab.

Step 3: Tilt-Cab Apparatus: Check that the cab lift motors and pumps operate properly. Inspect the cab lift cylinder(s), pins, mounts, and trunnions for signs of cracking, corrosion, or excessive wear.

Leaks

Step 4: Inspect the condition of all hoses and hydraulic lines for leaking fluids. These include antifreeze, water, windshield wiper fluid, oil, fuel, transmission fluid, hydraulic fluid, power steering fluid, and/or battery fluid.

NOTE: Checking for leaks should be done throughout inspection and maintenance.

Engine (Crankcase) Oil

Step 5: Determine the oil level by using the dipstick.

NOTE: Perform this task when the apparatus is parked on a flat/level surface and oil has had a chance to settle.

Step 6: Add oil through the fill port on the engine block, if necessary. Consult the operator's manual for the proper type of oil and fill parameters.

Engine Air Filter

Step 7: Inspect the air intake system for signs of damage or dirt buildup. Do not remove filter for inspection.

Step 8: Change the air filter if the air filter restriction gauge indicates excessive resistance per the manufacturer's recommendations. Follow instructions in the operator's manual and fire department policy.

NOTE: The air filter restriction shall be monitored per NFPA® 1911 (2012) 7.7.5.

Exhaust System

Step 9: Inspect the exhaust system for damage, recording any damage found on the inspection form.

Step 10: Test the rain cap (if so equipped) on the exhaust system ensuring that it operates freely.

Radiator Coolant

WARNING: Check coolant levels when the engine and radiator system are cool.

Step 11: Determine whether the antifreeze is at the proper level and mark inside the reservoir.

   a. Remove the cap on the antifreeze fill port or look through the sight glass, if one is provided.

   b. Read the coolant level correctly.

NOTE: Some vehicles' coolant reservoirs have two marks: one for when the engine is hot, and the other for when it is cool.

Step 12: Add coolant, using the type approved by the apparatus manufacturer, until amount reaches proper level mark per operator's manual guidelines.

Step 13: Check the radiator hoses, recording any leaks or undue wear in apparatus log or on maintenance form.

Step 14: Remove any debris, such as leaves or trash, resting against the radiator or air intake.

Cooling Fan

WARNING: Some engine cooling fans activate automatically without warning. Use caution when working near the fan.

Step 15: Inspect the cooling fan, record any cracks or missing blades in an apparatus log or on a maintenance form.

Windshield Washer Fluid

Step 16: Check the windshield washer fluid level.

Step 17: Add windshield washer fluid if tank is less than half full.

Battery Condition

WARNING: Batteries give off explosive hydrogen gas. Ventilate area when servicing. Wear safety goggles and acid resistant gloves. Exploding batteries can injure or kill.

NOTE: Depending on the design of the vehicle, the batteries may be located in the engine compartment or in a separate compartment elsewhere on the vehicle. Most modern vehicle batteries are the sealed type that do not require internal inspection by the driver/operator.

Step 18: If the apparatus has unsealed batteries, carefully remove the caps and check the electrolyte (water) level.

Step 19. Add distilled water, or water recommended by the manufacturer, to cells if the electrolyte level is low.

Step 20: Check all battery connections.

    a. Tighten any loose connections.

    b. Clean away any corrosion around terminals with a mixture of baking soda and water poured on the connections, scrubbed with a wire brush, and rinsed with clear water. If batteries are washed, dry batteries to prevent parasitic current.

    c. Clean road debris, dirt, dust, moisture from the top of the batteries to prevent any 'bleed' of current from terminal to terminal that can result in electronics issues.

Step 21: Check the battery tie-downs, ensuring that the battery is held firmly in place.

Step 22: Check the built-in battery charger if the apparatus is so equipped, ensuring proper operation.

Automatic Transmission Fluid Level

NOTE: Depending on the manufacturer's recommendations, it may be necessary to check the transmission fluid level after the vehicle has been driven and shifted through all forward gears, and while the vehicle is running.

Step 23: Check the automatic transmission fluid level and condition on the dipstick and/or electronic readout according to manufacturer instructions and fire department policy.

Step 24: Add fluid to the automatic transmission if the reading on the dipstick or readout indicates that the fluid is low. Add the proper type and amount per operator's manual.

Manual Transmission Oil Level

Step 25: If so equipped, check the manual transmission oil level to ensure that it is within the normal range. Report low levels and add more fluid.

Power Steering Fluid Level

NOTE: Before shutting down the apparatus, perform the power steering fluid level check if you did not do it earlier.

Step 26: Check the manufacturer's indicator marks to determine the power steering fluid level, according to manufacturer instructions and fire department policy. Report any drop in levels.

Step 27: Add fluid if the reading indicates that the fluid is low. Make sure to add the proper type and amount according to the operator's manual.

CAUTION: Do not overfill the reservoir because damage can occur to the system.

Brake Fluid (Hydraulic Brake Systems)

Step 28: Following the procedure outlined in the operator's manual, check the level of the brake fluid in the master brake cylinder.

Step 29: Add fluid if the fluid is low. Be sure to add the proper type and amount per operator's manual.

Air System
Step 30: Check for leaks in the system.

    a. The air system should be at normal operating pressure and the engine shut off. Walk around the apparatus and listen for leaks.

    b. On air tanks not equipped with automatic drains, drain any accumulated condensation. If the wet tank has excessive amounts of water, the air dryer desiccant may need to be replaced and /or the system needs to be serviced by an AHJ approved Emergency Vehicle Technician.

Belts
WARNING: Never attempt to check the belts while the vehicle's engine is running. Doing this with the engine running could result in severe injuries or entrapment in the belt and pulley(s).

Step 31: Check all engine compartment belts for tightness and excessive wear. These belts include water pump, air compressor, fan, alternator, etc.

NOTE: You should be familiar with the proper feel for tightness of each belt when it is properly adjusted. Most engines have multiple drive pulleys.

Electrical Wiring
Step 32: Check the electrical wiring in the engine compartment.

    a. Look for frayed, cracked, loose, or otherwise worn wiring.

    b. Record any wiring problems in the apparatus log or on maintenance forms.

    c. Refer any wiring problems to a mechanic for correction.

Steering Linkage
Step 33: Check the general condition of the steering linkage.

    a. Check for looseness and free play. Report any excessive free play.

    b. Check for missing fasteners.

Fuel System

Step 34: Store the apparatus with a minimum fuel tank level required by local SOPs.

Step 35: Check for any leaks.

Step 36: Check the fuel system filters for any indication of contamination, water, or debris via the filter sight bowls.

Step 37: Inspect fuel tank mounting straps for security and corrosion.

Documentation
Step 38: Document the inspection, record any maintenance actions, and report any deficiencies per local policy.

WARNING!: Batteries produce explosive hydrogen gas when being charged. Chargers must be used correctly to prevent accidents, injury, and even fatalities. Ventilate the area when servicing. Wear safety goggles and acid-resistant gloves. Always follow apparatus and battery charger manufacturer's instructions.

NOTE: The following are general steps for charging an apparatus battery. Always follow manufacturer specific instructions.

Step 1: Read manufacturer's operators manual for the battery charger. Ensure you are familiar with information on the specific vehicle and battery used.

Step 2: Don appropriate PPE.

Step 3: Ensure the charging area is appropriately set up. Change batteries in a designated area that is well ventilated.

Step 4: Make sure that the battery and ignition switch(es) are in their OFF positions.

Step 5: Clean the battery terminals prior to charging.

Step 6: Identify the polarity and voltage of the charging system of the battery to be charged (positive or negative ground).

Step 7: Connect the charging cables in accordance with manufacturer's instructions. For example, the positive cable to the positive post of the battery and the negative cable to the stand-alone negative post or vehicle frame.

NOTE: The positive charger cable is usually marked "Pos or +" and is often colored red. The negative charger cable is usually marked "Neg or –" and is colored black.

Step 8: Follow manufacturer instructions on connecting the battery charger to a power source.

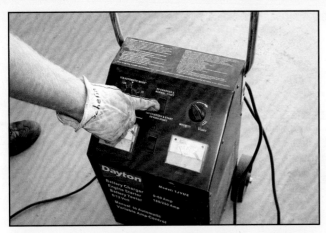

Step 9: Follow manufacturer instructions for charging the battery.

Step 10: Follow manufacturer instructions for disconnecting the battery charger.

2-7

Perform daily inspections for apparatus equipped with a fire pump.

NOTE: This skill sheet provides general guidelines for inspections. Ensure that the apparatus is in a proper location and all safety precautions are followed before beginning this skill. Always follow manufacturer's recommendations and local SOPs.

Step 1: Set up inspection area. Chock the vehicle's wheels.

Step 2: Check the underside of the apparatus and inside compartments for evidence of water or foam leaks.

Step 3: Inspect the water and foam tanks (if applicable) for proper fluid level.

Step 4: Check all components of the auxiliary fire suppression systems on board (halon, dry chemical, etc., if applicable) for damage, leaks, or corrosion.

    a. Ensure that all connections are secure.

    b. Check that all the valves are in the normal position for operation.

    c. Check the agent level in the tank by means of an agent level or sign gauge.

    d. Check dry chemical systems for signs of lumping.

    e. If the system is equipped with a hose reel, check it for proper operation.

Step 5: Make sure that the auxiliary fuel tank is full in the case of separate auxiliary engine-driven pumps with fuel supplies independent of the main apparatus fuel tank.

Step 6: Make sure that the fluid level in the priming oil tank is full and that (if equipped) the siphon-break hole in the oil line and the vent hole in the oil tank cap are open.

Step 7: Check for damage, leaks, or obstructions in any auxiliary winterization system used to prevent fire suppression water from freezing.

Step 11: Once water is introduced to the pump, initiate flowing water.

NOTE: Flowing water is usually done through an available discharge on the side or back of the truck. It is sometimes done using a truck-mounted master stream device. If using a discharge, remove the discharge cap prior to flowing water. To actually flow water out the discharge, open the appropriate discharge valve.

Step 8: Operate the pump drive control and make sure that the pump can be engaged. Depending on the design of the apparatus, the pump may be powered by a power take-off (PTO), split shaft transmission, or separate engine.

Step 9: Make sure that all gauges and valves on the pump panel are in working order.

    a. Check any gauges that are duplicated on the pump panel and dashboard to make sure they are in agreement.

    b. Open and close each valve several times to make sure it operates smoothly.

    c. Make sure that all pump drains are closed.

Step 10: Ensure an adequate supply of water so that the pump is capable of flowing water.

NOTE: Water supply can be from a positive pressure water source, such as a fire hydrant, or from the fire truck's onboard water tank by engaging the tank-to-pump valve.

Step 12: Increase the flow by increasing the water pressure. Manipulate the engine throttle (either by turning a knob or pushing a button).

Step 13: Once water is flowing, stop the operation by performing the steps in reverse order.

  a. Throttle down the engine to 0 psi or idle.

  b. Close the discharge valve.

  c. Replace any discharge cap that was removed.

Step 14: Check the relief valve.

  a. Throttle the engine to a point higher than the desired relief valve pressure setting.

  b. Slowly engage the relief valve by turning the knob.

  c. Set the relief valve.

  d. Depending on department policy, either leave the relief valve set at a specific level or disengage the relief valve by turning the knob in the opposite direction.

  e. Fully disengage the throttle back down to idle.

NOTE: Checking the relief valve can be done while water is flowing or is not flowing. The relief valve is usually operated by a turn-knob and is set using the pressure gauge and hearing.

Step 15: Test roof and bumper turrets (if applicable) for proper operation and full range of motion.

  a. Test to ensure that the length and pattern of discharge conform to the specifications in the operator's manual.

  b. Follow your department's SOPs regarding frequency for checking the agent-dispensing system.

Step 16: Reservice the vehicle. Refill the tank if water was used from the onboard water tank.

Step 17: Drain water completely from fire pump, discharges, and all booster lines to prevent unnecessary damage caused from water freezing in cold climate conditions (if required by local SOPs).

Step 18: Document the inspection, record any maintenance actions, and report any deficiencies per local policy.

NOTE: This skill sheet provides general guidelines for inspections. Ensure that the apparatus is in a proper location, and all safety precautions are followed before beginning this skill. Always follow manufacturer's recommendations and local SOPs.

Step 1: Set up inspection area. Chock vehicle's wheels.

Step 2: Flush the pump with water if it is a department policy to carry the pump full of water.

　a. Open all of the valves and drains, and push water through the system until it runs clear and no debris is being discharged.

　b. Pump water into the system through both an intake and a discharge connection (at different times).

Step 3: Check and clean intake strainers.

　a. After flushing, take away strainers to remove debris that has lodged against them.

　b. Replace any strainers that are damaged or corroded.

Step 4: Check the pump gear box for proper oil level and traces of water.

Step 5: Operate the pump primer with all pump valves closed.

Step 6: Operate the changeover valve while pumping from the booster tank in the case of a multistage (two- or three-stage) pump.

Step 7: Check the packing glands for excessive leaks.

Step 8: Ensure an adequate supply of water so that the pump is capable of flowing water.

NOTE: Water supply can be from a positive pressure water source, such as a fire hydrant, or from the fire truck's onboard water tank by engaging the Tank-to-Pump valve.

Step 9: Once water is introduced to the pump, initiate flowing water.

NOTE: Flowing water is usually done through an available discharge on the side or back of the truck. It is sometimes done using a truck-mounted master stream device. If using a discharge, remove the discharge cap prior to flowing water. To actually flow water out the discharge, open the appropriate discharge valve.

Step 10: Increase the flow by increasing the water pressure. Manipulate the engine throttle (either by turning a knob or pushing a button).

Step 11: Once water is flowing, stop the operation by performing the steps in reverse order.

    a. Throttle down the engine to 0 psi or idle.

    b. Close the discharge valve.

    c. Replace any discharge cap that was removed.

Step 12: Check the relief valve.

    a. Throttle the engine to a point higher than the desired relief valve pressure setting.

    b. Slowly engage the relief valve by turning the knob.

    c. Set the relief valve.

    d. Depending on department policy, either leave the relief valve set at a specific level or disengage the relief valve by turning the knob in the opposite direction.

    e. Fully disengage the throttle back down to idle.

NOTE: Checking the relief valve can be done while water is flowing or is not flowing. The relief valve is usually operated by a turn-knob and is set using the pressure gauge and hearing.

Step 13: Refer to the pump manufacturer's recommendations for additional instructions, if any.

Step 14: Reservice the vehicle. Refill the tank if water was used from the onboard water tank.

Step 15: Document the inspection, record any maintenance actions, and report any deficiencies per local policy.

NOTE: Ensure that the apparatus is in a proper location and all safety precautions are followed before beginning this skill. Always follow manufacturer's recommendations and local SOPs.

Step 1: Set up test area. Chock vehicle's wheels.

Step 2: Make sure that the pump is completely drained of all water.

Step 3: Inspect all gaskets of intake hose. Remove the gasket from the intake cap for use in Step 9.

Step 4: Look for foreign matter in the intake hose. Clean the hose if necessary.

Step 5: Place a lighted flashlight into the hose, just inside the female coupling, that will be connected to the intake.

Step 6: Connect 20 feet (6 m) of the correct intake hose to the pump intake connection (check original test records for correct diameter of hose). Support the hose so that it is relatively straight.

Step 7: Connect an accurate vacuum gauge (or mercury manometer) to the threaded test gauge connection on the intake side of the pump.

CAUTION: If the gauge is not connected to the intake side, it will be irreparably damaged.

Step 8: Check oil level of priming pump reservoir and replenish if necessary.

Step 9: Place the cap gasket against the male end of the hose and then use a sheet of 3/8-inch (9 mm) Lexan™, or other hard, clear plastic, large enough to cover the entire opening against the gasket. Hold the gasket and plastic in place until the priming device is operated.

Step 10: Run the priming device until the test gauge shows 22 inches of mercury (-75 kPa) developed.

NOTE: Reduce the amount of mercury developed 1 inch (3.5 kPa) for each 1,000 feet (300 m) of altitude.

Step 11: Compare readings of the apparatus intake gauge and test gauge. Record any difference.

Step 12 Shut off the engine. Listen for air leaks. No more than 10 inches (35 kPa) of vacuum should be lost in 5 minutes.

Step 13: Look through the clear plastic and examine the inside of the hose for any faults such as signs of bubbling or liner separation.

Step 14: Identify the faults by marking with chalk or other markings; remove hose from service if needed.

Step 15: Document the inspection, record any maintenance actions, and report any deficiencies per local policy.

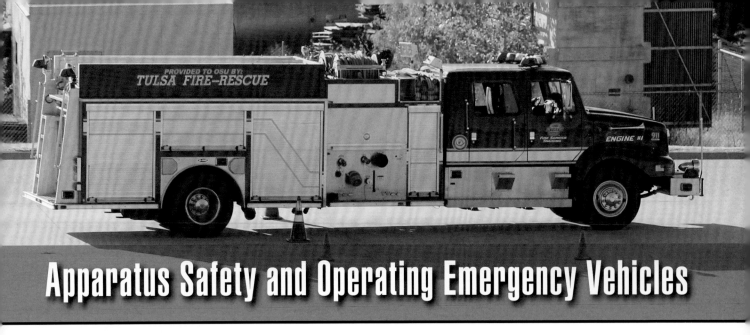

Apparatus Safety and Operating Emergency Vehicles

Chapter Contents

Key Terms

NFPA® Job Performance Requirements

This chapter provides information that addresses the following job performance requirements of NFPA 1002, *Standard for Fire Apparatus Driver/Operator Professional Qualifications (2014 and 2017)*.

4.3.1, 4.3.2, 4.3.3, 4.3.4, 4.3.5, 4.3.6, 7.2.1, 7.2.2, 7.2.3, 10.1.1

Apparatus Safety and Operating Emergency Vehicles

Learning Objectives

After reading this chapter, students will be able to:

1. Identify the considerations taken when selecting qualified driver/operators.

2. List driving regulations that affect apparatus driver/operators. (*NFPA 1002, 2014 and 2017:* 4.3.1, 4.3.6)

3. Detect reasons for accidents. (*NFPA 1002, 2014 and 2017:* 4.3.1, 4.3.6)

4. Review apparatus rider safety considerations. (*NFPA 1002, 2014 and 2017:* 4.3.1, 4.3.6)

5. Explain considerations to take when starting, idling, and shutting down apparatus. (*NFPA 1002, 2014 and 2017:* 4.3.1)

6. Explain considerations for operation of an apparatus. (*NFPA 1002, 2014 and 2017:* 4.3.1, 4.3.6, 7.2.2, 10.1.1)

7. Explain apparatus emergency response considerations. (*NFPA 1002, 2014 and 2017:* 4.3.1, 4.3.2, 4.3.3, 4.3.4, 4.3.5, 4.3.6)

8. Describe types of emergency operations warning devices. (*NFPA 1002, 2014 and 2017:* 4.3.1, 4.3.6)

9. Identify types of traffic control devices. (*NFPA 1002, 2014 and 2017:* 4.3.1, 4.3.6)

10. Explain considerations when stopping and braking apparatus. (*NFPA 1002, 2014 and 2017:* 4.3.1, 4.3.6)

11. Explain considerations when backing apparatus. (*NFPA 1002, 2014 and 2017:* 4.3.2, 4.3.3, 4.3.4, 4.3.6)

12. Explain considerations when performing tillering operations. (*NFPA 1002, 2014 and 2017:* 7.2.2)

13. Describe driving exercises and evaluation methods. (*NFPA 1002, 2014 and 2017:* 4.3.1, 4.3.2, 4.3.3, 4.3.4, 4.3.5, 4.3.6)

14. Summarize considerations for working safely on and around fire apparatus.

15. Start, idle, and shut down a fire service apparatus. (*NFPA 1002, 2014 and 2017:* 4.3.1, Skill Sheet 3-1)

16. Drive a fire service apparatus. (*NFPA 1002, 2014 and 2017:* 4.3.1, 4.3.6, 6.2.1, 7.2.2, 7.2.3, Skill Sheet 3-2)

17. Back apparatus using mirrors. (*NFPA 1002, 2014 and 2017:* 4.3.2, 4.3.3, 4.3.4, 4.3.5, 6.2.1, 7.2.1, 7.2.3, Skill Sheet 3-3)

18. Perform various driving exercises. (*NFPA 1002, 2014 and 2017:* 4.3.2, 4.3.3, 4.3.4, 4.3.5, 4.3.6, 6.2.1, 7.2.1, 7.2.3, Skill Sheet 3-4)

19. Perform various road tests in a fire service apparatus. (*NFPA 1002, 2014 and 2017:* 4.3.1, 7.2.2, Skill Sheet 3-5)

Chapter 3
Apparatus Safety and Operating Emergency Vehicles

Case History

A pumper, serving a rural area, responded late one evening to a reported auto accident. While responding, the pumper left the road while negotiating a turn. The passenger side rear wheels of the apparatus left the paved road, and the vehicle entered a roadside ditch and impacted trees and a utility pole. The passenger, who was not wearing a seat belt, was ejected from the apparatus and died as a result of injuries sustained in the crash. The driver, who was seat belted, self-extricated and began to render aid to the passenger.

Driver/operators must ensure that all members onboard the apparatus are seat belted before moving the vehicle. In addition, all driver/operators should be trained according to NFPA® 1002, *Standard for Fire Apparatus Driver/ Operator Professional Qualifications*. Training should include operation of apparatus on road conditions the driver/operator will likely encounter in local jurisdictions.

Source: NIOSH Report F2012-23

According to the United States Fire Administration (USFA), seventeen fire-fighters were killed responding to or returning from emergency incidents in 2010. This statistic underscores the need for well-trained driver/operators to exercise the utmost care in responding to and returning from incidents. Fire apparatus driver/operators are responsible for the safe transport of firefighters, apparatus, and equipment to and from the scene of an incident. The elements of safe fire apparatus operation require identifying qualified driver/operator candidates and knowing the common causes for accidents involving apparatus.

NFPA® 1002, *Standard for Fire Apparatus Driver/Operator Professional Qualifications*, has established minimum qualifications for apparatus driver/operators. In addition, it requires any driver/operator who is responsible for operating an aerial apparatus that is equipped with or without a pump to meet the requirements of NFPA® 1001, *Standard for Fire Fighter Professional Qualifications*.

This chapter describes the following:

- Selection of qualified driver/operators
- Driving regulations
- Reasons for accidents
- Apparatus rider safety

- Nonemergency apparatus operation
- Backing fire apparatus
- Emergency response considerations
- Tillering
- Driving exercises and evaluation methods

Selection of Qualified Driver/Operators

The method for selecting driver/operators varies among departments. In some career fire departments, the basic recruit academy includes an apparatus driver/operator component that qualifies all firefighters as driver/operators upon graduation. In other departments, driver/operators are promoted from the rank of firefighter. This promotion may require a minimum time of service in the department, a written test, a performance evaluation, and review of personnel records, or a combination of these criteria.

Another common method in the volunteer sector is for the chief officer to select a member who is ready for the added responsibility of the driver/operator position. The member may need to pass an evaluation after a training period to be allowed to drive to and operate at emergencies. In some departments, a member who has truck-driving experience may be allowed to enter into a driver/operator position after becoming a firefighter. Regardless of the selection process used for a candidate to become a driver/operator, a balance of experience, knowledge, maturity, sense of responsibility, and mental aptitude are necessary to safely and efficiently complete the many tasks which a driver/operator may be assigned.

NOTE: In order to meet the intent of NFPA® 1002, *Standard for Fire Apparatus Driver/Operator Professional Qualifications*, candidates must have successfully completed a Firefighter I course or equivalent course.

All fire departments must establish and maintain a thorough training program to include regularly scheduled review and refresher courses that maintain driver/operator skills and introduce new concepts as they evolve **(Figure 3.1)**. All such training should be thoroughly documented and maintained in department records. In addition to maintaining and enhancing skills, some departments may require a medical evaluation of the driver/operator's fitness for duty.

Abilities and Skills Common to Driver/Operators

Driver/operators should possess the following abilities and skills:

- **Reading skills** — Ability to read in English and comprehend a variety of complex and technical materials such as:
  - Manufacturer's operating instructions
  - Fire service manuals and periodicals
  - Maps, dispatch instructions, and preincident plans
  - Department standard operating procedures (SOP) or guidelines (SOG)

- **Computer skills** — Sufficient computer skills to:

  — Access computerized records, memos, bulletins, and manufacturers' manuals, and pertinent maintenance and inspection records.

  — Prepare and submit requests for supplies and equipment repair.

  — Operate mobile computer **(Figure 3.2)**.

  — Access and operate online mapping software and dispatch instructions.

⚠ CAUTION

While driving, the driver/operator should not operate a mobile computer. Driver/operators should focus on driving and driving only!

Figure 3.1 Driver/operators maintain their driving skills with a refresher course.

Figure 3.2 A driver/operator needs sufficient skills to operate a mobile computer.

— Operate and understand mechanical and electronic systems such as governors, foam systems, and information systems.

— Understand directions from a GPS.

- **Writing skills** — Complete maintenance forms, repair requests, and other standard forms and to write brief narratives on reports as required.

- **Mathematical skills** — Solve mathematical equations such as friction loss calculations.

NOTE: The review of basic mathematical skills is beyond the scope of this manual. Prospective or current driver/operators who are deficient in these skills may seek local resources for remedial or refresher instruction.

Figure 3.3 Firefighters maintain their fitness level by performing various exercises such as running.

- **Physical fitness** — Safely and efficiently perform strenuous tasks while under stressful fireground conditions **(Figure 3.3)**. Driver/operators may have to perform rigorous physical activities that include:

— Connecting an intake hose to a hydrant

— Hand-stretching a supply line to a hydrant

— Deploying a portable water tank

— Deploying hard sleeve hose for drafting operations

— Removing heavy or bulky equipment from compartments

NOTE: A periodic medical evaluation, in accordance with the NFPA® 1500, *Standard on Fire Department Occupational Safety and Health Program*, should be administered under the direction of the authority having jurisdiction (AHJ) in order to establish and maintain a driver/operator's fitness for duty.

- **Visual acuity** — NFPA® 1582, *Standard on Comprehensive Occupational Medical Program for Fire Departments,* provides specific standards that contain information and specific details on uncorrected vision and diseases of the eye. The authority having jurisdiction should develop standards for visual acuity.

- **Adequate hearing** — NFPA® 1582 contains a list of frequencies that a driver/operator must be able to hear and recommends rejecting a candidate who has hearing loss among those frequencies. Medical professionals conducting fire department hearing tests should be informed of the specifics of the NFPA® 1582 standard **(Figure 3.4)**.

Licensing Requirements that Affect Driver/Operator Selection

In the United States, the federal Department of Transportation (DOT) establishes the basic requirements for licensing a driver. In Canada, Transport Canada (TC) has similar authority. Both the DOT and TC have special requirements

Figure 3.4 A driver/operator must be able to hear certain frequencies, which are listed in NFPA® 1582.

for licensing drivers of large trucks. While these are national guidelines, each state or province has latitude to alter them as necessary for the needs of its jurisdiction. In some states and provinces, a fire apparatus driver/operator must obtain a commercial driver's license (CDL) in order to drive a large piece of fire apparatus. Other states or provinces may exempt fire apparatus driver/operators from these licensing requirements. Each fire department must be sure that its driver/operators are licensed according to the laws applicable in that jurisdiction.

Driving Regulations

Fire apparatus driver/operators must always exercise care for the safety of firefighters and civilians. You must maintain complete control, adjust speed for driving conditions, and operate in a manner consistent with the professional image of the fire service. Also be aware that you are subject to all traffic regulations when driving under *nonemergency* conditions

Federal laws, state or provincial motor vehicle codes, city ordinances, NFPA® standards, and department policies all regulate driver/operators in their duties. Because regulations vary from one state or province to another, they are discussed in general terms in this manual. Driver/operators should study the applicable laws and ordinances in their jurisdiction. Unless specifically exempt, fire apparatus driver/operators are subject to any statute, rule, regulation, or ordinance that governs any other vehicle operator. You must be familiar with all pertinent laws and procedures. Ignorance of the law does not limit your liability for failing to follow it. Failure to follow appropriate laws and policies may endanger fire personnel and/or civilians.

Most driving regulations pertain to dry, clear roads during daylight conditions. Driver/operators must adjust their speed to compensate for road conditions, such as rain, snow, fog, or darkness that may make driving more hazardous. You must be familiar with areas in your response district that are prone to traffic congestion, flooding, icing, or other road hazard issues.

Driving statutes usually describe vehicles that are in the emergency category; in most cases, this classification covers all fire department vehicles when they are responding to an emergency using their warning devices. In some jurisdictions, statutes may exempt emergency vehicles from driving regulations that apply to the general public if they are responding to a reported emergency and using their audible and visible warning devices. These exemptions could include the following:

- Speed limits
- Direction of travel
- Direction of turns
- Parking statutes and ordinances

Driver/operators must understand the content and scope of any exemptions. Legal decisions have held that a driver/operator who does not obey state, local, or departmental driving regulations can be subject to civil or criminal prosecution if the fire apparatus is involved in an accident. The organization that they represent may also be held responsible.

For example, in most jurisdictions, fire apparatus are not exempt from laws that require a vehicle to stop for a school bus when its flashing red lights indicate that it is loading or unloading students. Fire apparatus should proceed only after the bus driver or a police officer gives a signal that it is safe to proceed. The driver/operator should then proceed slowly, watching for children who may not be aware of the apparatus.

The driver/operator is not protected from the legal consequences of driving with **reckless disregard** for the safety of others. If the driver/operator is negligent in the operation of an emergency vehicle and is involved in a collision, both the driver/operator and the jurisdiction he or she represents may be held responsible. **Negligence** is usually found when the driver/operator has been found guilty of a gross violation of standing laws, policies, or ordinances. One example of gross negligence would be driving under the influence of alcohol. Driving under the influence of alcohol is not only an example of **gross negligence**, but recklessness as well.

Driver/operators must exercise care for the safety of others and must maintain complete control of the vehicle. The privileges extended to the driver/operator of an emergency vehicle do not relieve them of the duty to drive with **due regard** for the safety of the public. Obey all traffic control devices and rules of the road during nonemergency driving.

Common Collision Causes

The driver/operator's most important responsibility is to operate the apparatus safely during routine driving and while responding to emergency calls. If a fire apparatus is involved in a collision while responding to an incident, responders may be delayed and additional resources must be deployed to handle the fire apparatus accident. Damaged or destroyed apparatus will leave the jurisdiction with reduced capacity until the apparatus can be replaced. Additionally, the firefighters and authority having jurisdiction (AHJ) may be involved in time-consuming and costly litigation regarding injuries or damage sustained during the collision. Damaged apparatus may also present an enormous financial burden. Many departments may not be able to immediately replace a million dollar apparatus.

Reckless Disregard — An act of proceeding to do something with a conscious awareness of danger, while ignoring any potential consequences of so doing. Reckless disregard, while not necessarily suggesting intent to cause harm, is a harsher condition than ordinary negligence.

Negligence — Breach of duty in which a person or organization fails to perform at the standard required by law, or that would be expected by a reasonable person under similar circumstances.

Gross Negligence — Willful and wanton disregard.

Due Regard — Driver/operators drive with "due regard" for the safety of others using the highways. State vehicle codes provide and give special privileges to the operators or emergency vehicles; however, this does not relieve the operator from the duty and responsibility to drive with "due regard" for the safety of others.

A driver/operator's lapse in judgment and awareness and/or that of civilian motor vehicle operators can cause accidents or collisions (**Figure 3.5**). The most common place for a collision to occur is at an intersection. However, when the driver/operator drives with due caution and is fully aware of surrounding traffic, collisions are much less likely to occur. Although the driver/operator may be granted certain privileges while responding to emergency incidents, the driver/operator is responsible for the safe operation of the apparatus.

NOTE: The National Institute for Occupational Safety and Health (NIOSH) reviews and publishes reports concerning firefighter fatalities including vehicular accidents. Readers may review current as well as historical reports analyzing common fire apparatus accidents at the Institute's web site.

A fire apparatus driver/operator should maintain **situational awareness** in order to lower the chances of being involved in a collision with an object, pedestrian, or other vehicle. To establish the situational awareness necessary to safely drive an emergency vehicle, the driver/operator must train and practice with the apparatus to become familiar with its operation and the surrounding roadways. Knowledge of local traffic laws is also necessary for safe driving operation. Before allowing driver/operators to drive on public streets, they should have completed training in a practice area or other controlled environment. Driver training exercises are described in detail at the end of this chapter.

A collision en route to an emergency will end the response of the apparatus involved. The vehicle and the personnel assigned to it must remain at the scene of the collision to treat potential injuries, document damage, and await the police. Response to the original incident will be delayed as other units from farther away are dispatched.

Situational Awareness
— Perception of one's surrounding environment and the ability to anticipate future events.

Right-of-Way

Emergency vehicles on response have the right-of-way; however, this is not an excuse for a driver/operator getting into a collision. Proper situational awareness involves allowing the right-of-way if doing so decreases the chance of a collision.

It is best to anticipate unpredictable behavior from other drivers during emergency response. Emergency lights, sirens, and horns are a request for other drivers to yield to the emergency vehicle. Driver/operators must recognize that some motorists may not grant the right-of-way.

Figure 3.5 Lapses in judgment may cause a collision. *Courtesy of Mike Mallory.*

In general, fire apparatus collisions are grouped into seven basic causes, which reflect the lack of due regard and situational awareness.

1. Improper backing

2. Reckless driving

3. Excessive speed

4. Lack of driving skill and experience

5. Overloading and misuse

6. Mechanical failure

7. Driver/operator personal readiness

Improper Backing

While conducting emergency operations or during routine driving, fire apparatus must often be backed into or out of position. In addition, apparatus may be backed into the station or during hose loading operations. Backing accidents generally account for a significant percentage of all damage repair costs. Although most injuries sustained in these collisions are minor, fatalities have occurred during backing accidents. Proper backing techniques can eliminate these accidents (**Figure 3.6**).

Reckless Driving

Driver/operators have no control over the attitude or driving skills of the general public. However, fire apparatus drivers must conduct themselves professionally behind the wheel during all driving conditions and situations. Do not place firefighters or members of the public in situations where there is no alternative to a collision. You must give full attention to driving the apparatus, even under stressful conditions. Many actions are considered reckless when driving a piece of fire apparatus including:

- Driving at an excessive speed

- Letting the apparatus run off a paved surface, onto a soft road shoulder

- Attempting to read a map, electronic device, talking on a cell phone, or texting while driving

- Failing to abide by posted weight limits

- Following too close behind other apparatus or other vehicles

- Failing to obey posted traffic regulations or directions

- Failing to yield to other responding emergency vehicles

- Reacting with panic or unpredictable behavior to an approaching emergency vehicle

Driver/operators should develop a safety-conscious attitude. It is critically important to remain calm and drive in a safe manner. There is never a viable excuse for reckless driving. Driver/operators who drive aggressively, fail to observe safety precautions, and are easily agitated in traffic are a menace to other vehicles and pedestrians as well as a danger to other firefighters on the apparatus.

In addition to driving with a safety-conscious attitude, consider the public image of your department. Reckless operation of the apparatus and disrespectful gestures or words to members of the public will reflect negatively on

Figure 3.6 An example of proper backing techniques. *Courtesy of Ron Jeffers.*

the image of your department and the fire service in general. Communities in which your fire department is viewed to be professional, courteous, and skilled are more likely to offer support.

Finally, driver/operators must always remember that they have no control over the public's reaction to visual and audible warning devices. You must not put yourself or members of the public in a position where there is no alternative to a collision.

Excessive Speed

When responding to an emergency, the sense of urgency may cause a driver/operator to *want* to use excessive speed. This impulse must be controlled to maintain speeds that are safe for road conditions and the capabilities of the apparatus. Use of excessive speed may lead to loss of control of the apparatus or the inability to stop the apparatus.

Excessive speed also makes an apparatus more difficult to stop and can cause difficulties when braking. Additionally, driver/operators must be aware of the possibility of **brake fade**. Overheated brake components lose their ability to stop the vehicle, regardless of the configuration of the braking system. Disc and drum brakes will both overheat if braking and driving habits are poor. Radial tires and ABS braking systems do not reduce the potential for brake fade. Only effective handling and braking techniques can ensure maximum braking efficiency.

Brake Fade — Loss of braking function which occurs due to excessive use of the brakes.

Lack of Driving Skills

Fire departments must ensure that all driver/operator candidates complete a thorough training program before they are allowed to drive fire apparatus under emergency conditions **(Figure 3.7, p. 88)**. Driver/operators must also be trained or qualified to drive their assigned vehicles. Apparatus of similar function and manufacture may handle differently or have differing controls. It is essential that drivers are familiar with every vehicle they may be required to operate. Unfamiliarity with the controls or driving characteristics of the apparatus may lead to a collision, causing damage, injury, or fatalities. Lack of driving skills may result from:

Figure 3.7 Before driving fire apparatus under emergency conditions, all driver/operator candidates must complete a thorough training program.

- **Overconfidence in your driving ability.** You must not let the adrenaline rush of responding to an emergency impair good judgment and sound decisions. The task of safely driving the apparatus to the scene must always be foremost in your mind.

- **Inability to recognize a dangerous situation.** In a study conducted by the Society of Automotive Engineers (SAE), it was determined that in 42 percent of all collisions, the driver/operator was not aware of a problem until it was too late to correct. You may not have the ability to identify when you are approaching a dangerous situation.

- **False sense of security because of a good driving record.** You may not have had a previous collision and, therefore, do not believe a collision could occur.

- **Misunderstanding of apparatus capabilities.** Fire apparatus do not handle the same or stop as quickly as passenger vehicles. Inexperienced or poorly trained driver/operators may fail to consider the size and weight of the apparatus and drive it in the same manner as their personal vehicle. A full water tank provides better braking for the weight and subsequent road surface traction. When a water tank is empty, the apparatus is lighter, faster, and handles the road differently than when the water tank is full. Considering a pumper with a 1,000 gallon (4 000 L) tank, the difference in weight between a full and empty tank is over 8,000 pounds (4 000 kg). An apparatus with a properly baffled tank that is partially filled may be more dangerous than a full or empty tank. For safety reasons, many manufacturers recommend that tanks be either completely empty or full.

- **Insufficient training on a piece of apparatus.** This may result in a lack of knowledge about the controls of the apparatus.

Overloading and Misuse

Accidents can occur because of overloading, nonengineered modifications, and misuse. If manufacturers' design limitations are exceeded or the apparatus is modified from its original configuration and design, the apparatus will not perform according to specification, potentially resulting in unsafe operation. For example, if the apparatus is overloaded, it may not handle correctly when driven.

Mechanical Failure

Mechanical failure during travel may be an immediate occurrence and give no warning, resulting in an accident. This is a primary reason for the daily pretrip inspection whereby mechanical failures can be minimized and personnel and public safety is enhanced.

Poor maintenance of apparatus, especially braking systems, can lead to failures that result in collisions. Several fatal fire apparatus accidents have been traced back to improperly maintained apparatus braking systems. Follow an effective apparatus maintenance program to reduce the likelihood of mechanical failure.

Poor Vehicle Design

Many serious fire apparatus accidents have been attributed to poor vehicle design and maintenance. Vehicles built by apparatus manufacturers typically do not have design problems. "Homebuilt" apparatus that have been built by members of the fire department or local mechanics and custom-built, overloaded vehicles are more likely to have design problems. These vehicles are often built on government surplus or other used vehicle chassis that may be well worn even before the conversion. Many are operated over the gross vehicle weight (GVW) the chassis is designed to support and are top heavy after being retrofitted.

Driver/Operator Personal Readiness

The driver/operator must be prepared to report to duty without any compromise of physical or mental ability. Any firefighter, regardless of rank, should advise a driver/operator who may be mentally or physically impaired to seek appropriate assistance. Based on the policy of the jurisdiction, the appropriate superior officer should also be notified.

Some causes of driver/operator impairment (although temporary) may include, but are not limited to, effects from:

- Substance abuse
- Prescription drug and some over-the-counter drugs taken as directed
- Personal issues such as divorce, bankruptcy, or impending hardship
- Death in the family
- Illness
- Depression
- Fatigue

NOTE: A professional fire apparatus driver/operator is expected to adjust to and overcome driving challenges with intelligence, expediency, and safety. While driving fire apparatus, maintain a professional demeanor. Rude gestures, shouting, or using the horn to express anger are inappropriate actions.

Apparatus Rider Safety

Driver/operators must always ensure the safety of all personnel riding on the apparatus. It is SOP in most fire departments to don their protective gear before getting into the apparatus, with the exception of their helmets per NFPA® 1500 **(Figure 3.8)**. One possible exception to this is the driver/operator. Some driver/operators are not comfortable driving the apparatus wearing rubber fire boots or bulky protective clothing. If allowed by departmental SOP, the driver/operator may wish to don protective clothing after arriving at the scene.

All riders on the apparatus must be seated within the cab or body and wearing their seat belts before the apparatus is put into motion **(Figure 3.9)**. Some apparatus are equipped with a warning sound that alerts the driver/operator of an unbelted occupant. NFPA® 1901, *Standard for Automotive Fire Apparatus*, and NFPA® 1500, *Standard on Fire Department Occupational Safety and Health Program*, establish requirements for seat belt use on the apparatus. These standards also provide limited exceptions to the seat belt requirement.

⚠ WARNING

Crash Hazard

Do not wear helmet while seated .

Serious head or neck injury may result from helmet use in cab.

Failure to comply may injure or kill.

FAMA15 Do not paint over this label. Replace if damaged or lost

What This Means to You

The ultimate mission of any emergency response vehicle is to safeguard the health and welfare of the people it is meant to protect. This mission fails if the emergency responders themselves do not arrive safely. It is therefore essential that you drive the apparatus in a safe manner and that all occupants are seated and belted while the vehicle is in motion. During emergency responses, personnel may be inclined to take more risks than usual and to skip basic vehicle safety precautions. Resist this inclination. For example, it is important to don gear in the station before getting into the apparatus so that there is no need or temptation to unbuckle the seat belt. If a vehicle is in a crash, anyone who is unbelted becomes a hazard to anyone else in the vehicle. An unbelted occupant will become a lethal projectile with the potential to injure or kill those around them.

A seat belt that is held away from the body will not properly restrain you during a crash. Fasten seat belt low and snug on the hips and the shoulder belt snug against the chest. The shoulder belt is intended to restrain your upper body during a crash and keep your body in the best position to ensure the effectiveness of air bags if so equipped. Wear the shoulder belt on the outside shoulder only. Never wear the shoulder belt under your arm or swing it around the neck over the inside shoulder.

In certain vehicle configurations, the seat belt retractor may not retract the belt quickly or completely enough to prevent it from being caught in the door. Closing the door on the seat belt webbing will reduce its life. Before closing the door, check to be sure that the web will not get caught in the door. Place it completely inside the vehicle before closing the door to avoid web damage.

CAUTION

The driver/operator is responsible for confirming that all personnel are on board the apparatus with seat belts fastened. Confirmation must be verified verbally before moving the vehicle.

⚠ WARNING

Crash Hazard

Occupants must be seated and belted when vehicle is in motion.

Use only OEM approved belts.

Unbelted occupants are at greater risk of injury or death in a crash.

FAMA07 Do not paint over this label. Replace if damaged or lost.

Figure 3.8 This firefighter is removing his helmet before getting on the apparatus.

Figure 3.9 All personnel must be seated and wearing their seat belts before the apparatus is put into motion. *Courtesy of Ted Boothroyd.*

Loading fire hose while driving the apparatus is particularly common when loading large diameter (4-inch [100 mm] or larger) supply hose. It is common for large-diameter supply hose to be loaded as the driver/operator slowly drives the apparatus. NFPA® 1500 provides the following directions on how these operations should be performed:

- Train all members specifically on how to perform the moving hose-load operation. The procedure must be contained in the department's written standard operating procedures (SOPs).

- Assign at least one member, other than the driver/operator and the firefighters actually loading the hose, as a safety observer to the operation. The observer must have constant visual contact with the hose-loading operation, as well as visual and voice communication (usually via a portable radio) with the driver/operator **(Figure 3.10, p. 92)**.

- Close the area in which the hose loading is being performed to other vehicular traffic.

- Drive the apparatus only in a forward direction, straddling or to one side of the hose, and at a speed no greater than 5 mph (10 km/h).

- Do not allow members to stand on any portion of the apparatus while the vehicle is in motion.

Figure 3.10 Assign a safety observer who can see both the hose-loading operation and the driver/operator.

Firefighters should never be allowed to ride the tailboard, front bumper, or running boards of any moving apparatus. This is specifically prohibited by NFPA® 1500.

WARNING!
Firefighters must never ride on the outside of a moving apparatus for any reason. Serious injury or death could occur if the apparatus is involved in a collision or rollover or if the firefighter falls from the moving apparatus.

⚠ **WARNING**

Fall Hazard.

Never ride on vehicle when it is in motion.

Fall from moving vehicle may injure or kill.

FAMA24   Do not paint over this label. Replace if damaged or lost.

Newer apparatus are usually designed with fully enclosed cabs; however, many older apparatus are still in service with jump seat riding positions that are not totally enclosed. Some of these are equipped with safety bars or gates that are intended to prevent a firefighter from falling out of a jump seat. These devices are **not** substitutes for safety procedures that require firefighters to ride in safe, enclosed positions wearing their seat belts. Safety devices that are held in an upright or open position by straps or ropes provide no extra security for the firefighter riding in the jump seat.

Tiller training can be especially problematic in that most tiller apparatus only have a single seat within the confines of the tiller operator's enclosure.

This leaves no fixed riding position for an instructor who wishes to be in close contact with the tiller operator during training. NFPA® 1500 allows for a detachable seat to be placed next to the tiller operator's position in which the instructor may sit. This seat must be firmly attached to the apparatus and allow the instructor to be belted in position. The tiller operator and/or the instructor must wear a helmet and eye protection if they are not seated in the enclosed area. Newer apparatus designs may include a tiller operator enclosure that is capable of seating both the tiller operator and an instructor. If during the training exercise the apparatus is needed to make an actual emergency response, end the training session. A qualified tiller operator should take the controls of the tiller, and the student and instructor should take seated and belted positions inside the cab of the apparatus.

Safe Methods of Entering, Exiting, or Climbing

One of the most common causes of injury for the driver/operator is from slips and falls when entering and exiting the apparatus. Slips and falls can injure and kill. Be aware of the importance of using safe methods, and ensure that others using the apparatus use the same careful approach.

- Always face inward toward steps and handholds when entering, exiting, and climbing.
- Do not step or climb upon any vehicle surface unless it is slip resistant and handholds are provided.
- Be aware that certain steps may be a pivoting or folding design. Be certain that such steps are firmly engaged in the weight-bearing position before placing full weight on the step.

When climbing on or off vehicle, always:

- Face the vehicle.
- Use steps and handholds.
- Maintain three points of contact with vehicle (two feet and one hand or two hands and one foot).
- Keep steps, handholds, shoes, and walkways clean of grease, mud, dirt, fuel, ice, and snow.
- Use extra caution when wet, icy, or muddy.
- Replace surfaces when worn.

⚠ WARNING

Fall hazard
When climbing on or off vehicle, ALWAYS:
- Face vehicle.
- Use steps and handholds.
- Maintain three points of contact with vehicle (two feet and one hand or two hands and one foot).
- Keep steps, handholds, and walkways clean.
- Use extra caution when wet, icy or muddy.
- Replace surfaces when worn.

Slips and falls can injure or kill.

FAMA23   Do not paint over this label. Replace if damaged or lost.

Starting, Idling, and Shutting Down Apparatus

Driver/operators must be capable of starting, idling, and shutting down the apparatus in a safe and efficient manner. They must also understand components of the emission system such as diesel particulate filters (DPF) and diesel exhaust fluid (DEF) tanks that may be affected by these operations. The following sections address important considerations for starting, idling, and shutting down apparatus.

Starting the Apparatus

Vehicle manufacturers provide specific details regarding the features of their apparatus in operator manuals. Driver/operators should consult these publications for more detailed information.

When preparing to start the apparatus, whether for an emergency response or routine trip, the driver/operator must first know the destination and route of travel **(Figure 3.11)**. During emergency response, taking the time to review the incident location will allow the driver/operator to consider response factors such as road closings or traffic congestion. See **Skill Sheet 3-1** for the steps to start, idle, and shut down a fire service apparatus.

Figure 3.11 The driver/operator checking the map.

Idling the Engine

Follow manufacturer's recommendations on idling engines. Allowing a diesel engine to idle unnecessarily will waste fuel and may lead to the buildup of carbon in injectors, valves, and pistons and may cause damage to internal engine components and emission systems.

Diesel Particulate Filters

Beginning with engines produced in 2007, apparatus began to be equipped with a diesel particulate filter (DPF). The driver/operator needs to be familiar with the operation of the DPF and the significance of the following items:

- **High Exhaust System Temperature (HEST) indicator** — Lights when the exhaust system is very hot, usually due to an active regeneration in process.

- **DPF indicator** — Lights to indicate that the DPF is loading up with soot. See the owner's manual for details.

- **Manual (parked) regeneration switch** — Allows driver/operator to manually initiate an active regeneration to burn off the DPF soot load.

- **Regeneration inhibit switch** — Allows the driver/operator to keep the engine from initiating an active regeneration process. Used in limited circumstances if the apparatus is parked on dry grass or over other combustible material where there is a risk that high exhaust temperatures may start a fire.

The DPF collects particulates (soot) from the exhaust stream and burns them more completely. Apparatus equipped with a DPF will have very clean exhaust emissions and no black smoke as is common with older diesel engines. The soot burns out of the DPF naturally when the exhaust is very hot. If the apparatus makes frequent short runs, or operates in very cold climates, the exhaust may never get hot enough to burn out the soot and an active regeneration is required.

Active regeneration can occur in two manners, in automatic mode or in manual (parked) mode. Automatic regeneration occurs when the engine load, exhaust temperature, and engine speed are within an acceptable range. When the conditions are met, the engine will begin dosing fuel into the exhaust stream to raise the exhaust temperature and burn off the soot.

Active regeneration can also occur when the truck is parked. Parked regeneration allows the cleaning of the DPF in stationary truck operations and requires operator involvement to initiate. The operator will be notified of the need for a parked regeneration by illumination of the DPF light located in the cab. Parked regeneration cannot be initiated during pumping operations. Regeneration, whether automatic or manual, greatly increases the temperature of the exhaust exiting the tailpipe. Driver/operators should be aware of this and take precautions against harm from these high exhaust temperatures.

Parked Regeneration Hazards

Parked regeneration causes high exhaust gas temperatures at zero vehicle speed. Keep personnel away from exhaust outlet to avoid serious burns and injury. Do not perform parked regeneration while connected to an exhaust extraction system. Damage to the exhaust extraction system may result.

Exhaust gets extremely HOT without warning.
   KEEP AWAY from exhaust gas.
   Do NOT Touch pipes or parts.
   Do not park near flammable objects.
Hot metal and gas may burn skin or start fires.

FAMA04   Do not paint over this label. Replace if damaged or lost.

Diesel Exhaust Fluid Tanks

An apparatus equipped with Selective Catalyst Reductant (SCR) will have a tank in addition to the fuel tank that must be filled with Diesel Exhaust Fluid (DEF). It is the responsibility of the driver/operator to keep the DEF tank filled at all times. Failing to keep the DEF tank full may derate (reduce its **torque** output) the apparatus engine, or limit the vehicle speed. After a driver/operator continues to ignore an empty DEF tank, the apparatus may be limited in speed to 5 mph (10 km/h) and will need service from the dealer. Top off the DEF tank every time the apparatus is fueled and carry a spare jug of DEF on the apparatus just in case.

Shutting Down the Engine

The driver/operator should never shut down an engine immediately after a full load operation or when the temperature gauge indicates that the engine is overheated. A hot engine should cool to the normal operating temperature. Usually an idling time of three to five minutes is sufficient. Shutting down an engine without sufficient cool down may result in the following:

Torque — (1) Force that tends to create a rotational or twisting motion. (2) Measurement of engine shaft output. (3) Force that produces or tends to produce a twisting or rotational action.

- Immediate increase of engine temperature from lack of coolant circulation
- Oil film "burning" on hot surfaces
- Damage to heads and exhaust manifolds
- Damage to the turbocharger that can result in seizure

CAUTION

Never rev a diesel engine immediately before shutting it down. Damage to internal components may occur.

A driver/operator should never attempt to shut down the engine while the apparatus is in motion. You should always follow manufacturer recommendations for shutting down an apparaus. Shutting down the engine while the apparatus is in motion will cut off fuel flow from the injectors. Fuel flow through the injectors is required for lubrication anytime the injector plunger is moving. Fuel pressure can build up behind the shutoff valve and prevent the valve from opening.

Driving Apparatus

Driver/operators must be familiar with how to safely drive and operate the apparatus to which they are assigned. In most cases, apparatus will be equipped with automatic transmissions.

Driver/operators should also be aware of the following issues pertaining to driving the vehicle in nonemergency situations:

- Adjusting mirrors
- Potential points of contact
- Driving downhill
- Driving off-road
- Visual lead time
- Bridges and railroad crossings
- Adverse weather

Adjusting Mirrors

The large size of most apparatus makes it imperative that driver/operators have well-adjusted mirrors. These mirrors help to minimize blind spots before placing the apparatus in motion. Careful side view and rear-view mirror adjustment are critical to the safe operation of any vehicle. Since most apparatus are shared by multiple driver/operators, it is essential that mirror adjustment take place at the start of each shift, or any time the driving responsibility changes from one individual to another.

Have a partner walk around the vehicle to identify the blind spots. Adjust each mirror to minimize the number and extent of any blind spots **(Figure 3.12)**. Once blind spots are identified, compensate for this lack of vision while driving by slowing down before making turns or lane changes into areas where other vehicles or pedestrians may be hidden. Always keep side and rear view mirrors and cameras clean.

Transmissions

Apparatus equipped with automatic transmissions are becoming the norm for many fire departments. Eliminating much of the driver/operator's decision making regarding when to shift gears will reduce the likelihood of the engine sustaining damage from lugging. **Skill Sheet 3-2** provides the steps for driving both a manual and an automatic fire service pumping apparatus.

NOTE: Some jurisdictions may recommend manually shifting an apparatus equipped with an automatic transmission as a way to slow the vehicle in preparation for a stop. Local policy may specify this practice as a measure to extend the life of service brakes.

Manual transmission apparatus are becoming less prevalent in today's fire service. However, some mobile water supply apparatus and older model apparatus feature manual shift transmissions. The driver/operator should consult the operator's manual for specific information on driving apparatus with two-speed rear axles or a transmission with more than five speeds.

Figure 3.12 Adjust the mirrors to minimize blind spots.

Potential Points of Contact

Driver/operators of aerial apparatus must always be conscious that the aerial device may be hanging several feet (meters) over the front or rear of the apparatus. Take this into consideration whenever turning or parking the vehicle. The bumpers on the cab or rear of the vehicle may not be the only projections to mind while avoiding contact with other vehicles and objects.

Because of the large size of most aerial apparatus, there are several points of potential contact under the front, middle, and rear of the vehicle. Keep this in mind when traversing steep ramps, curbs, speed bumps, and similar obstacles on the road **(Figure 3.13)**. The classic definitions of these areas follow:

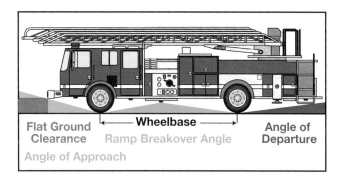

Figure 3.13 The driver/operator needs to keep in mind that the apparatus has several potential points of contact under the vehicle.

- **Angle of approach** — Angle formed by level ground and a line from the point where the front tires touch the ground to the lowest projection at the front of the apparatus.

- **Angle of departure** — Angle formed by level ground and a line from the point where the rear tires touch the ground to the lowest projection at the rear of the apparatus.

- **Breakover angle** — Angle formed by level ground and a line from the point where the rear tires touch the ground to the bottom of the frame at the wheelbase midpoint.

Driver/operators must have a keen awareness of these three angles for the apparatus they are driving. This awareness gives the driver/operator a sense of which objects can safely be traversed. Failure to realize this information could result in damage to the apparatus and property of others if it "bottoms out" while crossing an obstacle.

Weight Transfer/Center of Gravity

The effects of weight transfer must be considered in the safe operation of fire apparatus. Weight transfer follows the law of inertia which states that "objects in motion tend to remain in motion; objects at rest tend to remain at rest unless acted upon by an outside force." Whenever a vehicle undergoes a change in speed or direction, weight transfer takes place relative to the rate and degree of change. Apparatus driver/operators must be aware that the weight carried on most fire apparatus can contribute to skidding or possible rollover due to lateral weight transfer. These hazardous conditions can result from too much speed in turns, harsh or abrupt steering action, or driving on slopes too steep for a particular apparatus. Water tanks that are improperly baffled and partially filled with liquid (water or foam concentrate) are of particular concern when driving an apparatus.

The driver/operator should use only as much steering as needed to keep weight transfer to a minimum. Steering should be accomplished in a smooth and fluid motion rather than a series of multiple turns. Maintain a speed that is slow enough to prevent severe weight transfer from occurring.

Axle Weight Distribution

The driver/operator should ensure that the apparatus is properly loaded at all times. Poor weight distribution can make vehicle handling unsafe, such as the following:

- Too much weight on the steering axle can cause hard steering and can damage the steering axle and tires.

- Under-loaded front axles (caused by shifting weight too far to the rear) can make the steering axle weight too light to steer safely.

- Too little weight on the driving axles can cause poor traction.

- The drive wheels may spin easily.

During bad weather, the truck may not be able to keep going. Weigh the apparatus after loading it with all equipment and personnel to ensure that the axle loading is balanced within 7 percent from side to side and within the axle weight ratings front-to-back.

Driving Downhill

Use the service brake and auxiliary brake as well as manually shifting to lower gears to limit speed. To prevent engine damage, limit downhill speed to lower than maximum rpm. The engine governor cannot control engine speed downhill: The wheels turn the engine and driveshaft as gravity pulls the vehicle down the hill. Engine speed faster than the rated rpm can result in engine damage. It is unsafe and may be illegal to allow the apparatus to coast out of gear or "freewheel" while driving downhill. Failure to use alternate methods to slow the vehicle may result in brake failure, resulting in vehicle runaway.

NOTE: Some jurisdictions may recommend using the transmission to slow the vehicle and maintain a safe speed on the descent. Local policy may specify this practice as a measure to extend the life of service brakes.

Engine Lugging

Engine lugging occurs when the throttle is applied when a manual transmission is in too high a gear for the demand on the engine. A common example is trying to accelerate while a vehicle is moving up a steep grade. When this happens, the engine cannot respond to the amount of work being asked for at the throttle. When this **overthrottling** occurs with a diesel engine, more fuel is injected than can be burned. This results in an excessive amount of carbon particles in the exhaust, oil dilution, and additional fuel consumption. If lugging does occur, the driver/operator should not allow the engine rpm to drop below peak torque speed.

Overthrottling — Process of injecting or supplying the diesel engine with more fuel than can be burned.

Bridges and Railroad Crossings

Driver/operators must be actively familiar with the potential hazards, including bridges and railroads, associated with travel routes in their response areas. Always carry detailed maps of your response area and plan routes from the fire station to each potential emergency scene.

When determining a route to take, plot routes that avoid low overpasses and incompatible bridges. NFPA® 1901, *Standard for Automotive Fire Apparatus,* requires a placard in every apparatus that lists the vehicle height and weight in feet and tons to emphasize the importance of watching for bridge and overpass limits.

Aerial apparatus may be much longer than other commercial vehicles. This poses a hazard in areas where railroad crossings are located just before a controlled intersection. Drivers who cross the railroad tracks must ensure that there will be room between the tracks and the stop light to fit the apparatus while the light is still red. There are 19,824 locations in the U.S. where there is less than 100 feet (30 m) following the railroad tracks. These sites account for an average of 122 accidents annually. Driver/operators should survey their local roads, identify any problem areas, and be prepared to wait on the near side of the tracks until traffic has made sufficient room to proceed completely across before stopping.

Adverse Weather

Driver/operators must consider weather conditions as major factors while driving apparatus. Rain, snow, ice, and mud make roads slippery. Recognize these dangers and adjust your speed, factoring sharpness of curves, the crown of the road, road surface conditions, and other traffic. The driver/operator must recognize areas that may become slippery more easily, such as bridges and northern slopes of hills, as well as areas prone to blowing and drifting snow. The safe following distance between vehicles increases dramatically when the apparatus is driven on slippery roads. It may take 3 to 15 times greater distance for a vehicle to come to a complete stop on snow and ice than it does on dry pavement. It may be prudent for you to carefully apply the brakes in an area free of traffic to determine the slickness of the road.

Emergency Response Driving Considerations

Driver/operators must be aware of the many factors that will affect their safe and efficient response to an emergency. In most jurisdictions, when civilian drivers encounter emergency vehicles responding with warning lights activated and audible devices sounding, they must pull to the right, stop, clear intersections, and remain motionless until the emergency vehicle has passed. However, the fire apparatus driver/operator must never assume what another driver's actions will be especially when fire apparatus are responding in convoy. Drivers of private vehicles may pull over and stop for the first piece of apparatus and then pull out in front of the second apparatus, not realizing it was approaching. Additionally, some drivers may panic at the sight of approaching apparatus, or abruptly stop in the middle of an intersection. Other drivers of private vehicles may not hear a fire apparatus approaching for any number of reasons.

Anticipating that other drivers may not see, hear, or respond appropriately to approaching apparatus, the driver/operator should use the following guidelines to help avoid potential collisions:

- **Aim high in steering**. Find a safe path well ahead.
- **Get the big picture**. Stay back, and see the reaction of other motorists.
- **Keep your eyes moving**. Scan the area — do not stare at one view.
- **Leave yourself an "out."** Visualize an escape route to avoid a collision. Prepare for the unexpected.
- **Maintain enough distance from the vehicle ahead to pull out of traffic safely if the need arises.**
- **Make sure that others can see and hear you.** Use a combination of warning devices.

In addition to these guidelines, driver/operators must be familiar with warning devices and traffic control devices, as well as specific considerations involved with intersections and passing other vehicles.

Warning Devices

Fire apparatus are equipped with various combinations of audible and visual warning devices. Warning devices must be used to make the public aware of an approaching emergency vehicle. Use of warning devices should be limited to response to true emergencies. Use of these devices indiscriminately may promote a negative image of the fire service. Local jurisdictions should have policies governing what type of incident constitutes an actual emergency. Driver/operators should have a clear understanding of polices used in their jurisdiction with regard to emergency response.

Driver/operators must always drive with regard for the general motoring public. Some fire departments require apparatus warning devices to be turned off, and the apparatus to proceed with normal traffic on limited access highways. In reality, most fire apparatus are not capable of keeping up with other vehicular traffic at highway speeds. In slow moving traffic, warning devices may be used to help negotiate passage.

Some fire departments rely upon designated response routes. This practice may be hazardous if an apparatus is delayed or detoured for some reason.

Policies may require the use of radio reports to update location and status, particularly when approaching an intersection where another vehicle may be nearby. As previously stated, the driver/operator must come to a complete stop at intersections controlled with a red traffic light or stop sign.

Audible Warning Devices

Audible warning devices may include electronic or mechanical sirens as well as air horns. Studies have shown that civilian drivers respond better to sounds that change pitch. Short air horn bursts and the constant up and down oscillation of an electronic or mechanical siren may be the best way to get the attention of motorists. The sudden sounding of audible warning devices anywhere adjacent to unaware motorists may startle or panic civilians causing them to swerve or lose control of their vehicle.

At speeds above 50 mph (80 km/h), an emergency vehicle may outrun the effective range of its audible warning device. Sirens mounted on emergency vehicles operating at slower speeds project out much farther. In some instances, increasing the speed of an apparatus by 20 mph (30 km/h) can decrease the audible distance by 250 feet (75 m) or more.

There have been numerous collisions between fire apparatus and other emergency vehicles. It is not always possible to hear the audible warning devices of other approaching emergency vehicles. When more than one emergency vehicle is responding along the same route, they should travel at least 300 to 500 feet (90 to 150 m) apart. Some fire departments specify that different siren settings be used by apparatus responding together.

CAUTION
In-cab intercom headsets may make it more difficult to hear ambient noise or sirens of other emergency vehicles.

Visual Warning Devices

White lights are readily visible even during daylight hours. Because of this, the driver/operator should turn on the apparatus headlights as part of the emergency response. Dim headlights and turn off spotlights in situations where they may blind oncoming drivers. Do not drive with the high beam headlights constantly on as they may obscure other warning lights. Some jurisdictions use a combination of colored lights as part of their emergency light display. Fire department personnel must consult local laws and ordinances when designing the warning light array for a piece of apparatus.

In addition to dimming headlights and spotlights at an incident scene, driver/operators must be aware that warning lights and scene floodlights may reduce the effectiveness of the reflective trim on firefighters PPE. This may cause the drivers of approaching vehicles to be unable to see firefighters standing and working in the street. In certain situations, it may be appropriate to turn off some of the warning lights once the apparatus is in position. Some jurisdictions have equipped their apparatus with several yellow warning lights that are turned on when the apparatus is parked at an incident scene. These yellow lights allow approaching vehicles' head lights to more effectively illuminate the reflective trim worn by firefighters.

NOTE: Studies have shown that vehicles traveling with low beam headlights on during daylight hours have fewer accidents. It is the practice in some jurisdictions that fire apparatus travel with low beam headlights activated anytime that they are on the road.

Traffic Control Devices

The presence of a traffic control device does not relieve the driver/operator from the responsibilities of using defensive driving techniques. Even when traversing an intersection with a green light, maintain a speed that will allow for a quick stop or safe evasive maneuver in case another vehicle should enter the intersection. All intersections with a red light should be approached with extreme caution, and the apparatus should be brought to a complete stop before proceeding.

NOTE: Watch for other responding apparatus from different directions as multiple vehicles may confuse the signal preemption.

Local jurisdictions use various traffic control devices to assist emergency vehicle response. Driver/operators must understand the operation of any such devices used in their response areas. The sections that follow describe some of the systems that may be available to preempt traffic signals.

Traffic Signals at Stations and on Apparatus Routes

Traffic signals in front of fire stations allow apparatus to more safely enter the roadway. The signal may be controlled by a button in the station or remotely by a dispatcher. Some are activated by the station alerting system **(Figure 3.14)**.

Stations may also control traffic lights along routes heavily used by fire apparatus. These signals should be controlled by a dispatcher, from the fire station, or by a remote control on the apparatus.

Strobe Light Activated Preemption Devices

Some systems use strobe lights (emitters) mounted on the apparatus to activate sensors in the traffic lights **(Figure 3.15)**. The emitter generates an optical signal that is received by the traffic light as the apparatus approaches. The signal causes a green light for the fire apparatus direction of travel and a red light in all other directions. This system may also be formatted to turn off pedestrian crosswalk signals. On some systems, a white light mounted on the traffic light pole indicates that the signal has been received and a green light is forthcoming. When the vehicle's parking brake is set, the emitter is turned off so as not to affect any traffic signals nearby. Vehicles not equipped with this feature may require the driver/operator to manually turn off the emitter when the apparatus is parked at an emergency scene.

Traffic Signal Preemption Devices

Some traffic control systems may be activated by the vehicle's siren as it approaches an intersection. A microphone on the traffic signal receives the sound of an oncoming siren and orders the appropriate signal preemption.

Figure 3.15 Strobe lights mounted on the apparatus activate sensors in the traffic lights.

Figure 3.14 The traffic signals in front of the fire station may be controlled by the fire department.

This device may be adjusted to activate from distances of several hundred feet to about half a mile. Intersections equipped with this device will have 3-inch (77 mm) white and blue lights, mounted near the regular traffic light, facing each direction of travel.

Upon receipt of a signal and preemption of the traffic signal, a white light indicates the direction of the approaching apparatus, which further indicates that the green signal will be forthcoming. All other directions of travel will display a blue light to indicate that an emergency vehicle is approaching. When other emergency vehicles approach from different directions, the blue light will indicate that control of the signal has been gained from another direction. They will have a red signal requiring a stop at the traffic light while the other apparatus passes through the intersection.

GPS Based Traffic Signal Preemption

Using a GPS device and radio transmitter in the apparatus, data can be transmitted to a radio receiver on the traffic light in order to preempt a signal at the intersection. This system operates automatically as long as the apparatus is in range and the transmitter is turned on. This system also features a manual disable mode that will prevent preemption of traffic signals after a vehicle has arrived at the scene.

These devices are capable of determining location, speed, and status of the apparatus turn signal, as well as maintaining a recorded database of unit identification information for a historical record of signal use. In addition, a priority mode may be programmed allowing emergency vehicles a higher control level than other municipal vehicles such as transit buses, or snow plows.

Intersections

Intersections are the most likely place for a collision to occur involving an emergency vehicle. Driver/operators must know the motor vehicle statutes as well as department policy regarding proceeding through an intersection with and without traffic control devices. Many jurisdictions as well as NFPA® 1500 require fire apparatus to come to a full stop and account for vehicles in all lanes of traffic before proceeding through the intersection. A driver/operator coasting the apparatus through an intersection is not a substitute for making a complete stop. Make every attempt to make eye contact with other drivers to ensure that they are seen before proceeding.

Driver/operators must be cautious when driving on multilane roads or approaching multilane intersections because vehicles may stop in unconventional locations in order to allow apparatus to pass. Driving regulations commonly state that private vehicles should pull to the right to yield for emergency vehicles. On multilane roads, vehicles in the left lane may pull into a left turn lane instead of making lane changes to yield. Drivers waiting to make a left or right turn at an intersection may pull to the right or the left. Driver/operators should be prepared for a driver of a private vehicle to pull to either side when yielding for fire apparatus.

In situations where all lanes of travel are blocked, local policy may allow the driver/operator to drive the apparatus into the opposing lane of traffic in order to proceed through the intersection. During this maneuver, the apparatus must proceed at a greatly reduced speed.

Oncoming traffic must be able to see the apparatus in the opposing lane. Driving into the oncoming lane is not recommended in situations where oncoming traffic is unable to see the apparatus. Driver/operators must be alert for vehicles that may enter from side roads or driveways as well as other responding emergency vehicles. Avoid making sharp, quick motions and use broader movements with the apparatus to lessen weight transfer and make the intended path of the apparatus more obvious to other drivers.

Passing Other Vehicles

Generally, it is best to avoid passing vehicles that do not pull over to yield to fire apparatus. In some instances, the driver/operator will need to pass. Be prepared to do this in the safest manner possible. Use the following guidelines to ensure safety:

- Always travel on the innermost lane (fast lane) on multilane roads. Wait for vehicles in front of the apparatus to move to the right before passing.

- Avoid passing vehicles on the right side because drivers normally move to the right upon the approach of emergency vehicles.

- Be certain that opposing lanes of traffic are clear before crossing the center line.

- Avoid passing other emergency vehicles if at all possible. However, in some cases, it may be desirable for smaller, faster vehicles such as a chief's car to pass a larger, slower vehicle such as a mobile water supply apparatus. The drivers should coordinate these maneuvers by radio, with the slower apparatus pulling to the right to allow the faster vehicle to pass.

Stopping and Braking Apparatus

Before applying the brakes, the driver/operator must consider the weight of the apparatus and the condition of the brakes, tires, and road surface. Excessive or abrupt braking action can result in a skid that may cause injury to firefighters and lead to mechanical failure.

Some apparatus are equipped with engine brakes or other types of retarding devices that assist in stopping the apparatus. When the driver/operator releases pressure from the accelerator, the engine brake or retarder is activated. Because they provide a significant slowing action, the driver/operator is able to lessen the use of service brakes. Engine brakes and retarders help extend the life of service brake components and make apparatus easier to manage.

NOTE: Driver/operators of apparatus with retarders, engine brakes, or auxiliary braking systems should become familiar with local traffic laws and the manufacturers' recommendations for use during inclement weather or other road conditions.

Following sections will address visual lead time, braking and reaction time, and skids. Braking, traction, and stability control systems will also be explained in detail.

Visual Lead Time

The time needed to stop the apparatus or perform an evasive maneuver at the current rate of speed is visual lead time. Driver/operators establish visual lead time by scanning their path of travel far enough ahead based upon their speed. Your visual lead time determines whether or not reaction time and stopping distances will be sufficient in an emergency. You must match the distance surveyed ahead of the vehicle with the speed of travel. By aiming high in steering and getting the big picture, you may become aware of conditions that require action.

Braking and Reaction Time

Driver/operators should know the braking characteristics for the vehicle they are operating. The **braking distance** is the distance the vehicle travels from the time the brakes are applied until the apparatus comes to a complete stop. The **total stopping distance** is the sum of the driver/operator's reaction distance and the vehicle's braking distance. After perceiving the need to stop the vehicle, the driver/operator's **reaction distance** is the distance the apparatus travels while the driver/operator transfers his or her foot from the accelerator to the brake pedal (**Figure 3.16, p. 106**).

Apparatus manufacturers may provide information regarding stopping distances for specific apparatus. Stopping distances may vary greatly between apparatus; therefore, local jurisdictions should conduct braking distance tests using their vehicles (**Tables 3.1 a and b, p. 106 and 107**).

Other factors affect the driver/operator's ability to stop the apparatus including:

- Road conditions (wet, dry, snow, ice) and slope of driving surface
- Speed of apparatus
- Weight of the vehicle
- Type and condition of the vehicle's tires and braking system

Braking Distance — Distance the vehicle travels from the time the brakes are applied until it comes to a complete stop.

Total Stopping Distance — Sum of the driver reaction distance and the vehicle braking distance.

Reaction Distance — Distance a vehicle travels while a driver transfers a foot from the accelerator to the brake pedal after perceiving the need for stopping.

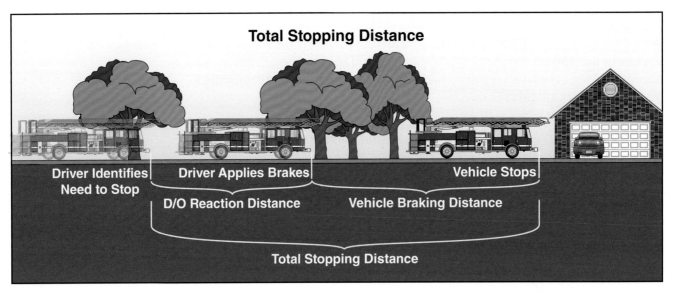

Figure 3.16 Driver/operators need to know the braking characteristics of the vehicle they are operating.

Table 3.1a (Customary) Braking and Stopping Distances (dry, level pavement)									
Speed (mph)	Average Driver Reaction Distance (feet)	Braking Distance (feet)				Total Stopping Distance (feet)			
		Vehicle A	Vehicle B	Vehicle C	Vehicle D	Vehicle A	Vehicle B	Vehicle C	Vehicle D
10	11		7	10	13		18	21	24
15	17		17	22	29		34	39	46
20	22	22	30	40	50	44	52	62	72
25	28	31	46	64	80	59	74	92	108
30	33	45	67	92	115	78	100	125	148
35	39	58	92	125	160	97	131	164	199
40	44	80	125	165	205	124	169	209	249
45	50	103	165	210	260	153	215	260	310
50	55	131	225	255	320	186	280	310	375
55	61	165	275	310	390	226	336	371	451
60	66	202	350	370	465	268	426	436	531

Typical Brake Performance
A–Average automobile
B–Light two-axle trucks
C–Heavy two-axle trucks
D–Three-axle trucks and trailers

A paved surface that is flat and dry provides for optimal stopping. Driver/operators must compensate for various road conditions that will hinder their ability to control the vehicle, such as when they must reduce the speed of an apparatus under less-than-ideal roadway or weather conditions.

Bringing a vehicle to a full and complete stop requires removing all of its forward momentum. As the mass or velocity of an object increases, it gains momentum. As a result, it takes longer to slow down or stop. For example, at

Table 3.1b (Metric)
Braking and Stopping Distances (dry, level pavement)

Speed (km/h)	Average Driver Reaction Distance (meters)	Braking Distance (meters)				Total Stopping Distance (meters)			
		Vehicle A	Vehicle B	Vehicle C	Vehicle D	Vehicle A	Vehicle B	Vehicle C	Vehicle D
16	3.4		2.1	3	4		5.5	6.4	7.3
24	5.2		5.2	6.7	8.8		10.4	11.9	14
32	6.7	6.7	9.1	12.2	15.2	13.4	15.8	18.9	21.9
40	8.5	9.4	14	19.5	24.4	18	22.6	28	32.9
48	10.1	13.7	20.4	28	35.1	23.8	30.5	38.1	45.1
56	11.9	17.7	28	38.1	48.8	29.6	39.9	50	60.7
64	13.4	24.4	38.1	50.3	62.5	37.8	51.5	63.7	75.9
72	15.2	31.4	50.3	64	79.2	46.6	65.5	79.2	94.5
80	16.8	39.9	68.6	77.7	97.5	56.7	85.3	94.5	114.3
88	18.6	50.3	83.8	94.5	118.9	68.9	102.4	113.1	137.5
96	20.1	61.6	106.7	112.8	141.7	81.7	129.8	133	161.8

Typical Brake Performance
A–Average automobile
B–Light two-axle trucks
C–Heavy two-axle trucks
D–Three-axle trucks and trailers

the same speed it will take a greater distance to stop a fully loaded tanker than a small initial attack apparatus. It will also take a greater distance to stop a vehicle traveling 50 mph (80 km/h) than the same vehicle when it is traveling 30 mph (50 km/h).

Skids

An important skill for the driver/operator is recognizing and avoiding conditions that may lead to skidding. Proficiency in **skid** control may be gained through practice at facilities equipped with skid pads. Any such training should be conducted under the supervision of qualified instructors using approved apparatus and specialized facilities (**Figure 3.17**).

Skid — An uncontrolled slide across a surface in a wheeled vehicle.

Figure 3.17 Driver/operators can practice skid control with skid pads on their apparatus.

Acceleration Skid — Accelerated skids usually occur when the gas pedal is applied too quickly.

Locked Wheel Skid — This type of skid is usually caused by braking too hard at a high rate of speed and locking the wheels. The vehicle will skid no matter which way the steering wheel is turned.

Two common types of skidding are acceleration and locked wheel skids. In an **acceleration skid**, the drive wheels lose traction on the road surface. To maintain control of the vehicle, the driver/operator should not apply the brakes, ease off the accelerator, and straighten out the front wheels as the vehicle begins to respond. A **locked wheel skid** generally results from braking too hard at a high rate of speed. The vehicle will skid no matter which way the steering wheel is turned. To regain proper control, ease off the brake to unlock the drive wheels and then straighten the front wheels as the apparatus begins to respond to control. The vehicle may then be slowed gradually until it is at a safe speed to continue driving.

A driver/operator driving a vehicle equipped with a standard transmission should not engage the clutch until the vehicle is under control and just before stopping the apparatus. Once the driver/operator has the skid under control, gradually apply power to the wheels to further control the vehicle by creating traction, or apply brakes as needed.

Driver/operators must balance the service brakes, transmission gear selection, and retarding device in order to maintain control when descending grades during icy conditions. Some of the most common causes involving driver error include the following:

● Driving too fast for road conditions

● Failing to anticipate obstacles (including other vehicles, debris, or pedestrians in the road)

● Improper use of auxiliary braking devices

● Improper maintenance of tire air pressure and adequate tread depth

Antilock Braking System (ABS)

Most new fire apparatus are equipped with an all-wheel, antilock braking system (ABS). ABS systems minimize the chance of the vehicle skidding when the brakes are applied forcefully as follows:

● Using an onboard computer that monitors each wheel and controls pressure to the brakes, maintaining optimal braking ability.

● Using a sensing device to monitor the speed of each wheel, sending a signal to the onboard computer.

● Receiving information from the computer when a wheel begins to lock up. The computer compares it to the information received from the other wheels to determine if this particular wheel should still be turning. Steering is maintained as long as the wheels do not lock.

● Reducing the brake pressure and allowing the wheel to continue to turn. Once it turns, it is braked again.

The computer makes these decisions many times per second, until the vehicle is brought to a stop. When driving a vehicle equipped with ABS, the driver/operator should maintain a steady pressure on the brake pedal, rather than pumping the pedal, until the apparatus comes to a complete stop.

Some apparatus will automatically shut off the auxiliary brake in the case of ABS activation. This does not help prevent skids or loss of traction unless the operator is applying the brakes. Apparatus without ABS require the auxiliary brake to be manually deactivated (inclement weather situations).

Apparatus Not Equipped with ABS

A driver/operator driving an apparatus NOT equipped with ABS that enters into a skid should release the brakes and allow the wheels to rotate freely. You should turn the steering wheel in the direction the vehicle should be traveling. If you oversteer, you will lose control of the vehicle.

Drivers should be aware that when apparatus with ABS is replaced with a reserve apparatus without ABS, you will need to alter the driving operations considerably. You must know the apparatus being operated.

Auxiliary Braking Systems

NFPA® 1901 requires that all apparatus with a GVWR of 36,000 lb (18 000 kg) or greater be equipped with an auxiliary braking system. Using an auxiliary braking system not only helps to reduce brake fade on long, steep grades, it can also significantly reduce service brake system maintenance costs.

There are four types of auxiliary brakes to aid the foundation brakes in slowing the vehicle:

- Exhaust brake
- Transmission output retarder
- Engine compression brake
- Electromagnetic retarder

The amount of retardation force available from any auxiliary braking system is a complex function of vehicle speed, engine speed, temperature, and control strategy. Transmission output retarders and electromagnetic retarders provide the highest level of braking torque and are unaffected by transmission gear shift changes. Engine brakes multiply their effectiveness through the transmission gearing, and the brake torque will increase as the transmission downshifts.

Auxiliary Brakes in Inclement Weather

Apparatus driver/operators should remember to turn off the auxiliary brake and reduce speed in inclement weather. In heavy rain, ice, or snow there is already a decreased level of traction due to the slippery road conditions. Although you may not be applying the service brakes, the simple action of taking your foot off of the accelerator may cause the application of the auxiliary brake. The sudden torque placed on the vehicle by the operation of the auxiliary brake may create a situation where the tires can no longer provide enough friction on the road surface to prevent the apparatus from entering a significant skid. Always refer to the auxiliary brake manufacturers' recommendations for more information.

Exhaust Brakes

The exhaust brake is the least capable of the four auxiliary brake devices. An exhaust brake uses a valve to restrict the flow of the exhaust, which creates back pressure that adds to the engine's inherent braking ability.

Engine Compression Brakes

An **engine compression brake** is an electronically-actuated mechanical system added to the engine valve train. The engine compression brake converts the mechanical energy of the vehicle into heat by compressing the engine intake air and then discharging the pressure to the atmosphere through the exhaust. The heat energy introduced into the engine cooling system is minimal. An engine compression brake has no impact on engine temperature.

Electromagnetic Retarders

An electromagnetic retarder is either mounted in the driveline, or supplied as an integral part of the rear axle. When activated, an electromagnetic field is created by supplying electrical power to a series of coils in the retarder. This field inhibits the rotation of the rotor and creates a braking torque at the rear wheels. Various options allow the retarder to be applied in stages either manually or by combinations of brake and accelerator pedal settings.

Electromagnetic retarders dissipate heat through cooling vanes into the surrounding air. Heat transfer becomes less efficient as the ambient temperature rises. Electromagnetic retarders will experience some loss of effectiveness at high temperatures.

Transmission Retarders

A transmission output retarder uses the viscous property of the automatic transmission fluid to retard the driveline. When activated, transmission fluid is introduced into the retarder housing and energy is absorbed into the fluid through the opposing action of spinning vanes. This retards the vehicle through the rear wheels and adds heat to the transmission fluid. This heat is dissipated through the transmission cooler and radiator.

Transmission retarders can provide high braking capacity but are limited in high ambient environments by the capacity of the vehicle cooling system. High transmission fluid temperatures caused by heavy retarder use increases the load on the engine cooling system and may cause the system to disengage.

Auxiliary Traction Control Systems

Traction can be improved by the use of more aggressive tire treads, tire chains, mechanical features in the driveline, or ABS-based automatic traction control. The driver/operator should be aware of these features on the apparatus and trained to use them.

Apparatus may be equipped with manually applied tire chains or automatic chains featuring short lengths of chain on a rotating hub in front of each drive wheel **(Figure 3.18)**. The hubs swing down into place upon activation from the cab. The hub with chains attached is driven by the drive wheel and the lengths of chain are spun under the tire by centrifugal force. These chains may be ineffective in snow deeper than 3 to 6 inches (75 to 150 mm) depending on consistency of the snow, or when the vehicle is moving at very slow speeds, or in reverse.

Automatic Traction Control (ATC)

Many vehicles that are equipped with ABS are also equipped with automatic traction control (ATC). This feature automatically reduces engine torque and applies the brakes to wheels that have lost traction and begin to spin. This transfers torque to the wheels that still have traction, which helps improve overall traction on slippery roads.

Some apparatus equipped with ATC have a mud and snow switch that increases available traction on extra soft surfaces. The switch may be activated until normal traction is regained. If the driver/operator needs to rock the apparatus out of a particular spot, and the ATC has deactivated the throttle, the mud and snow switch should be activated. The driver/operator must use caution when activating this switch. If the apparatus regains traction suddenly, axle damage may occur. Consult the manufacturer's operations manual for detailed instructions on operating the auxiliary braking systems on particular apparatus.

Figure 3.18 Automatic snow chains.

Driver Controlled Differential Lock

Some aerial apparatus may be equipped with Driver Controlled Differential Lock (DCDL). The purpose of this equipment is to improve traction and handling by locking the differential during off-road and wet weather conditions, such as snow or ice. The DCDL can be shifted while the vehicle is stationary or moving. When engaged, both wheels are forced to turn at the same speed, resulting in the differential being locked to maximize traction. While the DCDL is locked, the driver may feel a tendency for the vehicle to move straight ahead when turning and may hear tires "scrubbing;" this is normal. Disengage the DCDL feature when road conditions improve to prevent drive line damage, tire wear, and maximize vehicle control.

NOTE: Manufacturers recommend that the differential lock be disengaged while traveling and turning downhill. A dangerous condition can occur whereby the driver/operator loses positive steering control due to the differential lock not allowing differential rear wheel rotation.

Interaxle Differential Lock

The interaxle differential allows for speed differences between the rear driving axles. The interaxle differential lock feature allows the operator to lock-out the interaxle differential action between the rear tandem driving axles, creating one solid drive line between the rear axles. In this condition, each axle receives full torque from the engine. Under normal driving conditions where traction is favorable, leave the control in the unlock position. When approaching or anticipating poor tractive conditions, move the control to the lock position. After regaining normal traction move the control to the unlock position.

To reduce load on the drive train and avoid equipment damage:

- Ease up on the throttle pedal when shifting into or out of the locked condition.

- Do not activate this switch while one or more of the wheels are actually slipping or spinning.

- Do not spin the wheels with the inter-axle differential locked.

Stability Control Systems

Stability control systems are designed to help prevent roll-overs and tipping caused by cornering or sudden changes in direction. Two systems will be explained in the following sections: roll stability controls and electronic stability controls. Stability system safety will also be addressed.

Roll Stability Control

Roll Stability Control (RSC) is integrated into the ABS system. In addition to the usual ABS sensors, RSC includes a lateral accelerometer that senses when the side force caused by cornering approaches the roll-over threshold. It becomes active when the ABS computer senses an imminent roll over condition — even if the driver/operator does not. The driver will notice a difference in the vehicle when stability control is functioning but should continue to drive and correct as normal. The computer will attempt to slow the vehicle by first reducing the torque from the engine. If the vehicle has an engine compression brake, the driver will feel the additional deceleration as the retarder is applied. Finally, the computer may apply the service brakes at the wheels. If this happens, the driver will feel even more deceleration.

Electronic Stability Control

Electronic Stability Control (ESC), also referred to as Electronic Stability Program (ESP), is a more capable system than RSC. Where RSC merely slows the vehicle down, ESC applies the brakes independently to aim the vehicle in the direction that the operator positions the steering wheel. To accomplish this, the ESC system includes a steering wheel sensor in addition to the lateral accelerometer. Most ESC systems also reduce engine power until control is regained.

Stability System Safety

Neither RSC nor ESC improves a vehicle's cornering performance. Stability Control helps reduce vehicle instabilities when cornering or sudden changes in direction occur, however, it cannot prevent all instabilities from occurring. Always use safe driving techniques. The driver is always the most important player in safe vehicle operation.

⚠ WARNING

Crash Hazard.

This vehicle equipped with Electronic Stability Control (ESC).

ESC does not eliminate the need to drive safely.

Failure to comply will injure or kill.

FAMA13   Do not paint over this label. Replace if damaged or lost.

Backing Apparatus

Backing fire apparatus can be a hazardous action because of the vehicle's size and because the mirrors do not provide a full view around the apparatus. The sections that follow provide recommendations for backing policies and hand signals that are widely accepted for backing a vehicle. **Skill Sheet 3-3** provides the steps for backing an apparatus.

Recommended Backing Policies

All jurisdictions should develop a policy for backing fire apparatus. Always follow SOPs and local ordinances for backing procedures. IFSTA recommends that the driver/operator use the following general rules:

- If possible, position the apparatus so that backing will not be necessary.
- Walk all the way around the apparatus to clear any obstructions.
- Ensure that all equipment is secured and compartment doors are closed.
- Require the use of one or more spotters.
- Preposition lights to illuminate the area where the spotter will stand (approximately 8 to 10 feet [2.5 to 3 m]) behind the apparatus.
- Back the apparatus at a very slow speed and use caution to not outpace the spotter(s).
- Use hand signals that are agreed upon and understood by the spotter and driver/operator.
- Use portable radios, if feasible.
- Use backup cameras in addition to the mirrors, if the apparatus is so equipped.
- Sound two short blasts of the vehicle's horn immediately before backing the apparatus.
- Avoid mounting equipment on the apparatus that may interfere with the driver's rear visibility.

All apparatus should be equipped with a backup warning alarm. Driver/operators should continue to exercise caution, though, because the backup alarm may not be easily heard by members when operating at the scene of an emergency.

Some apparatus are equipped with backup cameras that also act as recorders. These devices provide a limited view of area behind the apparatus. The in-cab monitors are somewhat limited by screen size as well as environmental factors. To safely back the fire apparatus, driver/operators should use all means at their disposal including scanning between their direct field of vision, video screens, and spotters.

CAUTION

The driver/operator must not rely solely on backup cameras to provide a full and accurate view of the scene. Spotters are still required.

⚠️**WARNING**

Backing Hazard.

Ensure that personnel are clear before driving in reverse.

Always use a spotter when backing.

Failure to comply may injure or kill.

FAMA17   Do not paint over this label. Replace if damaged or lost.

Backing Communications

Communication between the driver and the spotter is important to avoid accidents and personal injury. Methods of communication between these individuals can be accomplished via radio and/or hand signals. Voice contact, unless through radio headphones, is often unreliable because of engine noise, distance, and local ambient noise.

Hand signals can be an effective way for a spotter to communicate with the driver/operator. A standard method of communication may be achieved using the hand signals outlined in this text. All firefighters, including those who may respond on mutual aid from nearby jurisdictions, should agree upon and train with the same hand signal system. The driver/operator and spotters should train together as a team for safety and efficiency. All firefighters performing spotting duties should be wearing a reflective safety vest.

The company officer should ensure that the appropriate number of spotters is deployed. The driver/operator must keep the spotters in sight at all times. If at any time during the operation the driver/operator loses sight of the spotters or feels unsafe, he or she should stop, set the parking brake, get out of the apparatus, and check that everyone involved understands the plan for backing the apparatus.

CAUTION
Upon losing sight of a spotter, the driver/operator must stop immediately because the spotter could be killed or injured by the apparatus.

When preparing to back the apparatus, the spotter should be positioned in the vision of the driver/operator, preferably in the left (driver's side) mirror, approximately 8 to 10 feet (2.5 to 3 m) behind and slightly to the left of the apparatus. On occasion, the spotter should position in view of the driver/operator in the right mirror, depending on the hazards present, always slightly behind and to the outside of the apparatus. Once the spotter's position has been established, he or she should not change mirrors. Generally, the best side for the spotter is on the driver's side of the apparatus if there is only one spotter.

Spotters must consider that during certain times of the day the position of the sun can create shadows or glare that may obscure the vision of a driver/operator while backing into an apparatus bay or other area. Glare may inhibit visibility in the side mirror. An additional spotter walking at the driver's side front fender may relay signals from the rear spotter to the driver/operator if necessary.

NOTE: Mirrors may become obscured in wet or snowy weather. Driver/operators should keep a squeegee or towel close by to keep mirrors clear during inclement weather.

Spotters must be prepared to simultaneously stop the apparatus as well as any oncoming vehicles or pedestrians. The spotter must remain in the spotlight created by apparatus lighting.

All hand signals should be done in a slow, exaggerated motion. Driver/operators should follow local SOPs for hand signals and communication between the driver and the spotter. The following are six hand signals that may be used to maintain clear communication between the spotter and driver/operator:

- **Backing straight** — The spotter uses a back and forth motion with both arms, which is visible to the driver/operator in the appropriate mirror. The spotter extends arms outward with elbows bent and both palms face the spotter. The apparatus moves only when the spotter moves his or her forearms. If the spotter fails to motion, the driver/operator stops the apparatus **(Figure 3.19)**.

- **Backing toward the left side of the apparatus** — The spotter is positioned in the appropriate mirror and motions with the right arm to back up (using the same motion as in straight backing) while pointing left to direct the rear of the apparatus. The left arm motions in an up-and-down motion with the palm facing the driver/operator. This up-and-down motion helps make the turning direction more visible to the driver/operator **(Figure 3.20)**.

- **Backing toward the right side of the apparatus** — The spotter is positioned in the appropriate mirror and motions with the left arm to back toward the right side of the apparatus. The spotter uses the right arm to point toward the right. The right palm faces the driver/operator while motioning the right arm up and down **(Figure 3.21)**.

Figure 3.19 A spotter wearing a safety vest demonstrates the "backing straight" signal.

Figure 3.20 A spotter wearing a safety vest demonstrates "backing to left" signal.

Figure 3.21 A spotter wearing a safety vest demonstrates "backing to right" signal.

- **Slowing down** — The spotter motions with the arms outstretched to the sides with palms facing down to slow down. The spotter should raise and lower the palms straight up and down **(Figure 3.22)**.

- **Stopping** — The spotter crosses both forearms into a large X to stop the apparatus **(Figure 3.23)**. The driver should interpret this signal as: backing complete, immediate but normal stop required. If an urgent stop is required, tap the crossed forearms together in an exaggerated manner, and use a voice command to *Stop Now!* The driver/operator should interpret this action as *Stop Now!*

- **Pull forward and reestablish backing** — In the event a backing operation is not working as planned, a signal may be given to stop backing, pull forward, and reestablish the operation. The spotter should first give the signal to stop. The signal to pull forward and reestablish backing is the opposite of straight line backing. The spotter turns palms out toward the driver/operator and motions back and forth in a pushing action **(Figure 3.24)**. After repositioning the apparatus, the driver/operator resumes contact with the spotter to complete the backing operation.

Spotters should use a slow, exaggerated motion for all hand signals. While the apparatus is being backed, it is still possible for the front of the apparatus to hit something. Spotters and driver/operators should monitor the front of the apparatus as well. Spotters should also watch for tree limbs, low overhead wires, sign posts, and other possible hazards.

Figure 3.22 A spotter wearing a safety vest demonstrates "slow down" signal.

Figure 3.23 A spotter wearing a safety vest demonstrates "stop" signal.

Figure 3.24 A spotter wearing a safety vest demonstrates "pull forward" signal.

Tillering

The tiller axle permits tillering of the tractor-trailer apparatus in and out of traffic and around turns that would be difficult or impossible for other vehicles. There is, however, much more to the job than steering and maneuvering the apparatus. All previously described driving practices concerning starting the engine, shifting gears, and braking apply to tractor-trailer apparatus as well as single- or dual-axle apparatus.

NOTE: Added weight increases the stopping distance of a tillered vehicle. There is less weight over the drive axle, which makes it much more prone to losing traction.

Tiller Operators

The tiller operator must be qualified to operate the aerial ladder and be familiar with the duties assigned to all truck company personnel. The tiller operator's driving assignments include:

- Straight-line driving
- Turning and backing
- Proper placement of the trailer at fires

These skills ensure the ready removal of ladders and equipment and the safe operation of the aerial ladder. Tiller operators must be particularly aware of the following:

- Distance of the trailer from the base of the building involved
- Angle of trailer placement in regard to the position of the tractor
- Proper overhead clearance
- Side and rear obstructions
- Grades and slopes of the working area

The tiller operator shares the driver's responsibility for the safety of the public and other vehicles when responding to or returning from alarms. Efficient tiller operation demands a thorough knowledge of prescribed routes to first alarm assignments and an awareness of conditions to be anticipated. In effect, the tiller operator is trained simultaneously with the driver/operator and responsible for knowing all laws, regulations, and SOPs for driving emergency apparatus on public streets.

Operator Training

Tillering, like other specialized operations, requires considerable practice and training. An expert tiller operator should always closely supervise beginners. See **Skill Sheets 3-3, 3-4,** and **3-5** for steps to complete driving exercises from the tiller operator position. During training, instructors should be in a position to take over the tillering instantly, if necessary. Officers and instructors should stress the importance of the following:

- Using good signal practices
- Trailing in-line on a straightaway always
- Bringing the trailer quickly into line again as soon as a turn is completed
- Observing the trailer overhang on turns

- Operating the tiller section in a smooth and safe manner
- Avoiding overtillering (overcorrecting)
- Keeping both hands on the wheel and giving undivided attention to the job

Driving Exercises and Evaluation Methods

After driver/operator candidates have been selected and trained, a standard evaluation method should be used to assess their performance. The evaluation should occur before the driver/operator is allowed to operate the apparatus under emergency conditions. NFPA® 1002 provides specific directions on driver/operator candidate's evaluation. These directions should be followed in order to certify personnel to the standard.

NOTE: All fire apparatus training and testing should follow NFPA® 1451, *Standard for a Fire and Emergency Service Vehicle Operations Training Program.*

Written Test

The written exam for driver/operators may include questions pertaining to the following areas:

- All applicable driving regulations for emergency and nonemergency situations
- Departmental regulations
- Hydraulic calculations
- Specific operational questions regarding pumping
- Department procedures or guidelines

Depending on local preference, the test may be open or closed book. The style of questions may also vary according to local needs.

Practical Driving Exercises

NFPA® 1002 specifies a number of practical driving exercises that driver/operator candidates should successfully complete before being authorized to drive apparatus on emergency calls. The standard requires that prospective driver/operators be able to perform these exercises with each type of apparatus they are expected to drive. Some jurisdictions prefer to have driver/operator candidates complete these evolutions prior to undergoing a road test. The exercises that follow are those specifically required in the standard. Individual jurisdictions may choose to add other evolutions that simulate local conditions. However, at a minimum, all of the following exercises must be completed. See **Skill Sheet 3-4** for the steps required in the alley dock exercise, the serpentine course, confined space turnaround, and diminishing clearance exercise.

NOTE: The descriptions for the exercises listed contain minimum dimensions for setting up these exercises. NFPA® 1002 notes that these dimensions may not be reasonable for extremely large apparatus. The authority having jurisdiction may modify, with suitable justification, particular dimensions to make them feasible for local conditions.

Road Tests

Driver/operators should demonstrate their ability to operate the apparatus on public roadways in order to be certified to drive emergency apparatus. Driver/operator candidates should only be allowed on the road after they have demonstrated their ability to control the apparatus that they are driving. Local jurisdictions may develop a road test route that will traverse any conditions particular to the area. However, as a minimum, NFPA® 1002 indicates that any road test must meet the AHJ's requirements. **Skill Sheet 3-5** shows a road test recommended in Annex A of NFPA® 1002.

Working Safely On and Around Fire Apparatus

Driver/operators and other personnel must work safely on and around apparatus. Safety issues include the following topics:

- Compartment doors
- Working on top of apparatus
- Hose restraints
- Hose chutes
- Intake/discharge caps

Compartment Doors

Driver/operators can improve the safety of the working environment around the apparatus by encouraging good practices with regard to compartment doors. Personnel in a hurry may tend to leave doors open after retrieving equipment. Always close swing-up or swing-out compartment doors to reduce the potential for personnel to be injured from accidentally walking into doors left open. Swing up doors should always be shut when not in use to avoid the potential that personnel working on top of the apparatus can mistake an open horizontal door for a walking surface. Keeping the swing-up or swing-out compartment doors closed at all times also prevents damage to the apparatus should the truck be driven outside of the station while a compartment door is still open.

WARNING!

NEVER step on open compartment doors. They do not support heavy weight. Falls can cause serious injury or death.

Operating on Top of Apparatus

There may be times when it is necessary to climb or walk on high areas of an apparatus where railings are not provided. Always have a second person present when working on, around, or under apparatus. Working on apparatus should be done with the utmost care, and only on surfaces that are provided with a slip resistant surface. Use the same methods recommended when getting on and off, always maintaining three points of contact. This means always holding on to a secure portion of the apparatus with at least one hand. If it is necessary to gain access to an area where a slip resistant surface is not provided, use rubber matting or other means to provide traction before attempting to step, stand, or walk on this area. Personnel operating on top of apparatus should wear PPE, including helmets, according to local policy.

Hose Restraints

New apparatus must include positive restraints for all hose carried on an apparatus. Any hose storage area shall be equipped with a positive means to prevent unintentional deployment of the hose from the top, sides, front, and rear of the hose storage area while the apparatus is underway in normal operations. Before ever placing the apparatus in motion, each driver/operator should ensure that any hose carried on the apparatus will not come loose during travel. Many fire departments have experienced fire hose inadvertently coming off apparatus while traveling on public streets. Several incidents have resulted in damage to property, serious injuries, and even death.

WARNING!
Secure hose and other equipment before placing vehicle in motion. Loose hose may drag behind vehicle and injure or kill.

Aerial Apparatus Hose Chutes

Certain aerial apparatus may carry hose on the top of the body under the aerial ladder. These apparatus have a "trough" or "chute" to guide the hose around the ladder turntable on its way out the back of the truck. While this method has many operational advantages, the hose chute must be watched carefully to ensure that hose connections do not get caught as the hose is exiting through the chute. Operators of this type of device must take special care to lay the hose in a manner conducive to the chute design and keep apparatus speeds very slow during deployment. Hose couplings that jam or catch on corners or other obstructions can cause the deploying hose to pull taught or whip, damaging equipment and injuring bystanders.

- Lay couplings so that they are pulled out straight, without flipping around.

- Lay hose so that it never crosses over itself when paying out.

- Maintain vehicle speed of 5 mph (10 km/h) or less. At 5 mph (10 km/h), 7 feet (2 m) of hose is pulled out each second. Travelling more than 5 mph (10 km/h) is likely to cause a hose jam in the hose chute.

Equipment Storage in Apparatus

Many fire departments choose to store equipment in the cab or other crew areas. This equipment can include SCBA packs, helmets, flashlights, axes, maps, medical supplies, and other items. NFPA® 1901 specifies that any equipment not needed while driving to the scene must be secured in brackets or contained in a storage cabinet. The bracket or cabinet must be capable of restraining the equipment against a force of up to ten times the equipment's weight. This will ensure that the equipment does not become a projectile during a crash. There have been many documented occurrences of unrestrained SCBA bottles flying through the front windshield during a frontal crash. Such a projectile would be lethal if it struck a firefighter in the back of the head. Driver/operators should minimize the amount of equipment stored in crew areas, and should ensure that equipment is secured before placing the apparatus in motion.

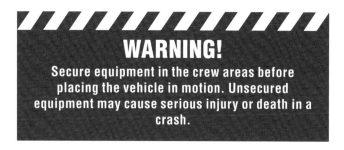

Hydraulic Equipment Hazards

Modern fire apparatus may have hydraulic components in addition to the hydraulic tools that may be used during emergency operations. All hydraulic tools and equipment have potential hazards.

Hydraulic fluids can leak from hydraulic hoses at high temperatures and high pressures causing burns or other injuries. Hydraulic fluid may also leak out when routine connections are made, and some hydraulic fluids are known to be toxic to human tissue. Other hydraulic fluids are synthetic and much less harmful. The driver/operator should be familiar with the SDS/MSDS on the hydraulic fluids used on their apparatus. Always wear appropriate PPE when working with hydraulic tools and equipment, including gloves and eye protection. Always wash away any fluid which has come in contact with human tissue.

The driver/operator should also know the maximum number of tools that may be attached to the system. Most manufacturers of hydraulic powered extrication tools have manifold blocks that can be connected to the end of the supply hose. Multiple tools may be attached to these manifold blocks. The driver/operator should understand the limitations of this equipment and make sure that design limitations have not been exceeded by attaching too many tools. For more information on hydraulically operated extrication equipment and its operation, see IFSTA's **Principles of Vehicle Extrication** manual.

High Pressure Hydraulic Fluid

Any apparatus or equipment may be powered by high pressure hydraulic fluid. Most heavy equipment operates on hydraulic power and it is common throughout industry. High pressure hydraulic fluid leaks are dangerous. When detecting a hydraulic leak, shut down the equipment and call in a service technician trained in safe methods of trouble-shooting and servicing hydraulic power equipment.

Never search for leaks with bare hands or other body parts. High pressure hydraulic fluid at pressures as low as 100 psi (700 kPa) can penetrate skin. Use a piece of wood or cardboard to detect leaks, keeping hands and other body parts well away from the potential source of the leak. In the case of a risk of exposure to a high pressure hydraulic skin penetration, seek medical help immediately. The high pressure injection of a fluid such as hydraulic oil, grease and paint constitutes a medical and surgical emergency, requiring access to appropriate specialist surgical expertise as soon as possible. Often the injury appears minor. Don't be fooled. Fluids injected under the skin are highly toxic. The injury will lead to gangrene, amputation, and death if not treated promptly.

Most doctors are not trained in treating hydraulic related injuries. Make sure they are aware of the potential problems and get the recommend treatment needed to treat the injury.

WARNING!
High pressure fluid leak will pierce skin.
Release pressure before working on system.

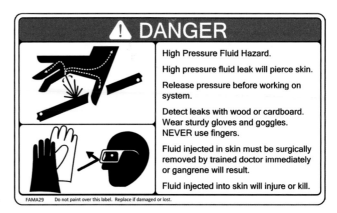

Intake and Discharge Cap Removal

Most apparatus include caps with chains on the end of inlet and discharge of water pipes. These caps often have a control valve in the pipe just behind them. If this valve is opened and then closed again while the plumbing is pressurized, this pressure can be trapped between the valve and the cap even if the fire pump is not operating and all the gauges read zero pressure.

NEVER attempt to remove any inlet or discharge cap on an apparatus until making certain there is no trapped pressure. Open the bleeder valve or drain valve between the control valve and the cap to ensure that any trapped pressure is released. Then remove the cap slowly and carefully. Do not stand in front of the cap. A cap that has pressure trapped behind it may fly off with great force when removed, potentially causing injury.

NOTE: One sign of trapped pressure is a cap that does not turn easily. If the cap is difficult to remove, double check that the drain valve or bleeder valve is not plugged and that all pressure is relieved before proceeding.

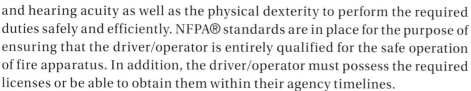

WARNING!

ALWAYS open drain/bleeder valve BEFORE removing inlet or discharge cap. Intake and discharge lines can trap pressure if the valve is opened and left closed. Intake and discharge cap under pressure will blow off with explosive force. Exploding cap will injure or kill.

⚠ WARNING

Pressure Hazard

ALWAYS OPEN Drain or Bleeder Valve to release pressure BEFORE removing Intake or Discharge Cap.

Caps can trap pressure.

Cap under pressure can fly off with great force.

Flying Cap will injure or kill.

FAMA18   Do not paint over this label. Replace if damaged or lost.

Chapter Summary

Driver/operators are required to be mentally and physically prepared to function each work period. Mental skills include reading, writing, and mathematical ability. Physical skills include, but are not limited to, the ability to lift and manipulate heavy objects. The driver/operator must have excellent near and distance vision and hearing acuity as well as the physical dexterity to perform the required duties safely and efficiently. NFPA® standards are in place for the purpose of ensuring that the driver/operator is entirely qualified for the safe operation of fire apparatus. In addition, the driver/operator must possess the required licenses or be able to obtain them within their agency timelines.

As part of emergency operations and the daily driving around the community, apparatus safety is of utmost importance. Driver/operators must understand all the rules and regulations regarding vehicle safety in their jurisdictions. In addition, they should have an excellent understanding of their apparatus' capabilities and systems and should arrive at work with a positive attitude with no physical or mental problems that could compromise their skills. Driver/operators must also be able to accurately and regularly inspect apparatus.

Review Questions

1. What abilities and skills are necessary for all driver/operators? (pp. 80-83)
2. How are driver/operators regulated in their duties? (pp. 83-84)
3. What are some common causes of collisions? (p. 86)
4. What must be ensured for all riders before the apparatus is put in motion? (p. 90)
5. What recommendations should always be followed when starting or shutting down an apparatus? (pp. 94-96)
6. What are some considerations the driver/operator must take into account when driving an apparatus? (pp. 96-99)
7. What are some types of traffic control devices? (pp. 102-103)
8. What are types of auxiliary braking systems? (pp. 109-110)
9. What are some recommended backing policies? (p. 113)
10. What are some factors tiller operators must be particularly aware of? (p. 117)
11. What are some methods of evaluating driver/operator candidates? (pp. 118-119)
12. What are some guidelines when operating on top of apparatus? (pp. 119-120)

NOTE: Ensure vehicle is properly prepared and all personnel are clear before performing this skill.

Step 3: Turn on the vehicle battery(ies).

CAUTION: Never operate the battery switch while the engine is running.

NOTE: Depending on the location of the battery switch, you may choose to operate this switch before entering the cab or immediately upon sitting in the driver's seat.

Step 1: Disconnect all external electrical cords, air hoses, or exhaust system hoses from the apparatus.

Step 2: Mount the apparatus, using appropriate steps and handrails.

    a. Don safety restraints.

    b. Ensure that all riders are wearing safety restraints and hearing protection.

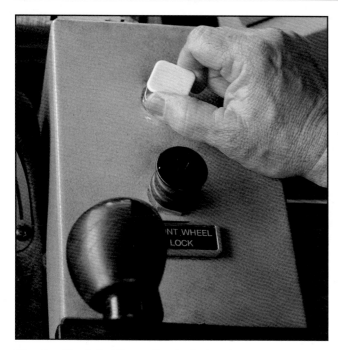

Step 4: Check that the parking brake is set.

Step 5: Manual transmissions only: Place the transmission in neutral.

Step 6: Turn on the ignition switches; wait until the vehicle computers and systems go through normal start-up.

Step 7: Operate the starter control, following manufacturer's recommendations.

Step 8: Observe the apparatus gauges.

    a. Shut down the engine immediately if oil pressure gauge does not fall within manufacturer's recommendations within 5 to 10 seconds.

    b. Check ammeter and/or voltmeter to make sure that electrical system is operating/charging properly.

    c. Check air pressure gauge to ensure that adequate pressure is built up to release parking brake and operate service brake.

Step 9: Shut off the engine following manufacturer's procedures.

CAUTION: Never operate the battery switch while the engine is running. Do not attempt to shut down the engine with the battery switch.

Step 10: Turn the battery switch to the OFF position.

Step 11: Reconnect external electrical cords, air hoses, or exhaust system hoses to the apparatus.

NOTE: Ensure vehicle is properly prepared and all personnel are clear before performing this skill.

Manual Shift Transmission with a Single-Speed Rear Axle

Step 1: Perform the steps in 3-1 to start the apparatus.

Step 2: Ensure that all riders are seated and wearing safety restraints and hearing protection.

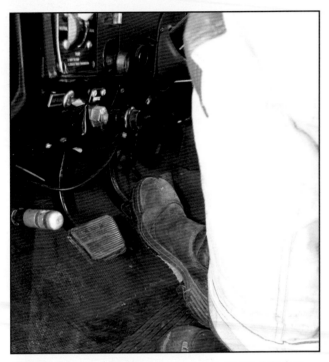

Step 3: Depress the service brake pedal with the right foot.

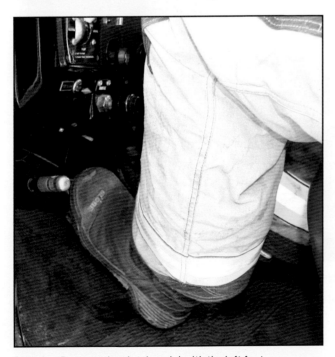

Step 4: Depress the clutch pedal with the left foot.

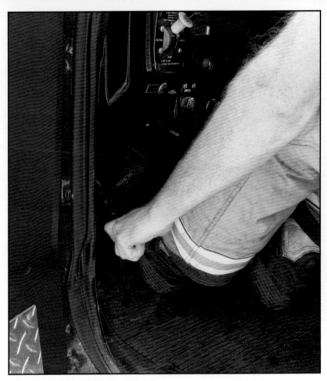

Step 5: Release the parking brake.

Step 6: Place the gear shifter into a low gear.

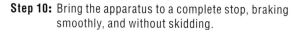
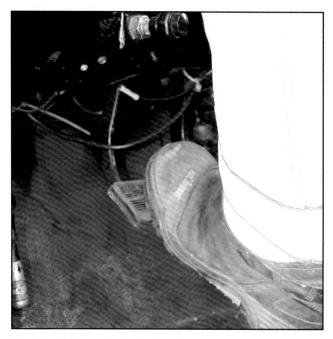

Step 7: Release the clutch slowly.

   a. Check surroundings before moving.

   b. Take care to avoid vehicle rollback before engaging the clutch.

Step 8: Drive forward, depressing the accelerator appropriately.

Step 9: Proceed from the station after proper speed or rpm is reached, apparatus clears the station, and you have an unobstructed view of street and traffic conditions.

   a. Go to an area that is out of normal traffic to practice forward driving.

NOTE: Some suggestions are an empty, large, open parking lot; a long driveway alongside the firehouse; or a rarely used dead-end street.

   b. Shift to a higher gear after proper speed or rpm is reached, after apparatus clears station, and you have an unobstructed view of street and traffic conditions.

   c. Shift to a lower gear, maintaining peak engine power, and remaining in gear at all times.

Step 10: Bring the apparatus to a complete stop, braking smoothly, and without skidding.

Step 11: Shut down the apparatus per Skill Sheet 3-1.

Automatic Transmission

Step 1: Perform the steps in Skill Sheet 3-1 to start the apparatus.

Step 2: Ensure that all riders are seated and wearing safety restraints and hearing protection.

Step 3: Depress the service brake pedal.

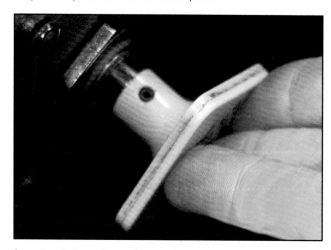

Step 4: Release the parking brake.

Step 5: Place the transmission into a gear for normal operation.

Step 6: Drive forward, depressing the accelerator appropriately.

Step 7: Proceed forward after apparatus clears station, and you have an unobstructed view of street and traffic conditions.

   a. Go to an area that is out of normal traffic to practice forward driving.

NOTE: Some suggestions are an empty, large, open parking lot; a long driveway alongside the firehouse; or a rarely used dead-end street.

Step 8: Bring the apparatus to a complete stop, braking smoothly, and without skidding.

Step 9: Shut down the apparatus per Skill Sheet 3-1.

Step 1: Perform the steps in Skill Sheet 3-1 to start the apparatus.

Step 2: Start the skill in an isolated practice area. Check both side mirrors. Maintain situational awareness, know the location of spotter(s), and know what is behind the apparatus. Follow local SOPs.

Step 3: Place the apparatus in reverse.

Step 4: Back the apparatus slowly, checking each mirror from time to time, always watching the spotter.

WARNING: If the driver needs to look away from the spotter, stop the vehicle until it is possible to see the spotter again.

    a. Follow the spotter's directions, and stop if you cannot see the spotter.

    b. Continue to back up until the spotter signals for you to stop.

Step 5: Repeat until the candidate is proficient enough for the cone course.

Step 6: Shut down the apparatus per Skill Sheet 3-1.

NOTE: Ensure vehicle is properly prepared and that all personnel are clear before performing this skill.

Prepare for Driving Exercises

Step 1: Mount the apparatus, secure your seat belt, and start the apparatus per Skill Sheet 3-1.

Step 2: Adjust all mirrors, sitting straight with both hands on the steering wheel, and moving your head from side to side until you can clearly see the spotter.

Alley Dock Driving Exercise

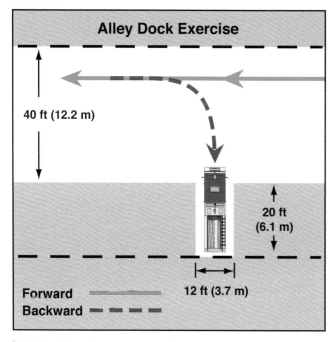

Step 3: Place the apparatus in drive.

Step 4: Drive the apparatus past the alley and bring the apparatus to a stop at a 90 degree angle from the alley.

Step 5: Place the apparatus in reverse.

Step 6: Back the apparatus slowly, making a left turn in reverse into the defined alley area.

Step 7: Bring the apparatus to a standstill, braking smoothly and without skidding.

Step 8: Repeat the exercise from the opposite direction.

Serpentine Course Driving Exercise

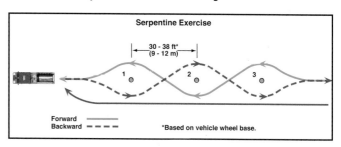

Step 9: Drive the apparatus along the left side of the cones in a straight line.

Step 10: Bring the apparatus to a standstill just beyond the last cone or until you see them lined up in the passenger's side mirror.

Step 11: Place the apparatus in reverse.

Step 12: Back the apparatus slowly, passing to the left of Cone 1, to the right of Cone 2, and to the left of Cone 3.

Step 13: Bring the apparatus to a standstill, braking smoothly and without skidding.

Step 14: Place the apparatus in drive.

Step 15: Drive the vehicle forward slowly, passing to the right of Cone 3, to the left of Cone 2, and to the right of Cone 1.

Step 16: Bring the apparatus to a standstill, braking smoothly and without skidding.

Confined Space Turnaround Exercise

Diminishing-Clearance Driving Exercise

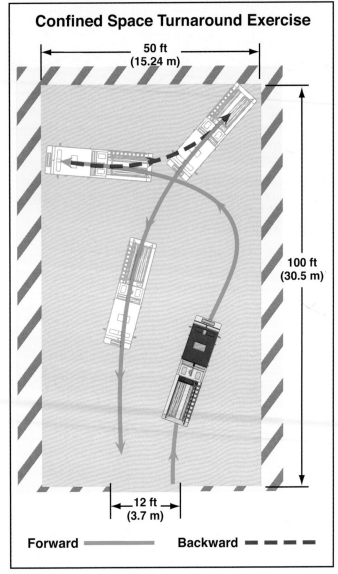

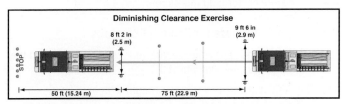

Step 22: Drive the apparatus forward, slowly, without touching any cones.

Step 23: Stop the vehicle, smoothly, at a point 50 feet (15.24 m) beyond the last cone within 6 inches (150 mm) of the backstop cone.

Step 24: A height clearance standard can be used to simulate a height restriction and test the candidate's judgment of the vertical clearance required by the apparatus.

Step 17: Place the apparatus in drive.

Step 18: Drive into the opening of the course, moving to one side or the other.

Step 19: Begin the turning process, making as many direction changes as needed to turn the apparatus 180 degrees without striking any cones.

Step 20: Drive the vehicle back through the opening of the course.

Step 21: Bring the apparatus to a standstill, braking smoothly and without skidding.

NOTE: This skill sheet provides a recommended checklist for conducting a road test based upon Annex A of NFPA® 1002. Candidates should perform all apparatus road tests as required by the AHJ where those tests vary from the NFPA®.

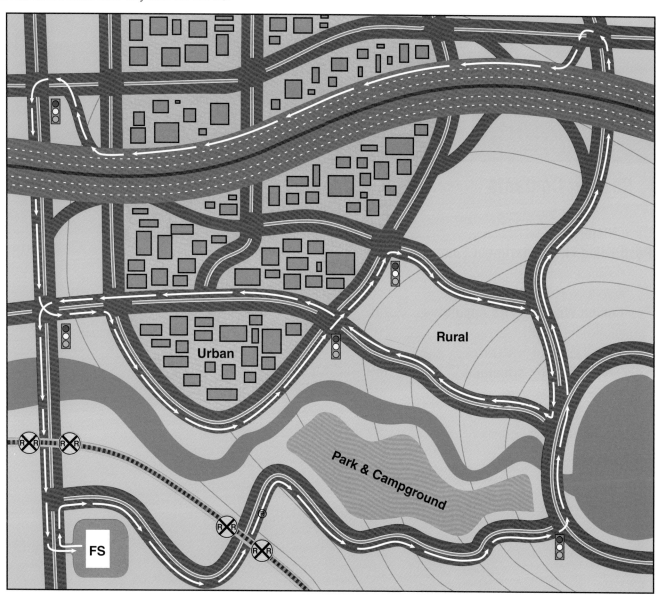

Step 1: Perform four left turns.

Step 2: Perform four right turns.

Step 3 Drive along a straight section of an urban business street or two-lane rural road at least one mile (1.6 km) in length.

Step 4: Drive along one through intersection and two intersections where a stop must be made.

Step 5: Drive over one railroad crossing.

Step 6: Drive around one curve, either left or right.

Step 7: Drive along a section of limited-access highway that includes a conventional ramp entrance and exit and a section of road long enough to allow two lane changes.

Step 8: Drive on a downgrade steep enough and long enough to require down-shifting and braking.

Step 9: Drive on an upgrade steep enough and long enough to require gear changing to maintain speed.

Step 10: Drive under one underpass or a low-clearance bridge.

Positioning Apparatus

Courtesy of Bob Esposito.

Chapter Contents

Key Terms

NFPA® Job Performance Requirements

This chapter provides information that addresses the following job performance requirements of NFPA 1002, *Standard for Fire Apparatus Driver/Operator Professional Qualifications (2014)*.

5.2.1, 5.2.2, 5.2.4

NFPA 1002, *Standard for Fire Apparatus Driver/Operator Professional Qualifications (2017)*.

5.2.4, 5.2.5, 5.2.7

Positioning Apparatus

Learning Objectives

After reading this chapter, students will be able to:

1. Describe positioning of pumpers for fire attack. (*NFPA 1002, 2014:* 5.2.1, 5.2.2, 5.2.4 & *NFPA 1002, 2017:* 5.2.4, 5.2.5, 5.2.7)

2. Describe positioning water source supply pumpers. (*NFPA 1002, 2014:* 5.2.1, 5.2.2, 5.2.4 & *NFPA 1002, 2017:* 5.2.4, 5.2.5, 5.2.7)

3. Summarize apparatus positioning considerations for wildland fire attack.

4. Identify considerations for special positioning situations. (*NFPA 1002, 2014:* 5.2.1, 5.2.2, 5.2.4 & *NFPA 1002, 2017:* 5.2.4, 5.2.5, 5.2.7)

5. Position pumper and make large diameter intake hose connections. (*NFPA 1002, 2014:* 5.2.1, 5.2.2, 5.2.4, Skill Sheet 4-1 & *NFPA 1002, 2017:* 5.2.4, 5.2.5, 5.2.7, Skill Sheet 4-1)

6. Position pumper and connect to 2½-inch (65 mm) hydrant outlets. (*NFPA 1002, 2014:* 5.2.1, 5.2.2, 5.2.4, Skill Sheet 4-2 & *NFPA 1002, 2017:* 5.2.4, 5.2.5, 5.2.7, Skill Sheet 4-2)

7. Position pumper and make multiple intake connections. (*NFPA 1002, 2014:* 5.2.1, 5.2.2, 5.2.4, Skill Sheet 4-3 & *NFPA 1002, 2017:* 5.2.4, 5.2.5, 5.2.7, Skill Sheet 4-3)

8. Position pumper and make connections for a dual pumping operation. (*NFPA 1002, 2014:* 5.2.1, 5.2.2, 5.2.4, Skill Sheet 4-4 & *NFPA 1002, 2017:* 5.2.4, 5.2.5, 5.2.7, Skill Sheet 4-4)

9. Position pumper and make connections for a tandem pumping operation. (*NFPA 1002, 2014:* 5.2.1, 5.2.2, 5.2.4, Skill Sheet 4-5 & *NFPA 1002, 2017:* 5.2.4, 5.2.5, 5.2.7, Skill Sheet 4-5)

Chapter 4
Positioning Apparatus

Case History

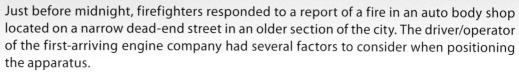

Just before midnight, firefighters responded to a report of a fire in an auto body shop located on a narrow dead-end street in an older section of the city. The driver/operator of the first-arriving engine company had several factors to consider when positioning the apparatus.

No smoke or fire was evident until the apparatus rolled up to the scene. At that time, the company officer noticed smoke coming from the rear of the building. The driver/operator knew that the engine company must be positioned properly on the narrow dead-end street in order for the first-arriving ladder company to have access for its aerial device. Furthermore, the second-arriving engine would need to approach from the same direction with a 5-inch (125 mm) LDH supply line.

To accommodate access for the aerial device, the driver/operator sized up the available options and positioned the apparatus well past the building. With the ladder truck in position, the engine completing a forward lay for water supply would be blocked out a significant distance from the attack pumper. Realizing this, the driver/operator and another firefighter back-stretched supply hose from the attack pumper's hose bed to a point just past the rear of the ladder truck, making it easier to complete the hose lay.

Driver/operators must always apply size-up skills when positioning their vehicle. They must consider the immediate task of their apparatus as well as the needs of other units responding to the incident. Once a pumper is in position with hoselines stretched and operating, it is nearly impossible to reposition the apparatus.

Driver/operators should position their apparatus for the safest and most advantageous use of the features of the apparatus. Driver/operators must be well trained and knowledgeable in local policies and procedures in order to efficiently execute any maneuvers and tasks that the Incident Commander (IC) or the IAP may require. This chapter describes proper positioning for pumping apparatus based on several common functions, including fire attack and water supply. It will also describe positioning for wildland operations and special situations.

NOTE: The reader will find information concerning the positioning of pumpers for relay pumping operations and during water shuttle operations in Chapters 12 and 13 respectively.

Positioning Fire Department Pumpers

A fire department pumper's primary function on the fireground is to provide water directly for fire streams or to support other pumpers or aerial apparatus **(Figure 4.1)**. Driver/operators must know how to properly position apparatus in many different scenarios including fire attacks and water supply operations.

Fire Attack Pumpers

Local policies, the company officer, and the driver/operator will determine the best placement for the first-arriving and later-arriving pumpers on the fireground. **Preincident planning** and district familiarization will assist the driver/operator to make informed decisions regarding apparatus positioning. The following sections address considerations that may help determine proper positioning for fire attack, supporting aerial apparatus, and supporting fire department connections.

Positioning for Fire Attack

Incident scene **size-up** determines the most advantageous position

Figure 4.1 This pumper is positioned on the fireground for support operations. *Courtesy of Ron Jeffers.*

for the attack pumper. The driver/operator and company officer of the first-arriving apparatus must observe conditions and determine the best apparatus position based on initial attack strategy and department policy. The position of the initial company, along with local operating guidelines and orders from the **Incident Commander (IC)**, will set the scene for later-arriving apparatus to support. When fire conditions are evident upon arrival, the driver/operator should place the apparatus in a safe position that offers the best tactical advantage. This includes an exit route for the apparatus should a withdrawal become necessary. A variety of size-up factors and local guidelines influence this decision. When positioning the apparatus, the driver/operator should:

- Pull the apparatus past the front of the building, if feasible, when arriving at an incident where no fire is evident (investigation mode). This position allows personnel on the apparatus to view three sides of the building.

- Consider the best access point for personnel and equipment entering the occupancy when parking the apparatus. This will allow personnel efficient access to the building to begin an investigation.
- Remain with the apparatus (based on local policy) in the event connections for water supply or fire department connections need to be made or to assist in pulling attack hoselines and operating the pump.

In cases where circumstances prohibit standard apparatus placement, incoming apparatus must be notified of the situation and changes made to accommodate the particulars of the incident. The following text describes proper placement for numerous situations that may occur.

NOTE: IFSTA's **Pumping and Aerial Apparatus Driver/Operator Handbook 3rd edition,** Chapters 16-20, contains further information on deploying aerial devices.

Rescue situations. Life safety is the first tactical priority at any incident. If there is an indication of an obvious rescue situation, position the apparatus to facilitate the most efficient deployment of ground ladders (or aerial device if so equipped).

Exposures. Position the apparatus so that fire streams can be deployed to protect the exposures if the fire has the potential to threaten exposures. When positioning for exposure protection, consider the apparatus as a potential exposure. Avoid placing the apparatus in a location that may subject it to high levels of radiant heat, falling embers, or other products of combustion.

Water supply. Establishing water supply is a primary concern of the driver/operator and company officer in the placement of the pumper. If a confirmed fire is located in an area of limited access, such as a narrow driveway or alley, the personnel of the first-arriving pumper should consider laying their own supply line. The driver/operator should also be aware that supply lines, especially LDH, may block the access of later-arriving apparatus. Guidelines based on local conditions and resources should be in place to minimize this occurrence. Supply lines should be laid where they are accessible to later-arriving apparatus.

Only after a proper size-up confirms the location and extent of the fire can a pumper's onboard tank be considered for water supply. If additional water may be required, the company officer and driver/operator must consider this factor in the placement of the apparatus. If the first-arriving pumper is located in an area that is difficult for other apparatus to access, such as a narrow driveway or alley, a supply line may be laid to the scene as the first apparatus moves into position.

Method of attack. Determine the positioning of the apparatus. If handlines or portable master streams are to be used, the pumper must be positioned in close proximity to the building or incident scene to allow effective water supply. If a fixed appliance is to be operated, the apparatus must be positioned in a safe location close enough for the fire stream to reach its intended target, but with consideration for the collapse potential of the structure.

Hoseline deployment. Position pumpers to better support the deployment of hoselines for fire attack or supply lines to fire department connections. Also consider the accessibility of water supply to the pumper.

Wind direction. Attempt to position the apparatus upwind of an incident whenever possible **(Figure 4.2)**. This positioning may negate the need for the driver/operator to wear protective breathing apparatus while operating the vehicle and reduce the possibility of the apparatus becoming an exposure if fire conditions worsen.

Terrain. Park apparatus on hard surfaces whenever practical. This will eliminate the chance of getting stuck in an unpaved area. In cold weather climates, a buildup of ice and snow before or during an incident should be considered relevant to apparatus safety. When operating at an incident involving hazardous or flammable liquids, an uphill position eliminates the chance of a hazardous liquid flowing underneath the apparatus. Similarly, at vehicle fires, an uphill position will protect the apparatus from burning fuel that may leak from the vehicle. One exception to the uphill rule involves wildland fires. Apparatus and personnel should be downhill of the main body of fire as wildland fires move uphill faster than on flat terrain or downhill.

Roadway response. Position the apparatus in a manner or location that will be safe from the hazards of the incident and protect personnel from oncoming traffic. Block lanes of the road where firefighters are operating as well as an additional lane for a safety zone.

When laying supply hose into the fire scene, lay the hose to the side of the street if at all possible **(Figure 4.3)**. Large diameter hose is almost impossible to move once charged with water, and later-arriving apparatus may be unable to drive over the hose without causing damage

Structural collapse. Another important consideration when determining the proper position for an attack pumper is the potential for structural collapse. Buildings with extensive fire involvement or those in poor condition before an incident may be more likely to suddenly collapse. Apparatus and personnel should maintain a collapse zone of at least one and a half times the height of any building determined likely to collapse **(Figure 4.4)**. When practical, the corners of a building may be advantageous positions for apparatus placement, especially aerial apparatus operating master streams. The corners of a structure are generally considered the safest position should a collapse occur.

Figure 4.2 Apparatus should be positioned upwind of an incident. *Courtesy of Rich Mahaney.*

Figure 4.3 Lay supply hose to the side of the street from hydrant to pumper.

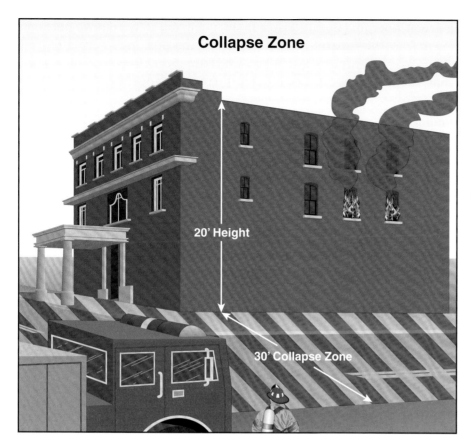

Figure 4.4 Position the apparatus outside of the collapse zone.

Preincident planning. Buildings that are old or poorly maintained may pose a higher risk even before a fire or other catastrophic incident. Preincident planning aids in identifying buildings with a high potential for collapse. Indicators that factor into the Incident Commander's decision to withdraw firefighters and apparatus from an area or building include buildings with reinforcement rods which may be identified by ornamental stars or bolts, those with bulging walls, traveling exterior cracks, and falling bricks. Those indicators, plus interior collapses, are all signs that a large-scale structural collapse may occur and a collapse zone should be established.

Overhead utility lines. Other factors, such as the location of overhead utility lines, dictate the position of apparatus on the fireground **(Figure 4.5)**. Positioning apparatus directly below these lines may be dangerous, especially if fire or weather conditions are likely to cause them to fall. Other factors, such as large fires or fires that have the potential to spread to exposures, dictate that apparatus be positioned farther away with an open route to withdraw.

Figure 4.5 Parking a pumper directly below a large number of utility lines may be dangerous, especially if fire or weather conditions cause them to fall. *Courtesy of Ron Jeffers.*

Falling debris. Falling debris from buildings, especially during high-rise fires, can be extremely dangerous to firefighters and damaging to apparatus and hoselines in the vicinity of the building. Depending on the incident, apparatus, equipment, and personnel operating within 200 feet (60 m) of the base of a high-rise fire may need to be protected from falling glass and debris.

The driver/operator should also consider the ability to remove portable equipment from the apparatus. Therefore, park in a position where compartment doors may be fully opened and ground ladders or other portable equipment may be removed safely and efficiently from the apparatus.

Positioning to Support Aerial Apparatus

In many cases, pumpers may arrive before the first aerial apparatus. Pumping apparatus driver/operators must seek a position of best advantage for their apparatus while keeping in mind the needs of aerial apparatus that have yet to arrive. Blocking access for aerial apparatus can seriously jeopardize the outcome of an incident.

Many jurisdictions' guidelines require that pumpers yield an optimum position close to a building for aerial apparatus. The aerial device, with its fixed length ladder or boom, is of no use positioned beyond its maximum reach. Most pumping apparatus carry a considerable length of various hose diameters. If an incident is beyond the reach of a preconnected handline, additional hose may be added to extend its reach.

In certain instances, the "inside/outside" method of apparatus placement may be used to position aerial and pumping apparatus at a fire scene **(Figures 4.6 a and b).** If a building is less than five floors tall, the attack pumper(s) is (are) positioned on the side of the street closest to the building and aerial apparatus are placed outboard of the pumper(s). The assumption is that the aerial device is long enough to reach over the pumper if necessary to reach the roof of a building of this height. In cases where the fire building is greater than five floors, the attack pumper(s) take(s) the outside position to allow the aerial apparatus maximum reach to the building. Additional considerations for driver/operators of both apparatus are the spread of the stabilizing system of the aerial apparatus and the placement of its complement of ground ladders. Apparatus with rear-loaded ladders must maintain enough clear space behind the vehicle to allow for removal of the longest ladder

Figure 4.6a The aerial is positioned outside the pumper because the building is less than five stories tall.

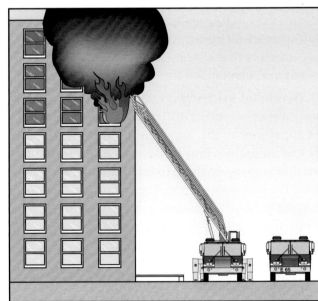

Figure 4.6b The aerial is positioned inside the pumper because the building is more than five stories tall.

Driver/operators should position pumpers providing water supply for elevated stream operations as closely to the aerial apparatus as practical. Friction loss due to distance and elevation are major considerations when supporting elevated streams. Position pumping apparatus equipped with elevated master stream devices in the same manner as aerial apparatus providing fire suppression.

Some cities may contain re-designed urban living or shopping districts that have been renovated to make pedestrian use more appealing. However, prior to construction, fire prevention planners should have reviewed these designs because they may hamper apparatus access.

Positioning to Support Fire Department Connections

In order to supply a fire department connection most efficiently, a pumper should position as closely as possible to the water source. This location is best determined through preincident planning. In some fire departments, the first-arriving pumper supports the **fire department connection (FDC)**; however, other jurisdictions may provide different guidelines.

In many locations, a fire hydrant is located in close proximity to the FDC. This allows the pumper to connect to the FDC and achieve water supply from the hydrant with relative ease. On some occasions, as when a static water supply is in use, the pumper may need to locate at the source. If the distance is great, a **relay** or water shuttle may be necessary to achieve support to the sprinkler or standpipe system.

> **CAUTION**
>
> Driver/operators should not cross-contaminate a nonpotable (nondrinkable) water source and a potable water supply.

Water Source Supply Pumpers

Not all pumpers are positioned at the incident scene to pump water into attack lines. In some cases, a pumper may need to position at a distant water source and pump water to the apparatus at the fire scene. The following sections discuss considerations for apparatus pumping from the location of static and pressurized water sources.

Drafting Operations

Drafting operations are required when a pumper must be supplied from a **static water supply** source such as a dry hydrant, storage tank, lake, or stream. Drafting pumpers may supply apparatus at the fireground directly or may serve as source pumpers for relay or water shuttle operations **(Figure 4.7, p. 142)**. These operations are common in rural areas, but they may occasionally be needed in urban areas as well. Relay and water shuttle operations are discussed in Chapters 12 and 13.

During preincident planning, fire departments should identify suitable drafting sites in their response district and record their location, approximate volume, and how to access them. This information will help driver/operators

Fire Department Connection (FDC) — Point at which the fire department can connect into a sprinkler or standpipe system to boost the water pressure and flow in the system. This connection consists of a clappered siamese with two or more 2½-inch (65 mm) intakes or one large-diameter (4-inch [100 mm] or larger) intake.

Relay — To shuttle water between a source and an emergency scene using mobile water supply apparatus.

Drafting —Process of acquiring water from a static source and transferring it into a pump that is above the source's level; atmospheric pressure on the water surface forces the water into the pump where a partial vacuum was created.

Static Water Supply — Supply of water at rest that does not provide a pressure head for fire suppression but may be employed as a suction source for fire pumps; for example, water in a reservoir, pond, or cistern.

Figure 4.7 A pumping apparatus set up for a drafting operation from a static water supply.

plan their water supply operation. Preference should be given to drafting locations that are accessible from a hard surface and require a minimum length of hard intake hose or lift. Limiting lift is of critical importance in achieving the best possible discharge capabilities. Some bridges and boat ramps make good drafting locations.

Driver/operators must be wary of drafting from locations that are off hard surfaces. These areas may become soft when wet and cause the apparatus to sink into the ground or become stuck when attempting to drive off. Surfaces near the banks of waterways may become unstable and collapse into the water injuring firefighters and creating a tipping hazard for apparatus. Conduct a risk/benefit analysis when considering any questionable location.

> ### CAUTION
> Any personnel working near the edge of bodies of water are required to wear a personal flotation device (PFD).

Dry Hydrant — Permanently installed pipe that has pumper suction connections installed at static water sources to speed drafting operations.

Upon identifying suitable drafting locations, many rural jurisdictions install **dry hydrants** at these sites **(Figure 4.8)**. A dry hydrant consists of an intake hose connection on the shore and a length of pipe extended into the water with a strainer on the end. This allows intake hose from the pumper to be quickly connected to the water supply source when a drafting operation is required. These hydrants should be flow tested by the AHJ in order to determine their capabilities. Chapter 10 of this text contains specific information about operating a pumper from draft.

Hydrant Operations

In many jurisdictions, the most common source of water is a fire hydrant. A pumper may be connected to a fire hydrant in a number of ways. The following sections detail information concerning each method.

Some departments have used hard intake hose to connect a pumper to a hydrant. However, driver/operators should be aware that hard intake hose is designed to withstand the vacuum associated with drafting operations. Some are not designed or intended to be used under positive pressure conditions. There have been instances of hard intake hose coupling failure or hose rupture when connected to hydrants with very high static pressure.

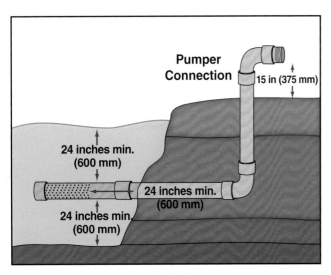

Figure 4.8 A dry hydrant installation.

CAUTION
Only hard intake hose that has been designated to withstand positive pressure should be connected to a fire hydrant.

The procedures for many fire departments require that driver/operators place gate valves on the small diameter discharges of dry barrel hydrants before connecting to the large diameter discharge. Additional hoselines are then connected to the hydrant later without having to shut down the hydrant.

Large diameter intake hose connections. The preferred type of hose for hydrant connection is large diameter **intake hose**. This hose is common in 100 foot (30 m) lengths. Shorter sections of 10 to 50 feet (3 to 15 m) are also available for use when the pumper is in close proximity to a hydrant. In order to properly position the apparatus, the driver/operator must know the position of the intake hose on the side of his or her vehicle **(Figure 4.9)**. Through practice, the driver/operator will learn to judge the proper distance to place the apparatus from the hydrant. This distance must be judged from the hydrant rather than the curb line because hydrants are located different distances from the curb. **Skill Sheet 4-1** explains how to position the pumper to make large diameter intake hose connections.

Intake Hose — Hose used to connect a fire department pumper or a portable pump to a nearby water source; may be soft sleeve or hard suction hose.

Side intake connections. To avoid blocking the street with the apparatus, the driver/operator must stop close to the curb with the pump intake a few feet short of being in line with the hydrant **(Figure 4.10)**.

Figure 4.10 The pumper is close to the curb and in proper position to make a hydrant connection.

Figure 4.9 This driver/operator is using a short section of LDH to connect the pumper and hydrant.

Stopping short of the hydrant allows the intake hose to curve slightly, preventing kinks that can drastically restrict flow.

A good way to minimize the chance of the intake hose kinking is to put a counterclockwise twist in the hose when making the connection between the hydrant and pumper. These twists help prevent the formation of kinks and do not restrict water flow. Practice with the hose is required in order to become proficient and to determine the number of twists needed for a given length of hose. When opening hydrants, it is advantageous to stand behind the hydrant to prevent injury should a coupling disconnect or fail.

Front and rear intake connections. Use similar precautions and judgment when positioning pumpers with front and rear intakes. The driver/operator should stop the apparatus either a few feet short or a few feet beyond the hydrant to allow the intake hose to curve. Take care not to block access for later-arriving apparatus. The only way to achieve proficiency with these operations is to practice with your assigned vehicle.

Connection to 2½-inch (65 mm) hydrant outlets. When the maximum flow from a hydrant is not required or large diameter intake hose is not available, connection to a hydrant may be made using one or two of the hydrant's 2½ inch (65 mm) outlets **(Figure 4.11)**. This is accomplished by connecting one or more sections of 2½ or 3-inch hose (65 or 77 mm) from the hydrant to the pump intake. **Skill Sheet 4-2** describes how to connect the pumper and supply water with a minimum of delay.

Figure 4.11 An apparatus connected to a hydrant using two 2½ inch (65 mm) hoselines.

Multiple intake connections. Occasionally, a pumper will be required to use a large diameter intake (sometimes called a *steamer intake*) and smaller hoselines from an exceptionally well-pressurized (strong) hydrant. **Skill Sheet 4-3** provides the steps for making multiple intake connections.

Dual Pumping Operations

With **dual pumping**, one strong hydrant is used to supply two pumpers. Generally, the pumpers are in close proximity to each other as both of them are being used as attack pumpers at the same incident. **Skill Sheet 4-4** outlines the steps for a dual pumping connection **(Figure 4.12).**

Tandem Pumping Operations

Tandem pumping operations are actually a form of relay pumping with the pumpers positioned close together rather than evenly spaced in the supply hose layout. Tandem pumping may be needed when pressures higher than a single engine is capable of supplying are required. A tandem pumping operation may be required when it is necessary to supply a high-rise sprinkler or standpipe

Dual Pumping — Operation where a strong hydrant is used to supply two pumpers by connecting the pumpers intake-to-intake. The second pumper receives the excess water not being pumped by the first pumper, which is directly connected to the water supply source.

Tandem Pumping — Short relay operation in which the pumper taking water from the supply source pumps into the intake of the second pumper; the second pumper then boosts the pressure of the water even higher. This method is used when pressures higher than the capability of a single pump are required.

system. Tandem pumping operations may also be used in situations where the attack pumper is located a relatively short distance from the water source, but a great distance from the fire. A second pumper can connect directly to the hydrant to supply water to the attack pumper at pressures greater than the hydrant is capable of supplying. In tandem pumping operations apparatus may be located up to 300 feet (90 m) apart. The pumper directly connected to the water source pumps water through its discharge outlet(s) to the intake(s) of the second engine **(Figure 4.13).** This enables the second engine to discharge water at a much higher pressure than it could generate on its own. The higher

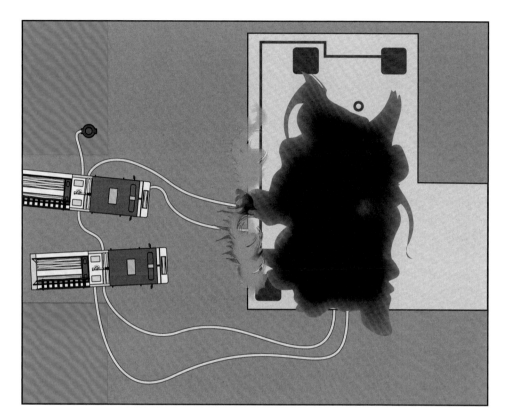

Figure 4.12 Dual pumping operations.

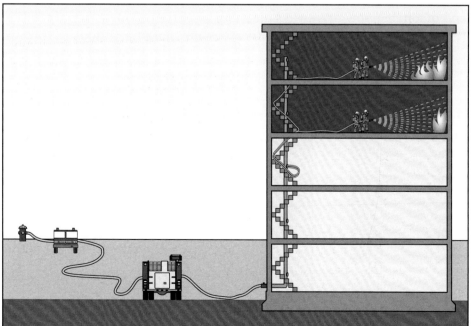

Figure 4.13 Tandem pumping operations.

pressure is a result of the two pumpers acting in series. Relay pumping is generally used to increase the volume of water available at a fire scene, while tandem pumping (another form of relay) is most often undertaken to increase water pressure. **Skill Sheet 4-5** explains how to position the pumper and make connections for a tandem pumping operation. Chapter 12 explains the specifics of relay pumping operations.

NOTE:A tandem pumping operation may be capable of pumping water at a greater pressure than fire hose and adapters can withstand. Pressure supplied to fire hose should not exceed that at which the hose is annually tested. NFPA® 1962, *Standard for the Inspection, Care, and Use of Fire Hose, Couplings, Nozzles, and the Service Testing of Fire Hose,* contains test pressures for various types of fire hose.

Positioning Wildland Fire Apparatus

Positioning apparatus for fighting wildland fires differs greatly from structural fire fighting considerations. Due to the dynamic nature of wildfires, apparatus are seldom positioned in the same location for the duration of an incident. Changing conditions may cause apparatus to reposition many times. Some wildland fire apparatus are capable of conducting mobile (pump and roll) attack operations **(Figure 4.14)**. Therefore, guidelines for positioning and operation must be more flexible than those for structural fire apparatus. Structural fire pumpers may serve in several ways to assist wildland firefighting operations. In addition to operating as water resupply sources for brush trucks, pumpers may provide direct fire attack and protection of structures. The following sections describe important considerations for some of these operations.

Structure Protection

Second only to life safety is the protection of property (structures) during fire fighting operations. The boundary between wildland and structural development, often referred to as the ***wildland/urban interface***, is a challenging environment for fire fighting operations.

Many of the structures threatened by wildfires are on rural lanes, at the end of long narrow driveways and may be surrounded by dry vegetation **(Figure 4.15)**. These access points are made more hazardous to traverse

Wildland/Urban Interface — Line, area, or zone where an undeveloped wildland area meets a human development area.

Figure 4.14 A wildland fire apparatus using pump and roll attack operations.

Figure 4.15 Structures in rural areas and surrounded by dry vegetation may be threatened by wildfires.

when obscured by smoke. Driver/operators should back the apparatus into position from the last known turnaround point and note the location of landmarks along the route.

Once the apparatus arrives at the structure it is assigned to protect, position it according to the following guidelines for safety and efficiency:

- Park the apparatus off the roadway (if conditions permit) to avoid blocking other apparatus or evacuating civilians.

- Clear away any nearby brush that may serve as fuel for a fire.

- Position the apparatus on the leeward side of the structure to minimize exposure to heat and blowing embers.

- Place the apparatus at a nearby but safe distance from the structure in order to keep hoselines short.

- Keep doors and windows closed to keep out burning material.

- Place the vehicles air conditioning on recirculation mode to avoid drawing in smoke from the outside.

- Do not position apparatus in close proximity to power lines, large trees, LPG tanks or other pressure vessels, and exposed structures

Wildland Fire Attack

Apparatus used in wildland fire attacks generally operate from several different positions during the course of an operation. The driver/operator must constantly be aware of the location and direction of spread to keep the apparatus and personnel out of a dangerous position. Any fire attack should begin with the apparatus positioned in an **anchor point** — a natural or man-made barrier that will prevent the fire from encircling the vehicle and crew. Typical anchors are roads, lakes, ponds, or previously burned areas.

Brush, vegetation, and smoke may limit the driver/operators ability to see during wildland operations. When driving the vehicle under conditions of reduced visibility, speed must be reduced appropriately. A spotter may be needed to walk ahead of the apparatus to help avoid obstacles such as logs, stumps, rocks, ditches, and low hanging branches. Spotters must be equipped with hand lights, wear high visibility clothing, and remain within the driver/operator's field of view at all times (**Figure 4.16**).

When the apparatus is operated in a stationary position, it should be placed in an area that affords maximum protection from heat and flames. Natural or man-made anchor points may be used. Consideration should be given to falling trees, incoming air drops, as well as access points for other

Anchor Point — Point from which a fire line is begun; usually a natural or man-made barrier that prevents fire spread and the possibility of the crew being "flanked" while constructing the fire line. Examples include lakes, ponds, streams, roads, earlier burns, rockslides, and cliffs.

Figure 4.16 When vision is limited, a spotter may be used to alert the driver/operator of upcoming obstacles. *Courtesy of Monterey County Training Officers.*

equipment in the area. A short attack line should be deployed and charged for protection of the apparatus. The vehicle should be positioned facing the direction of an exit path, with its front wheels straight and always parked with its wheels chocked and the emergency brake engaged.

Apparatus driven on steep hillsides or on loose or unstable ground surfaces may slide or overturn, leaving it stuck and vulnerable to being overrun by fire. Vehicles should not be driven over bridges unless the weight of the apparatus is known to be within the capacity of the structure **(Figure 4.17)**. Driver/operators should not attempt to **ford** streams with a vehicle unless it has been specifically designed to operate in such conditions.

Driving apparatus along the shoulders of railroad beds may be a dangerous tactic as the coarse rock that makes up most railroad beds may cause tire damage or sliding and rollovers. In addition, this is a vulnerable and dangerous position unless it can be confirmed from the railroad operator that train traffic has been halted.

For apparatus capable of mounting mobile fire attack, during these operations hoselines should be kept short in order to facilitate movement. A portion of the onboard water tank should be kept for the protection of the vehicle and its crew. When progressing along the edge of the fire, a crew should be sure to completely extinguish the fire. This may be accomplished with multiple apparatus working in tandem. Additional personnel and apparatus may be used to **mop up** after the initial fire attack and patrol the fire line to ensure that extinguishment is complete. Experience using pumping apparatus in the wildland environment has resulted in the following apparatus operation safety guidelines:

- Position apparatus in a safe area and do not leave apparatus unattended.
- Communicate with the entire fireground organization for safe and efficient operations.
- Keep headlights on whenever the engine is running.
- Back apparatus into a position facing an escape route.

Fording — Ability of an apparatus to traverse a body of standing water. Apparatus specifications should list the specific water depths through which trucks must be able to drive.

Mop-Up — (1) Overhaul of a fire or hazardous material scene. (2) In wildland fire fighting, the act of making a fire safe after it is controlled by extinguishing or removing burning material along or near the control line, felling dead trees (snags), and trenching logs to prevent rolling.

Figure 4.17 The driver/operator must know the weight of the apparatus before driving over a bridge.

- Close all windows and doors to prevent burning embers from entering the cab.

- Establish an anchor point before beginning fire attack.

- Draw apparatus and crews to the flanks of the fire rather than attempting a frontal attack if the fire is spreading rapidly upslope.

- Position apparatus to maximize protection from heat and fire, taking into consideration overhead power lines, heavy fuel load areas, and incoming air drops.

- Keep a charged line ready for apparatus protection.

- Do not drive apparatus into unburned fuels higher than the vehicle's underside clearance.

- Position apparatus using previously burned areas whenever possible **(Figure 4.18)**. Attacks made from the unburned side must allow sufficient distances to accommodate loss of water supply or mechanical failure.

- Consider the location of operating crews when moving apparatus. Do not drive into smoke near the location of other crews. Whenever driving through smoke, proceed very slowly, sounding the horn or siren intermittently.

NOTE: IFSTA's **Wildland Fire Fighting for Structural Firefighters** manual offers additional information about operating fire apparatus at wildland fires.

Special Positioning Situations

There are many other incidents and scenarios where the positioning of pumping apparatus is crucial. Considerations for safe and efficient placement for staging, highway operations, hazardous materials incidents, control zones, operations near railroads, and emergency medical incidents are explained in the following sections.

Figure 4.18 Wildland apparatus operating from previously burned areas.

Staging

Locally developed apparatus staging policies govern the general placement of apparatus at an incident scene. These policies allow for orderly placement of vehicles and enable the IC to maximize the potential of each piece of apparatus.

Many fire departments use two different **staging** protocols. Level I Staging is applied to the initial response of more than one fire department unit. Level II Staging is enacted when a large number of units are responding to an incident. This level is initiated by the IC or Operations Section Officer when requesting additional resources.

Level I

Level I Staging is often used on any multiunit response of two or more units. If the first arriving unit has no immediate orders for later-arriving apparatus, the officer may call for Level I Staging to be implemented while the incident is investigated. Upon transmittal of this order, other units stop (stage) approximately one block away from the scene in their direction of travel and await further instructions. Engine companies in this scenario typically stage near a hydrant or water source. While staged, driver/operators should not allow their position to be blocked.

Level II

Level II Staging is implemented when numerous units are responding to operate at the same incident, particularly those that require mutual aid or result in the transmittal of multiple alarms. One or more apparatus staging areas may be designated by the Operations Section Officer from which the IC can draw additional resources. Units responding to the incident are advised of the staging area location when dispatched and they respond directly to that location. A parking lot or other large open area such as a field may be designated for use as a staging area so long as it can be secured and is free of civilian traffic. The company officer of the first unit to arrive in staging may become the initial Staging Area Manger. As an incident develops, this officer may be replaced by a Chief Officer. The **Staging Area Manager** advises the Planning Section or IC as to the status of resource availability. Upon arrival at Staging, the Company Officer of the incoming unit should report to the Staging Area Manager. Apparatus in staging should shut off its emergency warning lights but maintain readiness to deploy rapidly when requested.

Base

Base may be established as an area from which large numbers of personnel and quantities of equipment may be deployed. This area serves as the primary point outside the incident area to which responding units report and receive initial orders for action.

Highway Operations

Firefighters face dangerous situations when operating on highways or other busy roadways. There are numerous challenges relative to apparatus placement in order to provide safety to responders and operational effectiveness. The most common incidents on roadways are traffic accidents and/or vehicle fires. Some of these incidents may involve multiple injuries or hazardous materials.

Staging — Standardized process or procedure by which available resources responding to a fire or other emergency incident are held in reserve at a location away from the incident while awaiting assignment.

Level I Staging — Used on all multiple-company emergency responses. The first-arriving vehicles of each type proceed directly to the scene, and the others stand by a block or two from the scene and await orders. Units usually stage at the last intersection on their route of travel before reaching the reported incident location.

Level II Staging — Used on large-scale incidents where a larger number of fire and emergency services companies are responding; these companies are sent to a specified remote location to await assignment.

Staging Area Manager — Company officer of the first-arriving company at the staging who takes command of the area and is responsible for communicating available resources and resource needs to the operations section chief.

Base — Location at which the primary Incident Management Logistics functions are coordinated and administered; the Incident Command Post may be co-located with the Base. There is only one Base per incident.

Problems associated with response are commonplace on limited access highways where there are long distances between interchanges. In some cases, apparatus must travel a considerable distance in the opposite direction of the incident before a turnaround or interchange is available that allows a reversal of direction. Apparatus should not travel opposing the normal flow of traffic on highways or ramps unless the police have closed the road to traffic. In some cases, aerial devices or ground ladders may be needed for operations on incidents involving bridges.

Water supply issues are also common during operations on limited access urban highways and rural roadways. Long hose lays or water shuttle operations may be required when hydrants are not available or are spread at wide intervals. Some jurisdictions have established a policy that calls for an additional pumper to respond to the nearest over/underpass during a highway incident. This unit will assist the pumper on the highway by establishing water supply with an off-highway source. It may also be necessary to stretch hoselines via ground ladder or aerial device to supply water to the level of the highway. Some highway systems are equipped with dry standpipe risers. These risers require one pumper that is off the highway to establish water supply and pump the standpipe inlet. The pumper on the highway can use the standpipe discharge to receive a steady flow of water for fire fighting.

Driver/operators must use their judgment when responding on a highway or turnpike. Many fire apparatus are incapable of traveling as fast as the normal flow of traffic on these roads. The use of warning devices under these conditions may only cause confusion for civilians drivers and serve to slow the actual response of the apparatus. Use sirens only to clear slow moving traffic. *The U.S. Department of Transportation Manual on Uniform Traffic Control Devices (MUTCD)* advises that emergency vehicle warning lights should be used as necessary to reach the incident, but once on scene their use should be reduced as much as possible. Warn drivers in advance of the incident by the use of warning signs and traffic control devices. The MUTCD further states that consideration should be given to reducing the amount of forward facing lights displayed (including headlights) to reduce interference with oncoming drivers. Driver/operators must be knowledgeable concerning their jurisdictions' policies regarding the display of emergency lights while responding to and positioned at incident scenes.

Cooperation between fire departments and law enforcement agencies is critical during operations on any roadway. To protect personnel and victims, a safe zone must be established around a roadway incident. There are numerous ways to re-direct and control traffic around an incident scene. Fire apparatus are often placed to act as a shield between oncoming traffic and firefighters working in the roadway **(Figure 4.19, p. 152)**. There are other traffic control devices that may be used in conjunction with apparatus or police vehicles; including traffic cones and signs. Driver/operators should be aware of local policies regarding positioning of apparatus and traffic control measures for incidents along roadways. All firefighters must exercise extreme caution when exiting the apparatus. Firefighters of the first-arriving apparatus may be in a dangerous position with traffic continuing to flow as they step off the vehicle. Similarly, the driver/operator must exercise care when stepping beyond the protection offered by the tailboard of a properly placed apparatus. Some juris-

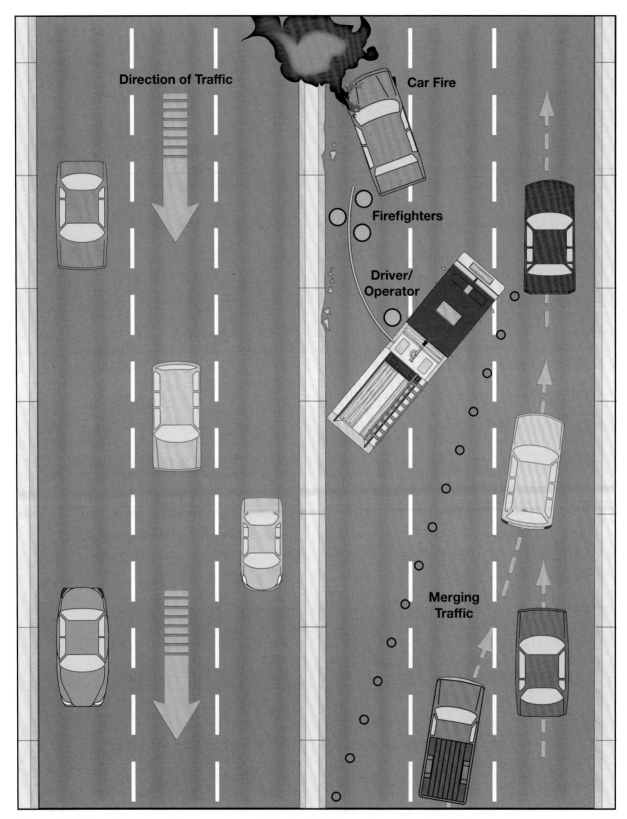

Direction of Traffic

Car Fire

Firefighters

Driver/ Operator

Merging Traffic

Figure 4.19 The placement of the apparatus shields the firefighters from oncoming traffic.

dictions specify the use of top mounted pump panels for units that respond to numerous highway incidents. Apparatus equipped with side mounted pump panels should position facing the incident scene, if at all possible, so that the driver/operator at the pump panel controls has a view of the incident scene.

Hazardous Materials Incidents

Hazardous materials responses are becoming ever more common in the fire service. Incidents involving the potential release of hazardous materials may occur at a fixed facility or during transport. The possibility for haz mat involvement should be considered during every response to a transportation incident. IFSTA's **Hazardous Materials for First Responders** manual discusses the subject of response to these incidents in detail. However, the following guidelines are basic principles the driver/operator must consider when responding to any potential hazardous materials incident.

- Obtain information regarding wind speed and direction from the dispatcher or by direct observation.

- Approach from upwind and uphill.

- Do not drive the apparatus directly to the scene until the material involved can be identified.

- Position apparatus and personnel well short of the scene until the nature of the hazard can be determined.

Control Zones

Once on scene, a series of **hazard-control zones** may be established to organize the incident. These zones assist in regulating the movement of response personnel for safety reasons and prevent unauthorized entry. Control zones may be expanded or contracted with the changing dynamics of an incident. The most common terminology divides the zones into hot, warm, and cold with corresponding levels of hazard **(Figure 4.20)**.

Hazard-Control Zones — System of barriers surrounding designated areas at emergency scenes, intended to limit the number of persons exposed to a hazard and to facilitate its mitigation. A major incident has three zones: Restricted (Hot) Zone, Limited Access (Warm) Zone, and Support (Cold) Zone.

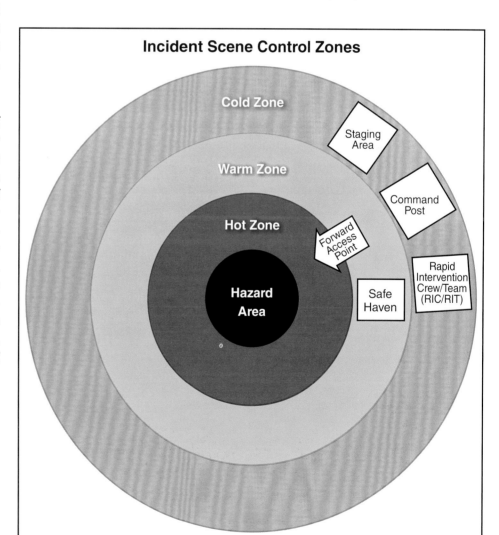

Incident Scene Control Zones

Cold Zone

Staging Area

Warm Zone

Command Post

Hot Zone

Forward Access Point

Hazard Area

Safe Haven

Rapid Intervention Crew/Team (RIC/RIT)

Figure 4.20 Control zones help organize an incident scene.

Hot Zone

The **hot zone** (also called *restricted, exclusion,* or *red zone*) is the area closest to the release of material. This area is exposed to gases, vapors, dust, or runoff of the hazardous substance. The perimeter of the hot zone must extend far enough to prevent people from suffering from the effects of the release.

Warm Zone

The **warm zone** (also called the *limited access zone* or *yellow zone*) is the area abutting the hot zone and extending to the border of the cold zone. It may be considered safe for personnel to enter briefly without special protective clothing, unless assigned a task requiring special protection. The warm zone is used to provide support for operations in the hot zone and to decontaminate personnel and equipment exiting the hot zone. The decontamination process usually takes place within the decon corridor located in the warm zone.

Cold Zone

The **cold zone** (also called the *support* or *green zone*) surrounds the warm zone and is the area where all incident support functions are conducted. Personnel in the cold zone are not required to wear special PPE because this area is considered safe. The Command Post, Staging Area, and Triage/ Treatment area are located in the cold zone. It is likely that driver/operators will stage their apparatus in the cold zone.

Operating Near Railroads

When incidents occur on or near railroad tracks, driver/operators must understand the specific hazards posed by rail operations and take steps to minimize the danger for personnel and apparatus. Fire department personnel must consider all railroad tracks "live." Because it is not always possible to stop the flow of trains on a track during emergency operations and it may require one to two miles (1.5 to 3 km) for a fully loaded train to make a complete stop, fire apparatus should never position on railroad tracks. Use the following guidelines when operating near a railroad:

- Take care not to position the apparatus close enough to a track where a passing train may contact the vehicle.

- Cross railroad tracks only at designated crossing points in order to avoid the possibility of becoming stuck on the tracks due to the ground clearance of the apparatus and the height of the track bed.

- Park on the same side of the track as the incident in order to avoid stretching hoselines across the track and to keep firefighters from making repeated crossings of the track.

- Notify the rail company to confirm that rail traffic has been halted along the section in question if stretching a hoseline across a track is absolutely necessary. If this is not possible, the hose may be run underneath the rails or an aerial apparatus may be used to provide access for a hoseline over the top of a track location.

- Use consideration for railroads that operate using high voltage overhead wires.

CAUTION

Apparatus should maintain a clear zone of at least 30 feet (9 m) from railroad tracks to prevent contact with objects on the railroad cars.

Emergency Medical Incidents

The majority of incidents to which many fire departments respond are emergency medical calls. The driver/operator and the fire apparatus itself can have a major impact on the safety of these incidents by choosing the best position for personnel safety as well as tactical deployment. An important consideration when positioning the fire apparatus is to leave the ambulance enough room for patient loading and protection of the firefighters who may be working on a street or highway.

The policy of some jurisdictions require that fire apparatus and EMS vehicles park off the street or highway whenever possible, shutting off all emergency warning lights. Where practical, this practice virtually eliminates hazards from oncoming traffic. When attempting to position the apparatus in a driveway, lot, or yard, make sure that the surface is stable enough to support the weight of the vehicle.

When an incident requires the driver/operator to position the apparatus in a street or highway, use the vehicle as a shield between the work area and oncoming traffic. Place larger apparatus (pumpers) between the flow of traffic and smaller vehicles (ambulances). Use traffic cones or other traffic control devices when possible to warn drivers of the incident before they drive upon it. The proximity of the exhaust discharge from parked apparatus should be considered relative to the location of patients being extricated or treated nearby.

Chapter Summary

Whether responding to an incident along a limited-access highway, city street, rural road, or urban/wildland interface, apparatus must be positioned for maximum safety and efficiency. In order to accomplish this goal, the driver/operator must understand the role of the apparatus in the overall IAP. This understanding will be based on preincident planning, knowledge of department policies, and communication from the IC.

The driver/operator must also position the apparatus in such a way as to support the safety of firefighters and civilians. This is accomplished by placing the vehicle in different locations based on the type of incident, terrain, and potential exposures.

Review Questions

1. What size-up factors affect positioning of the apparatus at an incident? (pp. 136-141)

2. What situations may require tandem pumping operations? (pp. 144-145)

3. What safety guidelines should be followed when positioning pumping apparatus in wildland fire attack? (pp. 148-149)

4. What is the difference between Level I Staging and Level II Staging? (p. 150)

5. What basic principles should be considered when responding to any potential hazardous materials incident? (pp. 153-154)

NOTE: This skill sheet provides general steps for positioning a pumper to make large diameter intake hose connections. Always follow the SOPs of the jurisdiction.

Side Intake

Step 1: Position apparatus a few feet (meters) short of hydrant. Chock wheels.

Step 2: Connect LDH to hydrant and lay hose to street, folding approx 3 feet (1 m) back onto itself (place two full counterclockwise twists in the hose if sexless couplings are not used).

4-1
Position pumper and make large diameter intake hose connections.

SKILL SHEETS

Step 3: Connect LDH to intake.

Step 4: Charge LDH and bleed air if required.

Step 5: Place apparatus into pump gear.

Front or Rear Intake

Step 1: Position apparatus a few feet (meters) short of hydrant (for front intake) or a few feet (meters) beyond the hydrant (for rear intake).

Step 2: Connect LDH to hydrant (place two full counterclockwise twists in the hose if sexless couplings are not used). Connect 2 ½ inch (65 mm) gate valves to unused outlets on a dry barrel hydrant, in case more water is needed.

Step 3: Connect LDH to intake.

Step 4: Charge LDH.

Step 5: Place apparatus into pump gear.

Step 1: Position apparatus as close to the hydrant as possible. Chock wheels.

Step 2: Lay out needed amount of 2½- or 3-inch (65 or 77 mm) hose, as required.

Step 4: Connect 2½- or 3-inch (65 or 77 mm) hoselines to the gate valves.

Step 3: Attach 2½-inch (65 mm) gate valves to hydrant.

4-2
Position pumper and connect to 2½-inch (65 mm) hydrant outlets.

SKILL SHEETS

Step 5: Connect 2½- or 3-inch (65 or 77 mm) hoselines to the apparatus intake.

Step 6: Charge supply lines, bleeding air as necessary.

SKILL SHEETS

4-3

Position pumper and make multiple intake connections from a hydrant.

NOTE: This skill sheet provides general steps for positioning a pumper and making multiple intake connections. Always follow the SOPs of the jurisdiction.

Step 1: Properly position apparatus in relation to fire hydrant. Chock wheels.

Step 2: Connect LDH and a 2½-inch (65 mm) gate valve to the hydrant. Lay hose to street, folding approx 3 feet (1 m) back onto itself (place two full counterclockwise twists in the hose if sexless couplings are not used).

Step 3: Connect LDH to intake.

Step 4: Charge LDH and bleed air.

Step 5: Connect additional 2½- or 3-inch (65 or 77 mm) lines to gate valve and apparatus.

Step 6: Charge additional hoselines.

Step 7: Place apparatus into pump gear.

NOTE: This skill sheet provides general steps for positioning the pumper and making connections for a dual pumping operation. Always follow the SOPs of the jurisdiction.

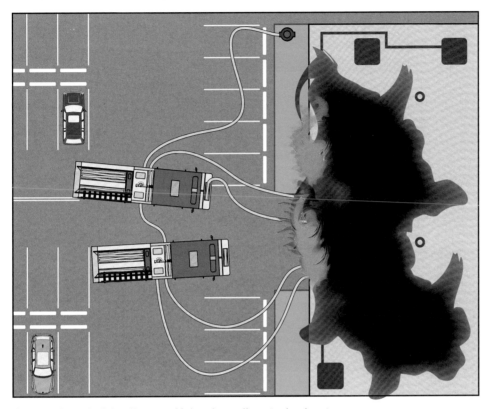

Step 1: First-Arriving Pumper: Make a large diameter hookup to the hydrant.

Step 2: First-Arriving Pumper. Begin supplying flow as required.

a. Minimize residual pressure to 0-5 psi (0-35 kPa) by equalizing the flow pressure with the intake pressure. This allows the unused apparatus steamer cap to be removed.

b. If the unused steamer has been replaced with some type of valve, the residual does not have to be reduced.

Step 3: Second-Arriving Pumper: Take a position and make an LDH connection from the open intake on the operating pumper to the open intake on the second pumper.

Step 4: Second-Arriving Pumper: Begin supplying flow as required.

Step 5: Both pumpers will have to adjust throttles to maintain required flows.

Step 6: If the residual pressure coming in to the second pumper falls off too sharply (approaches or drops below 20 psi [140 kPa]), a second supply line should be connected from the hydrant's 2½-inch (65 mm) outlet to a gated LDH or pony suction connection on the second engine.

NOTE: The instructor will provide students with information on positioning the pumper. The instructor may choose to provide details of an incident scenario.

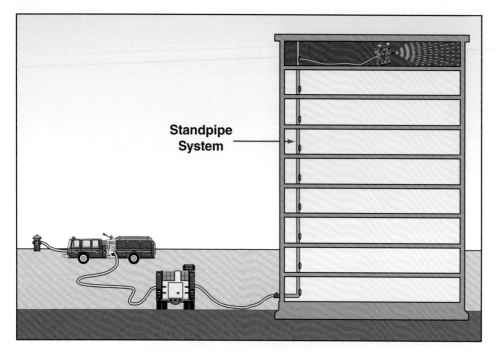

Standpipe System

Attack Pumper

Step 1: Position at the scene according to the needs of the incident.

Step 2: Supply attack lines, elevated master streams, or FDC. Complete hookups per local SOPs.

Step 3: After the supply pumper has reverse laid toward the hydrant, connect the supply hose to the appropriate intake.

Step 4: Switch from onboard to external water supply when supply hoses are charged.

Supply Pumper

Step 5: Reverse lay supply hose from the attack pumper to the hydrant.

Step 6: Put the pump in gear and prepare to flow water.

Step 7: Establish a water supply.

Step 8: Connect supply hose to the appropriate pump discharge.

Step 9: Discharge water through the supply hose to the attack pumper.

Step 10: Coordinate pressure with the attack pumper driver/operator.

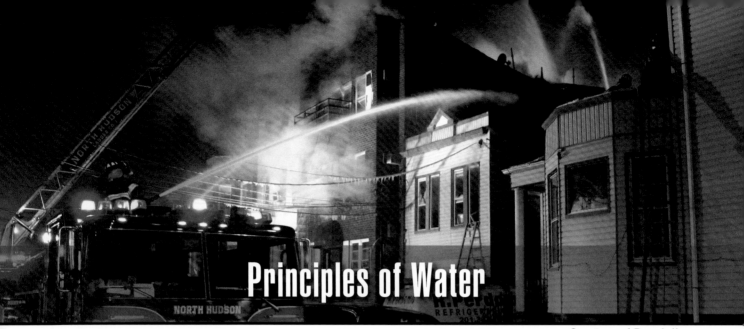

Courtesy of Ron Jeffers.

Principles of Water

Chapter Contents

Key Terms

NFPA® Job Performance Requirements

This chapter provides information that addresses the following job performance requirements of NFPA 1002, *Standard for Fire Apparatus Driver/Operator Professional Qualifications (2014)*.

5.2.1, 5.2.2

NFPA 1002, *Standard for Fire Apparatus Driver/Operator Professional Qualifications (2017)*.

5.2.4, 5.2.5

Principles of Water

Learning Objectives

After reading this chapter, students will be able to:

1. Describe the characteristics of water.

2. Identify the advantages and disadvantages of water.

3. Summarize facts about water pressure and velocity.

4. Summarize the principles of friction loss. (*NFPA 1002, 2014:* 5.2.1, 5.2.2 & *NFPA 1002, 2017:* 5.2.4, 5.2.5)

5. Identify how friction loss principles can be applied to the fire service. (*NFPA 1002, 2014:* 5.2.1, 5.2.2 & *NFPA 1002, 2017:* 5.2.4, 5.2.5)

6. Identify the principles of municipal water supply systems.

7. Describe private water supply systems. (*NFPA 1002, 2014:* 5.2.1, 5.2.2 & *NFPA 1002, 2017:* 5.2.4, 5.2.5)

Chapter 5
Principles of Water

Case History

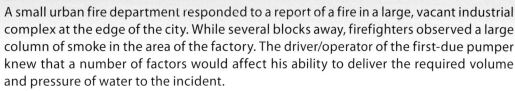

A small urban fire department responded to a report of a fire in a large, vacant industrial complex at the edge of the city. While several blocks away, firefighters observed a large column of smoke in the area of the factory. The driver/operator of the first-due pumper knew that a number of factors would affect his ability to deliver the required volume and pressure of water to the incident.

The hydrant closest to the complex had been recently placed out of service due to vandalism. The supply line would need to be laid from another hydrant farther away. In addition, the water mains in this older section of the city were smaller and often contained large amounts of sediment further reducing their capacity to flow water.

The driver/operator must have an understanding of the factors that influence water supply capability and how the availability of water for fire suppression is achieved using a variety of methods.

The fire service has a variety of chemical agents and additives at its disposal to aid in the extinguishment of fires. However, plain water remains the most common weapon in the firefighter's arsenal. A pumping apparatus driver/operator must have an understanding of why water is an effective extinguishing agent and the physics associated with moving water. This chapter will describe these principles.

Characteristics of Water

Water (H_2O) is a compound (molecule) of hydrogen and oxygen formed when two hydrogen atoms (H_2) combine with one oxygen atom (O). Below 32°F (0°C) (the freezing point of water), it converts to a solid state of matter, called *ice*. Above 212°F (100°C) (the boiling point of water), it converts to a gas, water vapor, or steam. Water cannot be seen in its vapor form. It only becomes visible as it rises away from the surface of the liquid and begins to condense (**Figure 5.1, p. 168**).

Water is considered to be virtually incompressible, and its weight varies at different temperatures. Water's density, or its weight per unit of volume, is measured in pounds per cubic foot (kg/m³). For fire protection purposes, ordinary fresh water is considered to weigh 62.4 lb/ft³ (1 000 kg/m³) or 8.3 lb/gal (1 kg/L).

Water has the ability to extinguish fire in several ways. It can cool or absorb heat from the fire, as well as smother (exclude oxygen from) fires. Water may also be used to smother fires in combustible liquids whose specific gravity is higher than 1 (heavier than water) **(Figure 5.2)**. Smothering may also occur when water converts to steam within a closed space.

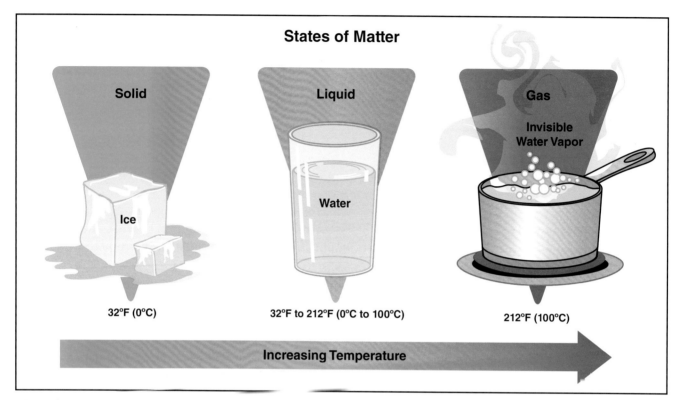

Figure 5.1 Water in three physical states.

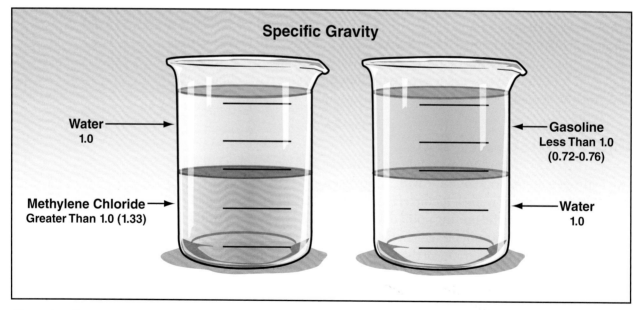

Figure 5.2 Combustible liquids have a specific gravity greater than or lesser than water.

Advantages and Disadvantages of Water

The following characteristics make water an excellent extinguishing agent:

● Water has a greater heat-absorbing capacity than other common extinguishing agents.

● A large amount of heat is required to change water to steam, allowing more heat to be absorbed from the fire.

● The greater the surface area of water exposed, the more rapidly heat is absorbed. The amount of surface area can be increased with the use of a fog stream or deflection of a solid stream off an object.

● At 212°F (100°C), water converted to steam occupies approximately 1,700 times its original volume, helping to dissipate heat in a well-vented room **(Figure 5.3)**. The expansion ratio is even greater at higher temperatures.

● Although some areas experience water shortages, generally it is an inexpensive and readily available commodity.

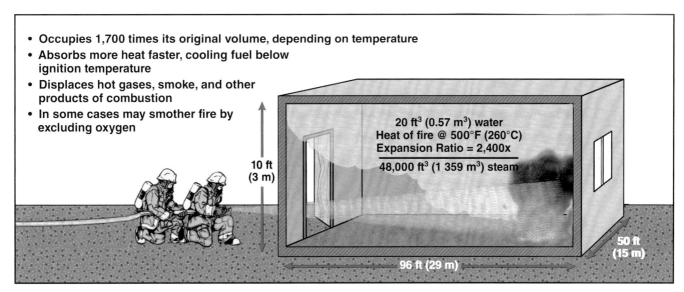

- Occupies 1,700 times its original volume, depending on temperature
- Absorbs more heat faster, cooling fuel below ignition temperature
- Displaces hot gases, smoke, and other products of combustion
- In some cases may smother fire by excluding oxygen

10 ft (3 m)

$$20\ \text{ft}^3\ (0.57\ \text{m}^3)\ \text{water}$$
Heat of fire @ 500°F (260°C)
$$\frac{\text{Expansion Ratio} = 2,400\text{x}}{48,000\ \text{ft}^3\ (1\ 359\ \text{m}^3)\ \text{steam}}$$

50 ft (15 m)

96 ft (29 m)

Figure 5.3 Water expands 1,700 times or more when converted to steam.

Some disadvantages are involved in the use of water as an extinguishing agent. Under certain circumstances, the properties of water may hinder fire fighting efforts:

● Water has a high surface tension that makes it somewhat difficult to soak into dense materials.

● Wetting agents may be mixed with water to reduce its surface tension and increase its penetrating ability. Water may be reactive with certain fuels, combustible metals, sodium metal, and triethyl aluminum. Due to low levels of opacity and reflectivity, radiant heat easily passes through water, rendering water curtains ineffective.

● In cold weather climates, the 32°F (0°C) freezing temperature of water may create operational problems such as frozen pumps and hoselines. Safety hazards such as ice dams and slippery surfaces occur in below-freezing temperatures **(Figure 5.4, p. 170)**.

Figure 5.4 Freezing temperatures create operational problems such as when the apparatus is covered in ice. *Courtesy of the Chicago (IL) Fire Department*

- Water is a good conductor of electricity. This characteristic may pose a danger to firefighters using water near energized electrical equipment.

- At 8.3 pounds per gallon (1 kg/L), water is a relatively heavy agent. Accumulations of water within a structure can lead to an increased potential for structural collapse.

Water Pressure and Velocity

The term *pressure* may have a variety of meanings. In this manual, pressure is defined as *force per unit area*. Pressure may be expressed as pounds per square foot (psf), pounds per square inch (psi), or kilopascals (kPa).

Pressure is easily confused with **force**. Force is a simple measure of weight and is expressed in pounds or Newtons. This measurement is directly related to the force of gravity, the amount of attraction the earth has for all bodies. If several objects of the same size and weight are placed on a flat surface, they all exert the same force on that surface.

For example, three square containers are placed next to each other. They are of equal size (1 ft x 1ft x 1 ft) containing 1 cubic foot of water and weighing 62.4 pounds. Each container exerts a force of about 62.4 pounds per square foot with a total of about 187.2 pounds of force over a 3 square foot area. If the containers are stacked on top of each other, the total force exerted – 187.2 pounds – remains the same, but the area of contact is reduced to 1 square foot. The pressure then becomes 187.2 pounds per square foot **(Figure 5.5 a).**

In metrics, three square containers are placed next to each other. They are of equal size (1 m x 1 m x 1 m) containing 1 cubic meter of water weighing 1 000 kg. Each container exerts a force of about 1 000 kilograms per square meter with a total of about 3 000 kilograms of force over a 3 square meter area. If the containers are stacked on top of each other, the total force exerted – 3 000 kilograms – remains the same, but the area of contact is reduced to 1 square meter. The pressure then becomes 3 000 kilograms per square meter **(Figure 5.5b).**

Pressure — Force per unit area exerted by a liquid or gas measured in pounds per square inch (psi) or kilopascals (kPa).

Force — Simple measure of weight, usually expressed in pounds or kilograms.

How Force Is Determined

Force is an influence that causes a change in the speed, direction, or shape of a substance. The force exerted by water is based on the impact of its weight within a specific area.

To understand how force is determined, it is necessary to know the weight of water and the height that a column of water occupies. The weight of 1 cubic foot of water is approximately 62.4 pounds. Because 1 square foot contains 144 square inches, the weight of water in a 1-square-inch column of water 1 foot high equals 62.4 pounds divided by 144 square inches or 0.434 pounds. A 1-inch square column of water 1 foot high therefore exerts a pressure at its base of 0.434 psi. The height required for a 1-square-inch column of water to produce 1 psi at its base equals 1 foot divided by 0.434 psi/ft or 2.304 feet: Therefore, a column of water 2.304 feet high exerts pressure of 1 psi at its base.

In metrics, a cube that is 0.1 m x 0.1 m x 0.1 m (a cubic decimeter) holds 1 liter of water. The weight of 1 liter of water is 1 kilogram. The cube of water exerts 1 kPa (1 kg) of pressure at the bottom of the cube. One cubic meter of water holds 1 000 liters of water and weighs 1 000 kg. Because the cubic meter of water is comprised of 100 columns of water, each 10 decimeters tall, each column exerts 10 kPa at its base.

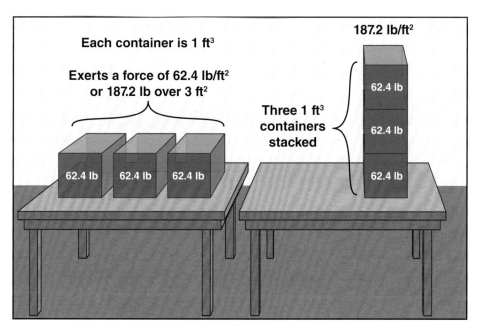

Figure 5.5a Stacking the water containers increases the pressure per square foot.

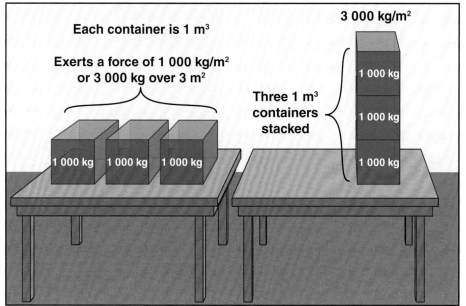

Figure 5.5b Stacking the water containers increases the pressure per square meter.

Principles of Pressure

The speed at which a fluid travels through a hose or pipe is determined by the pressure upon that fluid as well as the size of the orifice through which it is flowing. This speed is often called *velocity*. It is important to identify the type of pressure because the term *pressure*, in connection with fluids, has a broad range of meanings. Six principles determine the action or pressure on fluids. The driver/operator must understand these principles before attempting to understand the types of pressure.

First Principle

Fluid pressure is perpendicular to any surface on which it acts. The first principle is illustrated by a vessel having flat sides and containing water. Pressure exerted by the weight of the water is perpendicular to the walls of the container **(Figure 5.6)**. If this pressure is exerted in any other direction, the water would begin to move downward along the sides and rise at the center.

Second Principle

Fluid pressure at a point in fluid at rest is the same intensity in all directions. This principle is used in hydrostatic testing.

Third Principle

Pressure applied to a confined fluid is transmitted equally in all directions. This principle is illustrated by a hollow sphere to which a water pump is attached. A series of gauges is set into the sphere around its circumference. When the sphere is filled with water and pressure is applied by the pump, all the gauges will register the same pressure, providing they are on the same grade line with no changes in elevation **(Figure 5.7)**. For example, if a pumper is connected to a closed standpipe 100 feet (30 m) tall, and 100 psi (700 kPa) is applied to the

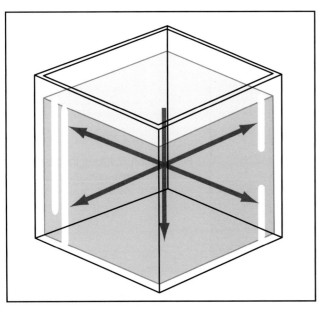

Figure 5.6 A vessel having flat sides and containing water illustrates the first principle.

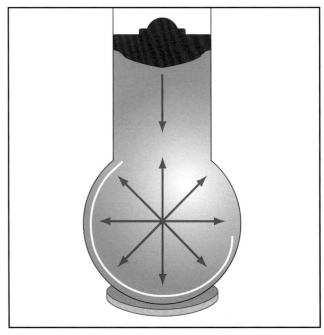

Figure 5.7 Pressure applied to a confined fluid is transmitted equally in all directions.

standpipe, a gauge at the top of the standpipe would read 100 psi (700 kPa). However, a gauge at the bottom of the standpipe would read 143.4 psi (1000 kPa) because of the weight of the water in the standpipe.

NOTE: Due to the increase in water pressure requirements necessary for the height of the building, pressure-regulating devices are installed in standpipe systems that serve high-rise buildings. These devices allow hoselines on lower floors to be more easily controlled, while allowing the high pressures required to access upper floors.

Fourth Principle

The pressure of a liquid in an open vessel is proportional to its depth. This principle is illustrated by three vertical containers, each 1 square inch (625 mm^2) in a cross-sectional area.

The depth of the water is 1 foot (300 mm) in the first container, 2 feet (600 mm) in the second, and 3 feet (900 mm) in the third container. The pressure at the bottom of the second container is twice that of the first, and the pressure at the bottom of the third container is three times that of the first. Thus, the pressure of a liquid in an open container is proportional to its depth **(Figure 5.8)**.

Fifth Principle

The pressure of a liquid in an open vessel is proportional to the density of the liquid. This principle is illustrated by two containers. One container holds mercury 1 inch (25 mm) deep, the other holds water 13.55 inches (340 mm) deep, yet the pressure at the bottom of each container is approximately the same **(Figure 5.9).** Thus, mercury is 13.55 times denser than water. Therefore, the pressure of a liquid in an open vessel is proportional to the density of the liquid. Mercury also has a specific gravity greater than one, as it will sink in water.

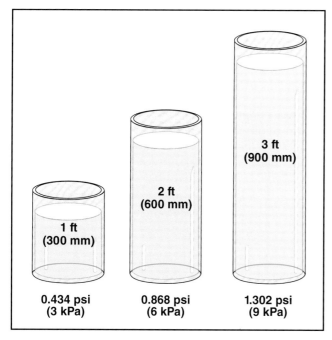

Figure 5.8 The pressure of a liquid in an open vessel is proportional to its depth.

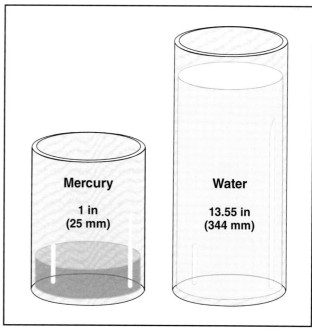

Figure 5.9 One inch (25 mm) of mercury creates the same pressure at the bottom of a container as 13.55 inches (344 mm) of water.

Sixth Principle

The pressure of a liquid at the bottom of a vessel is independent of the shape of the vessel. This principle is illustrated by observing water in several different shaped containers, each having the same cross-sectional area at the bottom and the same height. The pressure is the same in each container.

Types of Pressure

Several terms are used to define the types of pressure encountered in water supply systems and in the fire service. Driver/operators should be acquainted with these terms in order to understand the factors that affect delivery of water to the fireground.

Atmospheric Pressure

The atmospheric pressure that surrounds the earth has depth and density, exerting pressure on everything. This pressure is greatest at low altitudes and least at very high altitudes. Atmospheric pressure at sea level is 14.7 psi (100 kPa), which is considered standard atmospheric pressure.

A common method of measuring atmospheric pressure is by comparing the weight of the atmosphere with the weight of mercury. When observing a vertical cylinder, the greater the atmospheric pressure, the taller the column of mercury. A pressure of 1 psi (7 kPa) makes the column of mercury about 2.04 inches (50 mm) tall. At sea level, the column of mercury is 2.04 x 14.7, or 29.9 inches (759 mm) tall **(Figure 5.10)**.

NOTE: Refer to Chapter 11, Static Water Supply Sources, for detailed information regarding how atmospheric pressure affects pumping operations.

The readings of most pressure gauges are psi (or kPa) in addition to the existing atmospheric pressure. This reading is distinguished from actual atmospheric pressure by indicating psig, which means pounds per square inch gauge. The notation for an actual atmospheric pressure reading is psia, which is *pounds per square inch absolute* (the psi above a perfect vacuum is absolute zero).

For the purposes of this text, psi means psig (pounds per square inch gauge). A gauge reading 10 psi (70 kPa) at sea level means that it is actually 10 psig plus the atmospheric pressure of 14.7 psi. This pressure is not normally accounted for, as the

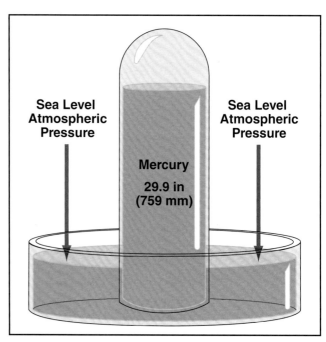

Figure 5.10 Atmospheric pressure is commonly measured using the weight of mercury.

gauge is calibrated to zero at ambient pressure. Therefore, 10 psig is 24.7 psia at sea level. The pressure actually is 24.7 psi (170 kPa) plus 10 psi (70 kPa).

Any pressure less than atmospheric pressure is called *vacuum*, and absolute zero pressure is called a *perfect vacuum*. For example, when a gauge reads 10 inches of Hg (35 kPa) of vacuum on the compound gauge, it actually indicates less than atmospheric pressure.

Head Pressure

In the fire service, *head* refers to the height of a water supply above the discharge orifice **(Figure 5.11)**. In this example, the water supply is 100 feet (30 m) above the hydrant discharge opening. This is referred to as *100 feet (30 m) of head*.

To convert head in feet to head pressure, you must divide the number of feet by 2.304 (the number of feet that 1 psi will raise a one square inch column of water). The result is head pressure in psi. In metrics, divide the number of meters by 0.1 to get head pressure in kPa. The water source has a head pressure of 43.4 psi (300 kPa).

Static Pressure

The water flow definition of static pressure is stored potential energy available to force water through pipes, fittings, hose, and adapters. *Static* means at rest, or without motion. Water pressure may be produced by an elevated water supply, atmospheric pressure, or a pump. If the water is not moving, the pressure exerted is static. True static pressure is seldom found in municipal water systems because there is always some flow in the pipes due to normal use. However, the pressure in a system before it flows from a hydrant is considered static for fire service purposes.

Vacuum — In the fire and emergency services, a pressure that is somewhat less than atmospheric pressure; a vacuum is needed to facilitate drafting of water from a static source.

Head — Alternate term for pressure, especially pressure due to elevation. For every 1-foot increase in elevation, 0.434 psi is gained (for every 1-meter increase in elevation, 9.82 kPa is gained). *Also known as* Head Pressure.

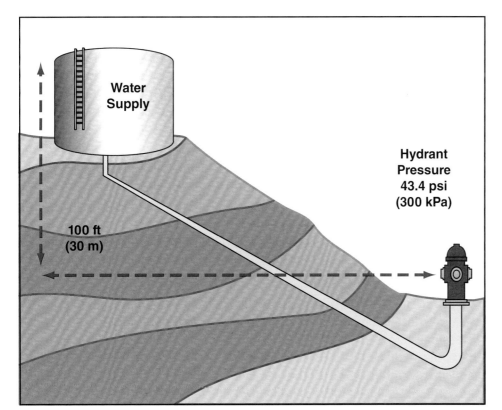

Figure 5.11 The height of the water supply above the fire hydrant creates the head pressure.

Normal Operating Pressure

The pressure found in a water distribution system during normal consumption demands is considered the normal operating pressure. Technically, as soon as water begins to flow through the system, static pressure no longer exists. Consumption demands within a water distribution system fluctuate continuously, causing water flow to increase or decrease accordingly. The difference between static pressure and normal operating pressure is the friction caused by water flowing through the pipes, valves, and fittings of the system.

Residual Pressure

Residual pressure is the portion of the total available pressure not used to overcome friction loss or gravity while forcing water through pipes, fittings, hoses, or adapters. Residual is the remainder or that which is left. For example, during a flow test in a water distribution system, the residual represents the pressure left in the system near the vicinity of one or more flowing hydrants. This residual pressure will reflect the water flowing from the open hydrant(s), other water consumption demands, and the size of the pipe.

NOTE: Identify the residual pressure at the location where the reading is taken and not at the flow hydrant.

Flow Pressure (Velocity Pressure)

While water is flowing from a discharge opening, the forward velocity pressure is considered *flow pressure*. Because a stream of water emitted from a discharge opening is not encased within a tube it exerts forward, but not lateral pressure. Use a Pitot tube and gauge to measure the forward velocity of flow pressure. If the size of the discharge opening is known, a firefighter can use the measurement of flow pressure to calculate the quantity of water flowing in gpm or L/min.

NOTE: When measuring the forward velocity of flow pressure using a nozzle; a smooth bore nozzle must be used with the pitot tube and gauge.

Pressure Loss and Gain: Elevation and Altitude

Although the terms *elevation* and *altitude* are often used interchangeably, a distinction is made between the two in the fire service. Elevation refers to the center line of the pump or the bottom of a static water supply source above or below ground level. Altitude is the position of an object in relation to sea level. Both terms have an effect on pumping and producing fire streams.

When a nozzle is above the level of the pump, there is pressure loss. Conversely, when a nozzle is below the pump, there is pressure gain. The pressure losses or gains due to gravity are called *elevation pressure*.

Altitude impacts the production of fire streams because atmospheric pressure drops as height above sea level increases. This drop is of little consequence between sea level and approximately 2,000 feet (600 m). Above this height, the lessening of atmospheric pressure means fire department pumpers must work increasingly harder to produce the pressures required for effective fire streams. This is because the less dense atmospheric pressure reduces a pumper's effective lift when drafting. Above sea level, atmospheric pressure decreases approximately 0.5 psi (3.5 kPa) for every 1,000 feet (300 m).

Residual Pressure — Pressure at the test hydrant while water is flowing; represents the pressure remaining in the water supply system while the test water is flowing and is that part of the total pressure that is not used to overcome friction or gravity while forcing water through fire hose, pipe, fittings, and adapters.

Elevation — Height of a point above sea level or some other reference point.

Altitude — Geographic position of a location or object in relation to sea level. The location may be either above, below, or at sea level.

Elevation Pressure — Gain or loss of pressure in a hoseline due to a change in elevation. *Also known as* Elevation Loss.

Friction Loss

An important factor in operating a fire pump and producing effective fire streams is the loss of pressure in a pipe or hose due to friction. The common term for pressure loss due to friction is *friction loss*. The fire service definition of friction loss is that part of the total pressure lost while forcing water through pipe, fittings, fire hose, and adapters.

The following causes friction loss in a fire hose:

- Movement of water molecules against each other
- Linings of fire hose/delaminating hose
- Couplings
- Sharp bends/kinks
- Change in hose size or orifice by adapters
- Improper gasket size

Anything that affects the movement of water has the potential to cause additional friction loss **(Figure 5.12)**. Friction loss in older hose may be much greater than that of brand new hose. Modern fire hose has a smoother inner lining and causes less friction loss than older hose. The friction loss in older hose may be as much as 50 percent greater than that of new hose.

The principles of friction loss in piping systems are the same as in fire hose. The following are causes of friction loss in piping:

- Movement of water molecules against each other
- Inside surface of piping
- Pipe fittings
- Valves

The rougher the inner surface of the pipe (commonly referred to as the *coefficient of friction*), the greater the friction loss will be. Friction loss can be measured by inserting in-line gauges in a hose or pipe. The difference in the

Friction Loss — Loss of pressure created by the turbulence of water moving against the interior walls of the hose or pipe.

Figure 5.12 Several factors may cause friction loss in a fire hose.

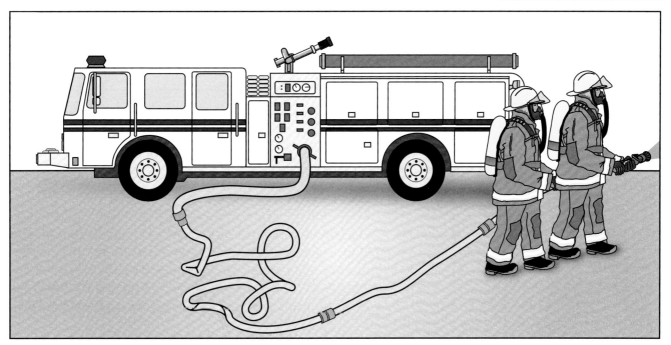

residual pressure between two gauges placed a distance apart in the same diameter hose or pipe when water is flowing is the friction loss for that distance. A common fire service example compares the difference in pressure between a nozzle and pumper.

Principles of Friction Loss

The four basic principles that govern friction loss in fire hose and pipes are explained in the following sections. These principles are accompanied by equations so that the friction loss due to each effect can be calculated.

First Principle

If all other conditions are the same, friction loss varies directly with the length of the hose or pipe. This principle can be illustrated by one hose that is 100 feet (30 m) long and another hose that is 200 feet (60 m) long. A constant flow of 200 gpm (800 L/min) is maintained in each hose. The 100-foot (30 m) hose has a friction loss of 10 psi (70 kPa). The 200-foot (60 m) hose has twice as much friction loss or 20 psi (140 kPa) **(Figure 5.13)**.

NOTE: You will learn how to calculate friction loss in Chapter 7.

Figure 5.13 In the first principle of friction loss, if all other conditions are the same, friction loss varies directly with the length of the hose or pipe.

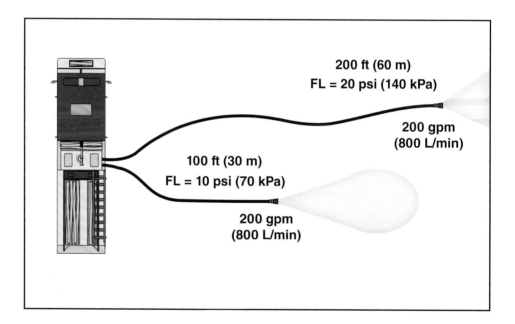

Second Principle

When hoses are the same size, friction loss varies approximately with the square of the increase in the velocity of the flow. This principle illustrates that friction loss develops much faster than the change in velocity.

NOTE: Velocity is proportional to flow.

For example, a length of 3-inch (77 mm) hose flowing 200 gpm (800 L/min) has a friction loss of 3.2 psi (22 kPa). As the flow doubles from 200 to 400 gpm (800 L/min to 1 600 L/min), the friction loss increases four times ($2^2 = 4$) to 12.8 psi (88 kPa). When the original flow is tripled from 200 to 600 gpm (800 L/min to 2 400 L/min), friction loss increases nine times ($3^2 = 9$) to 28.8 psi (199 kPa).

Third Principle

For the same discharge, friction loss varies inversely as the fifth power of the diameter of the hose. This principle readily proves the advantage of larger size hose and can be illustrated by one hose that is 2½ inches (65 mm) in diameter and another that is 3 inches (77 mm) in diameter. The friction loss in the 3-inch (77 mm) hose is:

$$\frac{(2\frac{1}{2})^5}{3^5} = \frac{97.66}{243} = 0.4 \text{ that of the 2½-inch hose}$$

$$\frac{(65)^5}{(77)^5} = \frac{1\,160\,290\,625}{2\,706\,784\,157} = 0.4 \text{ that of the 65 mm hose}$$

When the flow remains constant, the friction loss in a hose will decrease when the diameter of the hose is increased. Mathematically, friction loss varies inversely to the fifth power as the diameter of the hose. The following example shows the advantage of using larger size hose to reduce friction loss.

The friction loss in the 4-inch hose is:

$$\frac{(3)^5}{(4)^5} = \frac{3 \times 3 \times 3 \times 3 \times 3}{4 \times 4 \times 4 \times 4 \times 4} = \frac{243}{1024} = 0.24 \text{ that of the 3-inch hose}$$

The previous example shows the enormous reduction in friction loss by using 4-inch supply hose instead of 3-inch supply hose. It equates to a 76% reduction in friction loss by using 4-inch hose instead of 3-inch hose. Whenever possible the driver/operator, in conjunction with the unit officer, should consider using larger diameter hose sizes to reduce friction loss.

Fourth Principle

For a given velocity, friction loss is approximately the same, regardless of the pressure on the water. This principle explains why friction loss is the same when hoses or pipes at different pressures flow the same amount of water. For example, if 100 gpm (400 L/min) passes through a 3-inch (77 mm) hose within a certain time, the water must travel at a specified velocity (feet per second). For the same rate of flow to pass through a 1½-inch (38 mm) hose, the velocity must be greatly increased. Four 1½-inch hoses (38 mm) are needed to flow 100 gpm (400 L/min) at the same velocity as a single 3-inch (77 mm) hose.

While pipe sizes are fixed, some brands of fire hose may expand to a larger inside diameter than other brands when under pressure. Although both brands may be sold as 1¾-inch (45 mm) hose, one may actually expand close to 2 inches (50 mm) when charged. The tendency to expand decreases velocity and therefore decreases friction loss.

Applying Friction Loss Principles

With water being virtually incompressible, a pressure of 30,000 psi (210 000 kPa) is required to reduce its volume one percent. For this reason, the same volume of water supplied into a fire hose under pressure at one end will be discharged at the other end. The diameter of the hose determines the velocity for a given volume of water. The smaller the hose, the greater the velocity needed to deliver the same volume.

Friction loss in a water system increases as the length of hose or piping increases. Flow pressure will always be greatest near the source of supply and lowest at the farthest point in the system. An elevated tank is filled with water to a height of 150 feet (45 m). The pipe connections to a fire hydrant are located at the bottom of the tank. From the hydrant, 300 feet (90 m) of 2½-inch (65 mm) hose is laid out along a street with a valve at the end. Visualize a glass tube connected to the hose every 100 feet (30 m) standing upright 150 feet (45 m) to the same height as the elevated tank. With the valve closed, the water in all the tubes would stand at Line A, which is the same level as the water in the tank. This line indicates the static pressure.

When the valve on the nozzle end is opened, water flows moderately at a low pressure. If the opening is made directly at the hydrant, the flow will be much greater at a higher pressure. In other words, the flow pressure is not as great at the end of the hose as it is at the hydrant. Instead of the water being up to the level of the tube, it is up to Line B. The difference in the water level of the tubes indicates the pressure used to overcome the friction loss in the sections of hose between the tubes. The loss of pressure at each 100-foot (30 m) interval and the reduced discharge indicate the friction loss in the line.

An open fire hose (open butt) produces a stream that normally has no use in fire fighting. Some type of nozzle is needed to shape the stream. When a closed nozzle with a 1-inch (25 mm) tip is added to the system, the water level in the glass tubes returns to Line A. When the nozzle is opened, the water level drops to Line C (**Figure 5.14**).

If the 1-inch (25 mm) tip is replaced with a ¾-inch (19 mm) tip, the water level in the glass tubes rises even higher. The velocity of the water exiting the nozzle increases, but the amount of flow decreases. By decreasing the amount of water flowing, a firefighter reduces the speed of the water in the hose; consequently, there is less friction loss.

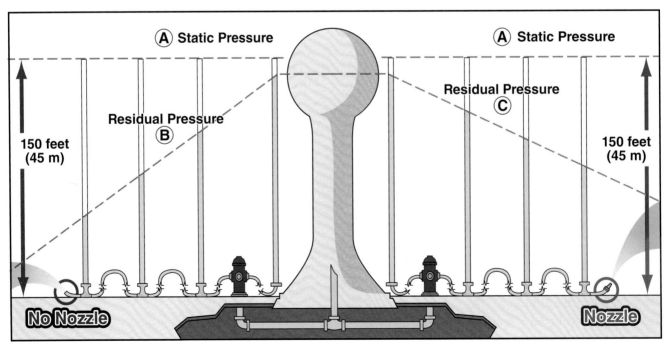

Figure 5.14 A nozzle can help recover pressure as friction loss increases.

Observe the height of the water in the first glass tubes in Figures 5.14. The water level in these tubes indicates a good supply of residual pressure left in the water main. Under these conditions, it is advisable to place a pumper in the line at the hydrant. Using a pump at this point provides additional force, thus increasing the pressure in the hose. Before water supply operations begin, the number of pumpers required to meet the requirements of the incident should be determined and positioned for maximum efficiency. This additional pressure makes it possible to produce effective fire streams. Using a pump also makes it possible to add hose, even to the extent of providing master streams.

There are practical limits to the velocity at which a stream can travel. If the velocity is increased beyond this point, the friction will become so great that the entire system is agitated by resistance. This agitation causes a degree of turbulence known as *critical velocity*. For this reason, hoselines of various diameters have a specific hose length at which the reduction in flow makes their use undesirable. Beyond this point, it is necessary to use parallel hoselines or siamese lines to increase flow and reduce friction.

Reducing Friction Loss

The following characteristics of a hose layout will affect friction loss:

- **Hose length** — To reduce friction loss caused by hose length or diameter, reduce the length of the lay and increase the diameter of the hose (this is normally not possible during fireground operations).

- **Hose diameter** — By using a larger diameter hose for a long water supply distance, the hose may then be reduced to a diameter appropriate for a master stream or handline. Because it is generally safe to increase the flow of water for fire fighting, it is usually acceptable to use larger diameter hose to reduce friction loss. However, hose size should not be increased so much that the hose becomes difficult to handle.

- **Sharp bends (kinks) in the hose** — Sharp bends or kinks can usually be minimized by employing proper hose handling techniques.

Water Hammer

Water moving through a pipe or hose has both mass and velocity. The mass of water increases as the pipe or hose size increases. Suddenly stopping water, moving through a hose or pipe, results in an energy surge being transmitted in the opposite direction, often at many times the original pressure. Each time this occurs there is an amplification of the wave causing pressure to increase. This surge is referred to as *water hammer* (**Figure 5.15, p. 182**). Where large volumes of water are involved, such as in large diameter hose layouts, water hammer is especially critical and can damage the pump, appliances, hose, or the municipal water system itself. To prevent water hammer when water is flowing, slowly close nozzles, valves, and hose clamps. When flowing from a water system, the entire operation should be stopped very slowly. When master streams are flowed or hydrants opened, they should be partially closed, stopped, and then closed more as a prevention measure.

Water Hammer — Force created by the rapid deceleration of water; causes a violent increase in pressure that can be powerful enough to rupture piping or damage fixtures. Generally results from closing a valve or nozzle too quickly.

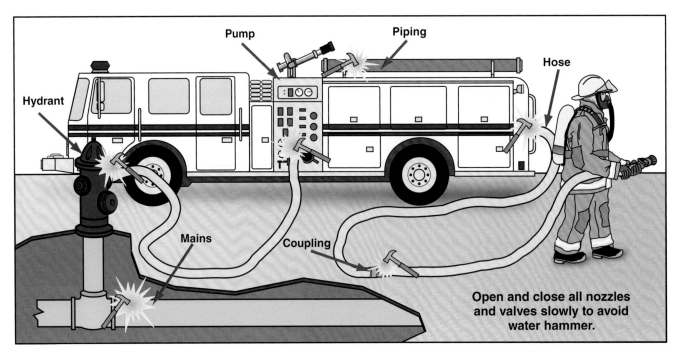

Figure 5.15 Multiple factors may cause water hammer.

Principles of a Municipal Water Supply System

Public and/or private water systems provide the methods for supplying water to populated areas. As the population increases in rural areas, the affected communities seek to improve water distribution systems from reliable sources.

The local water department may be a separate, city-operated utility, or a regional or private water authority. Because the department's principal function is to provide potable water, its officials are the experts in water supply problems. The fire department must work with the water department in planning fire protection coverage. Water department officials should realize that fire departments are vitally concerned with water supply and work with them on water supply needs and the locations and types of fire hydrants. When a large volume of water is needed, the fire department should request the water utility department to increase the water pressure in an area where there is a very large fire fighting operation.

The intricate working parts of a water system are many and varied and composed of the following fundamental components, which are explored in the following subsections:

* Sources of water supply
* Means of moving water
* Water processing or treatment facilities
* Water distribution system

Sources of Water Supply

The primary water supply can be obtained from either surface water or groundwater. Although most water systems are supplied from only one source, there are instances where both sources are used. Two examples of surface water supply are rivers and lakes **(Figure 5.16)**. Groundwater supply can be water wells or water-producing springs. Some communities have started using desalination plants to supply municipal requirements from seawater.

An engineering estimate can determine the amount of water that a community needs. This estimate is the total amount of water needed for domestic and industrial use and for fire fighting use. In cities, the domestic/industrial requirements far exceed that required for fire protection. In small towns, the requirements for fire protection may exceed other requirements.

Figure 5.16 This lake is used as a water supply for the area.

Means of Moving Water

There are three methods of moving water in a system **(Figure 5.17)**:

- **Direct pumping system** — Uses one or more pumps that takes water from the primary source and discharges it through the filtration and treatment processes. From there, a series of pumps force the water into the distribution system. If purification of the water is not needed, the water can be pumped directly into the distribution system from the primary source. Duplicating these pumping units and providing a secondary power source provides redundancy against failures in supply lines or pumps.

- **Gravity system** — Uses a primary water source located at a higher elevation than the distribution system. The gravity flow from the higher elevation provides the water pressure. This pressure is usually only sufficient when the primary water source is located at least several hundred feet (meters) higher than the highest point in the water distribution system. The most common examples include a reservoir at a higher elevation that supplies water to a city below or a system of elevated tanks in a city itself.

- **Combination system** — Most communities use a combination of the direct pumping and gravity systems. In most cases, elevated storage tanks supply the gravity flow. These tanks serve as emergency storage and provide adequate pressure through the use of gravity. When the system pressure is high during periods of low consumption, automatic valves open and allows the elevated storage tanks to fill. When the pressure drops during periods

Figure 5.17 Three methods to move water in a system.

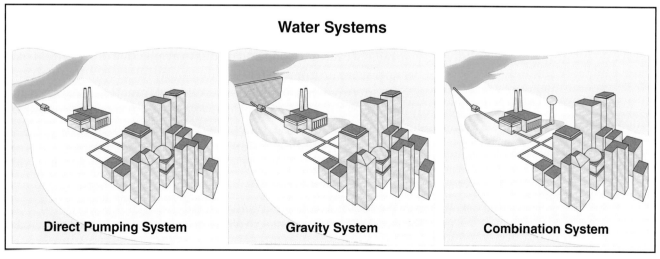

Water Systems

Direct Pumping System

Gravity System

Combination System

of heavy consumption, the storage containers provide extra water by feeding it back into the distribution system. A dependable combination system involves reliable, duplicated equipment and proper-sized, strategically located storage containers.

The storage of water in elevated reservoirs can also ensure water supply when the system becomes otherwise inoperative. Storage should be sufficient to provide domestic and industrial demands plus the demands expected in fire fighting operations. Such storage should also be sufficient to allow downtime necessary for most repairs, alterations, or additions to the system. Location of the storage and the capacity of the mains leading from this storage are also important factors in the functioning of the system.

Many industries provide their own private systems, such as elevated storage tanks, that are available to the fire department. Water for fire protection may be available to some communities from storage systems, such as cisterns, that are considered a part of the distribution system. The fire department pumper removes the water from these sources by drafting and provides pressure by its pump.

Water Processing or Treatment Facilities

The treatment of water for the water supply system is a vital process **(Figure 5.18)**. Water is treated to remove contaminants that may be detrimental to the health of those who use or drink it. Water may be treated by coagulation, sedimentation, filtration, or the addition of chemicals, bacteria, or other organisms. In addition to removing things from the water, fluoride or ozone may be added, for example.

The fire department's main concern regarding treatment facilities are that a maintenance failure, a natural disaster, the loss of power supply, or a fire could disable the pumping station(s) or severely hamper the purification process. Any of these situations would drastically reduce the volume and pressure of water available for fire fighting operations. Another problem would be the inability of the treatment system to process water fast enough to meet the demand. In either case, fire officials must have a plan to deal with potential shortfalls.

Water Distribution System

Distribution Systems — Part of an overall water supply system that receives the water from the pumping station and delivers it throughout the area to be served.

Grid System — Water supply system that utilizes lateral feeders for improved distribution.

The **distribution system** of the overall water supply system receives the water from the pumping station and delivers it throughout the area served. The ability of a water system to deliver an adequate quantity of water relies upon the carrying capacity of the system's network of pipes. When water flows through pipes, its movement causes friction and results in a reduction of pressure. There is much less pressure loss in a water distribution system when fire hydrants are supplied from two or more directions. A fire hydrant that receives water from only one direction is known as a dead-end hydrant. When a fire hydrant receives water from two or more directions, it is said to have circulating feed or a looped line. A distribution system that provides circulating feed from several mains constitutes a grid system **(Figure 5.19)**. A **grid system** should consist of the following components:

- **Primary feeders** — Large pipes (mains), with relatively widespread spacing, that convey large quantities of water to various points of the system for local distribution to the smaller mains

Figure 5.18 A water treatment facility.

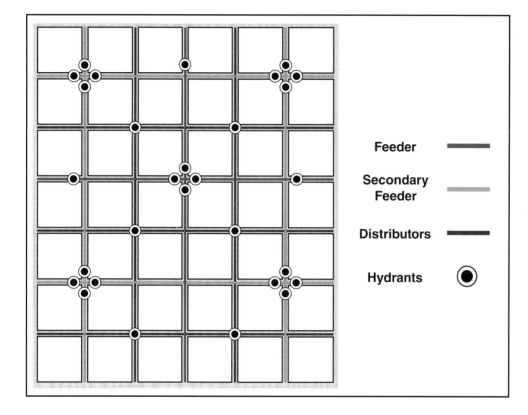

Feeder

Secondary Feeder

Distributors

Hydrants

Figure 5.19 A water grid system.

- **Secondary feeders** — Network of intermediate-sized pipes that reinforce the grid within the various loops of the primary feeder system and aid the concentration of the required fire flow at any point

- **Distributors** — Grid arrangement of smaller mains serving individual fire hydrants and blocks of consumers

Water supply distribution systems should be constructed with sufficient supply for routine consumption as well as fire protection needs in specific areas. Industrial and business districts require larger mains than those serving most residential neighborhoods. This system should include cross-connected mains at intervals sufficient to ensure adequate supply. Large mains are found on principal streets connected to smaller mains serving specific neighborhoods or developments.

Water Main Valves

The function of a valve in a water distribution system is to provide a means for controlling the flow of water through the distribution piping. Valves should be located at frequent intervals in the grid system so that only small districts are cut off if it is necessary to stop the flow at specified points. At least once a year, valves should be operated to keep them in good condition. The actual need for valve operation in a water system rarely occurs, sometimes not for many years. Space the valves within the distribution system so that a minimum portion of a main may be isolated for repair or maintenance, impacting only a small area of service. Provide hydrants with individual control valves in order to minimize the affect repairs will have on fire protection capabilities.

One of the most important factors in a water supply system is the water department's ability to promptly operate the valves during an emergency or breakdown of equipment. A well-run water utility has records of the locations of all valves. Valves should be inspected and operated yearly by the water supply utility. Valves for water systems are broadly divided into indicating and nonindicating types.

Indicating valves. An indicating valve visually shows whether the gate or valve seat is open, closed, or partially closed. Valves in private fire protection systems are usually of the indicating type. Two common indicator valves are the **post indicator valve (PIV)** and the **outside screw and yoke (OS&Y) valve (Figure 5.20)**. The post indicator valve is a hollow metal post that is attached to the valve housing. The valve stem inside the post is threaded and has a target that moves as the valve is opened or closed. The words *open* or *shut* appear in a window as the valve approaches one position or the other. These valves are commonly used on private water supply systems. The OS&Y valve has a yoke on the outside with a threaded stem that controls the gate's opening or closing. The threaded portion of the stem is out of the yoke when the valve is open and inside the yoke when the valve is closed. These are most commonly used on sprinkler systems but may be found in some water distribution system applications.

Nonindicating valves. These are the most common type of valves used on most public water distribution systems. In a water distribution system, these are normally installed in valve boxes or manholes. If a below-grade valve is

Figure 5.20 Examples of a post indicator valve (PIV) and an outside screw and yoke (OS&Y) valve.

properly installed, the valve can be operated aboveground with a special socket wrench on the end of a reach rod. Many fire departments carry these wrenches on their engines.

NOTE: Fire department policy may prohibit firefighters from operating the control valves of a water distribution system. For jurisdictions where it is permissible to operate these valves, firefighters should be familiar with the opening direction of nonindicating valves, as they may open clockwise or counterclockwise. Consult the local water authority before operating these valves.

Control valves in public water distribution systems are generally gate valves. Gate valves may be of the rising stem or the nonrising-stem type. The rising-stem type is similar to the OS&Y valve. On the nonrising-stem type, the gate either rises or lowers to control the water flow as the valve nut is turned by the valve key (wrench). Nonrising-stem gate valves should be marked with a number indicating the number of turns necessary to completely close the valve. If a valve resists turning after fewer than the indicated number of turns, it usually means debris or other obstructions are in the valve, or it may be corroded due to lack of maintenance. This condition should be reported to the agency responsible for maintaining the system.

The advantages of proper valve installation in a distribution system are readily apparent. If valves are installed according to established standards, it normally will be necessary to close off only one or perhaps two fire hydrants from service while a single break is being repaired. The advantage of proper valve installation is, however, reduced if all valves are not properly maintained and kept fully open. High friction loss is caused by valves that are only partially open. When valves are closed or partially closed, the condition may not be noticeable during ordinary domestic water usage. As a result, the impairment will not be known until a fire occurs or until detailed inspections and fire flow tests are made. A fire department may have difficulty in obtaining a sufficient volume of water for fire fighting in areas where there are closed or partially closed valves in the distribution system.

Water Pipes

Water pipe that is used underground is generally made of cast iron, ductile iron, asbestos cement, steel, plastic, or concrete. Whenever pipe is installed, it should be the proper type for the soil conditions and pressures to which it will be subjected. When water mains are installed in unstable or corrosive soils or in difficult access areas, steel or reinforced concrete pipe may be used to give the strength needed. Some locations that may require extra protection include areas beneath railroad tracks and highways, areas close to heavy industrial machinery, areas prone to earthquakes, or areas of rugged terrain.

The internal surface of the pipe, regardless of the material from which it is made, offers resistance to water flow. Some materials, however, have considerably less resistance to water flow than others. Personnel from the engineering division of the water department should determine the type of pipe best suited for the conditions at hand.

The amount of water able to flow through a pipe and the amount of friction loss created can also be affected by other factors. Frequently, friction loss is increased by encrustation of minerals on the interior surfaces of the pipe. Another problem is sedimentation that settles out of the water. Both of these conditions result in a restriction of the pipe size, increased friction loss, and a proportionate reduction in the amount of water available from the system. The adverse effects of encrustation and sedimentation can be reduced by flushing hydrants periodically. The fire department should coordinate with the local water authority before flushing hydrants in nonemergency situations. Hydrant flushing may cause water customers to receive rusty or foul smelling water for a period of time.

Water System Capacity

When engineers design a water distribution system, three basic rates of consumption are considered in their design, which form an established base to which the fire flow requirements can be added during the design process. The rates of consumption also allow the engineers and fire protection personnel alike to determine the adequacy of the water distribution system. The driver/operator should be familiar with these terms because they encounter them often during water supply testing.

- The average daily consumption (ADC) is the average amount of water used per day based on the total amount of water used in a water distribution system over the period of one year.

- The maximum daily consumption (MDC) is the maximum total amount of water that was used during any 24-hour interval within a 3-year period. Unusual situations, such as refilling a reservoir after cleaning, should not be considered in determining the maximum daily consumption.

- The peak hourly consumption (PHC) is the maximum amount of water used in any 1-hour interval over the course of a day.

Private Water Supply Systems

In addition to the public water supply systems that service most communities, fire department personnel must also be familiar with the basic principles of any private water supply systems that may be found within their response jurisdiction. Private water supply systems are most commonly found on large commercial, industrial, or institutional properties, but may also be found in some residential developments. They may service one large building or a series of buildings on the complex. In general, the private water supply system exists for one of the three following purposes:

- To provide water strictly for fire protection purposes

- To provide water for sanitary and fire protection purposes

- To provide water for fire protection and manufacturing processes

The design of private water supply systems is typically similar to that of the municipal systems described earlier in this chapter. Most commonly, private water supply systems receive their water from a municipal water supply system. In some cases, the private system may have its own water supply source, independent of the municipal water distribution system.

In a few cases, a property may be served by two sources of water supply for fire protection: one from the municipal system and the other from a private source. In many cases, the private source of water for fire protection provides nonpotable water (not for drinking). When this is the case, measures must be taken to prevent cross contamination of the municipal water supply system with nonpotable water. There are a variety of backflow prevention measures that can be employed to avoid this problem. Interconnecting potable and nonpotable water systems is restricted by the Environmental Protection Agency and numerous state and local water quality codes. This means that the protected property must maintain two completely separate systems if the combined water capacity is required for fire protection.

Almost universally, private water supply systems maintain separate piping for fire protection and domestic/industrial services. This is in distinct contrast to most municipal water supply systems in which fire hydrants are connected to the same mains that supply water for domestic/industrial use. Separate systems are cost prohibitive for most municipal applications but are economically practical in many private applications. A number of advantages are available to having separate piping arrangements in a private water supply system, including the following:

- The property owner has control over the water supply source.
- Either of the systems (fire protection or domestic/industrial) are unaffected by service interruptions to the other system.

NOTE: Private water supply systems that rely solely on the municipal water distribution system as their water supply source are subject to service interruptions in the event that the municipal system experiences a failure.

If there is any question about the reliability of a private water supply system or its ability to provide an adequate amount of water for a large-scale fire fighting operation, the fire department should make arrangements to augment the private water supply. This may be accomplished by relaying water from the municipal water supply system or by drafting from a reliable static water supply source close to the scene.

Chapter Summary

Pumping apparatus driver/operators must understand the properties of water and how it functions as an efficient and economical extinguishing agent. The principles of pressure and friction loss are factors that must be considered during every water supply operation in order to properly supply pumpers and attack hoselines. Preincident knowledge of the water distribution system serving a local jurisdiction and an understanding of the design and proper maintenance of a municipal or private water system is vital to providing needed water flow and will aid driver/operators in planning for large-scale fire fighting operations.

Review Questions

1. What are the ways that water can extinguish fire? (p. 168)
2. What are some advantages and disadvantages of water as an extinguishing agent? (pp. 169-170)
3. What are the different types of pressure? (pp. 174-176)
4. What are the principles of friction loss? (pp. 178-179)
5. How can friction loss caused by hose length or diameter be reduced? (p. 181)
6. What are the various means of moving water for a system? (pp. 183-184)
7. What are the purposes of a private water supply system? (pp. 188-189)

Hose Nozzles and Flow Rates

Chapter Contents

chapter 6

Key Terms

NFPA® Job Performance Requirements

This chapter provides information that addresses the following job performance requirements of NFPA 1002, *Standard for Fire Apparatus Driver/Operator Professional Qualifications (2014)*.

   5.2.1

NFPA 1002, *Standard for Fire Apparatus Driver/Operator Professional Qualifications (2017)*.

   5.2.4

Hose Nozzles and Flow Rates

Learning Objectives

After reading this chapter, students will be able to:

1. Distinguish among types of fire hose nozzles. (*NFPA 1002, 2014:* 5.2.1 & *NFPA 1002, 2017:* 5.2.4)

2. Identify considerations for selecting nozzles. (*NFPA 1002, 2014:* 5.2.1 & *NFPA 1002, 2017:* 5.2.4)

3. Distinguish among types of special purpose nozzles. (*NFPA 1002, 2014:* 5.2.1 & *NFPA 1002, 2017:* 5.2.4)

4. Summarize facts about nozzle pressure and reaction. (*NFPA 1002, 2014:* 5.2.1 & *NFPA 1002, 2017:* 5.2.4)

Chapter 6
Hose Nozzles and Flow Rates

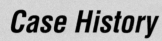

Case History

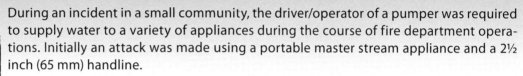

During an incident in a small community, the driver/operator of a pumper was required to supply water to a variety of appliances during the course of fire department operations. Initially an attack was made using a portable master stream appliance and a 2½ inch (65 mm) handline.

After the main body of fire was knocked down, several 1¾-inch (45 mm) handlines were stretched to conduct overhaul operations. One handline was outfitted with a selectable gallonage nozzle, and the other featured a smooth bore nozzle.

The driver/operator must understand the different features of each appliance that they may be responsible for pumping. The required pressure and flow rates are crucial if the stream is to be deployed in a safe and effective manner. Driver/operators that supply too little or too much pressure for the appliance they are pumping may cause equipment damage or endanger firefighters operating the appliance.

The following chapter provides basic information about handlines, nozzles, and master stream appliances. Although driver/operators may not be responsible for the selection of a particular handline or nozzle for use during an incident, they must be knowledgeable about the capabilities of each handline, nozzle, and master stream appliance on their apparatus in order to provide proper pressure and volume of water.

Operating pressure, nozzle design and adjustment, as well as the condition of the nozzle orifice affect the condition of the stream as it leaves the nozzle. Upon leaving the nozzle orifice, water forms a fire stream. Until it reaches its destination, the fire stream is influenced by velocity, gravity, wind, and friction with the air. Driver/operators must ensure that the optimum flow rate and discharge pressure are applied to each fire stream in order to achieve maximum efficiency during incident operations.

Fire Hose Nozzles

The fire service operates three types of nozzles to produce three basic fire streams: solid, fog, and broken stream **(Figure 6.1, p. 191)**. This chapter describes the operating characteristics of each nozzle to assist the driver/operator in supplying water safely and efficiently.

Solid Stream Nozzles

A **solid fire stream** is produced with a fixed orifice and a smooth bore nozzle. The solid stream is tight with little spray or shower effect **(Figure 6.2)**. This type of nozzle may be found on handlines as well as all types of master stream appliances.

Solid stream nozzles are designed so that the water flowing through the nozzle is gradually reduced until just before the orifice. At this point the nozzle becomes a cylindrical bore that gives the water a round shape at discharge. The smooth waterway of the nozzle allows the stream to maximize its effective reach.

The nozzle pressure and size of the discharge orifice determine the flow and reach of a solid stream. Solid stream nozzles on handlines should generally be operated at a maximum of 50 psi (350 kPa) nozzle pressure, while master stream appliances should be operated at a maximum 80 psi (560 kPa).

Determining the Flow from a Solid Stream Nozzle

Driver/operators may need to determine the amount of water discharged from a solid stream nozzle in order to perform friction loss calculations, determine

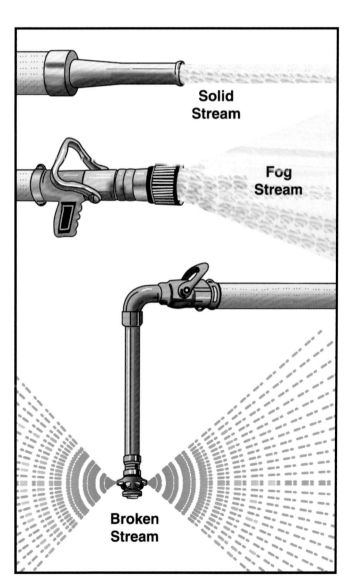

Figure 6.2 The solid fire stream has little spray or shower effect.

Figure 6.1 Basic fire streams: solid stream, fog stream, and broken stream.

pump discharge pressure, or to test the water supply when a nozzle is attached to a hydrant.

Formula 6.1 (Customary) - Discharge Rate

GPM = 29.7 x d² x √NP

Where:

GPM = Discharge in gallons per minute (gpm)

29.7 = A constant

d = Diameter of the orifice in inches (in)

NP = Nozzle Pressure in pounds per square inch (psi)

Formula 6.1 (Metric) - Discharge Rate

L/min = 0.067 x d² x √NP

Where:

L/min = Discharge in liters per minute (L/min)

0. 067 = A constant

d = Diameter of the orifice in millimeters (mm)

NP = Nozzle Pressure in kilopascals (kPa)

Using this formula, the driver/operator may determine water flow from any solid stream nozzle when the nozzle pressure and tip diameter is known. **Table 6.1, p. 196** lists various nozzle tip diameters. The following example illustrates an application of this formula:

Example 6.1 (Customary)

Determine the water flow from a 1-inch tip operating at 50 psi.

GPM = (29.7)(d)²(√NP)

GPM = (29.7)(1)² (√50)

GPM = **210.01 (app. 210)**

Example 6.1 (Metric)

Determine the flow of water from a 25 mm tip operating at 350 kPa.

L/min = (0.067)(d)²(√NP)

L/min = (0.067) (25)²(√350)

L/min = **783.41 (app. 780)**

Fog Stream Nozzles

In order for a stream of water to be broken into finely divided particles, it must be driven against an obstruction with sufficient force to diffuse the water and shatter the mass. Upon encountering an obstruction, the angle of deflection off its surface will determine the forward velocity of the stream of water as well as its pattern or shape. Therefore, a wide deflection produces a wide-angle fog pattern and a narrow deflection will produce a narrow-angle fog pattern **(Figure 6.3, p. 196)**.

Table 6. 1 Common Nozzle Diameters		
Customary (Inches)	Metric (mm) (Known As)	Metric (mm) (Actual)
½	13	12.700
⅝	16	15.880
¾	19	19.050
⅞	22	22.225
1	25	25.400
1⅛	29	28.575
1¼	32	31.750
1⅜	35	34.925
1½	38	38.100
1¾	45	44.450
2	50	50.800
2¼	57	57.150
2½	65	63.500
2¾	70	69.850
3	77	76.200

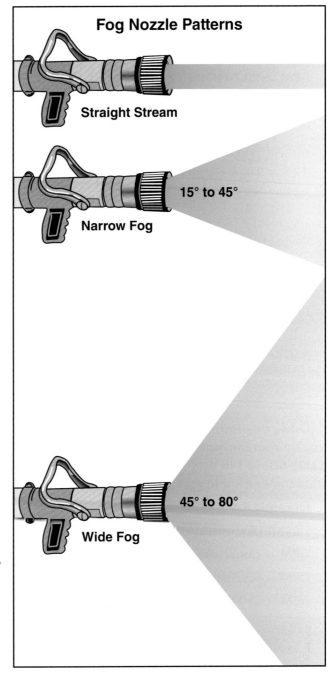

Fog Nozzle Patterns

Straight Stream

15° to 45°

Narrow Fog

45° to 80°

Wide Fog

Figure 6.3 Fog nozzle patterns: straight stream, narrow fog, and wide fog.

Fog Stream — Water stream of finely divided particles used for fire control.

A fog stream may be produced by deflection at the periphery, by impinging jets of water, or a combination of these methods. Periphery-deflected streams are produced by deflecting water around an inside circular stem in the nozzle. The water is then deflected by the exterior barrel of the nozzle. The position of the stem relative to the barrel will determine the shape of the **fog stream** **(Figure 6.4)**.

Impinging stream nozzles break water into fine, evenly divided particles by driving several jets of water together at an angle. Although a narrow pattern is possible, impinging stream nozzles most often provide a wide-angle fog pattern. Impinging jets may also be used in some periphery deflected stream nozzles.

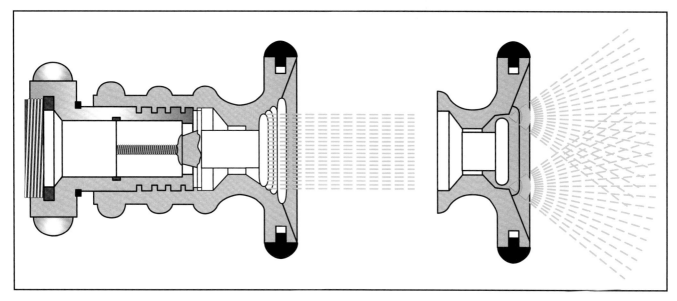

Figure 6.4 The relative positions of the deflection stem and the exterior barrel of a periphery-deflected nozzle determine the stream pattern.

The reach of the fog stream is directly related to its width, the size of the water particles (droplets), the wind, and the volume of water flowing. There are a variety of fog stream nozzles available with differing capabilities. The following sections will explain basic design and operation of some of these nozzles.

Constant Flow Fog Nozzles

A constant flow nozzle is designed to flow a specific volume of water on all stream patterns at a specific nozzle discharge pressure. Most constant flow nozzles feature a periphery-deflected stream and are equipped with an adjustable pattern range **(Figure 6.5)**. The principle of operation is based on rotating the exterior of the barrel to change pattern settings. During this rotation, the space between the deflecting stem and the interior throat of the nozzle remains the same, allowing for the discharge of a fixed gallonage of water on all pattern settings. Most constant flow nozzles are designed to operate at a nozzle pressure of 100 psi (700 kPa). However, some nozzles may operate at 50 (350 kPa) or 75 psi (525 kPa).

Selectable Gallonage Nozzles

Some nozzles may be designed for adjustable gallonage settings. These nozzles allow the firefighter operating the handline to select the flow rate to suit fire and operating conditions **(Figure 6.6, p. 198)**. The nozzle will supply this flow at the rated nozzle discharge pressure. If the driver/operator does not supply the proper pressure, the handline will not achieve the gallonage selected at the nozzle. Many of these nozzles

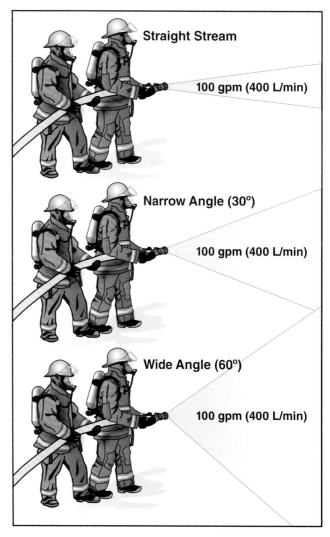

Straight Stream

100 gpm (400 L/min)

Narrow Angle (30°)

100 gpm (400 L/min)

Wide Angle (60°)

100 gpm (400 L/min)

Figure 6.5 Example of constant flow fog nozzles in operation.

Figure 6.6 A manually adjusted/selectable gallonage nozzle.

Figure 6.7 Firefighters operating an automatic fog nozzle.

are designed to flow the gallonage indicated at 100 psi (700 kPa) nozzle pressure. However, some models are available that are capable of operating at lower nozzle pressures.

Selectable gallonage nozzles and constant flow nozzles are similar in that when properly supplied, both discharge predetermined gallonage. When operating a selectable gallonage nozzle, the driver/operator sets its discharge gallonage with a specified range before use. Departmental SOPs may specify predetermined discharge gallonage. With a constant flow nozzle, the gallonage is based on the specifications established by the manufacturer of the nozzle.

NOTE: The driver/operator must know the gallonage setting in which the nozzle will be operated in order to properly calculate friction loss and determine an appropriate pump discharge pressure.

Automatic Fog Nozzles

Automatic nozzles are a type of variable flow nozzle with the ability to change patterns while maintaining the same nozzle pressure **(Figure 6.7)**. If the gallonage supplied to the nozzle changes, the automatic nozzle adjusts to maintain virtually the same pressure and consistency of pattern. This ability is made possible by a spring-activated device in the nozzle that constricts or expands the space between the baffle and the interior throat of the nozzle depending on the water pressure.

Although the stream produced by an automatic nozzle may appear adequate, if the proper discharge pressure is not applied the stream may not flow sufficient water for fire suppression. Automatic nozzles adjust to fluctuating water flow to maintain effective pressure and a consistent fire stream in all flow ranges. Most fog nozzles are designed to operate at 100 psi (700 kPa) tip pressure. However, some models may operate at 75 or even 50 psi (525 kPa or 350 kPa). Driver/operators must be knowledgeable about the equipment used in conjunction with the apparatus for which they are responsible.

CAUTION
Driver/operators must ensure that adequate discharge pressure is supplied to all hoselines, especially those equipped with automatic nozzles. Hoselines supplied with inadequate pressure may not provide sufficient flow for fire suppression even though the stream may appear well formed.

Within the limitation of its design, an automatic nozzle maintains its constant operating pressure even if the pump discharge pressure rises above this level. As pump pressure increases the nozzle enlarges its opening size — within a specific range — to compensate for the increased flow.

High Pressure Fog Nozzles

Operating at a pressure of up to 800 psi (5 600 kPa), high pressure fog nozzles produce a stream with significant forward velocity, but a relatively low volume of water delivery. Featuring a stream of fast-moving, fine spray, high-pressure fog nozzles may use an impinging stream. These nozzles are best suited for wildland fires and are not recommended for structural fire fighting due to their low water flow of only 8 to 15 gpm (30 L/min to 60 L/min).

Selecting Nozzles

Depending on department policy, the driver/operator may aid in the selection of the correct nozzle to perform suppression operations during a particular incident. The following sections describe types of nozzles common to most fire department pumpers.

Handline Nozzles

Nozzles for use on handlines may be solid, fog, or broken stream design, ranging in size from a ¾-inch (20 mm) "booster" nozzle to a nozzle suitable for a 3-inch (77 mm) diameter hoseline. Generally, 350 gpm (1 400 L/min) is the maximum flow for a handline. Greater flows will produce a nozzle reaction (discussed later in this chapter) that is difficult or dangerous for firefighters to handle.

Master Stream Nozzles

Master stream nozzles are capable of water flow in excess of 350 gpm (1 400 L/min) and must be properly secured for safe operation. These appliances may produce solid or fog streams and generate considerable nozzle reaction due to their higher flow rate **(Figure 6.8)**.

Master stream appliances are generally operated during incidents where handlines would be ineffective, conditions require a defensive posture, or personnel are limited. Smooth bore streams are generally operated at 80 psi (560 kPa) nozzle pressure, while fog appliances are generally operated at 100 psi (700 kPa). Driver/operators should consult manufacturer's recommendations for specific appliances. In addition to their large flow capability, master streams offer firefighters the ability to operate at a greater distance from the fire, taking advantage of a longer reach than handheld streams.

Designed for use from a fixed position, master stream appliances generally change the direction of water through the device in order to reduce nozzle reaction and achieve delivery of the fire stream. Water must often

Figure 6.8 Master stream nozzles are capable of high flow rates.

pass through one or more sharp bends that create friction in the appliance. Although friction loss in a master stream device is assumed to be a specific number, each jurisdiction should determine the actual loss of their specific equipment through field tests.

Master Stream Appliances

The three basic types of master stream appliances are fixed, combination, and portable. Each type of monitor has the ability to change the stream direction or angle while water is being discharged. The driver/operator should be familiar with the capabilities of the equipment to which he or she is assigned.

- **Fixed monitors** — Commonly called *deck guns* and permanently mounted on the apparatus.

- **Combination monitors** — May be used in a mount on the apparatus or removed and used remotely from the vehicle. Combination monitors often have flow limitations when they are removed from the apparatus and placed on the ground.

- **Portable monitors** — Stored on the apparatus for deployment to the location where they are to be used.

Elevated Master Streams

An elevated master stream may be pre-plumbed and permanently attached to an aerial ladder, platform, or other aerial device. It may also be designed as a detachable appliance designed to be set up only when needed. A detachable ladder pipe is one such device used in conjunction with aerial ladders. Movement of ladder pipes is limited to a vertical up and down motion. This action is accomplished by placing a firefighter at the tip or by using of ropes with a detachable ladder pipe. Pre-piped waterways generally feature a master stream that may be remotely controlled from the apparatus turntable and is generally able to move both up and down and side to side.

Master streams found on elevating platforms are similar in design to pre-plumbed aerial ladders. The difference is that the master stream appliance is attached to the platform for easy control by firefighters operating from the platform. Some platforms are equipped with two such devices. For more information on elevated master streams, refer to Chapters 16-20 of the **Pumping and Aerial Apparatus Driver/Operator Handbook, 3rd edition.**

Special Purpose Nozzles

Depending on the incident, firefighters may need to deploy special nozzles to operate effectively in unusual locations, or on specific fuels. Jurisdictions may have unique needs that are best met by special nozzles not required as part of the NFPA® 1901 standard list of pumping apparatus equipment. When using special purpose nozzles, consult the manufacturer for the correct use and operating pressure.

Cellar Nozzles

Cellar nozzles (some varieties are referred to as *distributors*) are most often lowered through holes or other openings to the cellar of an occupancy (**Figure 6.9**). These devices may also be deployed for attic or other void space fires.

Because some of these nozzles are not equipped with shutoffs, the insertion of an inline shut off valve at a location back from the nozzle increases safety and ease of operation.

NOTE: Though cellar nozzles may be referred to as *distributors*, distributor nozzles have unique flow rates that may differ from cellar nozzles.

Piercing Nozzles

Piercing nozzles, also called *penetrating nozzles*, are commonly used in aircraft fire fighting, car fires, or to apply water to voids, attics, or other areas inaccessible to standard fire streams **(Figure 6.10)**. The piercing nozzle is generally designed as 3 to 6 foot (1 to 2 m) hollow steel rod 1½ inches (38 mm) in diameter. The tip of the device is a hardened steel point capable of being driven through a variety of material including concrete block and other building materials. An impinging jet nozzle capable of flowing approximately 125 gpm (500 L/min) at 100 psi (700 kPa) is part of the hardened tip. At the opposite end of the nozzle a striking surface allows the device to be driven with a sledgehammer or maul axe through various obstructions.

Chimney Nozzles

Designed to suppress fires in chimney flues, the chimney nozzle is supplied by a booster hose. This device consists of a solid piece of brass or steel with many small impinging holes. Flowing only 1.5 to 3 gpm (6 to 12 L/min) at a nozzle

> **Piercing Nozzle** — Nozzle with an angled, case-hardened steel tip that can be driven through a wall, roof, or ceiling to extinguish hidden fire. *Also known as* Piercing Applicator Nozzle, Puncture Nozzle, *or* Penetrating Nozzle.

Figure 6.9 A cellar nozzle in operation.

Figure 6.10 Piercing nozzles are used in areas that are inaccessible to standard fire streams.

Figure 6.11 The chimney nozzle suppresses fires in chimney flues.

pressure of 100 psi (700 kPa), the impinging holes of the chimney nozzle produce a very fine mist which turns to steam in the hot interior of the chimney flue **(Figure 6.11)**.

Nozzle Pressure and Reaction

Nozzle Reaction — Counterforce directed against a person holding a nozzle or a device holding a nozzle by the velocity of water being discharged.

As water is discharged from a nozzle at a given pressure, a counterforce pushes back against firefighters operating the hoseline. This force, called *nozzle reaction*, illustrates Newton's Third Law of Motion: *For every action there is an equal and opposite reaction.* One of the limitations of nozzle pressure is the ability of firefighters to withstand the resulting nozzle reaction and continue to safely operate the hoseline.

WARNING!
Excessive nozzle reaction may seriously injure firefighters and hamper fire suppression efforts.

Most fog nozzles are designed to operate at or below 100 psi (700 kPa) nozzle pressure. Above this pressure, handlines become unwieldy for firefighters attempting to advance and maneuver during fire suppression operations. This operating pressure is also acceptable for master stream devices equipped with fog nozzles.

In most cases, solid stream nozzles for handline use should operate at 50 psi (350 kPa) nozzle pressure. Portable master stream devices should be operated at pressures not to exceed the manufacturer's recommendations. Generally for fixed master stream appliances, a nozzle pressure of 80 psi (560 kPa) is required.

Even when you are not responsible for determining the best configurations for preconnected attack lines and nozzle choices, you should be familiar with the nozzle reaction that a fire attack team will encounter. Determining realistic layouts for jurisdictional requirements and personnel availability will help ensure safety and efficiency on the fireground.

Calculating Nozzle Reaction for Solid Stream Nozzles

In order to calculate nozzle reaction when utilizing solid stream nozzles, use the following formulas:

Formula 6.2 (Customary) – Nozzle Reaction for Solid Stream Nozzles

NR = 1.57 x d² x NP

Where:

NR = Nozzle Reaction in pounds (lb)

1.57 = A constant

d = Nozzle diameter in inches (in)

NP = Nozzle Pressure in pounds per square inch (psi)

Formula 6.2 (Metric) – Nozzle Reaction for Solid Stream Nozzles

NR= 0.0015 x d² x NP

Where:

NR = Nozzle Reaction in Newtons (N)

0.0015 = A constant

d = Nozzle diameter in millimeters (mm)

NP = Nozzle Pressure in kilopascals (kPa)

Example 6.2 (Customary)

Determine the nozzle reaction from a hoseline equipped with a 1¼ inch tip operating at a nozzle pressure of 50 psi.

NR = **(1.57)(d)²(NP)**

NR = $(1.57)(1.25)^2(50)$

NR = **122.66 lb (app. 120)**

Example 6.2 (Metric)

Determine the nozzle reaction from a hoseline equipped with a 32 mm tip operating at a nozzle pressure of 350 psi.

NR = **(0.0015)(d)²(NP)**

NR = $(0.0015)(32)^2(350)$

NR = **537.6 N (app. 540)**

A simple guideline for the Customary system of measurement is NR = Q/3. This may be used to achieve the approximate solid stream nozzle reaction on the fireground. Q equals the total flow of water in gpm flowing through the nozzle.

Calculating Nozzle Reaction for Fog Stream Nozzles

In order to calculate the nozzle reaction when using fog stream nozzles, the following formulas may be used:

Formula 6.3 (Customary) – Nozzle Reaction for Fog Stream Nozzles

NR= 0.0505 x Q x √NP

Where:

NR = Nozzle Reaction in pounds (lb)

0.0505 = A constant

Q = Total flow through the nozzle in gallons per minute (gpm)

NP = Nozzle Pressure in pounds per square inch (psi)

Formula 6.3 (Metric) – Nozzle Reaction for Fog Stream Nozzles

NR = 0.0156 x Q x √NP

Where:

NR = Nozzle Reaction in Newtons (N)

0.0156 = A constant

Q = Total flow through the nozzle in liters per minute (L/min)

NP = Nozzle Pressure in kilopascals (kPa)

NOTE: The value Q in the previous formulas represent the total flow of water through the nozzle. This is not to be confused with the value of Q (Q = Flow/100) that is expressed in friction loss formulas in Chapter 7.

The following example illustrates the application of this formula:

Example 6.3 (Customary)

Find the nozzle reaction of a hoseline with a fog nozzle flowing 200 gpm at 100 psi.

NR = (0.0505)(Q)(√NP)

NR = (0.0505)(200)(√100)

NR = **101 lb (app. 100)**

A simple guideline for the customary system of measurement is NR = Q/2. This may be used to achieve the approximate fog stream nozzle reaction on the fireground. Q equals the total flow of water in gpm through the nozzle.

Example 6.3 (Metric)

Find the nozzle reaction of a hoseline with a fog nozzle flowing 800 L/min at 700 kPa.

NR = (0.0156)(Q)(√NP)

NR = (0.0156)(800)(√700)

NR = **330.19 N (app. 330)**

Chapter Summary

Driver/operators are not always responsible for selecting the appropriate nozzle for use during fireground operations. However, they must be familiar with the capabilities and limitations of each nozzle carried on the apparatus as well as the specified flow rate and discharge pressure required to ensure safe and effective operations. Driver/operators must understand the hydraulic calculations that must be performed in order to achieve the desired results on the fireground.

Review Questions

1. What are the main types of fire hose nozzles available? (p. 193)

2. When would special purpose nozzles be used? (pp. 200-202)

3. Why is it important to take into account nozzle pressure and reaction? (p. 202)

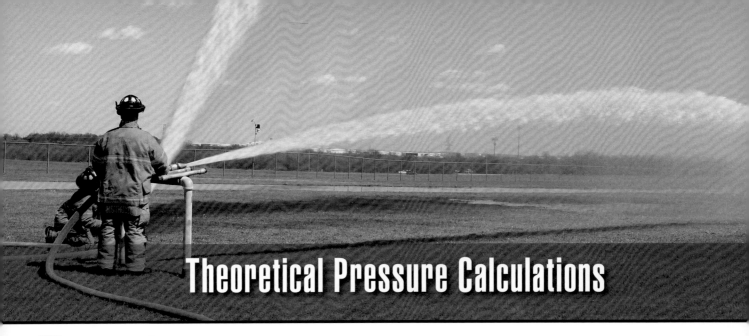

Theoretical Pressure Calculations

Chapter Contents

Key Terms

NFPA® Job Performance Requirements

This chapter provides information that addresses the following job performance requirements of NFPA 1002, *Standard for Fire Apparatus Driver/Operator Professional Qualifications (2014)*.
   5.1.1, 5.2.1, 5.2.2, 5.2.4

NFPA 1002, *Standard for Fire Apparatus Driver/Operator Professional Qualifications (2017)*.
   5.1.2, 5.2.4, 5.2.5, 5.2.7

Theoretical Pressure Calculations

Learning Objectives

After reading this chapter, students will be able to:

1. Summarize facts about total pressure loss. (*NFPA 1002, 2014:* 5.2.1, 5.2.2 & *NFPA 1002, 2017:* 5.2.4, 5.2.5)

2. Identify how various hose layouts affect total pressure loss. (*NFPA 1002, 2014:* 5.2.4 & *NFPA 1002, 2017:* 5.2.7)

3. Explain how to determine pump discharge pressure. (*NFPA 1002, 2014:* 5.2.1, 5.2.2 & *NFPA 1002, 2017:* 5.2.4, 5.2.5)

4. Test hose carried on fire department apparatus to determine friction loss. (*NFPA 1002, 2014:* 5.1.1, 5.2.1, 5.2.2, Skill Sheet 7-1 & *NFPA 1002, 2017:* 5.1.2, 5.2.4, 5.2.5, Skill Sheet 7-1)

Chapter 7
Theoretical Pressure Calculations

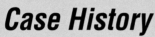

Case History

As members of a small fire department, driver/operators and company officers may be expected to assist in the development of standard operating procedures and preincident plans for their primary response district. With several high-rise apartment buildings under construction in their district, the captain of Engine 1 met with the driver/operators assigned to the company and asked that they review department policy for operating handlines from standpipe systems and supplying water to a FDC. The driver/operators must determine how to meet the requirements of the SOP for the new buildings in question. In order to predetermine the required pressures, the driver/operators must employ theoretical pressure calculations using standard formulas. After the correct pressures have been determined, they may be recorded in the preincident plan or posted on a sign next to the FDC for quick reference during incident operations.

The primary function of the driver/operator on the fireground is to provide water to attack crews in sufficient volume and pressure to achieve control and extinguishment of fires. In order to accomplish this task, an understanding of the theoretical aspects of fire stream development is required.

Driver/operators must consider the effects of friction loss and elevation on hose layouts. The ability to correctly factor variables encountered at incident scenes and develop the proper pump discharge pressure for specific fire streams is paramount to safe and efficient operations.

Driver/operators on the fireground rarely perform the theoretical calculations contained in the following sections. Due to the dynamic nature of fire fighting, driver/operators are more likely to use the methods described in Chapter 9, Fire Pump Theory. However, you should have the ability to calculate theoretical friction loss because understanding the factors that influence flow rates provides:

- A better understanding of the basis for the methods used in Chapter 9.

- The ability to predetermine approximate pump discharge pressures for preconnected hoselines and common hose lays for the apparatus and district to which you are assigned.

- The skill to conduct preincident planning of hose deployment at target hazards or unusual occupancies in the jurisdiction.

Throughout this chapter, numerous example problems will aid in familiarizing you with the concepts used in performing hydraulic calculations. Examples are presented in a step-by-step format to illustrate the entire problem-solving method to allow you to use multiple variables to find a resolution

Before proceeding to the main body of this chapter, review the sizes of fire hose and solid stream tip sizes commonly used in the fire service. These figures will be used for calculations throughout the chapter and are contained in **Tables 7.1** and **7.2**. All metrics in IFSTA publications follow a document titled "Training Guidelines for the Metric Conversion of Fire Departments in Canada." The NFPA® does not follow these guidelines. This may result in some differences in what a particular size hose is called in metric terms.

Formula Examples, Tables, Figures, and Conversions

Examples of all formulas found in this chapter are located at the end of the chapter. The examples are first included in the Customary System and then in the International System of Units (metrics). Tables and figures containing numerical information for completing the following examples are found in these sections and include the following:

- Friction loss coefficients
- Appliance pressure loss
- Elevation pressure
- Hose layout applications
- Pump discharge pressure

The numbers used in the examples for the Customary System and the International System are not conversions one to the other. Different numbers are used in each section to make the calculations simpler. In the main body of the chapter, the metrics are approximate conversions to make the formulae and instructions easier to understand.

Total Pressure Loss: Friction Loss, Elevation Pressure Loss, and Appliance Loss

In order to effectively provide water for fire streams, it is necessary to know the amount of friction loss in the fire hose and the pressure loss or gain due to elevation **(Figure 7.1)**. Friction loss is caused by a number of factors including the condition of the hose and couplings as well as any kinks in the hoseline. However, the primary consideration is the volume of water flowing per minute.

When making a friction loss calculation, the driver/operator must also account for the length and diameter of the hose as well as appliances that may be in use with the hoseline. In addition, pressure may be lost or gained due to elevation differences. Friction loss and elevation pressure loss (when applicable) are combined with the loss associated with appliances added to the layout to create Total Pressure Loss (TPL). These factors are expressed in pounds per square inch.

Table 7.1 Common Hose Sizes		
U.S. (Inches)	Canada (mm)	NFPA (mm)
¾	20	20
1	25	25
1½	38	38
1¾	45	44
2	50	51
2½	65	65
3	77	76
3½	90	89
4	100	100
4½	115	113
5	125	125
6	150	150

Table 7.2 Common Nozzle Diameters		
Customary (Inches)	Metric (mm) (Known As)	Metric (mm) (Actual)
½	13	12.700
⅝	16	15.880
¾	19	19.050
⅞	22	22.225
1	25	25.400
1⅛	29	28.575
1¼	32	31.750
1⅜	35	34.925
1½	38	38.100
1¾	45	44.450
2	50	50.800
2¼	57	57.150
2½	65	63.500
2¾	70	69.850
3	77	76.200

Determining Friction Loss

Friction loss may be determined using calculations, or for more precise information, by performing tests using the actual equipment and conditions likely to be encountered in the field. This method involves the use of in-line gauges to measure friction loss at various flows through specific hose layouts, while the calculation method relies on the use of mathematical equations or field application methods that may not be completely accurate based on current equipment and conditions.

The only truly accurate method for determining pressure loss in a particular hose lay involves measuring the pressure at both ends of the hoseline and subtracting the difference. This method is not practical during fireground operations. The use of standard formulas and field applications often produce slightly different results than actual testing. However, these results are reasonably close and generally are relied upon for safe fireground operations.

Figure 7.1 An elevated master stream being used on a structure fire. *Courtesy of Chris Mickal.*

The current formula for friction loss accounts for the diameter of the hose, the volume of water flowing, as well as the length of the hose layout. These factors are expressed in the following formula:

Formula 7.1 (Customary): Friction Loss

$FL = CQ^2L$

Where:

FL = Friction Loss in pounds per square inch (psi)

C = Friction loss coefficient

Q = Flow rate in hundreds of gallons per minute (gpm) (gpm/100)

L = Hose length in hundreds of feet (ft) (feet/100)

Formula 7.1 (Metric): Friction Loss

$FL = CQ^2L$

Where:

FL = Friction Loss in kilopascals (kPa)

C = Friction loss coefficient

Q = Flow rate in hundreds of liters per minute (L/min) (L/min/100)

L = Hose length in hundreds of meters (m) (meters/100)

Using Formula 7.1, the following steps are used to determine friction loss:

Step 1: Obtain the friction loss coefficient for the hose being used.

Step 2: Determine the number of gallons (liters) per minute of water (Q) flowing through the hose by using the equation Q = gpm/100 (Q= L/min/100).

Step 3: Determine the number of feet of hose (L) by using the equation L = feet/100 (L = meters/100).

Step 4: Use the numbers obtained in steps one through three in conjunction with Formula 7.1 to determine the total friction loss.

NOTE: Examples 7.1-7.3 at the end of this chapter demonstrate how to use **Formula 7.1: Friction Loss**.

Determining Friction Loss Coefficients

In order to achieve more accurate results, some jurisdictions perform tests using the equipment they own. Before undertaking this task, several principles must be considered.

- Conduct testing using the actual hose that will be used during fire fighting operations.

- Test one diameter of hose at a time, as well as hose of the same construction and manufacturer. Different kinds of hose may provide inconsistent results as material, construction, and wear affect friction loss.

- Base the results of the test on the measuring devices used to record the data. Properly calibrated pitot tubes, in-line gauges, and flowmeters achieve reliable readings.

Figure 7.2a A pitot tube and gauge is used to measure water flow pressure in psi or kPa.

Figure 7.2b A flowmeter measures water flow in gpm or L/min.

The following equipment is commonly used during testing:

- Pitot tube or flowmeter **(Figures 7.2 a** and **b).**
- Two in-line gauges, preferably calibrated in increments of 5 psi or less (50 kPa or less for metric gauges)
- Hose
- Smooth bore nozzle (if using pitot tube)
- Any type of nozzle (if using flowmeter)

To determine friction loss, see **Skill Sheet 7-1** for instructions to test hose carried on fire department apparatus.

Appliance Pressure Loss (APL)

Fireground operations often require the use of **appliances** such as reducers, gates, wyes, and manifolds. The friction loss created by each device varies, based on the appliance.

NOTE: Friction loss in cases where the total flow through the appliance is less than 350 gpm (1 400 L/min) is generally considered to be insignificant and is not considered in this manual.

Friction loss in these appliances varies with the rated capacity of the device as well as the flow. For this text, it is assumed that there is a 0 psi (0 kPa) loss for flows less than 350 gpm (1 400 L/min) and a 10 psi (70 kPa) loss for each appliance (other than master stream devices) in a hose assembly when flowing 350 gpm (1 400 L/min) or greater. For this manual, a friction loss of 25 psi (175 kPa) for all master stream appliances, regardless of flow, will be used. Friction loss for handline nozzles will not be considered, as this is generally insignificant in the overall pressure loss of a hose assembly. Fire departments can calculate accurate friction loss for master stream appliances (portable monitors and turrets) using the method found in **Appendix C**.

Determining Elevation Pressure

During fireground operations hoselines are often deployed at a range of elevations. Elevation pressure, which is created by a difference between the nozzle and the pump, must be factored into total pressure loss.

Appliance — Generic term applied to any nozzle, wye, Siamese, deluge monitor, or other piece of hardware used in conjunction with fire hose for the purpose of delivering water.

In order to conduct rapid elevation pressure loss calculations on the fire-ground, driver/operators may employ the following formula:

Formula 7.2 (Customary): Elevation Pressure Loss

EP = 0.5H

Where:

EP = Elevation Pressure in pounds per square inch (psi)

0.5 = A constant

H = Height in feet (ft)

Formula 7.2 (Metric): Elevation Pressure Loss

EP = 10H

Where:

EP = Elevation Pressure in kilopascals (kPa)

10 = A constant

H = Height in meters (m)

In order to determine elevation pressure in a multistory building, the following formula is generally used:

Formula 7.3 (Customary): Elevation Pressure Loss in a Multistory Building

EP = (5 psi) x (Number of Stories – 1)

Formula 7.3 (Metric): Elevation Pressure Loss in a Multistory Building

EP = (35 kPa) x (Number of Stories – 1)

NOTE: Examples **7.4** and **7.5** at the end of this chapter demonstrate how to use **Formula 7.2: Elevation Pressure Loss** and **Formula 7.3: Elevation Pressure Loss in a Multistory Building.**

Hose Layout Applications

In each hose layout, friction loss is affected by factors such as hose diameter and the length of the layout. The following section describes several types of layouts and the effect of friction loss on each. For a list of tables that includes friction loss calculations for specific types of hose layouts, see **Appendix D** (Customary) or **Appendix E** (Metric).

Total pressure loss involves friction loss, loss or gain due to elevation, as well as appliance friction loss (when flow exceeds 350 gpm [1 400 L/min]). Hose layouts are divided into simple or complex layouts depending on the complexity of the friction loss calculation for the purposes of this manual. The principles used to determine the total pressure loss in each category are essentially the same.

Single Hoseline

The single hose lay, whether used as a supply or attack line, presents the simplest friction loss calculation. **Examples 7.6** and **7.7** demonstrate how to determine the total pressure loss in this type of layout.

Multiple Hoselines (Equal Length)

When using more than one hoseline of equal length and equal diameter, friction loss calculations need only be made for one line. When the diameters vary, calculations must be made for each hoseline. The pump discharge pressure may then be set based on the higher pressure because the discharge valve for the hoseline requiring less pressure may be partially closed to reduce pressure in that hoseline. **Example 7.8** illustrates the procedure for calculating total pressure loss when multiple hoselines are used.

Wyed Hoselines (Equal Length)

Common fireground operations include a 2½-, 3-, or 4-inch (65 mm, 77 mm, or 100 mm) hoseline wyed into two or more smaller lines for fire attack. The attack lines generally range from 1½- to 2½-inches (38 to 65 mm) in diameter. These attack lines must be the same length and diameter to avoid having two different nozzle pressures.

In order to determine friction loss in this assembly, only one of the wyed hoselines need be considered as long as the nozzle pressure, hose length, and diameter are the same. The following steps will allow the driver/operator to calculate friction loss in an equal length wyed line hose layout.

Step 1: Compute the number of gpm (L/min) flowing in each wyed hoseline by using the equation:

$$Q = \frac{\text{flow rate (gpm or L/min)}}{100}$$

Step 2: Determine the friction loss in one of the wyed attack lines using **Formula 7.1 - Friction Loss.**

$$FL = CQ^2L$$

Step 3: Compute the total number of gpm (L/min) flowing through the supply hoseline to the wye:

$$Q_{Total} = \frac{\text{(flow in Attack Line 1) + (flow in Attack Line 2)}}{100}$$

Step 4: Determine the friction loss in the supply hoseline using **Formula 7.1: Friction Loss adjusted for the total for Q.**

$$FL = (C)(Q_{Total})^2(L)$$

Step 5: Add the friction loss from the supply hoseline, one of the attack lines, 10 psi (70 kPa) for the wye (if total flow is above 350 gpm [1 400 L/min]), and elevation pressure (if applicable) to determine the total pressure loss.

NOTE: Examples 7.9 and **7.10** illustrate how to compute total pressure loss in an equal length wyed hose assembly.

Siamesed Hoselines (Equal Length)

Additional pressure is needed to overcome friction loss as the rate of flow is increased through a hoseline. To accommodate larger volumes of water and keep friction loss rates reasonable, two or more parallel hoselines may be laid. These lines may be brought together with a Siamese at a point close to the fire. When two hoselines of equal length are Siamesed to supply a fire stream, friction loss is approximately 25 percent less than that of a single hoseline at the same nozzle pressure.

Use the following steps to determine the amount of friction loss in Siamesed hoselines. The equation $FL=CQ^2L$ is used to determine the amount of pressure loss due to friction loss in a single hoseline. However, when making a calculation for Siamesed lines, a different set of coefficients is used.

Step 1: Compute the total gallons per minute (L/min) flowing by using the equation:

$$Q = \frac{\text{flow rate (gpm or L/min)}}{100}$$

Step 2: Determine the friction loss in the Attack Line using **Formula 7.1 - Friction Loss** ($FL=CQ^2L$) and the coefficients for a single hoseline from Table 7.3, p. 222.

Step 3: Determine the amount of friction loss in the Siamesed lines using **Formula 7.1 - Friction Loss** ($FL=CQ^2L$) and the coefficients for Siamesed hoselines from Table 7.4, p. 229.

Step 4: Add the friction loss from the Siamesed lines, the Attack Line, plus 10 psi (70 kPa) for the Siamese appliance (if the flow is greater than 350 gpm [1 400 L/min]). Add elevation pressure (if applicable) to determine the total pressure loss.

NOTE: Examples 7.11 and **7.12** illustrate how to calculate the total pressure loss in Siamesed lines of equal length.

Standpipe Operations

Many fire departments have predetermined pressures that a driver/operator is expected to supply to the fire department connection (FDC) in standpipe equipped occupancies. These pressures may be referenced in department policies, preincident plans, or labeled on the faceplate of the FDC. In order to determine the required pressure for a standpipe system, the total pressure loss must be calculated. **Example 7.13** provides an example of how to calculate total pressure loss for a standpipe system.

Multiple Hoselines (Unequal Length)

Occasionally, an incident may require the use of multiple hoselines of the same or different diameter that are of unequal length. When presented with this scenario, the driver/operator must calculate the friction loss for each hoseline supplied by separate discharges to individual nozzles. The hose with the highest friction loss represents the total pressure loss at the pump, assuming that there is minimal change in elevation. **Examples 7.14** and **7.15** illustrate the total pressure loss calculations for this hose layout.

Wyed Hoselines (Unequal Length) and Manifold Lines

The addition of lengths of hose to an established wyed hose layout may result in unequal lengths of attack lines. It is necessary to determine friction loss for each attack line because the length of the hoselines is different.

Some jurisdictions conduct operations using a manifold appliance fed by a large diameter hoseline that supplies several smaller attack lines. These attack lines may have different lengths and diameters. When hose lengths are unequal and/or the diameter is different, the total pressure loss in the system is based on the highest pressure loss in any of the lines. Hoselines requiring less than the maximum pressure may be gated down by the driver/operator. However, unless each manifold discharge is equipped with a pressure gauge, gating down hoselines is based on guesswork and may endanger attack crews working on that line.

Use the following steps to calculate friction loss in unequal length wyed or manifold hoselines.

Step 1: Determine the gpm (L/min) flow in each of the wyed hoselines by using the following equation:

$$Q = \frac{\text{flow rate (gpm or L/min)}}{100}$$

Step 2: Use **Formula 7.1: Friction Loss** to determine the friction loss in each of the wyed hoselines.

$$FL = CQ^2L$$

Step 3: $$Q_{Total} = \frac{(\textit{flow in Hoseline 1}) + (\textit{flow in Hoseline 2})}{100}$$

Step 4: Determine the friction loss in the supply line using **Formula 7.1: Friction Loss adjusted for the total for Q:**

$$FL = (C)(Q_{Total})^2L$$

Step 5: To determine total pressure loss, the friction loss from the supply line is added, along with the wye or manifold appliance (if greater than 350 gpm [1 400 L/min]), elevation loss, and the wyed line with the greatest amount of friction loss.

NOTE: Examples 7.16 and **7.17** illustrate the computation of total pressure loss in an unequal wyed hose layout and a manifold assembly.

Master Streams

Although master streams evolved from the same basic principles as other fire streams, they require a greater volume of water and are generally supplied by multiple hoselines with a Siamese or a large diameter hoseline. When calculating pressure loss with a master stream device, the driver/operator must add 25 psi (175 kPa) to the pressure loss calculation. **Examples 7.18** and **7.19** illustrate pressure loss in master stream hose layouts.

Elevated Waterways

A pumping apparatus driver/operator may encounter a scenario where an aerial apparatus is providing an elevated waterway at an emergency scene. When supplying an elevated waterway, such as an elevated master stream or elevated standpipe, the driver/operator will have to consider pressure loss in the aerial device when determining total pressure loss calculations. In an aerial device, the water must navigate several bends in the aerial piping. It is these bends that cause pressure loss due to the turbulence that is created as the water forcefully makes its way through the piping. For the purpose of this manual, when considering pressure loss in an elevated waterway, assume a loss of 25 psi (175 kPa) for the waterway and master stream appliance. In addition, the elevation of the master stream must be considered as part of the total pressure loss.

The pressure loss of each apparatus will vary slightly based on manufacturer and truck to truck. As a driver/operator, it is your responsibility to become familiar with the particular apparatus you will be using. For more precise figures, the manufacturer may be consulted, or an individual fire department may perform field tests to achieve results specific to their apparatus and equipment. When a detachable ladder pipe is employed, friction loss for the hose, ladder pipe, elevation, and any appliances must be considered. **Examples 7.20** and **7.21** illustrate total pressure loss calculations for pumping scenarios with elevated waterways.

Pump Discharge Pressure

In order to arrive at the correct pressure for the development of adequate fire streams driver/operators must understand pump discharge pressure and its relation to nozzle pressure. Pump discharge pressure must be sufficient to overcome all pressure loss.

Determining Pump Discharge Pressure

The sum of the pressure loss encountered as well as the required nozzle pressure will be used to determine the pump discharge pressure. The following formula is used to calculate **pump discharge pressure (PDP)**.

Formula 7.4 (Customary): Pump Discharge Pressure

PDP = NP + TPL

Where:

PDP = Pump Discharge Pressure in pounds per square inch (psi)

NP = Nozzle Pressure in pounds per square inch (psi)

TPL = Total Pressure Loss in pounds per square inch (psi)

(TPL accounts for pressure loss due to friction, elevation, and appliances)

Formula 7.4 (Metric): Pump Discharge Pressure

PDP = NP + TPL

Where:

PDP = Pump Discharge Pressure in kilopascals (kPa)

NP = Nozzle Pressure in kilopascals (kPa)

TPL = Total Pressure Loss in kilopascals (kPa)

(TPL accounts for pressure loss due to friction, elevation, and appliances)

Pump Discharge Pressure (PDP) — Actual pressure of the water as it leaves the pump and enters the hoseline; total amount of pressure being discharged by a pump. In mathematical terms, it is the pump intake pressure plus the net pump discharge pressure. Measured in pounds per square inch or kilopascals.

In some fireground situations, attack lines must be supplied with water before the driver/operator has time to calculate the correct pump discharge pressure. Some jurisdictions calculate the discharge pressure for their pre-connected attack lines in advance. This method provides the driver/operator with a reasonably accurate starting point to which differences in elevation or appliances may be factored based on the specific hose layout.

When supplying multiple hoselines, the driver/operator will need to compensate for the specific pressure requirements of individual lines. Calculate and set the pump discharge pressure based on the hoseline with the greatest pressure requirement. In order to safely supply any other hoseline pressures, the pumper discharge valves or appliance valves must be gated back to accommodate the necessary pressure. The following are safe and efficient nozzle pressures for common fire streams:

- Solid stream nozzle (handline) = 50 psi (350 kPa)

- Solid stream nozzle (master stream) = 80 psi (560 kPa)

- Fog nozzle = 100 psi (700 kPa)

- Low pressure fog nozzle = 50 or 75 psi (350 or 525 kPa)

NOTE: Examples 7.22 – 7.26 illustrate the calculation of pump discharge pressure using Formula 7.4 – Pump Discharge Pressure.

Determining Net Pump Discharge Pressure

When required to discharge a specified pressure, fire apparatus pumps take advantage of the water pressure coming into the pump's water supply and add the required pressure to achieve **net pump discharge pressure (NPDP)**. This pressure represents the action of water into the pump, through it, and then out a discharge. In order to determine the net pump discharge pressure, all forces that affect the amount of work required of the fire pump must be considered. In the case of a pumper being supplied by a hydrant or another pumper, the net pump discharge pressure is the difference between the pump discharge pressure and the incoming pressure from the supply source. For example, if a pumper is required to discharge 150 psi (1 050 kPa) and it has an intake pressure of 50 psi (350 kPa), the pump will develop the additional 100 psi (750 kPa) to meet the demand and achieve the net pump discharge pressure of 150 psi (1 050 kPa). This is illustrated by the following formula:

Formula 7.5 (Customary & Metric): Net Pump Discharge Pressure

$NPDP_{PPS}$ = PDP – Intake Reading

Where:

$NPDP_{PPS}$ = Net pump discharge pressure from a positive pressure source

PDP = Pump discharge pressure

NOTE: Formula 7.5 illustrates a pumper operating from a pressurized source. For further information regarding static sources, refer to Chapter 11, Static Water Supply Sources. Example 7.27 applies Formula 7.5 – Net Pump Discharge Pressure to calculate net pump discharge pressure.

Net Pump Discharge Pressure (NPDP) — Actual amount of pressure being produced by the pump; difference between the intake pressure and the discharge pressure. *Also known as* Engine Pressure or Net Pressure.

Chapter Summary

In order to expedite and simplify pump operations on the fireground, many commonly used hose layouts may be precalculated as part of policy and preplanning functions. However, the driver/operator must have an understanding and ability to make certain hydraulic calculations in the field in order to operate safely and efficiently. Each driver/operator must possess the ability to provide the correct pressure and volume of water for various lengths and diameters of hose and consider pressure loss due to friction and changes due to elevation.

Review Questions

1. What factors contribute to total pressure loss? (p. 210)

2. What are the steps for computing total pressure loss in an equal length wyed hose assembly? (p. 215)

3. How is pump discharge pressure calculated? (p. 218)

Formula Examples — Customary System

Formula Examples — Customary System

Formula 7.1: Friction Loss

$$FL = CQ^2L$$

Where:

FL = Friction Loss in pounds per square inch (psi)

C = Friction loss coefficient

Q = Flow rate in hundreds of gallons per minute (gpm) (gpm/100)

L = Hose length in hundreds of feet (ft) (feet/100)

The friction loss coefficients listed in **Table 7.3** are approximations used by IFSTA and the NFPA® for each diameter of hose. Exact coefficients for a specific piece of hose will vary based on the manufacturer and condition of the hose. The coefficients represented in this chart reflect results that are usually slightly higher than actual friction loss, providing the driver/operator with a "worst case" scenario. In order to achieve more exact results, individual fire departments may conduct tests and perform calculations using their own hose and appliances. The next section explains calculating friction loss coefficients.

Table 7.3 Friction Loss Coefficients — Single Hoselines	
Hose Diameter (Inches)	**Coefficient**
¾ (booster)	1,100
1 (booster)	150
1¼ (booster)	80
1½	24
1¾ with 1½-inch couplings	15.5
2	8
2½	2
3 with 2½-inch couplings	0.8
3 with 3-inch couplings	0.677
3½	0.34
4	0.2
4½	0.1
5	0.08
6	0.05
Standpipes	
4	0.374
5	0.126
6	0.052

Example 7.1

If 300 gpm is flowing from a nozzle, what is the total pressure loss due to friction for 400 feet of 2½-inch hose?

FL = CQ²L

C = 2 from Table 7.3

$Q = \dfrac{gpm}{100} = \dfrac{300}{100} = 3$

$L = \dfrac{feet}{100} = \dfrac{400}{100} = 4$

FL = $(2)(3)^2(4)$ = **72 psi (app. 70)**

Example 7.2

What is the total pressure loss due to friction in 600 feet of 4-inch hose when 750 gpm is flowing?

FL = CQ²L

C = 0.2 from Table 7.3

$Q = \dfrac{gpm}{100} = \dfrac{750}{100} = 7.5$

$L = \dfrac{feet}{100} = \dfrac{600}{100} = 6$

FL = $(0.2)(7.5)^2(6)$ = **67.5 psi (app. 70)**

Example 7.3

What is the total pressure loss due to friction in 250 feet of 1¾-inch hose when 150 gpm is flowing?

FL = CQ²L

C = 15.5 from Table 7.3

$Q = \dfrac{gpm}{100} = \dfrac{150}{100} = 1.5$

$L = \dfrac{feet}{100} = \dfrac{250}{100} = 2.5$

FL = $(15.5)(1.5)^2(2.5)$ = **87.19 psi (app. 90)**

Formula 7.2: Elevation Pressure Loss

EP = 0.5H

Where:

EP = Elevation Pressure in pounds per square inch (psi)

0.5 = A constant

H = Height in feet (ft)

Example 7.4

Calculate the pressure loss due to elevation for a hoseline operating at the top of a 100-foot hill **(Figure 7.3)**.

EP = 0.5H

EP = (0.5)(100) = **50 psi**

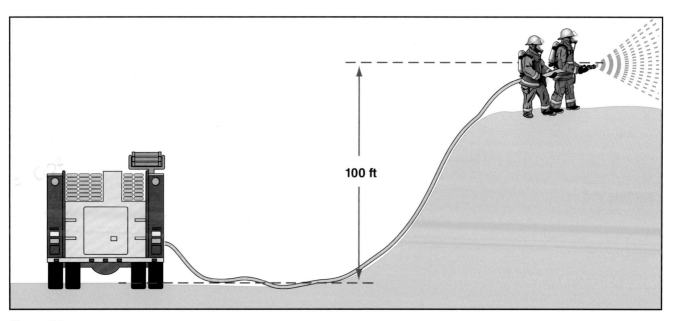

100 ft

Figure 7.3

Formula 7.3: Elevation Pressure Loss in a Multistory Building

EP = (5 psi) x (Number of Stories – 1)

Example 7.5

A hoseline is operating on the ninth floor of a building **(Figure 7.4)**. What is the pressure loss due to elevation?

EP = (5 psi) x (Number of Stories – 1)

EP = (5)(9 - 1) = **40 psi**

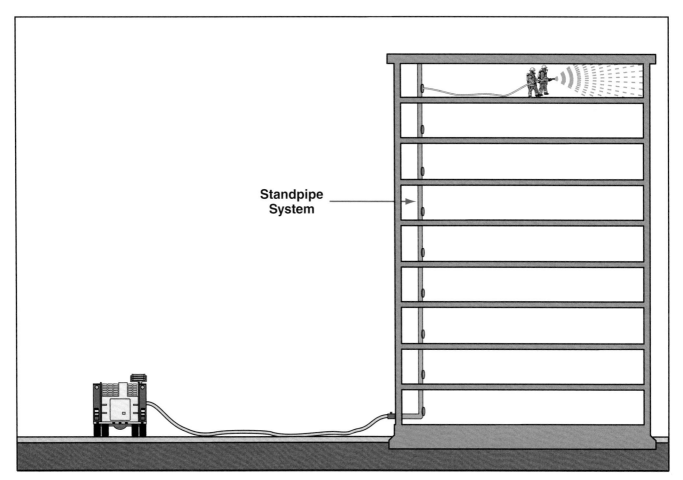

Figure 7.4

Total Pressure Loss Calculations — Single Hoseline

Example 7.6

What is the pressure loss due to friction for a pumper that is supplying a 300-foot hoseline that is flowing 125 gpm? The hoseline is composed of 200 feet of 2½-inch hose reduced to 100 feet of 1½-inch hose **(Figure 7.5, p. 226)**.

2½-inch Hoseline

FL = CQ²L

C = 2 from Table 7.3

$Q = \dfrac{gpm}{100} = \dfrac{125}{100} = 1.25$

$L = \dfrac{feet}{100} = \dfrac{200}{100} = 2$

FL = $(2)(1.25)^2(2)$ = **6.25 psi**

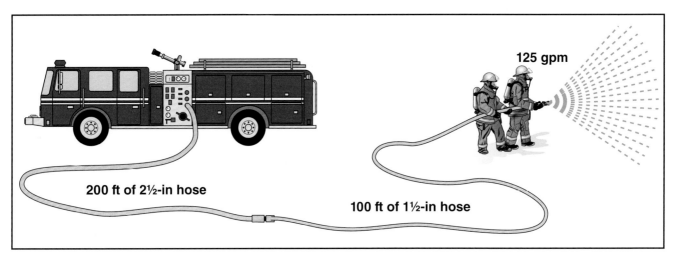

Figure 7.5

1½-inch Hoseline

FL = CQ²L

C = 24 from Table 7.3

$$Q = \frac{gpm}{100} = \frac{125}{100} = 1.25$$

$$L = \frac{feet}{100} = \frac{100}{100} = 1$$

FL = (24)(1.25)²(1) = **37.5 psi**

Total Pressure Loss

TPL = 6.25 + 37.5 = **43.75 psi (app. 40)**

Example 7.7

An engine company advances 150 feet of 1¾-inch hose to the third floor of a building for fire attack. Determine the total pressure loss due to friction and elevation when flowing 175 gpm.

1¾-inch Hoseline

FL = CQ²L

C = 15.5 from Table 7.3

$$Q = \frac{gpm}{100} = \frac{175}{100} = 1.75$$

$$L = \frac{feet}{100} = \frac{150}{100} = 1.5$$

FL = (15.5)(1.75)²(1.5) = **71.2 psi**

Elevation Pressure

EP = (5 psi) x (Number of Stories – 1)

EP = (5)(3 - 1) = **10 psi**

Total Pressure Loss

TPL = 71.2 + 10 = **81.2 psi (app. 80)**

Total Pressure Loss Calculations — Multiple Hoselines (Equal Length)

Example 7.8

Three 2½ -inch hoselines, which are each 400 feet long and operated at 50 psi nozzle pressure using 1-inch tips, are put into use. What is the total pressure loss due to friction in each hoseline?

$$GPM = 29.7 \times d^2 \times \sqrt{NP}$$

d = 1

NP = 50

$GPM = (29.7)(1)^2(\sqrt{50}) = $ **210.01 (app. 210)**

$$FL = CQ^2L$$

C = 2 from Table 7.3

$Q = \dfrac{gpm}{100} = \dfrac{210}{100} = 2.1$

$L = \dfrac{feet}{100} = \dfrac{400}{100} = 4$

$FL = (2)(2.1)^2(4) = $ **35.28 psi (app. 35) per hoseline**

Total Pressure Loss Calculations — Wyed Hoselines (Equal Length)

Example 7.9

Determine the pressure loss due to friction in a layout consisting of 400 feet of 2½-inch hose wyed off into two 1½-inch hoselines, 100 feet in length, each flowing 95 gpm (**Figure 7.6, p. 228**).

1½-inch Hoselines

$$FL = CQ^2L$$

C = 24 from Table 7.3

$Q = \dfrac{gpm}{100} = \dfrac{95}{100} = 0.95$

$L = \dfrac{feet}{100} = \dfrac{100}{100} = 1$

$FL = (24)(0.95)^2(1) = $ **21.66 psi per hoseline**

2½-inch Hoseline

$$FL = CQ^2L$$

C = 2 from Table 7.3

$Q = Q_{Total} = \dfrac{(gpm\ in\ Hoseline\ 1) + (gpm\ in\ Hoseline\ 2)}{100}$

$Q_{Total} = \dfrac{95 + 95}{100} = \dfrac{190}{100} = 1.9$

$L = \dfrac{feet}{100} = \dfrac{400}{100} = 4$

$FL = (2)(1.9)^2(4) = $ **28.88 psi**

Total Pressure Loss

TPL = 21.66 + 28.88 = **50.54 psi (app. 50)**

NOTE: The total flow was less than 350 gpm, so it was not necessary to factor in pressure loss for the wye.

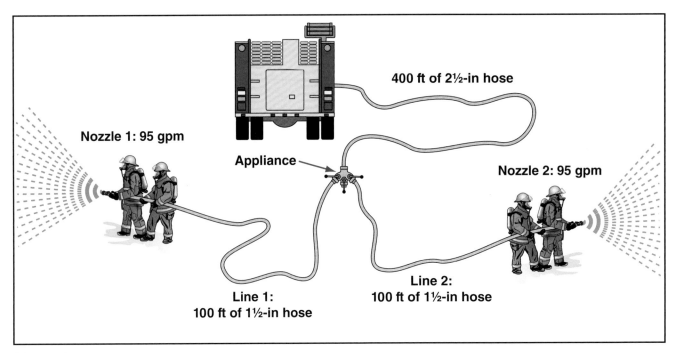

400 ft of 2½-in hose

Nozzle 1: 95 gpm

Appliance

Nozzle 2: 95 gpm

Line 1:
100 ft of 1½-in hose

Line 2:
100 ft of 1½-in hose

Figure 7.6

Example 7.10

Determine the pressure loss given a hose assembly featuring two 2½-inch hoselines, each 200 feet long, flowing 250 gpm, wyed off a supply line of 500 feet of 4-inch hose:

2½-inch Hoselines

FL = CQ²L

C = 2 from Table 7.3

$Q = \dfrac{gpm}{100} = \dfrac{250}{100} = 2.5$

$L = \dfrac{feet}{100} = \dfrac{200}{100} = 2$

FL = (2)(2.5)²(2) = **25 psi per hoseline**

4-inch Hoseline

FL = CQ²L

C = 0.2 from Table 7.3

$Q_{Total} = \dfrac{(gpm \text{ in Hoseline 1}) + (gpm \text{ in Hoseline 2})}{100}$

$Q_{Total} = \dfrac{250+250}{100} = \dfrac{500}{100} = 5$

$L = \dfrac{feet}{100} = \dfrac{500}{100} = 5$

$FL = (0.2)(5)^2(5) = \textbf{25 psi}$

Total Pressure Loss

$TPL = 25 + 25 + 10 = \textbf{60 psi}$

NOTE: Because the total flow through this assembly was greater than 350 gpm, it was necessary to include 10 psi for pressure loss in the wye.

Total Pressure Loss Calculations — Siamesed Hoselines (Equal Length)

Example 7.11

What is the pressure loss due to friction in a hose assembly with two 3-inch hoselines with 2½-inch couplings, each 1,000 feet long, being used to supply a Siamese appliance to which 300 feet of 2½ inch hose is attached, equipped with a solid stream nozzle, featuring a 1¼-inch tip, at 50 psi nozzle pressure **(Figure 7.7)**.

NOTE: Table 7.4 lists friction loss coefficients for Siamesed lines of equal length.

2½-inch Hoseline

GPM = 29.7 x d² x √NP

$d = 1.25$

$NP = 50$

$GPM = (29.7)(1.25)^2(\sqrt{50}) = \textbf{328.14 (app. 328)}$

FL = CQ²L

$C = 2$ from Table 7.3

$Q = \dfrac{gpm}{100} = \dfrac{328}{100} = 3.28$

$L = \dfrac{feet}{100} = \dfrac{300}{100} = 3$

$FL = (2)(3.28)^2(3) = \textbf{64.55 psi}$

Table 7.4 Friction Loss Coefficients — Siamesed Lines of Equal Length	
Number of Hoses and Their Diameter (inches)	**Coefficient**
Two 2½"	0.5
Three 2½"	0.22
Two 3" with 2½" couplings	0.2
One 3" with 2½" couplings, one 2½"	0.3
One 3" with 3" couplings, one 2½"	0.27
Two 2½", one 3" with 2½" couplings	0.16
Two 3" with 2½" couplings, one 2½"	0.12

Figure 7.7

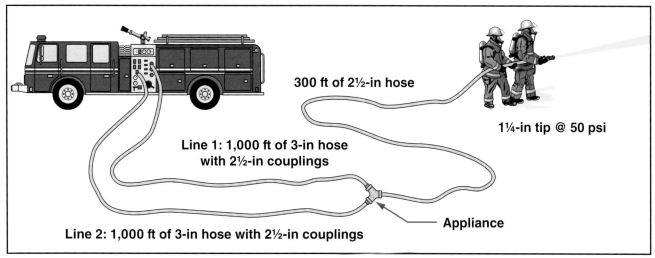

300 ft of 2½-in hose

1¼-in tip @ 50 psi

Line 1: 1,000 ft of 3-in hose with 2½-in couplings

Line 2: 1,000 ft of 3-in hose with 2½-in couplings

Appliance

3-inch hose with 2½-inch couplings Siamesed Hoselines

FL = CQ²L

C = 0.2 from Table 7.4

$$Q = \frac{gpm}{100} = \frac{328}{100} = 3.28$$

$$L = \frac{feet}{100} = \frac{1000}{100} = 10$$

FL = (0.2)(3.28)²(10) = **21.52 psi**

Total Pressure Loss

TPL = 64.55 + 21.52 = **86.07 psi (app. 85)**

NOTE: Because the total flow through the assembly was less than 350 gpm, it was not necessary to factor pressure loss in the Siamese appliance.

Example 7.12

Determine the total pressure loss in a hose assembly with two 2½-inch hoselines, each 750 feet long, supplying a Siamese appliance. Attached to the appliance is 200 feet of 2½-inch hose with a nozzle flowing 300 gpm, located 30 feet uphill of the Siamese appliance.

2½-inch Hoseline

FL = CQ²L

C = 2 from Table 7.3

$$Q = \frac{gpm}{100} = \frac{300}{100} = 3$$

$$L = \frac{feet}{100} - \frac{200}{100} = 2$$

FL = (2)(3)²(2) = **36 psi**

EP = 0.5H

EP = (0.5)(30) = **15 psi**

TPL = 36 + 15 = **51 psi**

2½-inch Siamesed Hoselines

FL = CQ²L

C = 0.5 from Table 7.4

$$Q = \frac{gpm}{100} = \frac{300}{100} = 3$$

$$L = \frac{feet}{100} = \frac{750}{100} = 7.5$$

FL = (0.5)(3)²(7.5) = **33.75 psi**

Total Pressure Loss

TPL = 51 + 33.75 = **84.75 psi (app. 85)**

Total Pressure Loss Calculations — Standpipe Operations

Example 7.13

A pumper responds to a fire on the fifth floor of a building. Two 2½-inch hoselines, each 150 feet long, are connected to the fire department connection. Utilizing the 4-inch diameter standpipe, firefighters make connections on the fourth floor of the building and advance the hoseline to the fifth floor. They are using 200 feet of 1¾-inch hose and flowing 125 gpm from a fog nozzle. What is the total pressure loss in the hose and standpipe assembly?

NOTE: Since the hoselines connected to the FDC are of equal size and length they can be treated like hoselines connected to a Siamese appliance for hydraulic calculations.

1¾-inch Hoseline

FL = CQ²L

C = 15.5 from Table 7.3

$Q = \dfrac{gpm}{100} = \dfrac{125}{100} = 1.25$

$L = \dfrac{feet}{100} = \dfrac{200}{100} = 2$

FL = (15.5)(1.25)²(2) = 48.44 psi

Standpipe

Based on 10 feet per floor, assume 40 feet of standpipe is used.

FL = CQ²L

C = 0.374 from Table 7.3

$Q = \dfrac{gpm}{100} = \dfrac{125}{100} = 1.25$

$L = \dfrac{feet}{100} = \dfrac{40}{100} = 0.4$

FL = (0.374)(1.25)²(0.4) = 0.23 psi (Friction loss within the standpipe is minimal)

Elevation Pressure

EP = (5 psi) x (Number of Stories – 1)

EP = (5)(5-1) = 20 psi

2½-inch Hoselines Connected to FDC

FL = CQ²L

C = 0.5 from Table 7.4

$Q = \dfrac{gpm}{100} = \dfrac{125}{100} = 1.25$

$L = \dfrac{feet}{100} = \dfrac{150}{100} = 1.5$

FL = (0.5)(1.25)²(1.5) = 1.17 psi

Total Pressure Loss

TPL = 48.44 + 0.23 + 20 + 1.17 = **69.84 psi (app. 70)**

Total Pressure Loss Calculations — Multiple Hoselines (Unequal Length)

Example 7.14

Two 2½-inch hoselines, Line 1 is 300 feet long and Line 2 is 500 feet long. They are both outfitted with 250 gpm fog nozzles **(Figure 7.8)**. Determine the total pressure loss due to friction for this hose layout.

Line 1

$$FL = CQ^2L$$

C = 2 from Table 7.3

$$Q = \frac{gpm}{100} = \frac{250}{100} = 2.5$$

$$L = \frac{feet}{100} = \frac{300}{100} = 3$$

$$FL = (2)(2.5)^2(3) = \textbf{37.5 psi}$$

Line 2

$$FL = CQ^2L$$

C = 2 from Table 7.3

$$Q = \frac{gpm}{100} = \frac{250}{100} = 2.5$$

$$L = \frac{feet}{100} = \frac{500}{100} = 5$$

$$FL = (2)(2.5)^2(5) = \textbf{62.5 psi}$$

Total Pressure Loss

The total pressure loss will be equal to the hoseline with the highest friction loss. In this case, it is Line 2, with a pressure loss of **62.5 psi (app. 60)**.

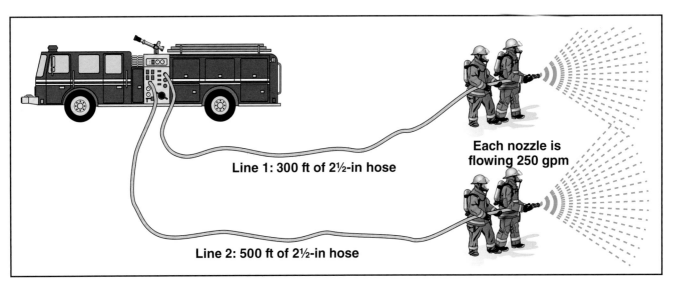

Line 1: 300 ft of 2½-in hose

Each nozzle is flowing 250 gpm

Line 2: 500 ft of 2½-in hose

Figure 7.8

Example 7.15

A pumper is supplying four lines. Lines 1 and 2 are 150 feet of 1½-inch hose equipped with a 5/8-inch solid stream tip operating at 50 psi. Lines 3 and 4 are 200 feet of 1¾-inch hose equipped with a ¾-inch solid stream tip operating at 50 psi **(Figure 7.9)**. Determine the total pressure loss due to friction for this hose layout.

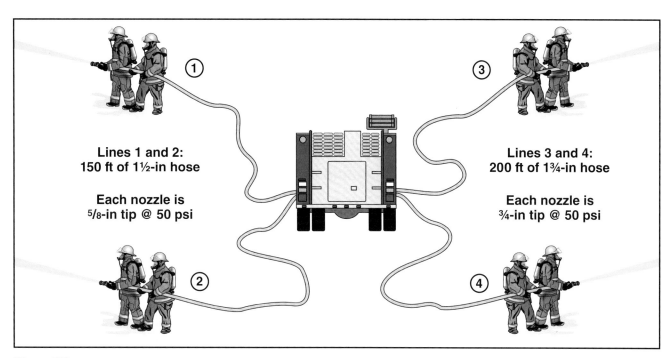

Figure 7.9

Lines 1 and 2

GPM = 29.7 x d² x √NP

d = 0.625

NP = 50

GPM = (29.7)(0.625)²(√50) = **82.04 (app. 82)**

FL = CQ²L

C = 24 from Table 7.3

$Q = \dfrac{gpm}{100} = \dfrac{82}{100} = 0.82$

$L = \dfrac{feet}{100} = \dfrac{150}{100} = 1.5$

FL = (24)(0.82)²(1.5) = **24.21 psi per Hoseline**

Lines 3 and 4

GPM = 29.7 x d² x √NP

d = 0.75

NP = 50

GPM = (29.7)(0.75)²(√50) = **118.13 (app. 118)**

$$FL = CQ^2L$$

C = 15.5 from Table 7.3

$$Q = \frac{gpm}{100} = \frac{118}{100} = 1.18$$

$$L = \frac{feet}{100} = \frac{200}{100} = 2$$

$$FL = (15.5)(1.18)^2(2) = \textbf{43.16 psi per Hoseline}$$

Total Pressure Loss

The total pressure loss will be equal to the hoselines with the highest friction loss. In this case, it is Lines 3 and 4, with a pressure loss of **43.16 psi (app. 40)** per hoseline.

Total Pressure Loss Calculations — Wyed Hoselines (Unequal Length) and Manifold Lines

Example 7.16

Determine the total loss of pressure due to friction and elevation pressure for a hose layout in which one 400 foot, 3-inch hoseline with 2½-inch couplings is supplying two attack lines **(Figure 7.10)**. Line 1 is a 200 foot 1¾-inch hose that is stretched horizontally through the front door of a dwelling. This line is flowing 150 gpm. Line 2 is 150 feet of 1½-hoseline that is deployed via ladder to the second floor. The second line is flowing 95 gpm.

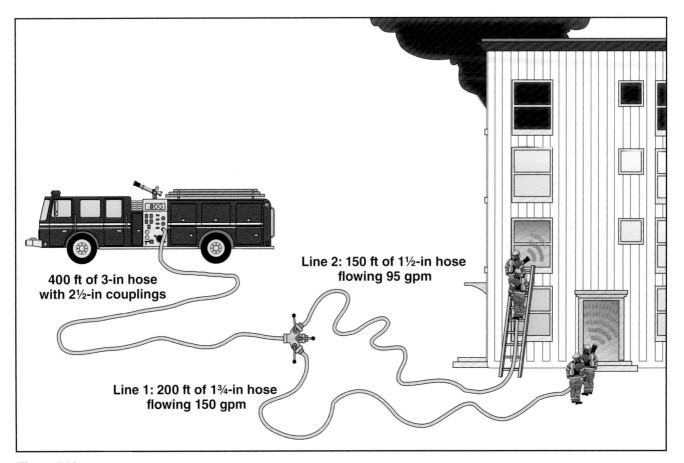

400 ft of 3-in hose with 2½-in couplings

Line 2: 150 ft of 1½-in hose flowing 95 gpm

Line 1: 200 ft of 1¾-in hose flowing 150 gpm

Figure 7.10

Line 1

FL = CQ²L

C = 15.5 from Table 7.3

$Q = \dfrac{gpm}{100} = \dfrac{150}{100} = 1.5$

$L = \dfrac{feet}{100} = \dfrac{200}{100} = 2$

FL = $(15.5)(1.5)^2(2)$ = **69.75 psi**

Line 2

FL = CQ²L

C = 24 from Table 7.3

$Q = \dfrac{gpm}{100} = \dfrac{95}{100} = 0.95$

$L = \dfrac{feet}{100} = \dfrac{150}{100} = 1.5$

FL = $(24)(0.95)^2(1.5)$ = **32.49 psi**

EP = (5 psi) x (Number of Stories - 1)

EP = (5)(2 - 1) = **5 psi**

TPL = 32.49 + 5 = **37.49 psi**

3-inch hose with 2½-inch couplings

FL = CQ²L

C = 0.8 from Table 7.3

$Q = Q_{Total} = \dfrac{(gpm\ in\ Line\ 1) + (gpm\ in\ Line\ 2)}{100}$

$Q_{Total} = \dfrac{150 + 95}{100} = \dfrac{245}{100} = 2.45$

$L = \dfrac{feet}{100} = \dfrac{400}{100} = 4$

FL = $(0.8)(2.45)^2(4)$ = **19.21 psi**

Total Pressure Loss

The total pressure loss will be equal to the friction loss in the supply hoseline plus the wyed hoseline with the highest friction loss. In this case, it is Line 1, with a pressure loss of **69.75 psi**. No friction loss for the appliance will be applied because the total flow rate was less than 350 gpm.

TPL = 69.75 + 19.21 = **88.96 psi (app. 90)**

Example 7.17

Determine the total pressure loss due to friction for a hose layout in which one 500 foot, 3-inch hose with 3-inch couplings is supplying three attack lines that are connected to a water thief appliance. Line 1 is 150 feet of 1½-hose that is flowing 125 gpm. Line 2 is 100 feet of 1½-hose that is flowing 95 gpm. Line 3 is 150 feet of 2½-inch hose that is flowing 225 gpm.

Line 1

FL = CQ²L

C = 24 from Table 7.3

$Q = \dfrac{gpm}{100} = \dfrac{125}{100} = 1.25$

$L = \dfrac{feet}{100} = \dfrac{150}{100} = 1.5$

$FL = (24)(1.25)^2(1.5) = \mathbf{56.25\ psi}$

Line 2

FL = CQ²L

C = 24 from Table 7.3

$Q = \dfrac{gpm}{100} = \dfrac{95}{100} = 0.95$

$L = \dfrac{feet}{100} = \dfrac{100}{100} = 1$

$FL = (24)(0.95)^2(1) = \mathbf{21.66\ psi}$

Line 3

FL = CQ²L

C = 2 from Table 7.3

$Q = \dfrac{gpm}{100} = \dfrac{225}{100} = 2.25$

$L = \dfrac{feet}{100} = \dfrac{150}{100} = 1.5$

$FL = (2)(2.25)^2(1.5) = \mathbf{15.19\ psi}$

3-inch hose with 3-inch couplings

FL = CQ²L

C = 0.677 from Table 7.3

$Q = Q_{Total} = \dfrac{(gpm\ in\ Line\ 1 + gpm\ in\ Line\ 2 + gpm\ in\ Line\ 3)}{100}$

$Q_{Total} = \dfrac{125 + 95 + 225}{100} = \dfrac{445}{100} = 4.45$

$L = \dfrac{feet}{100} = \dfrac{500}{100} = 5$

$FL = (0.677)(4.45)^2(5) = \mathbf{67.03\ psi}$

Total Pressure Loss

The total pressure loss will be equal to the friction loss in the supply hoseline plus the wyed hoseline with the highest friction loss. In this case, it is Line 1, with a pressure loss of **56.25 psi**. A friction loss of **10 psi** must be added for the water thief appliance because the total flow rate exceeded 350 gpm.

TPL = 56.25 + 67.03 + 10 = **133.28 psi (app. 130)**

Total Pressure Loss Calculations — Master Streams

If unequal length or diameter of hose is used to supply a master stream, use the average of the hose lengths to simplify calculation. In order to obtain the average, a driver/operator may add the length of each hoseline and then divide by the number of hoselines being used. Use the coefficients for Siamesed hoselines, referenced in Table 7.4 with the total flow through the nozzle to complete friction loss calculations.

In certain scenarios, multiple lines of equal diameter but unequal length may be used. No coefficient for that combination is shown in Table 7.4. The driver/operator should average the length of the lines and assume equal pressure through each one.

Example 7.18

Determine the total pressure loss due to friction for a hose layout that consists of one 700 foot, 5-inch hose that is supplying three hoselines that are attached to a large diameter hose manifold **(Figure 7.11)**. Two of the hoselines are 150 feet of 3-inch hose with 2½-inch couplings that are supplying a portable master stream appliance. The master stream is discharging 80 psi through a 1½-inch tip. The third hoseline is 150 feet of 2½-inch hose flowing 275 gpm.

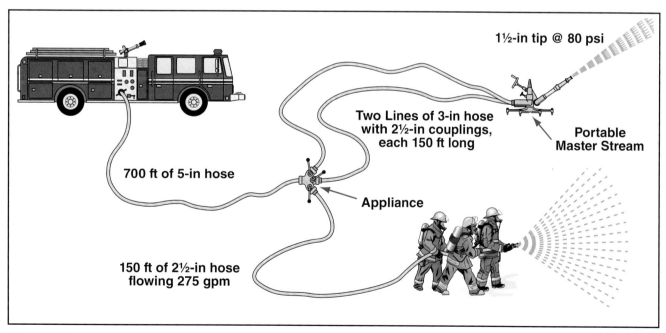

Figure 7.11

3-inch hose with 2½-inch couplings Supplying a Portable Master Stream

GPM = 29.7 x d² x √NP

d = 1.5

NP = 80

GPM = $(29.7)(1.5)^2(\sqrt{80})$ = **597.7 (app. 598)**

FL = CQ²L

C = 0.2 from Table 7.4

$Q = \dfrac{gpm}{100} = \dfrac{598}{100} = 5.98$

$L = \dfrac{feet}{100} = \dfrac{150}{100} = 1.5$

FL = $(0.2)(5.98)^2(1.5)$ = **10.73 psi**

TPL = 10.73 + 25 = **35.73 psi** (25 psi added for Master Stream device)

2½-inch Hoseline

FL = CQ²L

C = 2 from Table 7.3

$Q = \dfrac{gpm}{100} = \dfrac{275}{100} = 2.75$

$L = \dfrac{feet}{100} = \dfrac{150}{100} = 1.5$

FL = $(2)(2.75)^2(1.5)$ = **22.69 psi**

5-inch Hoseline

FL = CQ²L

C = 0.08 from Table 7.3

$Q = Q_{Total} = \dfrac{(gpm\ in\ Master\ Stream) + (gpm\ in\ 2\frac{1}{2}\text{-inch Hoseline})}{100}$

$Q_{Total} = \dfrac{598 + 275}{100} = \dfrac{873}{100} = 8.73$

$L = \dfrac{feet}{100} = \dfrac{700}{100} = 7$

FL = $(0.08)(8.73)^2(7)$ = **42.68 psi**

Total Pressure Loss

The total pressure loss will be equal to the friction loss in the supply hoseline plus the wyed hoseline with the highest friction loss. In this case, it is the hoselines supplying the portable master stream, with a pressure loss of **35.73 psi**. A friction loss of **10 psi** must be added for the large diameter hose manifold because the total flow rate exceeded 350 gpm.

TPL = 35.73 + 42.68 + 10 = **88.4 psi (app. 90)**

Example 7.19

Determine the total pressure loss in a hose layout where a 3,000 gpm master stream device is supplied by three 5-inch hoselines **(Figure 7.12)**. Two of the hoselines measure 900 feet in length, and the other is 1,200 feet in length. 1,000 gpm is flowing through each hoseline.

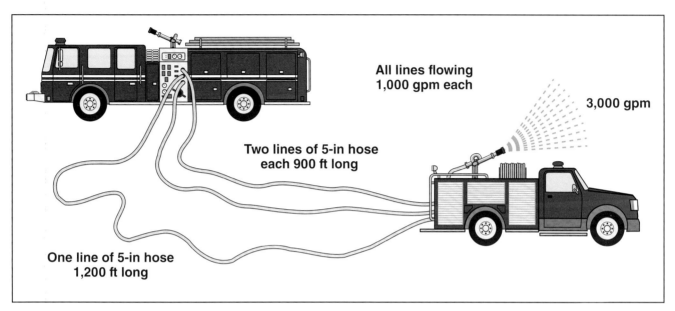

Figure 7.12

5-inch Hoselines

FL = CQ²L

C = 0.08 from Table 7.3

$$Q = \frac{gpm}{100} = \frac{1000}{100} = 10$$

$$\text{Average Length} = \frac{(\text{Sum of Hose Lengths})}{3} = \frac{(900 + 900 + 1200)}{3} = \frac{3000}{3} = 1000 \text{ feet}$$

$$L = \frac{feet}{100} = \frac{1000}{100} = 10$$

FL = (0.08)(10)²(10) = **80 psi per hoseline**

Total Pressure Loss

TPL = 80 + 25 = **105 psi** (25 psi added for Master Stream device)

Total Pressure Loss Calculations — Elevated Waterways

Example 7.20

A pumper is supplying 200 feet of 3-inch hose with 2½-inch couplings that is feeding an aerial device with a detachable waterway containing 100 feet of 3-inch hose with 2½-inch couplings. The aerial device is elevated 75 feet and is discharging 500 gpm **(Figure 7.13)**. Determine the total pressure loss in this hose layout.

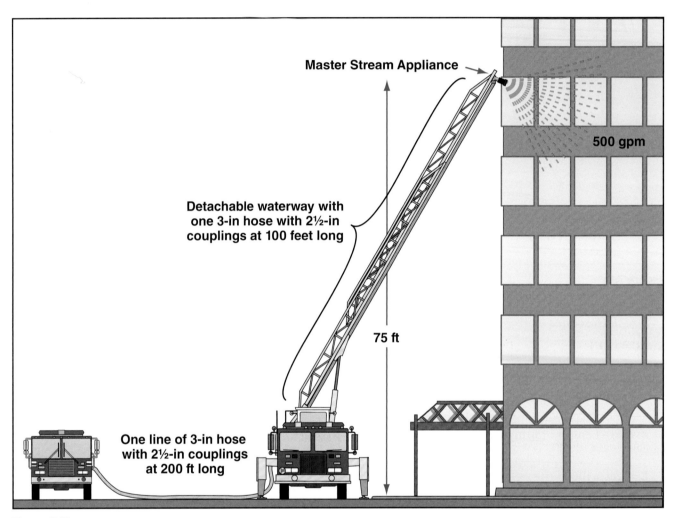

Figure 7.13

3-inch hose with 2½-inch couplings

FL = CQ²L

C = 0.8 from Table 7.3

$Q = \dfrac{gpm}{100} = \dfrac{500}{100} = 5$

$L = \dfrac{feet}{100} = \dfrac{200}{100} = 2$

FL = (0.8)(5)²(2) = **40 psi**

Detachable Waterway's 3-inch hose with 2½-inch couplings

FL = CQ²L

C = 0.8 from Table 7.3

$Q = \underline{gpm} = \underline{500} = 5$
    100   100

$L = \underline{feet} = \underline{100} = 1$
    100   100

FL = (0.8)(5)²(1) = **20 psi**

Elevation Pressure

EP = 0.5H

EP = (0.5)(75) = **37.5 psi**

Total Pressure Loss

TPL = 40 + 20 + 37.5 + 25 = **122.5 psi (app. 120)** (25 psi added for aerial device)

Example 7.21

Determine the total pressure loss in a hose layout where a pumper is supplying 800 feet of 5 inch hose that is connected to an aerial device positioned as an elevated master stream. The master stream is elevated 50 feet and is equipped with a solid stream nozzle with a 2-inch tip and is flowing 100 psi.

GPM = 29.7 x d² x √NP

d = 2

NP = 100

GPM = (29.7)(2)²(√100) = **1188**

FL = CQ²L

C = 0.08 from Table 7.3

$Q = \underline{gpm} = \underline{1188} = 11.88$
     100   100

$L = \underline{feet} = \underline{800} = 8$
    100   100

FL = (0.08)(11.88)²(8) = **90.33 psi**

EP = 0.5H

EP = (0.5)(50) = **25 psi**

Total Pressu re Loss

TPL = 90.33 + 25 + 25 = **140.33 psi (app. 140)** (25 psi added for aerial device)

Formula 7.4: Pump Discharge Pressure

PDP = NP + TPL

Where:

PDP = Pump Discharge Pressure in pounds per square inch (psi)

NP = Nozzle Pressure in pounds per square inch (psi)

TPL = Total Pressure Loss in pounds per square inch (psi)

(TPL accounts for pressure loss due to friction, elevation, and appliances)

Example 7.22

A pumper must supply 500 feet of 2½-inch hose that is flowing 300 gpm through a fog nozzle. Determine the pump discharge pressure required to adequately supply the hoseline.

FL = CQ²L

C = 2 from Table 7.3

$Q = \dfrac{gpm}{100} = \dfrac{300}{100} = 3$

$L = \dfrac{feet}{100} = \dfrac{500}{100} = 5$

FL = (2)(3)²(5) = **90 psi**

Pump Discharge Pressure

PDP = NP + TPL

PDP = 100 + 90

PDP= **190 psi**

Example 7.23

Determine the pump discharge pressure required to supply two 2½-inch hoselines, one that is 300 feet long and the other 500 feet long. Each line is outfitted with 250 gpm fog nozzles **(Figure 7.14)**.

Figure 7.14

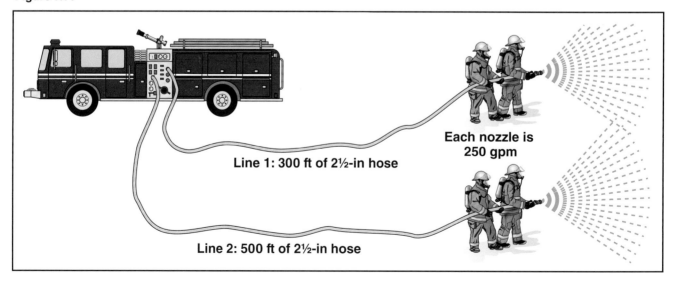

Each nozzle is 250 gpm

Line 1: 300 ft of 2½-in hose

Line 2: 500 ft of 2½-in hose

Line 1

FL = CQ²L

C = 2 from Table 7.3

$Q = \dfrac{gpm}{100} = \dfrac{250}{100} = 2.5$

$L = \dfrac{feet}{100} = \dfrac{300}{100} = 3$

FL = (2)(2.5)²(3) = **37.5 psi**

Line 2

FL = CQ²L

C = 2 from Table 7.3

$Q = \dfrac{gpm}{100} = \dfrac{250}{100} = 2.5$

$L = \dfrac{feet}{100} = \dfrac{500}{100} = 5$

FL = (2)(2.5)²(5) = **62.5 psi**

Pump Discharge Pressure (PDP)

The pump discharge pressure should be set for the hoseline with the highest pressure demand. In this case, it is Line 2 with a pressure loss of **62.5 psi**. The pump only produces one pressure using the available water supply. The driver/operator should gate back the discharge outlet for Line 1 to ensure the correct pressure when the line is flowing.

PDP = NP + TPL

PDP = 100 + 62.5 = **162.5 psi (app. 160)**

Example 7.24

Determine the pump discharge pressure for a pumper that is using two 3-inch hoselines with 2½-inch couplings, each 200 feet long, to supply an elevated master stream. The master stream is elevated 60 feet and features a master stream fog nozzle that is flowing 1,000 gpm at 100 psi.

FL = CQ²L

C = 0.2 from Table 7.4

$Q = \dfrac{gpm}{100} = \dfrac{1000}{100} = 10$

$L = \dfrac{feet}{100} = \dfrac{200}{100} = 2$

FL = (0.2)(10)²(2) = **40 psi**

EP = 0.5H

EP = (0.5)(60) = **30 psi**

Total Pressure Loss

TPL = 40 + 30 + 25 = **95 psi** (25 psi added for aerial device)

Pump Discharge Pressure

PDP = NP + TPL

PDP = 100 + 95 = **195 psi**

Example 7.25

Determine the pump discharge pressure in a hose layout with one 300 foot 3-inch hose with 3-inch couplings that is supplying three hoselines connected to a water thief. Line 1 is 100 feet of 1½-inch hose that is flowing 125 gpm. Line 2 is 200 feet of 1½-inch hose that is flowing 95 gpm. Line 3 is 150 feet of 2½-inch hose that is flowing 250 gpm. All hoselines feature fog nozzles.

Line 1

FL = CQ²L

C = 24 from Table 7.3

$Q = \dfrac{gpm}{100} = \dfrac{125}{100} = 1.25$

$L = \dfrac{feet}{100} = \dfrac{100}{100} = 1$

FL = (24)(1.25)²(1) = **37.5 psi**

Line 2

FL = CQ²L

C = 24 from Table 7.3

$Q = \dfrac{gpm}{100} = \dfrac{95}{100} = 0.95$

$L = \dfrac{feet}{100} = \dfrac{200}{100} = 2$

FL = (24)(0.95)²(2) = **43.32 psi**

Line 3

FL = CQ²L

C = 2 from Table 7.3

$Q = \dfrac{gpm}{100} = \dfrac{250}{100} = 2.5$

$L = \dfrac{feet}{100} = \dfrac{150}{100} = 1.5$

FL = (2)(2.5)²(1.5) = **18.75 psi**

3-inch hose with 3-inch couplings

FL = CQ²L

C = 0.677 from Table 7.3

$$Q = Q_{Total} = \frac{(gpm\ in\ Line\ 1 + gpm\ in\ Line\ 2 + gpm\ in\ Line\ 3)}{100}$$

$$Q_{Total} = \frac{125 + 95 + 250}{100} = \frac{470}{100} = 4.7$$

$$L = \frac{feet}{100} = \frac{300}{100} = 3$$

FL = (0.677)(4.7)²(3) = **44.86 psi**

Total Pressure Loss

The total pressure loss will be equal to the friction loss in the supply hoseline plus the hoseline connected to the water thief with the highest friction loss. In this case, it is Line 2 with a pressure loss of **43.32 psi**. A friction loss of **10 psi** must be added for the water thief because the total flow rate exceeded 350 gpm.

TPL = 43.32 + 44.86 + 10 = **98.18 psi**

Pump Discharge Pressure

The pump discharge pressure is established to accommodate the hoseline with the highest pressure demand. The discharge outlets for the other hoselines on the water thief may be gated back until the desired pressure is obtained.

PDP = NP + TPL

PDP = 100 + 98.18 = **198.18 psi (app. 200)**

Example 7.26

What is the pump discharge pressure for a pumper that is supplying 500 feet of 5-inch hose to an appliance connected to an aerial waterway that is elevated 60 feet? The top of the waterway features a master stream device with a 1¼-inch solid stream nozzle that is flowing 80 psi.

GPM = 29.7 x d² x √NP

d = 1.25

NP = 80

GPM = (29.7)(1.25)²(√80) = **415.07 psi (app. 415)**

FL = CQ²L

C = 0.08 from Table 7.3

$$Q = \frac{gpm}{100} = \frac{415}{100} = 4.15$$

$$L = \frac{feet}{100} = \frac{500}{100} = 5$$

FL = (0.08)(4.15)²(5) = **6.89 psi**

EP = 0.5H

$EP = (0.5)(60) =$ **30 psi**

Total Pressure Loss

$TPL = 6.89 + 30 + 10 + 25 =$ **71.89 psi** (10 psi added for appliance and 25 psi added for aerial device)

Pump Discharge Pressure

PDP = NP + TPL

$PDP = 80 + 71.89 =$ **151.89 psi (app. 150)**

Formula 7.5: Net Pump Discharge Pressure

$NPDP_{PPS} =$ **PDP - Intake Reading**

Where:

$NPDP_{PPS} =$ Net Pump Discharge Pressure from a Positive Pressure Source

PDP = Pump Discharge Pressure

Example 7.27

A pumper being supplied from a hydrant with 20 psi on the intake gauge is discharging water at 170 psi. Determine the net pump discharge pressure.

$NPDP_{PPS} =$ **PDP - Intake Reading**

$NPDP_{PPS} = 170 - 20 =$ **150 psi**

Formula Examples — International System of Units (Metric)

Formula Examples — International System of Units (Metric)

Formula 7.1: Friction Loss

$$FL = CQ^2L$$

Where:

FL = Friction Loss in kilopascals (kPa)

C = Friction loss coefficient

Q = Flow rate in hundreds of liters per minute (L/min) (L/min/100)

L = Hose length in hundreds of meters (m) (meters/100)

The friction loss coefficients listed in **Table 7.5** are approximations used by IFSTA and the NFPA® for each diameter of hose. Exact coefficients for a specific piece of hose will vary based on the manufacturer and condition of the hose. The coefficients represented in this chart reflect results that are usually slightly higher than actual friction loss, providing the driver/operator with a "worst case" scenario. In order to achieve more exact results, individual fire departments may conduct tests and perform calculations using their own hose and appliances. The next section of this chapter explains calculating friction loss coefficients.

Table 7.5 Friction Loss Coefficients – Single Hoselines	
Hose Diameter and Type (mm)	**Coefficient (C)**
20 mm booster	1 741.0
25 mm booster	238.0
32 mm booster	127.0
38 mm	38.0
45 mm	24.6
50 mm	12.7
65 mm	3.17
70 mm with 77 mm couplings	2.36
77 mm with 65 mm couplings	1.27
77 mm with 77 mm couplings	1.06
90 mm	0.53
100 mm	0.305
115 mm	0.167
125 mm	0.138
150 mm	0.083
Standpipes	
100 mm	0.600
125 mm	0.202
150 mm	0.083

Example 7.1

If 1 200 L/min is flowing from a nozzle, what is the total pressure loss due to friction for 120 meters of 65 mm hose?

$$FL = CQ^2L$$

C = 3.17 from Table 7.5

$$Q = \frac{L/min}{100} = \frac{1\ 200}{100} = 12$$

$$L = \frac{meters}{100} = \frac{120}{100} = 1.2$$

$$FL = (3.17)(12)^2(1.2) = \textbf{547.78 kPa (app. 550)}$$

Example 7.2
What is the total pressure loss due to friction in 180 meters of 100 mm hose when 3 000 L/min is flowing?

$$FL = CQ^2L$$

C = 0.305 from Table 7.5

$$Q = \frac{L/min}{100} = \frac{3\,000}{100} = 30$$

$$L = \frac{meters}{100} = \frac{180}{100} = 1.8$$

$$FL = (0.305)(30)^2(1.8) = \textbf{494.1 kPa (app. 495)}$$

Example 7.3
What is the total pressure loss due to friction in 75 meters of 45 mm hose when 600 L/min is flowing?

$$FL = CQ^2L$$

C = 24.6 from Table 7.5

$$Q = \frac{L/min}{100} = \frac{600}{100} = 6$$

$$L = \frac{meters}{100} = \frac{75}{100} = 0.75$$

$$FL = (24.6)(6)^2(0.75) = \textbf{664.2 kPa (app. 665)}$$

Formula 7.2: Elevation Pressure Loss

$$EP = 10H$$

Where:

EP = Elevation Pressure in kilopascals (kPa)

10 = A constant

H = Height in meters (m)

Example 7.4
Calculate the total pressure loss due to elevation for a hoseline operating at the top of a 30 meter hill (**Figure 7.15, p. 250**).

$$EP = 10H$$

$$EP = (10)(30) = \textbf{300 kPa}$$

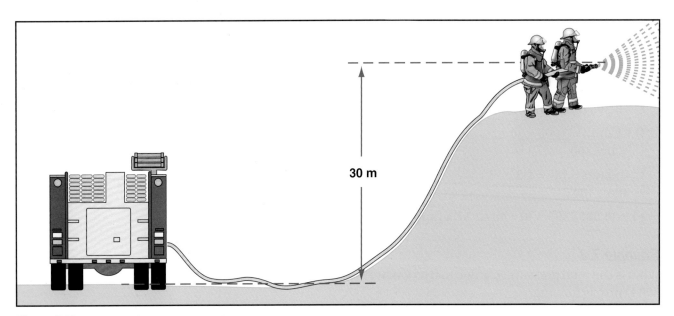

Figure 7.15

Formula 7.3: Elevation Pressure Loss in a Multistory Building
EP = (35 kPa) x (Number of Stories – 1)

Example 7.5
A hoseline is operating on the ninth floor of a building **(Figure 7.16)**. What is the pressure loss due to elevation?

EP = (35 kPa) x (Number of Stories – 1)

EP = (35)(9 –1) = **280 kPa**

Figure 7.16

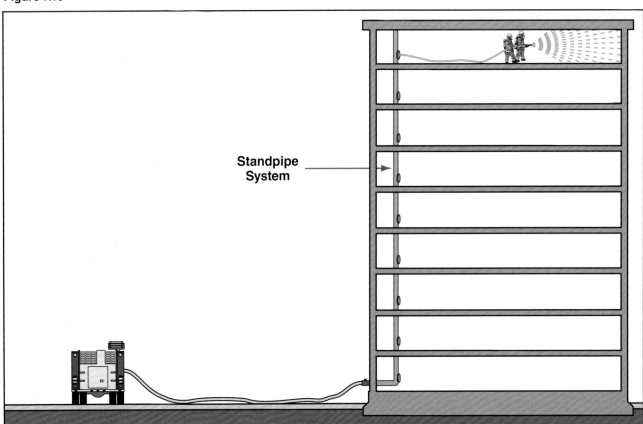

Standpipe System

Total Pressure Loss Calculations — Single Hoseline

Example 7.6

What is the pressure loss due to friction for a pumper that is supplying a 90 m hoseline that is flowing 500 L/min? The hoseline is composed of 60 meters of 65 mm hose reduced to 30 meters of 38 mm hose (**Figure 7.17**).

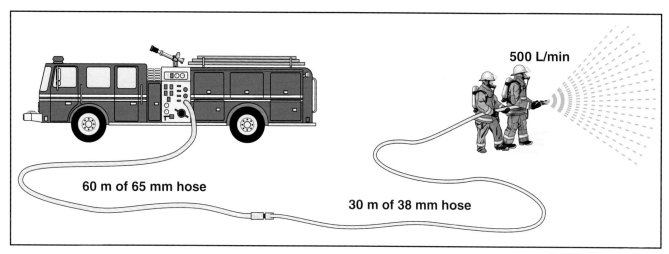

500 L/min

60 m of 65 mm hose

30 m of 38 mm hose

Figure 7.17

65 mm Hoseline

FL = CQ²L

C = 3.17 from Table 7.5

$Q = \dfrac{L/min}{100} = \dfrac{500}{100} = 5$

$L = \dfrac{meters}{100} = \dfrac{60}{100} = 0.6$

$FL = (3.17)(5)^2(0.6) =$ **47.55 kPa**

38 mm Hoseline

FL = CQ²L

C = 38 from Table 7.5

$Q = \dfrac{L/min}{100} = \dfrac{500}{100} = 5$

$L = \dfrac{meters}{100} = \dfrac{30}{100} = 0.3$

$FL = (38)(5)^2(0.3) =$ **285 kPa**

Total Pressure Loss

TPL = 47.55 + 285 = **332.55 kPa (app. 330)**

Example 7.7

An engine company advances 45 m of 45 mm hose to the third floor of a building for fire attack. Determine the total pressure loss due to friction and elevation when flowing 700 L/min.

45 mm Hose

FL = CQ²L

C = 24.6 from Table 7.5

$Q = \dfrac{L/min}{100} = \dfrac{700}{100} = 7$

$L = \dfrac{meters}{100} = \dfrac{45}{100} = 0.45$

FL = (24.6)(7)²(0.45) = **542.43 kPa**

Elevation Pressure

EP = (35 kPa) x (Number of Stories – 1)

EP = (35)(3 – 1) = **70 kPa**

Total Pressure Loss

TPL = 542.43 + 70 = **612.43 kPa (app. 610)**

Total Pressure Loss Calculations — Multiple Hoselines (Equal Length)

Example 7.8

Three 65 mm hoselines, each 120 m long, operating at 350 kPa nozzle pressure, and using 25 mm solid stream nozzles are put into use. What is the total pressure loss due to friction in each hoseline?

L/min = 0.067 x d² x √NP

d = 25

NP = 350

L/min = (0.067) (25)²(√350) = 783.41 (app. 783)

FL = CQ²L

C = 3.17 from Table 7.5

$Q = \dfrac{L/min}{100} = \dfrac{783}{100} = 7.83$

$L = \dfrac{meters}{100} = \dfrac{120}{100} = 1.2$

FL = (3.17)(7.83)²(1.2) = **233.22 kPa (app. 230) per hoseline**

Total Pressure Loss Calculations — Wyed Hoselines (Equal Length)

Example 7.9

Determine the pressure loss due to friction in a layout consisting of 120 m of 65 mm hose with two 38mm attack lines each flowing 400 L/min at a length of 30 m **(Figure 7.18)**.

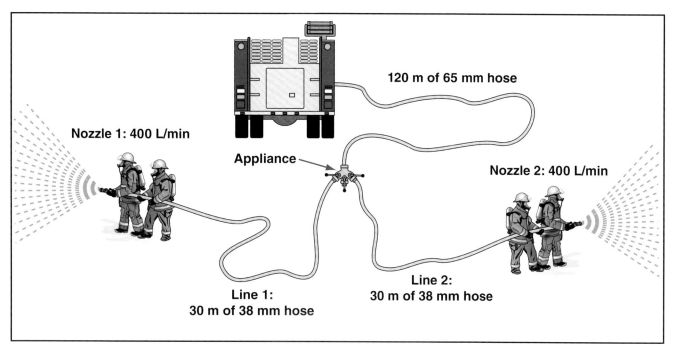

Figure 7.18

38 mm Hoselines

FL = CQ²L

C = 38 from Table 7.5

$Q = \dfrac{L/min}{100} = \dfrac{400}{100} = 4$

$L = \dfrac{meters}{100} = \dfrac{30}{100} = 0.3$

FL = $(38)(4)^2(0.3)$ = **182.4 kPa per hoseline**

65 mm Hoseline

FL = CQ²L

C = 3.17 from Table 7.5

$Q = Q_{Total} = \dfrac{(L/min\ Hoseline\ 1) + (L/min\ in\ Hoseline\ 2)}{100}$

$Q_{Total} = \dfrac{400 + 400}{100} = \dfrac{800}{100} = 8$

$L = \dfrac{meters}{100} = \dfrac{120}{100} = 1.2$

FL = $(3.17)(8)^2(1.2)$ = **243.46 kPa**

Total Pressure Loss

TPL = 182.4 + 243.46 = **425.86 kPa (app. 425)**

NOTE: The total flow through this hose layout was less than 1 400 L/min; therefore, it was not necessary to consider the pressure loss in the wye.

Example 7.10

Determine the pressure loss given a hose assembly featuring two 65 mm hoselines, each 60 m long and flowing 1 000 L/min, wyed off a supply line of 150 m of 100 mm hose.

65 mm Hoselines

FL = CQ²L

C = 3.17 from Table 7.5

$Q = \dfrac{L/min}{100} = \dfrac{1\,000}{100} = 10$

$L = \dfrac{meters}{100} = \dfrac{60}{100} = 0.6$

FL = $(3.17)(10)^2(0.6)$ = **190.2 kPa per hoseline**

100 mm Hoseline

FL = CQ²L

C = 0.305 from Table 7.5

$Q = Q_{Total} = \dfrac{(L/min\ in\ Hoseline\ 1) + (L/min\ in\ Hoseline\ 2)}{100}$

$Q_{Total} = \dfrac{1\,000 + 1\,000}{100} = \dfrac{2\,000}{100} = 20$

$L = \dfrac{meters}{100} = \dfrac{150}{100} = 1.5$

FL = $(0.305)(20)^2(1.5)$ = **183 kPa**

Total Pressure Loss

TPL = 190.2 + 183 + 70 = **443.2 kPa (app. 440)**

NOTE: The total flow through this hose layout exceeded 1 400 L/min; therefore, it was necessary to add 70 kPa for the pressure loss in the wye.

Total Pressure Loss Calculations — Siamesed Hoselines (Equal Length)

Example 7.11

Given a hose assembly in which two 77 mm hoselines with 65 mm couplings, each 300 m long, are used to supply a Siamese to which 100 m of 65 mm inch hose is attached and equipped with a solid stream nozzle, featuring a 32 mm tip, at 350 kPa nozzle pressure **(Figure 7.19)**. What is the pressure loss due to friction?

NOTE: Table 7.6 lists friction loss coefficients for Siamesed lines of equal length.

65 mm Hoseline

L/min = 0.067 x d² x √NP

d = 32

NP = 350

L/min = $(0.067) (32)^2(\sqrt{350})$ = **1 283.54 (app. 1 284)**

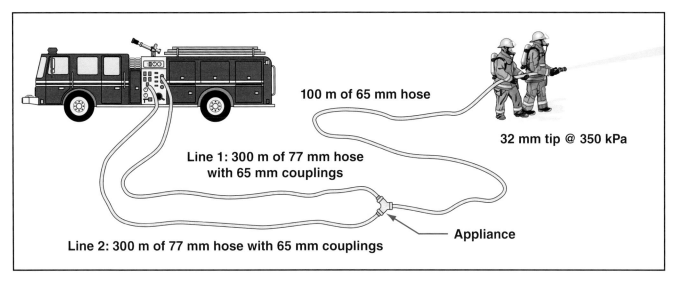

Figure 7.19

$FL = CQ^2L$

C = 3.17 from Table 7.5

$Q = \dfrac{L/min}{100} = \dfrac{1\,284}{100}\ Q = 12.84$

$L = \dfrac{meters}{100} = \dfrac{100}{100} = 1$

$FL = (3.17)(12.84)^2(1) = \mathbf{522.62\,kPa}$

77 mm hose with 65 mm couplings Siamesed Hoselines

$FL = CQ^2L$

C = 0.316 from Table 7.6

$Q = \dfrac{L/min}{100} = \dfrac{1\,284}{100} = 12.84$

$L = \dfrac{meters}{100} = \dfrac{300}{100} = 3$

$FL = (0.316)(12.84)^2(3) = \mathbf{156.29\,kPa}$

Total Pressure Loss

TPL = 522.62 + 156.29 = **678.91 kPa (app. 680)**

NOTE: The total flow through this hose assembly was less than 1 400 L/min; therefore, it was not necessary to consider the pressure loss in the Siamese appliance.

Table 7.6
Friction Loss Coefficients — Siamesed Lines of Equal Length

Hose Diameter and Type (mm)	Coefficient C
Two 65 mm	0.789
Three 65 mm	0.347
Two 77 mm with 65 mm couplings	0.316
Two 77 mm with 77 mm couplings	0.268
One 77 mm with 65 mm couplings, one 65 mm	0.473
One 77 mm with 77 mm couplings, one 65 mm	0.426
Two 65 mm lines, one 77 mm with 65 mm couplings	0.253
Two 77 mm with 65 mm couplings, one 65 mm	0.189

Example 7.12

Determine the total pressure loss in a hose assembly with two 65 mm hoselines, each 225 m long, being used to supply a Siamese to which 60 m of 65 mm hose is connected. The nozzle on the 65 mm hoseline is flowing 1 200 L/min. It is located 10 m uphill of the Siamese.

65 mm Hoseline

FL = CQ²L

C = 3.17 from Table 7.5

$Q = \dfrac{L/min}{100} = \dfrac{1\,200}{100} = 12$

$L = \dfrac{meters}{100} = \dfrac{60}{100} = 0.6$

FL = (3.17)(12)²(0.6) = **273.89 kPa**

EP = 10H

EP = (10)(10) = **100 kPa**

TPL = 273.89 + 100 = **373.89 kPa**

65 mm Siamesed Hoselines

FL = CQ²L

C = 0.789 from Table 7.6

$Q = \dfrac{L/min}{100} = \dfrac{1\,200}{100} = 12$

$L = \dfrac{meters}{100} = \dfrac{225}{100} = 2.25$

FL = (0.789)(12)²(2.25) = **255.64 kPa**

Total Pressure Loss

TPL = 373.89 + 255.64 = **629.53 kPa (app. 630)**

Total Pressure Loss Calculations — Standpipe Operations

Example 7.13

A pumper responds to a fire on the fifth floor of a building. Two 65 mm hoselines, each 45 meters long, are connected to the fire department connection. Utilizing the 100 mm diameter standpipe, firefighters make connections on the fourth floor of the building and advance the hoseline to the fifth floor. They are using 60 meters of 45 mm hose and flowing 500 gpm from a fog nozzle. What is the total pressure loss in the hose and standpipe assembly?

NOTE: Since the hoselines connected to the FDC are of equal size and length they can be treated like hoselines connected to a Siamese appliance for hydraulic calculations.

45 mm Hoseline

FL = CQ²L

C = 24.6 from Table 7.5

$Q = \dfrac{L/min}{100} = \dfrac{500}{100} = 5$

$L = \dfrac{meters}{100} = \dfrac{60}{100} = 0.6$

FL = (24.6)(5)²(0.6) = **369 kPa**

Standpipe

Based on 3 meters per floor, assume 12 meters of standpipe is used.

FL = CQ²L

C = 0.600 from Table 7.5

$Q = \dfrac{L/min}{100} = \dfrac{500}{100} = 5$

$L = \dfrac{meters}{100} = \dfrac{12}{100} = 0.12$

FL = (0.600)(5)²(0.12) = **1.8 kPa** (Friction loss within the standpipe is minimal)

Elevation Pressure

EP = (35 kPa) x (Number of Stories – 1)

EP = (35)(5-1) = **140 psi**

65 mm Hoselines Connected to FDC

FL = CQ²L

C = 0.789 from Table 7.6

$Q = \dfrac{L/min}{100} = \dfrac{500}{100} = 5$

$L = \dfrac{meters}{100} = \dfrac{45}{100} = 0.45$

FL = (0.789)(5)²(0.45) = **8.88 kPa**

Total Pressure Loss

TPL = 369 + 1.8 + 140 + 8.88 = **519.68 kPa (app. 520)**

Total Pressure Loss Calculations — Multiple Hoselines (Unequal Length)

Example 7.14

Two 65 mm hoselines, one 150 meters long and the other 100 meters long are outfitted with 1 000 L/min fog nozzles **(Figure 7.20)**. Determine the total pressure loss due to friction for this hose layout.

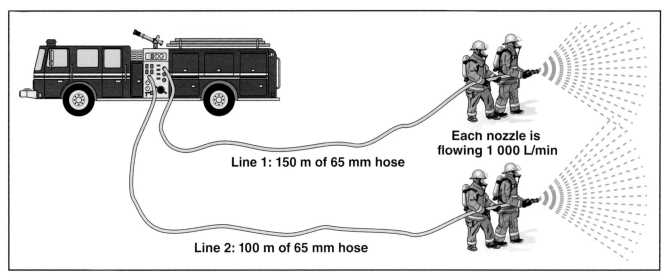

Figure 7.20

Line 1

$$FL = CQ^2L$$

C = 3.17 from Table 7.5

$$Q = \frac{L/min}{100} = \frac{1\,000}{100} = 10$$

$$L = \frac{meters}{100} = \frac{150}{100} = 1.5$$

$$FL = (3.17)(10)^2(1.5) = \textbf{475.5 kPa}$$

Line 2

$$FL = CQ^2L$$

C = 3.17 from Table 7.5

$$Q = \frac{L/min}{100} = \frac{1\,000}{100} = 10$$

$$L = \frac{meters}{100} = \frac{100}{100} = 1$$

$$FL = (3.17)(10)^2(1) = \textbf{317 kPa}$$

Total Pressure Loss

The total pressure loss will be equal to the hoseline with the highest friction loss. In this case, it is Line 1, with a pressure loss of **475.5 kPa (app. 475)**.

Example 7.15

A pumper is supplying four lines. Lines 1 and 2 are 45 meters of 38 mm hose equipped with a 16 mm solid stream tip operating at 350 kPa. Lines 3 and 4 are 60 meters of 45 mm hose equipped with a 19 mm solid stream tip operating at 350 kPa **(Figure 7.21)**. Determine the total pressure loss due to friction for this hose layout.

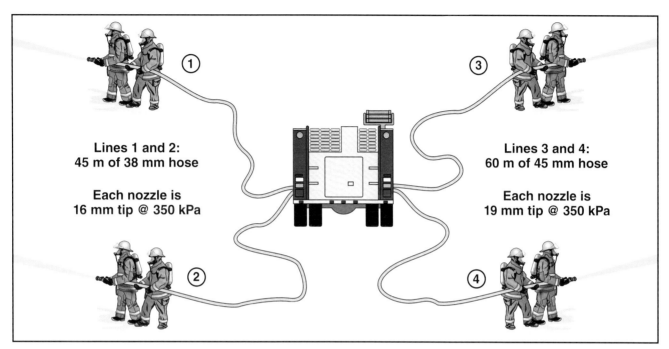

Figure 7.21

Lines 1 and 2

L/min = 0.067 x d² x √NP

d = 16

NP = 350

L/min = (0.067) (16)²(√350) = **320.88 (app. 320)**

FL = CQ²L

C = 38 from Table 7.5

$Q = \dfrac{L/min}{100} = \dfrac{320}{100} = 3.2$

$L = \dfrac{meters}{100} = \dfrac{45}{100} = 0.45$

FL = (38)(3.2)²(0.45) = **175.1 kPa per hoseline**

Lines 3 and 4

L/min = 0.067 x d² x √NP

d = 19

NP = 350

L/min = (0.067) (19)²(√350) = **452.5**

FL = CQ²L

C = 24.6 from Table 7.5

$$Q = \frac{L/min}{100} = \frac{452.5}{100} = 4.525$$

$$L = \frac{meters}{100} = \frac{60}{100} = 0.6$$

FL = (24.6)(4.525)²(0.6) = **302.22 kPa per hoseline**

Total Pressure Loss

The total pressure loss will be equal to the highest loss of the hoselines. In this case, it is Lines 3 and 4, with a pressure loss of **302.22 kpa (app. 300)** per hoseline.

Total Pressure Loss Calculations — Wyed Hoselines (Unequal Length) and Manifold Lines

Example 7.16

Determine the total loss of pressure due to friction and elevation pressure for a hose layout in which one 120 m, 77 mm hoseline with 65 mm couplings is supplying two attack lines **(Figure 7.22)**. Line 1 is a 60 m of 45 mm hose that is stretched horizontally through the front door of a dwelling. This line is flowing 600 L/min. The second hoseline is 45 m of 38 mm hose that is deployed via ladder to the second floor. The second line is flowing 400 L/min.

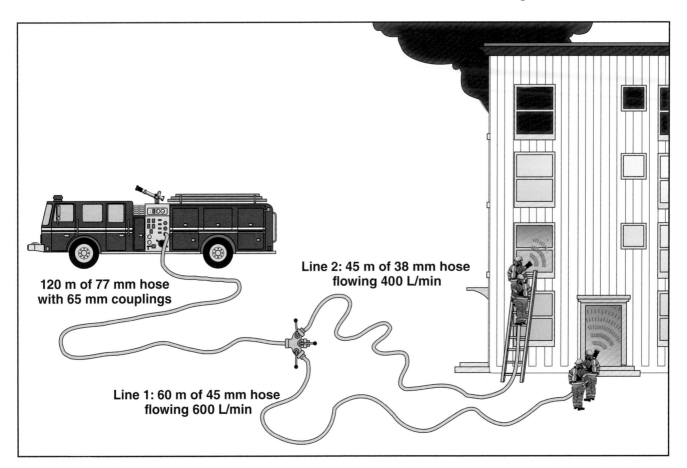

120 m of 77 mm hose
with 65 mm couplings

Line 2: 45 m of 38 mm hose
flowing 400 L/min

Line 1: 60 m of 45 mm hose
flowing 600 L/min

Figure 7.22

Line 1

FL = CQ²L

C = 24.6 from Table 7.5

$Q = \dfrac{\text{L/min}}{100} = \dfrac{600}{100} = 6$

$L = \dfrac{\text{meters}}{100} = \dfrac{60}{100} = 0.6$

FL = (24.6)(6)^2(0.6) = **531.36 kPa**

Line 2

C = 38 from Table 7.5

$Q = \dfrac{\text{L/min}}{100} = \dfrac{400}{100} = 4$

$L = \dfrac{\text{meters}}{100} = \dfrac{45}{100} = 0.45$

FL = (38)(4)^2(0.45) = **273.6 kPa**

EP = (35 kPa) x (Number of Stories - 1)

EP = (35)(2 –1) = **35 kPa**

TPL = 273.6 + 35 = **308.6 kPa**

77 mm hose with 65 mm couplings

FL = CQ²L

C = 1.27 from Table 7.5

$Q = Q_{\text{Total}} = \dfrac{(\text{L/min in Line 1}) + (\text{L/min in Line 2})}{100}$

$Q_{\text{Total}} = \dfrac{600 + 400}{100} = \dfrac{1\,000}{100} = 10$

$L = \dfrac{\text{meters}}{100} = \dfrac{120}{100} = 1.2$

FL = (1.27)(10)^2(1.2) = **152.4 kPa**

Total Pressure Loss

The total pressure loss will be equal to the friction loss in the supply hoseline plus the wyed hoseline with the highest friction loss. In this case, it is Line 1, with a pressure loss of **531.36 kPa**. No friction loss for the appliance will be applied because the total flow rate was less than 1 400 L/min.

TPL = 531.36 + 152.4 = **683.76 kPa (app. 680)**

Example 7.17

Determine the total pressure loss due to friction for a hose layout in which one 150 m, 77 mm hose with 77 mm couplings is supplying three attack lines that are connected to a water thief appliance. Line 1 is 45 m of 38 mm hose that is flowing 500 L/min. Line 2 is 30 m of 38 mm hose that is flowing 400 L/min. Line 3 is 45 m of 65 mm hose that is flowing 900 L/min.

Line 1

$FL = CQ^2L$

C = 38 from Table 7.5

$Q = \dfrac{L/min}{100} = \dfrac{500}{100} = 5$

$L = \dfrac{meters}{100} = \dfrac{45}{100} = 0.45$

$FL = (38)(5)^2(0.45) = \mathbf{427.5\ kPa}$

Line 2

$FL = CQ^2L$

C = 38 from Table 7.5

$Q = \dfrac{L/min}{100} = \dfrac{400}{100} = 4$

$L = \dfrac{meters}{100} = \dfrac{30}{100} = 0.3$

$FL = (38)(4)^2(0.3) = \mathbf{182.4\ kPa}$

Line 3

$FL = CQ^2L$

C = 3.17 from Table 7.5

$Q = \dfrac{L/min}{100} = \dfrac{900}{100} = 9$

$L = \dfrac{meters}{100} = \dfrac{45}{100} = 0.45$

$FL = (3.17)(9)^2(0.45) = \mathbf{115.55\ kPa}$

77 mm hose with 77 mm couplings

$FL = CQ^2L$

C = 1.06 from Table 7.5

$Q = Q_{Total} = \dfrac{(L/min\ of\ Line\ 1 + L/min\ of\ Line\ 2 + L/min\ of\ Line\ 3)}{100}$

$Q_{Total} = \dfrac{500 + 400 + 900}{100} = \dfrac{1\ 800}{100} = 18$

$L = \dfrac{meters}{100} = \dfrac{150}{100} = 1.5$

$FL = (1.06)(18)^2(1.5) = \mathbf{515.16\ kPa}$

Total Pressure Loss

The total pressure loss will be equal to the friction loss in the supply hoseline plus the wyed hoseline with the highest friction loss. In this case, it is Line 1, with a pressure loss of **427.5 kPa**. A friction loss of **70 kPa** must be added for the water thief appliance because the total flow rate exceeded 1 400 L/min.

TPL = 427.5 + 515.16 + 70 = **1 012.66 kPa (app. 1 000)**

Total Pressure Loss Calculations — Master Streams

If unequal length or diameter of hose is used to supply a master stream, use the average of the hose lengths to simplify calculation. To obtain the average, a driver/operator may add the length of each hoseline and then divide by the number of hoselines being used. Use the coefficients for Siamesed hoselines referenced in Table 7.6 with the total flow through the nozzle to complete friction loss calculations.

In certain scenarios, multiple lines of equal diameter but unequal length may be used. Coefficients for that combination are not shown in Table 7.6 . The driver/operator should average the length of the lines and assume equal pressure through each one.

Example 7.18

Determine the total pressure loss due to friction for a hose layout in which one 210-meter, 125 mm hose is supplying three hoselines that are attached to a large diameter hose manifold **(Figure 7.23)**. Two of the hoselines are 45 meters of 77 mm hose with 65 mm couplings that are supplying a portable master stream device. The master stream is discharging 560 kPa through a 38 mm tip. The third hoseline is 45 meters of 65 mm hose flowing 1 100 L/min.

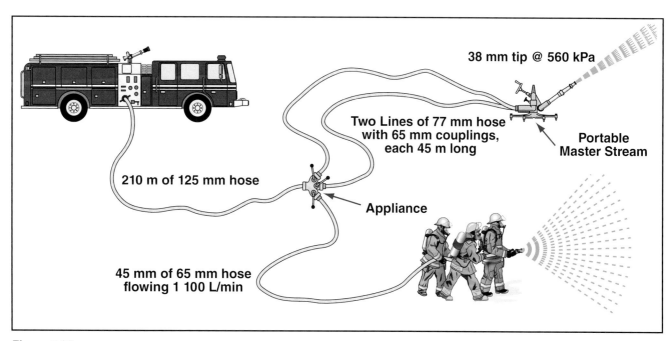

38 mm tip @ 560 kPa

Two Lines of 77 mm hose with 65 mm couplings, each 45 m long

Portable Master Stream

210 m of 125 mm hose

Appliance

45 mm of 65 mm hose flowing 1 100 L/min

Figure 7.23

77 mm hose with 65 mm couplings Supplying a Portable Master Stream

L/min = 0.067 x d² x √NP

d = 38

NP = 560

L/min = (0.067) (38)^2(√560) = **2 289.48 (app. 2 290)**

FL = CQ²L

C = 0.316 from Table 7.6

$Q = \dfrac{L/min}{100} = \dfrac{2\,290}{100} = 22.9$

$L = \dfrac{meters}{100} = \dfrac{45}{100} = 0.45$

FL = (0.316)(22.9)^2(0.45) = **74.57 kPa**

TPL = 74.57 + 175 = **249.57 kPa** (175 kPa added for Master Stream device)

65 mm Hoseline

FL = CQ²L

C = 3.17 from Table 7.5

$Q = \dfrac{L/min}{100} = \dfrac{1\,100}{100} = 11$

$L = \dfrac{meters}{100} = \dfrac{45}{100} = 0.45$

FL = (3.17)(11)^2(0.45) = **172.61 kPa**

125 mm Hoseline

FL = CQ²L

C = 0.138 from Table 7.5

$Q = Q_{Total} = \dfrac{(L/min\ in\ Master\ Stream) + (L/min\ in\ 65\ mm\ Hoseline)}{100}$

$Q_{Total} = \dfrac{2\,290 + 1\,100}{100} = \dfrac{3\,390}{100} = 33.9$

$L = \dfrac{meters}{100} = \dfrac{210}{100} = 2.1$

FL = (0.138)(33.9)^2(2.1) = **333.04 kPa**

Total Pressure Loss

The total pressure loss will be equal to the friction loss in the supply hoseline plust the wyed hoseline with the highest friction loss. In this case, it is the hoselines supplying the portable master stream, with a pressure loss of **249.57 kPa**. A friction loss of **70 kPa** must be added for the large diameter hose manifold because the total flow rate exceeded 1 400 L/min.

TPL = 249.57 + 333.04 + 70 = **652.61 kPa (app. 650)**

Example 7.19

Determine the total pressure loss in a hose layout where a 12 000 L/min master stream device is supplied by three 125 mm hoselines **(Figure 7.24)**. Two of the hoselines are 300 m in length, and one is 400 m. All lines are flowing 4 000 L/ min through each hoseline.

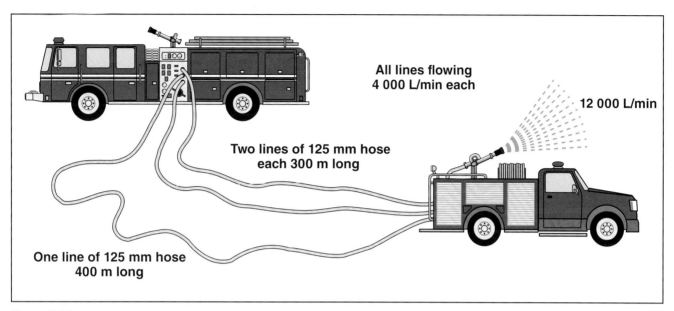

Figure 7.24

125 mm Hoselines

FL = CQ²L

C = 0.138 from Table 7.5

$Q = \dfrac{L/min}{100} = \dfrac{4\,000}{100} = 40$

$\text{Average Length} = \dfrac{\text{(Sum of Hose Lengths)}}{3} = \dfrac{(300 + 300 + 400)}{3} = \dfrac{1\,000}{3} = 333 \text{ meters}$

$L = \dfrac{\text{meters}}{100} = \dfrac{333}{100} = 3.33$

FL = (0.138)(40)²(3.33) = **735.26 kPa per hoseline**

Total Pressure Loss

TPL = 735.26 + 175 = **910.26 kPa (app. 910)** (175 kPa added for Master Stream device)

Total Pressure Loss Calculations — Elevated Waterways

Example 7.20

A pumper is supplying 60 meters of 77 mm hose with 65 mm couplings that is feeding an aerial device with a detachable waterway containing 30 meters of 65 mm hose. The aerial device is elevated 25 meters and is discharging 2 000 L/min **(Figure 7.25)**. Determine the total pressure loss in this hose layout.

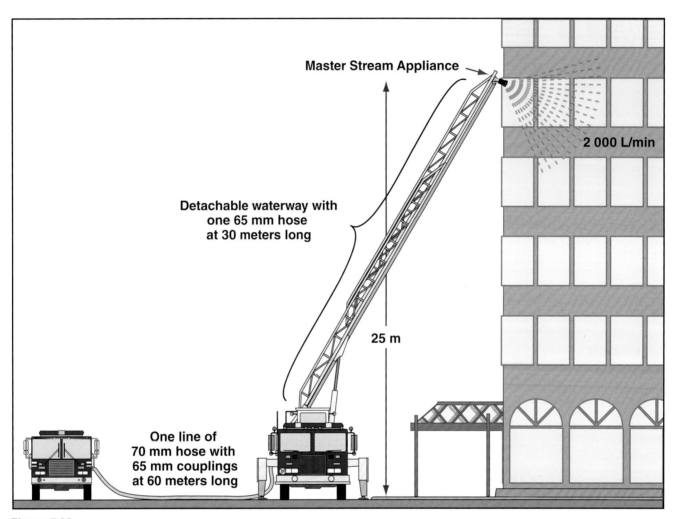

Figure 7.25

77 mm hose with 65 mm couplings

FL = CQ²L

C = 1.27 from Table 7.5

$Q = \dfrac{L/min}{100} = \dfrac{2\,000}{100} = 20$

$L = \dfrac{meters}{100} = \dfrac{60}{100} = 0.6$

FL = (1.27)(20)²(0.6) = **304.8 kPa**

65 mm Hoseline

FL = CQ²L

C = 3.17 from Table 7.5

$Q = \dfrac{L/min}{100} = \dfrac{2\,000}{100} = 20$

$L = \dfrac{meters}{100} = \dfrac{30}{100} = 0.3$

FL = (3.17)(20)²(0.3) = **380.4 kPa**

Elevation Pressure

EP = 10H

EP = (10)(25) = **250 kPa**

Total Pressure Loss

TPL = 304.8 + 380.4 + 250 + 175 = **1 110.2 kPa (app. 1 100)** (175 kPa added for aerial device)

Example 7.21

Determine the total pressure loss in a hose layout where a pumper is supplying 240 meters of 125 mm hose that is connected to an aerial device elevated master stream. The master stream is elevated 15 meters and is equipped with a solid stream nozzle with a 50 mm tip and is flowing 700 kPa.

GPM = 0.067 x d² x √NP

d = 50

NP = 700

GPM = (0.067)(50)²(√700) = **4 431.63 (app. 4 432)**

FL = CQ²L

C = 0.138 from Table 7.5

$Q = \dfrac{L/min}{100} = \dfrac{4\,432}{100} = 44.32$

$L = \dfrac{meters}{100} = \dfrac{240}{100} = 2.4$

FL = (0.138)(44.32)²(2.4) = **650.56 kPa**

EP = 10H

EP = (10)(15) = **150 kPa**

Total Pressure Loss

TPL = 650.56 + 150 + 175 = **975.56 kPa (app. 975)** (175 kPa added for aerial device)

Formula 7.4: Pump Discharge Pressure

PDP = NP + TPL

Where:

PDP = Pump Discharge Pressure in kilopascals (kPa)

NP = Nozzle Pressure in kilopascals (kPa)

TPL = Total Pressure Loss in kilopascals (kPa)

(TPL accounts for pressure loss due to friction, elevation, and appliances)

Example 7.22

A pumper must supply 150 m of 65 mm hose that is flowing 1 200 L/min through a fog nozzle. Determine the pump discharge pressure required to adequately supply the hoseline.

$FL = CQ^2L$

C = 3.17 from Table 7.

$Q = \dfrac{L/min}{100} = \dfrac{1\,200}{100} = 12$

$L = \dfrac{meters}{100} = \dfrac{150}{100} = 1.5$

$FL = (3.17)(12)^2(1.5) = $ **684.72 kPa**

Pump Discharge Pressure

PDP = NP + TPL

PDP = 700 + 684.72

PDP= **1 384.72 kPa (app. 1 400)**

Example 7.23

Determine the pump discharge pressure required to supply two 65 mm hoselines, one that is 100 m long and the other 150 m long. Each line is outfitted with 1 000 L/min fog nozzles **(Figure 7.26)**.

Figure 7.26

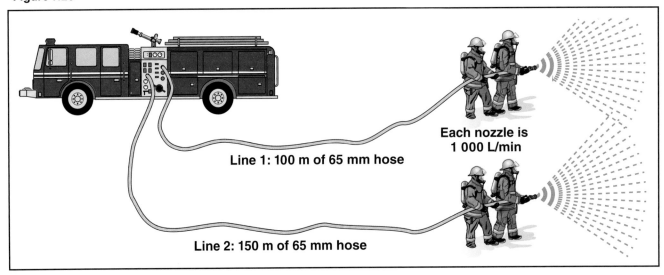

Each nozzle is 1 000 L/min

Line 1: 100 m of 65 mm hose

Line 2: 150 m of 65 mm hose

Line 1

FL = CQ²L

C = 3.17 from Table 7.5

$Q = \dfrac{L/min}{100} = \dfrac{1\,000}{100} = 10$

$L = \dfrac{meters}{100} = \dfrac{100}{100} = 1$

FL = (3.17)(10)²(1) = **317 kPa**

Line 2

FL = CQ²L

C = 3.17 from Table 7.5

$Q = \dfrac{L/min}{100} = \dfrac{1\,000}{100} = 10$

$L = \dfrac{meters}{100} = \dfrac{150}{100} = 1.5$

FL = (3.17)(10)²(1.5) = **475.5 kPa**

Pump Discharge Pressure

The pump discharge pressure should be set for the hoseline with the highest pressure demand. In this case, it is Line 2 with a pressure loss of **475.5 kPa**. The pump only produces one pressure using the available water supply. The driver/operator should gate back the discharge outlet for Line 1 to ensure the correct pressure when the line is flowing.

PDP = NP + TPL

PDP = 700 + 475.5 = **1 175.5 kPa (app. 1 200)**

Example 7.24

Determine the pump discharge pressure for a pumper that is using two 77 mm hoselines with 65 mm couplings, each 75 meters long, to supply an elevated master stream. The master stream is elevated 20 meters and features a master stream fog nozzle that is flowing 4 000 L/min at 700 kPa.

FL = CQ²L

C = 0.316 from Table 7.6

$Q = \dfrac{L/min}{100} = \dfrac{4\,000}{100} = 40$

$L = \dfrac{meters}{100} = \dfrac{75}{100} = 0.75$

FL = (0.316)(40)²(0.75) = **379.2 kPa**

EP = 10H

EP = (10)(20) = **200 kPa**

Total Pressure Loss

TPL = 379.2 + 200 + 175 = **754.2 kPa** (175 kPa added for aerial device)

Pump Discharge Pressure

PDP = NP + TPL

PDP = 700 + 754.2 = **1 454.2 kPa (app. 1 450)**

Example 7.25

Determine the pump discharge pressure in a hose layout with one 90 m, 77 mm hose with 77 mm couplings is supplying three hoselines connected to a water thief. Line 1 is 30 m of 38 mm hose that is flowing 500 L/min. Line 2 is 60 m of 38 mm hose that is flowing 400 L/min. Line 3 is 45 m of 65 mm hose that is flowing 1 000 L/min. All attack lines feature fog nozzles.

Line 1

Fl = CQ²L

C = 38 from Table 7.5

$Q = \dfrac{L/min}{100} = \dfrac{500}{100} = 5$

$L = \dfrac{meters}{100} = \dfrac{30}{100} = 0.3$

FL = (38)(5)²(0.3) = **285 kPa**

Line 2

FL = CQ²L

C = 38 from Table 7.5

$Q = \dfrac{L/min}{100} = \dfrac{400}{100} = 4$

$L = \dfrac{meters}{100} = \dfrac{60}{100} = 0.6$

FL = (38)(4)²(0.6) = **364.8 kPa**

Line 3

FL = CQ²L

C = 3.17 from Table 7.5

$Q = \dfrac{L/min}{100} = \dfrac{1\ 000}{100} = 10$

$L = \dfrac{meters}{100} = \dfrac{45}{100} = 0.45$

FL = (3.17)(10)²(0.45) = **142.65 kPa**

77 mm hose with 77 mm couplings

FL = CQ²L

C = 1.06 Table 7.5

$Q = Q_{Total} = \dfrac{(L/min\ in\ Line\ 1 + L/min\ in\ Line\ 2 + L/min\ in\ Line\ 3)}{100}$

$Q_{Total} = \dfrac{500 + 400 + 1\ 000}{100} = \dfrac{1\ 900}{100} = 19$

$L = \dfrac{meters}{100} = \dfrac{90}{100} = 0.9$

FL = (1.06)(19)²(0.9) = **344.39 kPa**

Total Pressure Loss

The total pressure loss will be equal to the friction loss in the supply hoseline plus the hoseline connected to the water thief with the highest friction loss. In this case, it is Line 2 with a pressure loss of **364.8 kPa**. A friction loss of **70 kPa** must be added for the water thief because the total flow rate exceeded 1 400 L/min.

TPL = 364.8 + 344.39 + 70 = **779.19 kPa**

Pump Discharge Pressure

The pump discharge pressure is established to accommodate the hoseline with the highest pressure demand. The discharge outlets for the other hoselines on the water thief may be gated back until the desired pressure is obtained.

PDP = NP + TPL

PDP = 700 + 779.19 = **1 479.19 kPa (app. 1 500)**

Example 7.26

What is the pump discharge pressure for a pumper that is supplying 150 meters of 125 mm hose to an appliance that is connected to an aerial waterway that is elevated 20 feet? The top of the waterway features a master stream device with a 32 mm solid stream nozzle that is flowing 560 psi.

GPM = 0.067 x d² x √NP

d = 32

NP = 560

GPM = (0.067)(32)²(√560) = **1 623.56 kPa (app. 1 624)**

FL = CQ²L

C = 0.138 from Table 7.5

$Q = \dfrac{L/min}{100} = \dfrac{1\ 624}{100} = 16.24$

$L = \dfrac{meters}{100} = \dfrac{150}{100} = 1.5$

FL = (0.138)(16.24)²(1.5) = **54.59 kPa**

EP = 10H

EP = (10)(20) = **200 kPa**

Total Pressure Loss

TPL = 54.59 + 200 + 70 + 175 = **499.59 psi** (70 kPa added for appliance and 175 kPa added for aerial device)

Pump Discharge Pressure

PDP = NP + TPL

PDP = 560 + 499.59 = **1 059.59 kPa (app. 1 050)**

Formula 7.5: Net Pump Discharge Pressure

$NPDP_{PPS}$ = PDP - Intake Reading

Where:

$NPDP_{PPS}$ = Net Pump Discharge Pressure from a Positive Pressure Source

PDP = Pump Discharge Pressure

Example 7.27

A pumper being supplied from a hydrant with 150 kPa on the intake gauge is discharging water at 1 700 kPa. Determine the net pump discharge pressure.

$NPDP_{PPS}$ = PDP - Intake Reading

$NPDP_{PPS}$ = 1 700 kPa – 150 kPa = **1 550 kPa**

Customary

Step 1: Lay out, on a level surface, the lengths of hose to be tested.

Step 2: Connect one end of the hoseline to a discharge on the pumper being used to carry out the tests. Connect a nozzle to the opposite end of the hoseline.

    a: Use a smooth bore nozzle if you use a pitot tube to determine the nozzle pressure and corresponding flow of water.

    b: Use any suitable nozzle if you use a flow meter to determine the flow.

Step 3: Insert Gauge 1 in the hoseline at the connection between the first and second sections of hose away from the discharge.

    a: Make this connection 50 feet from the pumper if the hose being tested is in lengths of 50 feet.

    b: If 100-foot sections of hose are used, Gauge 1 should be 100 feet from the pumper.

Step 4: Insert Gauge 2 at a distance of 200 feet from Gauge 1, regardless of the length of the hose sections.

    a: Depending on the length of the hose sections, there should be either 50 or 100 feet between Gauge 2 and the nozzle.

    b: If a portable flowmeter is being used, DO NOT insert it between the test gauges. However, it may be inserted in the hoseline anywhere else.

SKILL
SHEETS

7-1

Test hose carried on fire department apparatus to determine friction loss.

Step 5: When all appliances have been inserted into the hoseline, begin the tests.

a: Supply water to the hoseline at a constant pump discharge pressure for the duration of each test run. Because three or four test runs should be made for each size hose, different pump discharge pressures may be used for different runs as long as they are not changed within the same test run.

b: Use sufficient pump discharge pressure to produce a satisfactory fire stream from the nozzle.

Step 6: Once water is flowing, record the pump discharge pressure, the readings from Gauge 1 and Gauge 2, and the flowmeter or pitot gauge readings (whichever is being used) in the appropriate spaces of the chart used to determine friction loss for fire hose.

Test hose carried on fire department apparatus to determine friction loss.

Friction Loss Coefficient Determination Chart

Date: __ / __ / ____   Hose Size _____ Inches   Hose Construction _____

Person Conducting Tests _____

Column 1 Test Run No.	Column 2 Pump Discharge Pressure psi	Column 3 Pressure @ Gauge 1 psi	Column 4 Pressure @ Gauge 2 psi	Column 5 Nozzle Pressure* psi	Column 6 Flow From Flowmeter or by Equation**	Column 7 $\frac{(GPM)^2}{100}$ or $\frac{(Col.\ 6)^2}{100}$	Column 8 Friction Loss per 100 feet or $\frac{(Col.\ 3\text{-}Col.\ 4)}{2}$	Column 9 C $\left(\frac{Col.\ 8}{Col.\ 7}\right)$
1								
2								
3								
4								

Total of all Col. 9 Answers

Average C = ————————

No. of Tests Conducted

* Not necessary if flowmeter is used
**GPM = 29.7 d² √NP

Average C = [ ]

Step 7: Complete the chart used to determine friction loss for fire hose. This provides you with the friction loss coefficient for your particular hose.

7-1

Test hose carried on fire department apparatus to determine friction loss.

Metric

Step 1: Lay out, on a level surface, the lengths of hose to be tested.

Step 2: Connect one end of the hoseline to a discharge on the pumper being used to carry out the tests. Connect a nozzle to the opposite end of the hoseline.

a: Use a smooth bore nozzle if you use a pitot tube to deterine the nozzle pressure and corresponding flow of water.

b: Use any suitable nozzle if you use a flowmeter to determine the flow.

Step 3: Insert Gauge 1 in the hoseline at the connection between the first and second sections of hose away from the discharge.

a: Make this connection 15 meters from the pumper if the hose being tested is in lengths of 15 meters.

b: If 30-meter sections of hose are used, Gauge 1 should be 30 meters from the pumper.

Step 4: Insert Gauge 2 at a distance of 60 meters from Gauge 1, regardless of the length of the hose sections.

a: Depending on the length of the hose sections, there should be either 15 meters or 30 meters between Gauge 2 and the nozzle.

b: If a portable flowmeter is being used, DO NOT insert it anywhere between the gauges. It may be inserted in the hoseline anywhere but between the test gauges.

Step 5: When all appliances have been inserted into the hoseline, begin the tests.

a: Supply water to the hoseline at a constant pump discharge pressure for the duration of each test run. Because three or four test runs should be made for each size hose, different pump discharge pressures may be used for different runs as long as they are not changed within the same test run.

b: Use sufficient pump discharge pressure to produce a satisfactory fire stream from the nozzle.

Step 6: Once water is flowing, record the pump discharge pressure, the readings from Gauge 1 and Gauge 2, and the flowmeter or pitot gauge readings (whichever is being used) in the appropriate spaces of the chart used to determine friction loss for fire hose.

7-1

Test hose carried on fire department apparatus to determine friction loss.

Friction Loss Coefficient Determination Chart

Date: ___/___/_____   Hose Size _____Millimeters   Hose Construction _____

Person Conducting Tests _____

Column 1	Column 2	Column 3	Column 4	Column 5	Column 6	Column 7	Column 8	Column 9
Test Run No.	Pump Discharge Pressure kPa	Pressure @ Gauge 1 kPa	Pressure @ Gauge 2 kPa	Nozzle Pressure* kPa	Flow From Flowmeter or by Equation**	$\dfrac{(L/min)^2}{100}$ or $\dfrac{(Col.\ 6)^2}{100}$	Friction Loss per 100 meters or $\dfrac{(Col.\ 3\text{-}Col.\ 4)}{0.6}$	C $\dfrac{(Col.\ 8)}{Col.\ 7}$
1								
2								
3								
4								

Total of all Col.9 Answers

Average C = ————————

No. of Tests Conducted

Average C = [ ]

* Not necessary if flowmeter is used
**L/min = 0.067 d² √NP

Step 7: Complete the chart used to determine friction loss for fire hose. This provides you with the friction loss coefficient for your particular hose.

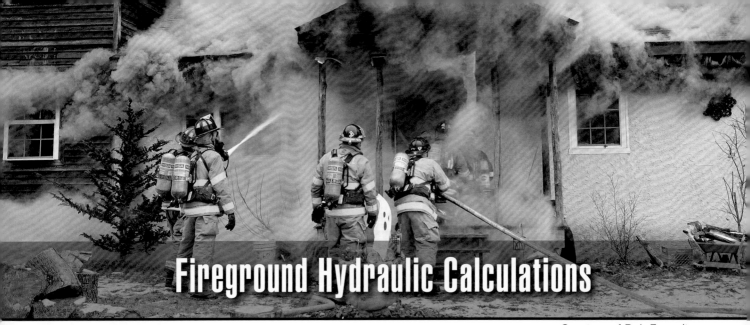

Courtesy of Bob Esposito.

Fireground Hydraulic Calculations

▉ Chapter Contents

Key Terms

NFPA® Job Performance Requirements

This chapter provides information that addresses the following job performance requirements of NFPA 1002, *Standard for Fire Apparatus Driver/Operator Professional Qualifications (2014)*.

5.2.1, 5.2.2

NFPA 1002, *Standard for Fire Apparatus Driver/Operator Professional Qualifications (2017)*.

5.2.4, 5.2.5

Fireground Hydraulic Calculations

Learning Objectives

After reading this chapter, students will be able to:

1. Describe flowmeters and flowmeter applications. (*NFPA 1002, 2014:* 5.2.1, 5.2.2 & *NFPA 1002, 2017:* 5.2.4, 5.2.5)

2. Distinguish between manual and electronic hydraulic calculators. (*NFPA 1002, 2014:* 5.2.1, 5.2.2 & *NFPA 1002, 2017:* 5.2.4, 5.2.5)

3. Describe how pump charts are used in the fire service. (*NFPA 1002, 2014:* 5.2.1, 5.2.2 & *NFPA 1002, 2017:* 5.2.4, 5.2.5)

4. Explain how the Condensed Q formula can be used on the fireground. (*NFPA 1002, 2014:* 5.2.1, 5.2.2 & *NFPA 1002, 2017:* 5.2.4, 5.2.5)

5. Describe the gpm flowing method. (*NFPA 1002, 2014:* 5.2.1, 5.2.2 & *NFPA 1002, 2017:* 5.2.4, 5.2.5)

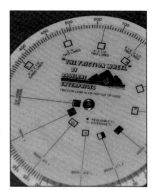

Chapter 8
Fireground Hydraulic Calculations

Case History

In a mid-size city fire department, the driver/operator of the second-arriving engine company was responding to a confirmed fire on the 12th floor of a local apartment building. During the response, the driver/operator began to anticipate his initial actions as the apparatus approached the occupancy.

This jurisdiction featured a few high rises as it was an infrequent task for firefighters to work from a building standpipe system. Most fires were combatted using preconnected handlines with pump discharge pressures that were posted at the pump panel.

Fortunately, the driver/operator and company officer were well versed in the department's equipment, operating policies, and basic hydraulic calculations. The apparatus was placed at a hydrant and the FDC was supplied as per department policy and building preplan. The driver/operator considered the vertical distance to the fire as well as the appliances, hose layout, and type of nozzle issued for high-rise fire attack. Combining knowledge of jurisdictional variables and standard hydraulic calculations, the driver/operator was able to successfully augment the water supply available for fire fighting.

The formulas described in the previous chapter provide the driver/operator with the background necessary to complete many calculations that may be required to determine pressure loss for a wide variety of situations. The dynamic environment of the fireground usually is not conducive to performing lengthy mathematical equations. During emergency operations, driver/operators commonly use one or more of the following methods of determining pressure loss and **pump discharge pressure**:

- Flowmeters
- Hydraulic calculators
- Pump charts
- Condensed Q method
- GPM flowing

Flowmeters

The driver/operator on the fireground must use hydraulic calculations to determine the appropriate amount of water to be discharged from hoselines and nozzles during an incident. **Flowmeters** reduce the number of pressure

Pump Discharge Pressure (PDP) — Actual pressure of the water as it leaves the pump and enters the hoseline; total amount of pressure being discharged by a pump. In mathematical terms, it is the pump intake pressure plus the net pump discharge pressure. Measured in pounds per square inch (kPa).

Flowmeter — Mechanical device installed in a discharge line that senses the amount of water flowing and provides a readout in units of gallons per minute or (liters per minute).

calculations required of the driver/operator. In order to ensure reliability, flowmeters must be maintained in accordance with the manufacturer's recommendations.

Flowmeters measure and display water flow in gallons (liters) per minute. This number requires no further calculation as it reflects the water pressure that will be discharged through the nozzle if the hoseline is functioning at its rated capacity.

The driver/operator's ability to quickly and accurately determine the flow of a particular hoseline in gallons (liters) per minute is especially advantageous when automatic nozzles are employed with handlines or master stream devices. Because handlines or master stream devices maintain a predetermined nozzle pressure and a stream that appears to be adequate, automatic nozzles may lead you to supply insufficient discharge pressures, creating a low gallon (liters) per minute flow. Insufficient discharge pressures are hazardous during fire suppression operations. Use of a flowmeter will make certain that you are aware of the gallon (liters) per minute flow and that you can develop the correct discharge pressure (within operation limits) to achieve the proper rate of flow. The flowmeter relieves you from relying on calculations based on the friction loss, elevation pressure, and length of the hoseline.

Based on the NFPA® 1901 standard, for every discharge outlet equipped with a flowmeter, a pressure gauge shall also be provided. These flowmeters must display flow in increments of 10 gpm (40 L/min) or less.

Types of Flowmeters

Several designs of flowmeters are available that operate by different principles. The two most common to the fire service are:

- **Paddlewheel** — Mounted at the top of a straight section of the discharge pipe so that only a small portion of the device extends into the waterway. This method of placement reduces the impediment to waterflow and lessens the chance of damage from any debris in the pipe. As water moves past the paddlewheel, a sensor measures the speed at which it spins and translates the information into a flow measurement.

- **Spring probe** — Employs a stainless steel spring probe to detect water movement in the discharge piping. The greater the flow, the more the spring is bent. An electrical charge is transmitted from the spring to a display unit for review by the driver/operator. With only one simple moving part, the spring probe design tends to require very little maintenance.

With proper calibration, a flowmeter in good working order should be accurate to a tolerance of plus or minus 3 percent. In other words, based on a flow of 100 gpm (400 L/min), the display should be no more than 3 gallons (12 L) higher or lower than the actual discharge.

Each discharge equipped with a flowmeter must have a digital readout display mounted within 6 inches (150 mm) of the control valve for that discharge **(Figure 8.1)**. If a pressure gauge is mounted at the 6-inch (150 mm) location, then the flowmeter must be mounted within 2 inches (50 mm) adjacent to the pressure gauge. Some apparatus also feature a monitoring device that offers additional information to the driver/operator including:

- The flow through any specific discharge
- The total water flow through the pump in "real time"
- Total water flowed through the pump for the duration of the incident
- The amount of foam being flowed

Flowmeter Applications

The following sections explain applications for flow-meters and their importance for driver/operators. The AHJ may determine when to use each type of flowmeter.

Figure 8.1 A flowmeter and a digital readout display.

Diagnosing Waterflow Problems

The driver/operator may use a flowmeter reading to help identify waterflow issues. For example, a kink or partially closed valve in the hose layout will cause the flowmeter to register a change in the meter's reading. Additionally, a hoseline may have burst if an attack team member sends a message saying that the volume of water at the nozzle has suddenly decreased without a corresponding change at the flowmeter.

Relay Pumping

When engaged in a relay pumping operation, the driver/operator may feed a supply line without having to know the volume of water flowing from the receiving pumper. This operation may be accomplished with the use of a flowmeter and the pumper's master discharge gauge during the initial phase of relay setup. As you increase the throttle, the discharge reading on the flowmeter will rise at a corresponding level. Increase the engine speed until the flowmeter reading no longer increases. This will establish the correct discharge pressure to supply an adequate volume of water to the receiving pumper. Throughout the duration of the incident, monitor the flowmeter as well as the intake pressure gauge. The intake pressure reading cannot be allowed to drop below 20 psi (140 kPa). Additionally, be careful not to overpressurize the next pumper in the relay. Apparatus equipped with electronic pressure governors involved in relay pumping, with the exception of the attack pumper, should operate in revolutions per minute (rpm). Information concerning relay pumping operations may be found in Chapter 12.

Standpipe Operations

The driver/operator may have difficulty determining the exact location of various hoselines, especially during the initial phase of operations in multifloor occupancies equipped with standpipes. When calculating discharge pressures, account for pressure loss due to elevation.

When operating an apparatus equipped with a flowmeter(s), the number and types of nozzles on lines operating from the standpipe may be factored by adding the flow rate for each nozzle together and pumping the volume of water that matches that rate. The driver/operator must monitor the status of each attack team to determine which lines are flowing. When a line is shut down, lower the pressure accordingly or the standpipe system will attempt to flow the excess through the remaining hoselines. Apparatus equipped with electronic pressure governors set in the psi mode should compensate for this shutdown. A pressure governor in the rpm mode will not automatically compensate for the reduced flow.

The driver/operator must consider that even when a standpipe or hoseline is charged, there is no flow through the system or hose layout until you open the nozzle. Rely upon experience, training, and operating guidelines to set pressures that are relatively close to what may be required when water is discharged. After you open the hoseline, finalize the pressure discharge based on the exact conditions.

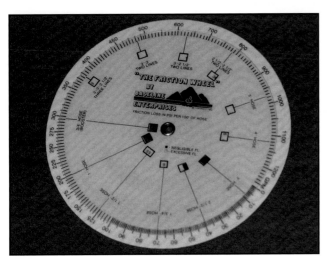

Figure 8.2 A manual friction loss calculator.

Hydraulic Calculators

The driver/operator can use a hydraulic calculator to determine the pump discharge pressure required for virtually any hose layout without relying on mental calculations. Hydraulic calculators may be either manual or electronic. The manual version of the calculator consists of a slide or dial that can be moved to cover or reveal rates of flow, size of hose, and length of hose layout in order to come to a conclusion to a problem **(Figure 8.2)**. Manual calculators are often supplied by fire equipment companies or fire service organizations.

Electronic hydraulic calculators are specially programmed to allow you to input the variables of each hose layout, including the length, diameter of hose, and elevation changes. The calculator then applies preprogrammed formulas to arrive at the pump discharge pressure. These calculators may be handheld devices or permanently affixed to a location near the pump operator's panel.

Pump Charts

Pump Charts — Charts carried on a fire apparatus to aid the pump operator in determining the proper pump discharge pressure when supplying hoselines.

Pump charts are often developed by a fire department and contain information specific to that jurisdiction's equipment and common hose layout operations. The charts specify pump discharge pressure and are often printed on laminated sheets carried on the apparatus or plaques that are mounted to the pump operator's panel. Some pump charts may also be available from equipment manufacturers featuring the specifications of their products.

In order to develop a customized pump chart, members of a fire department should set up a form that clearly identifies the nozzles and devices used by the department as well as any special layouts or applications, such as sprinkler systems, that would be useful to the driver/operator. Column headings that indicate flow, as well as nozzle pressure should be developed, along with distance in feet for hose layouts.

Once the information is gathered, the calculations must be made to determine the appropriate pump discharge pressure for each scenario developed by the fire department. Observe the following guidelines when making the initial calculations:

• Include friction loss for master stream appliances (those flowing in excess of 350 gpm [1 400 L/min].

- Ensure that the length of the wyed hoseline layout is the distance between the pumper and the wye.

- Factor each scenario in cases where a master stream may be supplied by a different number or diameter of hoselines.

- Round pump discharge pressure calculations to the nearest 5 psi (35 kPa).

- Do not let the pump discharge pressures exceed the test pressure for the diameter hose or the pumper involved in the calculation.

- Do not exceed the department's maximum PDP policy if the department has one and the policy maximum varies from the hose manufacturer's max PDP.

- To perform relay pumping calculations, the pump discharge pressure should provide for residual pressure at the intake of the pumper being supplied that is based on jurisdictional policy.

In order to use the chart, the driver/operator must locate the nozzle or the layout in question on the chart, account for the number of feet (meters) in the layout, then plot where each column intersects to find the required pump discharge pressure.

Customary Example

Using **Table 8.1a, p. 286,** determine the pump discharge pressure for a master stream equipped with a 1¾-inch solid stream tip that is supplied by three, 2½-inch hoselines that are 600 feet long.

Solution: Locate the master stream device equipped with a 1¾-inch tip in the appropriate column. Select the option that factors the device being supplied by three, 2½-inch hoselines. Follow the line to the appropriate column for a 600-foot hose lay. The result should indicate the 189 psi entry on the table.

Metric Example

Using **Table 8.1b, p. 286,** determine the pump discharge pressure for a master stream device that is equipped with a 45 mm solid stream nozzle tip and is supplied by three 65 mm hoselines, each 180 meters long.

Solution: Locate the master stream device equipped with a 45 mm nozzle tip in the left column of the chart. Choose the one the shows the device being supplied by three 65 mm lines. Follow this line to the column for a 180 meter hose lay. You should land on the figure 1 317 kPa. This is the required pump discharge pressure.

Table 8.1a (Customary)
Pump Chart

Length of Lay in Feet

Nozzles	GPM	NP	100	200	300	400	500	600	700	800	900	1,000	1,100	1,200
Booster 1"	23	100		115										
Preconnect 1¾"	150	100		170										
Wyed Line:														
200' of 1½" on 2½" skid	190	100	150	157	164	172	179	186	193	201	208	215	222	229
2½" Fog	250	100	112	125	138	150	162	175	187	200	212	225	237	250
Master Stream:														
1¾" (Two 2½" Lines)	800	80	137	169	201	233								
1¾" (Three 2½" Lines)	800	80	119	133	147	161	175	189	203					
1¾" (Two 3" Lines)	800	80	118	131	144	157	170	183	196	209				
Relay:														
One 3" Line	250	20	25	30	35	40	45	50	55	60	65	70	75	80
One 3" Line	500	20	40	60	80	100	120	140	160	180	200			
Two 3" Lines	750	20	31	43	54	65	76	88	99	110	121	133	144	155
Two 3" Lines	1,000	20	100	180										
Sprinklers	Maintain 150 psi													
Elevation	Add ½ psi per foot or 5 psi per floor													

NOTE: All pressures rounded to the nearest whole number for this table only. Computations rounded to the nearest 5 psi are acceptable.

Table 8.1b (Metric)
Pump Chart

Length of Lay in Meters

Nozzles	L/min	NP	30	60	90	120	150	180	210	240	270	300	330	360
Booster 25 mm	90	700		815										
Preconnect 45 mm	570	700		1 180										
Wyed Line:														
60 m of 38 mm on														
65 mm skid	760	700	1 085	1 140	1 195	1 250	1 305	1 360	1 415	1 470	1 525	1 580	1 635	
65 mm Fog	1 000	700	795	890	985	1 080	1 175	1 270	1 365	1 460	1 555	1 650	1 745	
Master Stream:														
45 mm (Two 65 mm Lines)	3 200	560	957	1 179	1 401	1 623	1 845	2 067						
45 mm (Three 65 mm Lines)	3 200	560	832	929	1 026	1 123	1 220	1 317	1 414	1 511	1 608	1 705	1 802	1 899
45 mm (Two 77 mm Lines)	3 200	560	824	913	1 002	1 091	1 180	1 269	1 358	1 447	1 536	1 625	1 714	1 803
Relay:														
One 77 mm Line	1 000	140	178	216	254	292	330	368	406	444	482	520	558	596
One 77 mm Line	2 000	140	292	444	596	748	900	1 052	1 204	1 356	1 508	1 660	1 812	1 964
Two 77 mm Lines	3 000	140	225	310	395	480	565	650	735	820	905	990	1 075	1 160
Two 77 mm Lines	4 000	140	292	444	596	748	900	1 052						
Sprinklers	Maintain 1 050 kPa													
Elevation	Add 10 kPa per meter or 35 kPa per floor													

NOTE: All pressures rounded to nearest whole number for this table only. Computations rounded to the nearest 25 kPa are acceptable.

Condensed Q Formula

The Condensed Q formula may be used for operations in which the friction loss can be determined for 3-, 4-, or 5- inch hose. The following formulas illustrate this method. The formulas cannot be used with metric measurements.

Formula 8.1 – Condensed Q Formula (3-inch hose)

$$FL = Q^2$$

Where:

FL = Friction Loss in pounds per square inch (psi) for 100 feet of 3-inch hose

Q = Flow rate in hundreds of gallons per minute (gpm/100)

This formula may be used for 3-inch hose with 2½- or 3-inch couplings. Although not as accurate as the FL= CQ²L formula, it is a quick, easy-to-use method with decent reliability during many fireground operations.

NOTE: Driver/operators must be aware of the margin of difference when using the Condensed Q formula. Although sufficient for many fireground calculations, the friction loss results will be 20 percent greater than when using the FL= CQ²L formula. In some instances, 20 percent will not amount to a major effect in psi. However, in a hose lay of 1,000 feet of 3-inch hose, the difference may be as great as 50 psi.

The following example illustrates the use of Formula 8.1:

Example 8.1

What is the total loss in pressure due to friction when 200 gpm is being discharged from a nozzle that is connected to 100 feet of 3-inch hose?

$$FL = Q^2$$

$$Q = \frac{gpm}{100} = \frac{200}{100} = 2$$

$$FL = 2^2 = \textbf{4 psi per 100 feet of 3 inch hose}$$

Formula 8.2 – Condensed Q Formula (4-inch hose)

$$FL = \frac{Q^2}{5}$$

Where:

FL = Friction Loss in pounds per square inch (psi) for 100 feet of 4-inch hose

Q = Flow rate in hundreds of gallons per minute (gpm/100)

The following example illustrates the use of Formula 8.2

Example 8.2

What is the total pressure loss in 500 feet of 4-inch hose flowing 1,000 gallons per minute?

$$FL = \frac{Q^2}{5}$$

$$Q = \frac{gpm}{100} = \frac{1000}{100} = 10$$

$FL = \dfrac{\underline{10^2}}{5}$ = **20 psi per 100 feet of 4-inch hose**

TPL = 20 x 5 = **100 psi**

Formula 8.3 – Condensed Q Formula (5-inch hose)

$FL = \dfrac{\mathbf{Q^2}}{\mathbf{15}}$

Where:

FL = Friction Loss in pounds per square inch (psi) for 100 feet of 5-inch hose

Q = Flow rate in hundreds of gallons per minute (gpm/100)

The following example illustrates the use of Formula 8.3:

Example 8.3

Determine the total pressure loss due to friction for an 800-foot layout of 5-inch hose flowing 1,000 gpm.

$FL = \dfrac{\mathbf{Q^2}}{\mathbf{15}}$

$Q = \dfrac{gpm}{100} = \dfrac{1000}{100} = 10$

$FL = \dfrac{\underline{10^2}}{15}$ = **6.67 psi per 100 feet of 5-inch hose**

TPL = 6.67 x 8 = **53.36 psi (app. 50)**

GPM Flowing

The gpm flowing method is applicable to both solid and fog streams and is calculated using flow in gallons per minute. It may be used for various diameter hose, although it is not applicable to the metric system of measurement.

The driver/operator may consult **Table 8.2** noting that the gpm flowing method is not applicable to 2½ inch hoselines flowing less than 160 gpm. Factoring the flow in gallons per minute from the nozzle at a given pressure, you must then subtract 10 from the first two numbers of the gpm flow. A sufficiently accurate estimation of friction loss per 100 feet of 2½-inch hose is obtained. A further review of Table 8.2 reveals that friction loss in 2½-inch hose increases 1 psi for every 10 gpm increase in flow.

Example 8.4

Determine the total pressure loss due to friction in a 400-foot layout of 2½-inch hose using a 250 gpm fog nozzle at 100 psi.

Flow = 250 gpm

FL = 15 psi per 100 feet of 2½-inch hose from Table 8.2

TPL = 15 x 4 = **60 psi in 400 feet of 2½-inch hose**

Table 8.3 shows the friction loss per 100 feet of 1½- or 2½-inch hose. The friction loss in a 1½-inch hose is equal to the friction loss in a 2½-inch hose that is flowing four times as much water. For example, a 1½-inch hose flowing 50 gpm has 10 psi friction loss per 100 feet. The friction loss is equal to a 2½-inch hose flowing 200 gpm.

Table 8.3 is divided into three sections:

- The upper section represents 1½-inch hose flowing 50 to 75 gpm and 2½-inch hose flowing 200 to 300 gpm. In this section, the friction loss increases by 2 psi for every 5 gpm flow increase in 1½-inch hose and for every 20 gpm flow increase in 2½-inch hose.

- The middle section represents 1½-inch hose flowing 80 to 100 gpm and 2½-inch hose flowing 320 to 400 gpm. In this section, the friction loss increases by 3 psi for every 5 gpm flow increase in 1½-inch hose and for every 20 gpm flow increase in 2½-inch hose.

- The lower section represents 1½-inch hose flowing 105 to 125 gpm and 2½-inch hose flowing 420 to 500 gpm. In this section, the friction loss increases by 4 psi for every 5 gpm flow increase in 1½-inch hose and for every 20 gpm flow increase in 2½-inch hose.

Table 8.2 GPM Flowing #1

GPM Flowing 2½" Hose		Friction Loss per 100 ft. 2½" Hose
100		3
110-120		4
130-140		5
150		6
160-170		7
180		8
190	Subtract "10"	9
200	from the first	10
210	two numbers	11
220	of gpm	12
230		13
240		14
250		15
260		16
270		17
280		18
290		19
300		20

Table 8.3 GPM Flowing #2

GPM Flowing 1½" Hose		GPM Flowing 2½" Hose		Friction Loss per 100 ft. 1½" or 2½" Hose
50		200		10
55		220		12
60	Same as	240	For increase of	14
65	4 times as	260	20 gpm flowing	16
70	much water	280	FL increases	18
75	flowing in 2½-inch	300	2 psi	20
80		320		23
85		340		26
90		360	For increase of	29
95		380	20 gpm flowing FL increases	32
100		400	3 psi	35
105		420		39
110		440	For increase of	43
115		460	20 gpm flowing	47
120		480	FL increases	51
125		500	4 psi	55

The following example illustrates the gpm flowing method using 1½-inch hose.

Example 8.5

Determine the total pressure loss due to friction in 200 feet of 1½-inch hose flowing 100 gpm.

Flow = 100 gpm

FL = 35 psi per 100 feet of 1½-inch hose from Table 8.3

TPL = 35 x 2 = **70 psi in 200 feet of 1½-inch hose**

Chapter Summary

The formulas presented for determining pump discharge pressure in Chapters 6 and 7 provide highly accurate results but may be somewhat complex to perform in the dynamic environment of emergency incidents. Driver/operators may employ a variety of other methods to achieve similar results with fewer calculations.

Other options on the fireground include using flowmeters, hydraulic calculators, and pump charts. Simplified calculations that reach results similar to traditional formulas are also available. However, driver/operators must be aware that results of these calculations are not exact answers, and, in some cases, may provide a considerable difference in final pump discharge pressure when used for more complex formulas.

Review Questions

1. What are some benefits of using flowmeters on the fireground? (pp. 281-282)

2. What is the difference between a manual and an electronic hydraulic calculator? (p. 284)

3. What guidelines should be followed when developing a pump chart? (pp. 284-285)

4. What is the Condensed Q Formula? (p. 287)

5. How can the GPM Flowing Method be used on the fireground? (pp. 288-289)

Fire Pump Theory

Chapter Contents

Key Terms

NFPA® Job Performance Requirements

This chapter provides information that addresses the following job performance requirements of NFPA 1002, *Standard for Fire Apparatus Driver/Operator Professional Qualifications (2014)*.

5.2.1, 5.2.2

NFPA 1002, *Standard for Fire Apparatus Driver/Operator Professional Qualifications (2017)*.

5.2.4, 5.2.5

Fire Pump Theory

Learning Objectives

After reading this chapter, students will be able to:

1. Distinguish among types of positive displacement pumps. (*NFPA 1002, 2014:* 5.2.1, 5.2.2 & *NFPA 1002, 2017:* 5.2.4, 5.2.5)

2. Summarize facts about the operation of centrifugal pumps. (*NFPA 1002, 2014:* 5.2.1, 5.2.2 & *NFPA 1002, 2017:* 5.2.4, 5.2.5)

3. Distinguish among various pump mounting and drive arrangements. (*NFPA 1002, 2014:* 5.2.1, 5.2.2 & *NFPA 1002, 2017:* 5.2.4, 5.2.5)

4. Describe intake and discharge piping. (*NFPA 1002, 2014:* 5.2.1, 5.2.2 & *NFPA 1002, 2017:* 5.2.4, 5.2.5)

5. Summarize facts about valves used in a piping system. (*NFPA 1002, 2014:* 5.2.1, 5.2.2 & *NFPA 1002, 2017:* 5.2.4, 5.2.5)

6. Explain the operation of automatic pressure control devices. (*NFPA 1002, 2014:* 5.2.1, 5.2.2 & *NFPA 1002, 2017:* 5.2.4, 5.2.5)

7. Summarize facts about priming methods and devices. (*NFPA 1002, 2014:* 5.2.1, 5.2.2 & *NFPA 1002, 2017:* 5.2.4, 5.2.5)

8. Identify characteristics of pump panel instrumentation. (*NFPA 1002, 2014:* 5.2.1, 5.2.2 & *NFPA 1002, 2017:* 5.2.4, 5.2.5)

9. Describe types of auxiliary cooling devices. (*NFPA 1002, 2014:* 5.2.1, 5.2.2 & *NFPA 1002, 2017:* 5.2.4, 5.2.5)

Chapter 9
Fire Pump Theory

Case History

While testing new 5-inch (125 mm) LDH pressurized by a pumper, two firefighters walked the length of the hose lay checking for leaks in the hose or at a coupling. After being under pressure for approximately 3 minutes, the hose catastrophically came off the coupling. The firefighters inspecting the hose were approximately 30 feet (9 m) from the burst and reported that the loose end of the hose came approximately 6 feet (2 m) off the ground. The defective hose landed about 40 feet (12 m) from its original position.

Fortunately, no one was injured during this incident. However, driver/operators must be aware of the pressure involved in pumping operations and the potential for injury to personnel and damage to equipment and property should a component fail. Full PPE must be worn during operations and nonessential personnel and civilians must be kept at a safe distance.

Source: *www.firefighterclosecalls.com / news/ full story/ newsid/30043/layout/no*

Some high pressure water systems serve industrial complexes or other specialized locations that may provide a sufficient volume of water at adequate pressure for fire fighting purposes without needing additional pumping. However, except for a few well developed municipal water systems, it is necessary to increase the existing pressure with fire department pumpers in order to maintain pressure sufficient for fire fighting operations. Fire department pumpers are also needed to supply attack hoselines using water from the apparatus water tank or other static sources such as portable tanks, lakes, or ponds.

Early pumps used by the fire service were hand-operated piston pumps. To supply water under pressure, a handle was pumped operating a piston in a cylinder, forcing water out of the pump. Rotary pumps followed, using a hand crank to rotate a gear, forcing water through the pump and hoses. Single and double action piston pumps of various diameters and strokes replaced rotary pumps. These types of pumps are referred to as **positive displacement pumps**. Positive displacement pumps are self-priming, deliver a definite volume of water or air, and exhaust air from the pump and deliver water. These pumps are "constant flow machines" in that they produce the same flow at a given speed regardless of discharge pressure. All the air and water are forced out of the pump with each operating cycle. Modern fire apparatus continue to have a form of positive pressure pump (priming pump) connected to the main fire pump in order to allow the apparatus to use static water sources.

Positive Displacement Pump — Self-priming pump that utilizes a piston or interlocking rotors to move a given amount of fluid through the pump chamber with each stroke of the piston or rotation of the rotors. Used for hydraulic pumps on aerial devices' hydraulic systems and for priming pumps on centrifugal fire pumps.

Modern fire department pumpers are equipped with centrifugal pumps as their main pump. This type of pump does not use positive action to force water from the pump; rather, it depends on the velocity of the water produced by centrifugal force to provide the pressure needed to achieve proper discharge pressure.

The following chapter outlines the basic concepts surrounding various types of pumps and their operation. The components that comprise the overall apparatus pumping system are also contained in this chapter. Specific information detailing the operation of a fire pump is detailed in a subsequent chapter, as are the particulars of foam extinguishing systems.

Positive Displacement Pumps

Although the positive displacement pump has been replaced by the centrifugal pump as the main pumping unit on fire apparatus, positive displacement pumps continue to serve a vital role on modern apparatus because of their ability to pump air and foam. In this capacity, they are used as priming devices to get water into the centrifugal pump during drafting operations. By removing air trapped in the centrifugal pump, water is forced into the pump by atmospheric pressure.

Piston Pumps

Piston Pump — Positive-displacement pump using one or more reciprocating pistons to force water from the pump chambers.

Piston pumps operate using a piston that moves back and forth in a cylinder **(Figure 9.1)**. The pressure developed by this action causes intake and discharge valves to operate and causes the movement of air, water, and foam. Although no longer used as high-capacity pumps, some are still in service for high pressure stream fire fighting. These multicylinder, PTO-driven pumps can provide pressures up to 1,000 psi (7 000 kPa) for high-pressure fog lines, or to inject foam concentrate into a water line or manifold at a higher pressure than the water pump is creating.

Rotary Pumps

From the standpoint of design, rotary-type pumps are the simplest of all fire apparatus pumps. In modern apparatus, the use of rotary pumps is confined to small capacity, booster-type pumps; low volume, high-pressure pumps; and priming pumps. Most of the rotary pumps in use today are either rotary-gear or rotary-vane construction. These pumps are driven by either a small electric motor or through a clutch that extends from the apparatus drive shaft.

Rotary Gear Pumps

Rotary gear pumps consist of two gears that rotate in a tightly meshed pattern inside a watertight case **(Figure 9.2)**. The gears are constructed so that they contact each other and are in close proximity to the case. The gears form watertight and airtight pockets as they turn from the intake to the outlet. As each gear tooth reaches the discharge chamber the air or water contained in that pocket is forced out of the pump. As the tooth returns to the intake side of the pump, the gears are meshed tightly enough to prevent the water or air that has been discharged from returning to the intake.

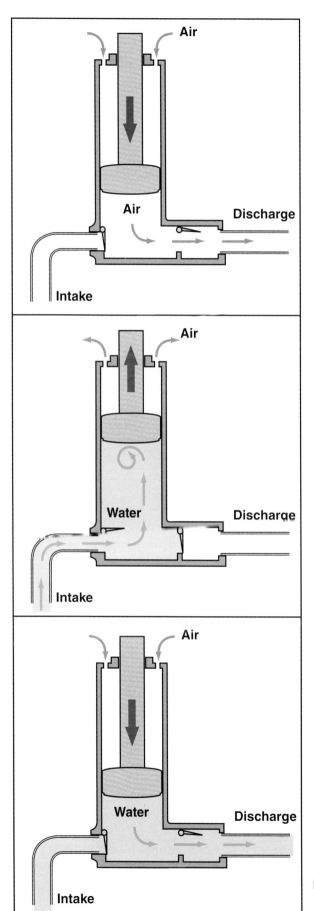

The total amount of water that can be pumped by a rotary gear pump depends on the size of the pockets in the gears and the speed of rotation. The rotary gear pump is a positive displacement pump because each pocket in the gears contains a definite amount of water, which is forced out of the pump each time the gears turn with a positive action. If the pump tries to move more water than the discharge lines can take away, pressure builds up. A pressure relief device must be provided to handle excess pressure.

Like piston pumps, the rotary gear pump is susceptible to damage from normal wear and tear, as well as from pumping water laden with sand or other debris. To prevent damage to the casings, most gear pumps feature gears made of bronze or another soft metal, while a strong alloy such as cast iron is used for the pump casing.

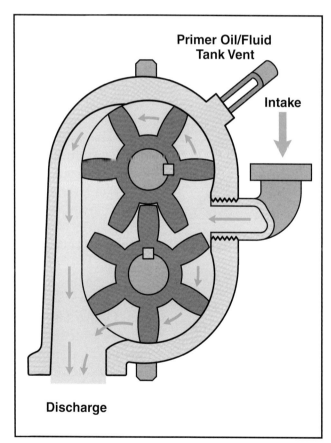

Figure 9.2 A rotary gear pump.

Figure 9.1 A piston pump.

Rotary Vane Pumps

Rotary vane pumps are constructed with moveable elements that automatically compensate for wear, maintaining a tighter fit with closer clearances as the pump is used. This is one of the most common types of pumps used to prime a centrifugal fire pump.

In a rotary vane pump, the rotor is mounted off center inside the housing. The distance between the rotor and the housing is much greater at the intake than at the discharge. The vanes are free to move within the slot where they are mounted. As the rotor turns, the vanes are forced against the housing by centrifugal force. When the surface of the vane that is in contact with the casing becomes worn, centrifugal force causes it to extend further, causing it to maintain a tight fit. This self-adjusting feature makes the rotary vane pump much more efficient at pumping air than a rotary gear pump.

As the rotor turns, air is trapped between the rotor and the casing in the pockets formed by adjacent vanes. As the vanes turn, this pocket becomes smaller, which compresses the air and causes pressure to build up. This pocket becomes even smaller as the vanes progress toward the discharge opening. At this point the pressure reaches its maximum level, forcing the trapped air out of the pump. The air or water is prevented from returning to the intake by the close spacing of the rotor at that

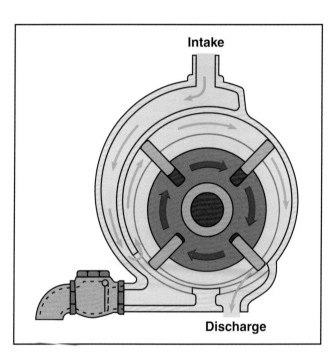

Figure 9.3 A typical rotary vane pump.

point **(Figure 9.3)**. As in the rotary gear pump, the air being evacuated from the intake side reduces pressure, creating a vacuum. This forces water into the pump by atmospheric pressure until it fills with water. At this point, the pump is primed and forces water out of the discharge in the same manner as air was forced out.

NOTE: Rotary pumps are prone to failure if not exercised regularly. These pumps should be operated during routine apparatus checks.

Centrifugal Pumps

Nearly all modern fire apparatus feature a **centrifugal pump** as their main pump. This pump is classified as a nonpositive displacement pump as it does not pump a definite amount of water with each revolution. The pump imparts velocity to the water and converts it to pressure within the pump itself.

Principles of Operation and Constructic

The operation of a centrifugal pump is based c
revolving disk tends to throw water introduced
edges of the disk **(Figure 9.4)**. The **impeller** acts
through the **eye** in its center. This water is thr
the outside edge of the pump housing. The spe
amount of pressure that is developed. The faste
the water is thrown, giving the water more velo
at the edge of the disk, the water at the center o
outward, toward the path of least resistance. T
verted to pressure by confining the water withi
which the water rises, or the extent to which it
is based on the speed of the impeller's rotation

NOTE: In order to develop the revolutions p
full use of the pump, the transmission must be p
on the manufacturer's recommendation.

A centrifugal pump contains an impeller
shaft, and seals. The impeller transmits energ
water. The pump casing houses the impeller
and confines it in order to convert the velocity to pressure. Then, the casing
directs the water to the discharge opening of the pump. The speed at which
the impeller rotates is a ratio based upon the power train configuration.
Water is introduced from the intake into the eye of the impeller. The volume
capacity of the pump is dictated by the size of the impeller. A larger impeller has a larger eye, allowing greater flow capacity. As the water comes into
contact with the vanes of the impeller, it is thrown by centrifugal force to the
outside of the impeller. This water is confined in its travel by the shrouds of
the impeller, which increase the velocity for a given speed of rotation. The
off-center mounting of the impeller within the casing creates a water passage
of gradually increasing size as it nears the discharge outlet of the pump. This
section of the pump is called the **volute**.

The increasing size of the volute is necessary because the volume of water
passing through it increases as it nears the discharge outlet. This gradual

Volute — Spiral, divergent chamber of a centrifugal pump in which the velocity energy given to water by the impeller blades is converted into pressure.

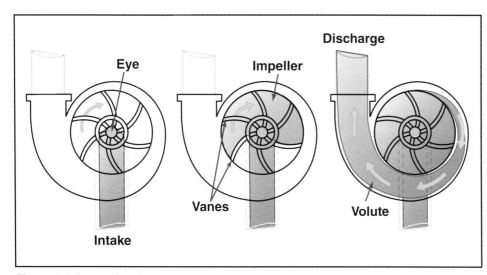

Figure 9.4 A centrifugal pump.

reduces the velocity of the water, enabling the pressure [to build up] proportionately. Three main factors influence a centrifugal fire [disch]arge pressure:

- [Amou]nt of water being discharged — If the discharge outlet is large [eno]ugh in diameter to allow the water to escape as it is thrown from the [im]peller and collected in the volute, the pressure buildup will be very small. If the discharge outlet is closed, a high pressure buildup will result. With all other factors remaining constant, the amount of output pressure that a pump may develop is directly dependent on the volume of water it is discharging. Thus the discharge volume affects both the intake and discharge pressures.

- **Speed at which the impeller is turning** — Greater pressure is developed with increased impeller speed. The increase in pressure is roughly equal to the square of the change in impeller speed. For example, with all other factors remaining constant, doubling the speed of the impeller will result in four times as much pressure.

- **Pressure of water when it enters the pump from a pressurized source (hydrant, relay, etc.)** — Water will flow through a centrifugal pump even if the impeller is not turning. When water is supplied to the eye of the impeller under pressure, it moves through the impeller by itself. Any movement of the impeller increases both the velocity and the corresponding pressure buildup of the water in the volute. Because the incoming pressure adds directly to the pressure developed by the pump, incoming pressure changes are reflected in the discharge pressure.

A centrifugal pump is unable to pump air and is not self-priming. There are several ways to prime a centrifugal pump to draft water from a static source. An external priming pump may be used to remove the air and allow atmospheric pressure to force water into the pump. As previously discussed, the Rotary Vane pump is typically used for this purpose. Another way to achieve priming is the use of a device that employs air from the apparatus braking system to power a Venturi device that removes air from the suction side of the pump.

NOTE: Another option involves the use of a foot valve attached to the suction hose strainer.

Two basic types of centrifugal pumps are used by the fire service: single stage and multistage. There is a phenomenon of cavitation due to recirculation in single-stage pumps, where excess capacity is not allowed to escape the impeller area. This may lead to pump damage.

Single-Stage Centrifugal Fire Pumps

Pumps used in the fire service constructed with a single impeller are referred to as *single-stage centrifugal pumps* (**Figure 9.5**). These may consist of front-mount pumps, power take off, auxiliary engine driven, and midship pumps that use a single intake impeller and a simple casing to provide flow capacities up to 2,250 gpm (9 000 L/min) (**Figure 9.6**).

High-capacity pumps require large impellers with waterways that present a minimum amount of opposition to the movement of water. Newton's Third Law of Physics states that for every action there is an equal and opposite reac-

Figure 9.5 A single-stage centrifugal pump is constructed with a single impeller.

Figure 9.6 A typical single-stage pump casing.

tion. The water in motion in the pump creates stress on the pump, its bearings, and other moving parts, as well as the casing mounted to the truck frame.

To minimize the lateral thrust of large quantities of water entering the eye of the impeller, a double-suction impeller may be used. The double-suction impeller takes water in from both sides; the reaction of each side being equal and opposite cancels out the lateral thrust. It also provides a larger waterway for movement of water through the impeller. Because the impeller turns at a high rate of speed, a radial thrust is developed as the water is delivered to the discharge outlet. Stripping edges in the opposed discharge volutes divert the water into two streams that are 180 degrees apart. Water being removed at two places and traveling in opposite directions cancels the radial thrust. This design provides a hydraulically balanced pump that reduces stress on the pump and vehicle chassis, helping to lengthen the service life of the pump and apparatus.

Multistage Centrifugal Fire Pumps

Multistage centrifugal pumps have an impeller for each stage mounted in a single housing. The impellers are usually mounted on a single shaft driven by a single drive train. Generally, the impellers are identical and have the same capacity. The feature that makes multistage pumps more efficient is the capability to connect the stages in series for maximum pressure or in parallel for maximum volume by use of a transfer valve.

Pumping in the parallel (volume) position. When the pump transfer valve is in the volume position, each of the impellers takes water from a source and delivers it to the discharge **(Figure 9.7)**. Each of the impellers is capable of delivering its rated pressure while flowing 50 percent of its rated capacity; therefore, the total amount of water the pump can deliver is equal to the sum of the stages. If a two-stage pump is rated at 1,000

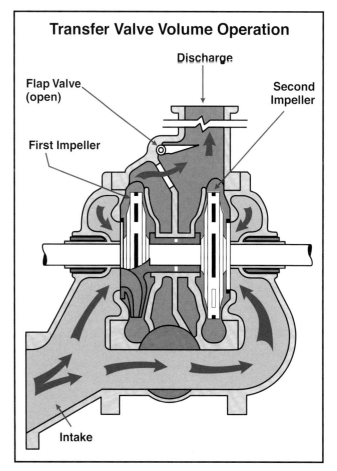

Figure 9.7 Pumping in the parallel (volume) position.

gpm (4 000 L/min) at 150 psi (1 050 kPa), each of the impellers supplies 500 gpm (2 000 L/min) to the pump discharge manifold. At that point, the two streams combine to create 1,000 gpm (4 000 L/min) available to the discharges at a net pressure of 150 psi (1 050 kPa). The driver/operator must know that although the pump receives its maximum flow rating at 150 psi (1 050 kPa), the volume of the pump may increase with the capability of the source.

Pumping in series (pressure) position. When the transfer valve is set in the pressure position, all water from the intake manifold is directed into the eye of the first impeller. Depending on the specific pump, the first stage increases the pressure and discharges 50 to 70 percent of the volume capacity through the transfer valve and into the eye of the second impeller. In a two-stage pump, the second impeller increases the pressure and delivers the water at a higher pressure into the discharge port. Setting the transfer valve to series (pressure) greatly increases the maximum pressure that may be attained; however, increasing the pressure results in a corresponding loss in volume. Setting the transfer valve to series (pressure) results in a much higher pressure than would be achieved in parallel operation. This is because the same stream of water has passed through two impellers with each boosting the pressure **(Figure 9.8)**. With only one impeller delivering the water to the pump discharge port, the volume of water available while operating in pressure position is limited to the amount that one impeller can supply.

Fire pump manufacturers have specific recommendations for when the transfer valve on their pumps should be operated in the volume or pressure positions **(Figure 9.9)**. The process of switching between pressure and volume is sometimes referred to as "changeover." Due to the improved efficiency of modern fire pumps, local jurisdictions should establish policy for switching between pressure and volume based on the manufacturer's recommendation for specific pumps.

NOTE: Driver/operators should consult the manufacturer's recommendation for the flow rate at which transfer should occur on the specific pump they are operating.

When the transfer valve is operated on a two-stage pump, sudden changes in pressure can occur as the water in the pump changes its direction of flow. Switching from volume to pressure can result in the immediate doubling of the previous discharge pressure. This change may result in damage to the pump and hoselines as well as injury to firefighters. The maximum net pump discharge pressure at which the transfer valve may be safely operated varies by manufacturer and age of the pump. The driver/operator should consult the manufacturer's recommendation for the correct maximum transfer

CAUTION

Switching from volume to pressure can result in the immediate doubling of the previous discharge pressure. This change may result in damage to the pump and hoselines as well as injury to firefighters.

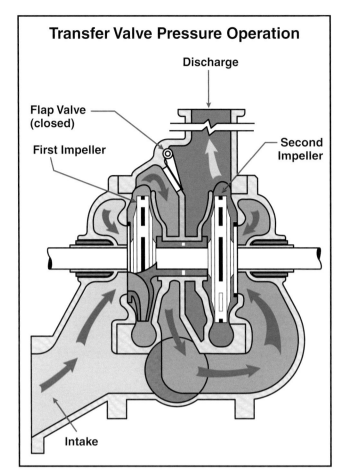

Transfer Valve Pressure Operation

Discharge

Flap Valve (closed)

First Impeller

Second Impeller

Intake

Figure 9.8 Pumping in series (pressure) position.

Figure 9.9 Pump operators use a transfer valve to switch between volume and pressure pumping operations.

pressure. Any changeover on the fireground must be carefully coordinated with attack crews so that they will be prepared for a slight interruption during the transfer.

The driver/operator must size up the incident in an attempt to anticipate the demands that may be placed on the pumper as the fire fighting operation progresses. If there is any question as to the correct position for the transfer valve, it is best to operate in parallel (volume) rather than series (pressure). In the parallel mode, the pump will be capable of supplying 100 percent of its rated capacity at 150 psi (1 050 kPa) at 10 feet (3 m) of lift with 20 feet (6 m) of suction hose while drafting.

Operation of the transfer valve is performed manually on many older two-stage pumps. These pumps feature a safeguard making it physically impossible to accomplish the transfer while pumping at a high pressure. Newer pumps use a power-operated transfer valve. This valve may be activated by electricity, air pressure, or by the water pressure itself. Many power-operated transfer valves operate at pressures as high as 200 psi (1 400 kPa). Exposure to pressures in this range poses a threat to equipment and personnel. Driver/operators must use care with these controls and be familiar with manual override features should the power equipment fail.

Clapper Valve — Hinged valve that permits the flow of water in one direction only.

Check Valve — Automatic valve that permits liquid to flow in only one direction. For example, the inline valve that prevents water from flowing into a foam concentrate container when eduction pressure is disrupted.

Clapper (check) valves are essential to the operation of a multistage pump **(Figure 9.10)**. Should a valve stick open or closed, or be hampered by debris, the pump will not operate properly in series (pressure). When the transfer valve is operated, water allowed to escape back into the intake will churn through the pump instead of building up pressure. The operation of the clapper valve may be checked by removing the strainer from a large intake opening and reaching into the pump with a long wooden dowel, or similar type of rod. The clapper valve must be able to swing freely.

Some fire pumps have been constructed using up to four impellers connected in series to develop pressures up to 1,000 psi (7 000 kPa) for high pressure fog fire fighting operations. Another method to increase pressure involves using a single-stage high-pressure centrifugal pump mounted outboard in conjunction with a conventional two-stage pump with a separate drive system. When pressures higher than 250 psi (1 750 kPa) are needed, the separate third stage is engaged and used to increase the pressure from the second stage. These types of pumps are usually found in cities with a large number of high rise buildings. The increased pressure capabilities allow fire department pumpers to supply sprinklers and standpipes on the upper floors of very tall high rises. These pumpers must be equipped with hose and adapters that are rated for use at these pressures.

Pump Wear Rings and Packing

Although there is no positive mechanical isolation of the discharge area of the pump from the intake in the impeller, the velocity of the water moving through the impeller prevents most of the water in the discharge from escaping back into the intake. The pressure in the volute is much higher than that in the intake side of the pump at the eye of the impeller. A very close tolerance must be maintained between the pump casing and the hub of the impeller. This opening is usually limited to .01 inch (0.25 mm) or less. Any increase in the opening lessens the effectiveness of the pump.

Some amount of sediment and dirt is found in all water supplies. As these impurities pass through the pump, they cause wear on the impeller as it turns at speeds of nearly 4,000 rpm when the pump approaches its capacity. Particles of sand passing between the impeller and pump casing act like an abrasive and wear down the metal surfaces. As gaps increase, greater amounts of water are allowed to slip back into the intake and are not available at the discharge. Eventually, the pump is no longer able to pump at its rated capacity. An initial indication of wear may occur during pump tests when increased engine rpm is required to pump at the rated capacity.

Wear Rings — Replaceable rings that are attached to the impeller and/or the pump casing to allow a small running clearance between the impeller and pump casing without causing wear of the actual impeller or pump casing material.

To restore the pumping capacity without replacing the entire pump, **wear rings** or clearance rings in the pump casing may be replaced to maintain the preferred spacing between the hub of the impeller and the pump casing. If the hub of the impeller is also worn down, it is possible to replace wear rings to maintain proper clearance.

Unlike the positive displacement pump, no harm results from shutting off all the pump discharges for short periods of time in a centrifugal pump. When discharges are closed, the energy being supplied to the impeller is dissipated in the form of heat as water within the pump is allowed to churn. If this situation continues for a long period of time, the water in the pump may become

Parallel or Volume Mode

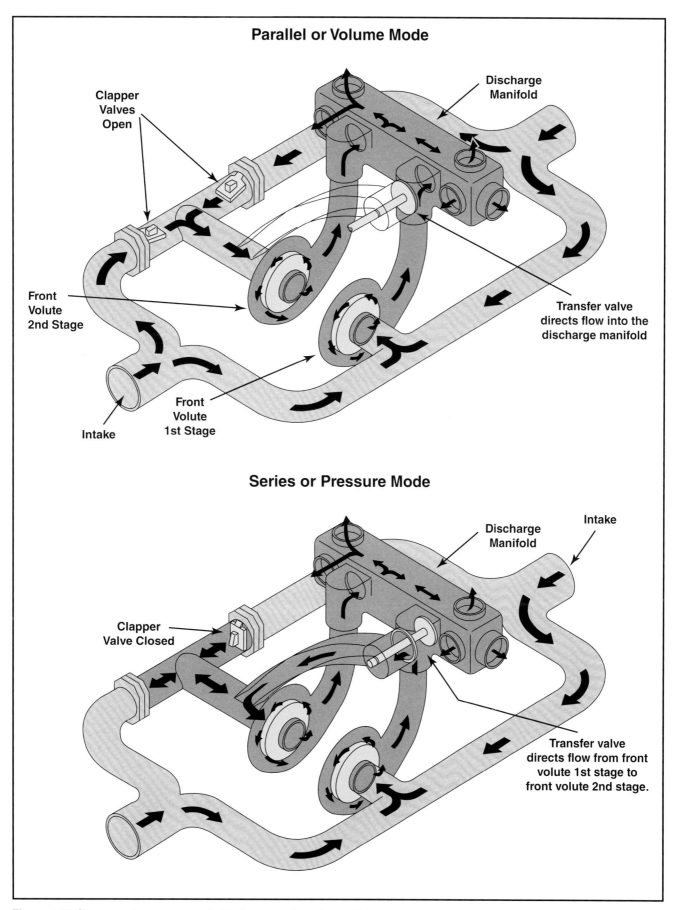

Clapper Valves Open

Discharge Manifold

Front Volute 2nd Stage

Front Volute 1st Stage

Intake

Transfer valve directs flow into the discharge manifold

Series or Pressure Mode

Discharge Manifold

Intake

Clapper Valve Closed

Transfer valve directs flow from front volute 1st stage to front volute 2nd stage.

Figure 9.10 Clapper valves are essential to the operation of a multistage pump.

quite hot and the metal parts of the pump may expand. If the wear rings and impellers expand too much, they may come in contact with each other and the friction of the two surfaces rubbing will create additional heat and may result in serious damage to the pump. In extreme cases, wear rings may seize causing serious pump damage.

Newer model centrifugal pumps may be equipped with a thermal relief valve that opens to allow overheated water to circulate between the pump and the main water tank or into the atmosphere. When operating a pump not equipped with a thermal relief valve, the best course of action to prevent overheating is to ensure that some water is moving through the pump at all times. The driver/operator can check for excessive pump temperature manually by placing a hand on the direct pump intake pipe. If it is warm to the touch, the driver/operator should open a discharge, tank fill, or circulator valve. If water is not expected to be discharged for an extended period of time, the pump should be throttled down to idle and disengaged.

Pump impellers are fastened to a shaft that connects to a transfer case. The transmission transfers the required energy to spin the impellers at a very high rate of speed. At the point where the shaft passes through the pump casing, a semi-tight seal must be maintained to prevent air leaks that may interfere with the pump's ability to conduct a drafting operation. Mechanical seals are the most common type in use today. They form a tight seal without dripping and do not require a periodic adjustment. It is, however, important to operate the pump regularly to lubricate the seals. Mechanical seals should not be allowed to freeze in cold weather. Damage may be incurred, requiring the disassembly of the entire pump and drive assembly in order to replace the seals. These seals must not be allowed to run waterless for any length of time as they will overheat and become damaged. The most common type of seal packing material is composed of rope fibers impregnated with graphite or lead. This material is pushed into a stuffing box by a packing gland driven by a packing adjustment mechanism. Some centrifugal fire pumps are equipped with ceramic or mechanical seals that are not adjustable.

Packing rings are primarily used in older fire pumps. As packing rings wear with the operation of the shaft, the packing gland can be tightened in order to control any leaks and allow the pump to draft. Heat develops by friction where the packing rings come into contact with the shaft. In order to overcome this, a spacer, known as a *lantern* or *slinger ring* is supplied with the packing to provide cooling. A small amount of water leaks out around the packing and prevents the buildup of excessive amounts of heat that may score the shaft.

If the packing is too loose, an excessive amount of water may leak from the pump during operation. Additionally, the pump may not be sealed sufficiently to draft from a static water source. The adjustment of packing must be made according to manufacturer's recommendations. However, generally when a pump is operating under pressure, water should drip at a rate specified by the pump manufacturer from the packing glands, but not run as a steady stream.

The packing only receives water for lubrication if the pump is full and operating under pressure. Most manufacturers recommend the pump to be drained between fire calls, especially in cold weather conditions. If the pump is not used for extended periods of time, the packing may dry out, causing excessive leaking. After a period of dryness, adjustment to the packing should be made only after the pump has operated under pressure and the packing has had a chance to seal properly.

CAUTION
If a pump is operated dry for any length of time, damage to the shaft may result. Any weakening may cause failure during future use.

Ceramic pump seals may also be available for use in certain pumps. This material offers superior resistance to warping, stretching, and corrosion.

Pump Mounting and Drive Arrangements

Fire department pumps are available with many different pump drive systems. When determining which pump would work best for the needs of a local fire department, factors include the intended use of the pump and its cost, appearance, space requirements, and ease of maintenance.

Auxiliary Engine Driven Pumps

Pumps powered by gasoline or diesel engines independent of the vehicle-drive engine are examples of auxiliary pumps. Some manufacturers have models that are powered by special fuels such as jet fuel for military or other special applications. Although used on some structural fire fighting pumpers, the most common applications for auxiliary engine driven pumps are:

- Airport rescue fire fighting (ARFF) vehicles
- Wildland fire apparatus
- Mobile water supply apparatus **(Figure 9.11)**
- Trailer mounted fire pumps
- Portable fire pumps

In some cases, these pumps may be part of a skid-mount assembly that includes a small water tank, booster reel, and small diameter attack lines. With a pumping capacity of generally 500 gpm (2 000 L/min) or less, some jurisdictions mount these assemblies on pickup trucks.

Figure 9.11 A mobile water supply apparatus. *Courtesy of Ron Jeffers.*

Power Take-Off (PTO) Drive

In this arrangement, the pump is driven by a driveshaft connected to the **power take-off (PTO)** **(Figure 9.12, p. 308)**. PTO driven fire pumps are most common to initial attack, wildland, or mobile water supply applications. In recent years, they are becoming widely used on structural apparatus pumpers.

Some manufacturers offer a rear-engine PTO design that is driven off the engine's flywheel. This type of system has been used with much success in the construction and refuse industries for many years. In addition to offering

Power Take-Off (PTO) System — Mechanism that allows a vehicle engine to power equipment such as a pump, winch, or portable tool; it is typically attached to the transmission.

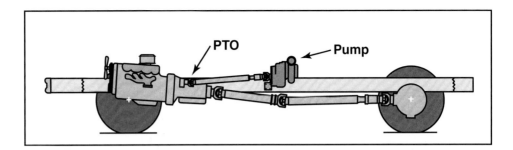

Figure 9.12 In this illustration, the pump is driven by a driveshaft connected to the power take-off (PTO).

Pump and Roll — Ability of an apparatus to pump water while the vehicle is in motion.

the versatility of **pump and roll** capability, the mounting of the pump offers an opportunity for a shorter wheelbase, additional room for compartments, as well as cross lays that are packed lower on the apparatus body where they are more accessible.

Proper mounting of these pumps is essential for dependable and smooth operation. The pump gear case must be mounted in a location that allows for a minimum of angles in the driveshaft. Additionally, it must not extend too far below the chassis or it may be damaged during driving.

The PTO unit is powered by an idler gear in the vehicle's transmission. The speed of the shaft is independent of the gear in which the road transmission is operating when the pump is in use but is under the control of the clutch. When the driver/operator disengages the clutch to stop or to change gears, the pump also stops turning. The PTO pump does permit pump and roll operation, but it is not as effective as the separate engine unit.

The pressure developed is determined by the speed of the engine; therefore, the pressure changes when the driver/operator changes the vehicle's speed. If the apparatus is used for pump and roll operations, mount a pressure gauge inside the cab of the vehicle. While hoselines are in operation, drive the vehicle using the pressure gauge rather than the speedometer. Generally using the lowest gear makes maintaining the balance between speed and pressure easiest. The driver/operator must always be cautious not to drive too fast for weather and scene conditions.

In the past, conventional PTO units were limited to powering pumps up to approximately 500 gpm (2 000 L/min). However, some manufacturers now provide full torque power take-offs that allow for the installation of pumps as large as 1,250 gpm (5 000 L/min). This type of PTO is commonly used with automatic transmissions where the flywheel of the engine drives the PTO unit. Apparatus must be equipped with properly rated engines, drive shafts, and PTO systems in order to provide the necessary power to operate the pump at capacity. Horsepower requirements of the vehicle must include accessories, such as warning lights, air compressor, and the vehicle's air conditioning system, that may be operated during pumping operations.

Front-Mount Pumps

Some fire department pumpers feature an extended front bumper with a pump mounted between the bumper and the grill of the vehicle **(Figure 9.13)**. This unit is typically driven through a gear box and a clutch connected by a drive shaft to the front of the crankshaft. The gear box uses a step up gear ratio, which causes the impeller of the pump to turn faster than the engine. This ratio is set to match the torque of the engine to the rotation speed required for the impeller to deliver the pump's rated capacity. The maximum capacity of the pump depends on the limitations of the engine driving it, typically up to 1,250 gpm (5 000 L/min). To use a **front-mount pump**, the chassis should have a front of engine PTO option that provides a coupling to the front of the crankshaft. The specifications of the pump and drive shaft must always be matched to the power source.

Front-Mount Pump — Fire pump mounted in front of the radiator of a vehicle and powered off the crankshaft.

One major disadvantage of the front-mount pump is the susceptibility of the pump and gauges freezing in cold weather due to their exposed position. The likelihood of freezing may be lessened through the use of external lines that circulate radiator fluid through the pump body. While driving the vehicle, a cover may be used to protect the pump, reducing the exposure to freezing weather conditions. During warm weather operations, front-mount pumps may obstruct airflow through the vehicles radiator and may contribute to overheating. In addition to these disadvantages, front-mount pumps must be installed with proper protection against damage from a front-end collision. Their position makes them vulnerable to damage from even a minor impact.

Most front-mount pumps are engaged and operated from the pump location in front of the apparatus. This may put the driver/operator in a vulnerable position directly in front of the vehicle. It is essential that a lock be provided to prevent the road transmission from being engaged while the pump is operating. Because the operating lever that engages the pump is usually located at the pump, a warning light in the cab should be provided to alert the driver that the pump is engaged. The pump may be severely damaged if the vehicle is driven with the pump engaged and without water being discharged.

Midship Pumps

Most fire departments operate pumpers that feature the pump mounted laterally across the frame behind the engine and transmission **(Figure 9.14)**. Power is supplied to the pump through the use of a split shaft gear case (transfer case) located in the drive line between the transmission and the rear axle. By shifting a gear and collar arrangement inside the gear box, power can be diverted from the rear axle and transmitted to the fire pump. The pump is then actually driven by either a series of gears or a drive chain or belt.

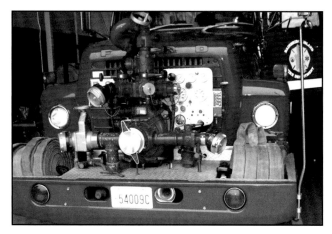

Figure 9.13 An apparatus with a front-mounted pump.

Figure 9.14 A midship mounted pump.

The gear ratio is set to match the engine torque curve to the speed of the rotation required for the impeller to deliver the rated capacity of the pump. This ratio is arranged so that the impeller turns faster than the engine, usually one and a half (1½) to two and a half (2½) times as fast. The maximum capacity that can be obtained by this system is limited only by the engine horsepower and the size of the pump. Most fire pumps can be configured to operate over a range of capacities determined by the piping arrangement and gear ratio used in the apparatus. Some pumps can be rated anywhere from 500 to 2,250 gpm (2 000 L/min to 9 000 L/min) with no major changes to the pump itself.

The usual arrangement provides control of the transfer case from inside the apparatus cab by using a mechanical linkage or by electrical, hydraulic, or air-operated controls. If so equipped, the driver/operator should engage the pump and put the road transmission in the proper gear (based on the manufacturer's instructions) before leaving the cab. If the road transmission is not placed in the correct gear, the pump will not turn at the needed rpm to operate effectively. When the driver/operator places the transmission in the correct gear, a lockout feature engages, preventing the transmission from switching gears as rpms are raised or lowered.

NOTE: The driver/operator should know how to manually shift the pump into gear in the event of a malfunction with the transfer case.

With the transmission turning, many apparatus register the engine speed in miles per hour (km/h) on the speedometer when the pump is operating. The driver/operator may check to see that the transmission is in the correct gear by observing the speedometer reading after the pump is engaged. With the engine idling and the pump engaged, most speedometers will indicate between 10 to 15 mph (15 to 25 km/h). However, there are some apparatus that are designed so that the speedometer does not register above 0 mph (0 km/h) including all PTO pumps when the pump is engaged. Driver/operators must be fully aware of the specific operation of the pumper to which they are assigned. Chapter 10 of this manual offers additional information on proper pumping procedures.

Some power transfer arrangements are provided with a manual override in case of difficulty with the power unit. Driver/operators should practice and become proficient with this manual override, if so equipped, so they will be prepared in case the primary system fails in an emergency **(Figure 9.15)**.

Because engaging the pump involves transferring the power from the rear axle to the pump drive gears, it is not possible to transmit power to the rear axle while the pump is engaged. This eliminated the possibility of pump and roll operation with a conventional gearing arrangement.

To prevent an automatic transmission gear selector from moving during a pumping operation or a manual transmission from slipping out of gear, a lock is provided on the transmission or shift lever to hold it in the proper gear for pumping. It is also possible to operate the pump shift control without the gears completing their travel. If this happens, the vehicle may begin to move as the engine rpm is increased to build pressure. Some apparatus, particularly newer models with automatic transmissions, are equipped with lockouts to prevent this from occurring. Most apparatus are equipped with an indicator light in the cab that signals when pumping operations may begin **(Figure 9.16)**.

Figure 9.15 The manual pump override is available in case the normal pump-engage operations fail.

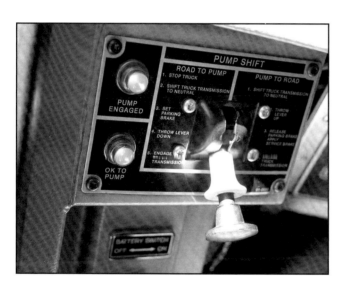

Figure 9.16 The pump indicator light will illuminate when the pump is "Ok to pump."

The driver/operator should not rely solely on the pump indicator light. Other signs that the apparatus is ready to pump, such as a speedometer reading or listening for the sound of the pump engaging, may be used as a fail-safe against the possible malfunction of the indicator light. On automatic transmissions, it is possible for the transmission to be momentarily engaged in the highest (fourth or fifth gear, depending on the model) forward ranges while the internal clutches are being applied and released. The transmission output shaft may begin to rotate at a low speed during the shifting process. Therefore, the transmission must be in neutral during this entire sequence.

NOTE: If the shift lever is moved from neutral during the process, the transmission may lock up and the engine may stall.

Hydrostatic pumps are used for auxiliary systems, including compressed air foam systems (CAFS) and generators on some apparatus.

Rear-Mount Pumps

Apparatus with rear-mount pumps are becoming increasingly popular **(Figure 9.17)**. This design offers a number of advantages, including a more even weight distribution on the chassis and more usable compartment space. A disadvantage of the rear-mount pump is that the driver/operator may be more directly exposed to oncoming traffic than in other pump-mounting positions. This situation may be somewhat alleviated by placing the pump controls on one of the rear sides of the apparatus so that the vehicle may be positioned on an angle to protect the driver/operator.

Figure 9.17 An apparatus with a rear-mount pump. *Courtesy of Ron Jeffers.*

Depending on the manufacturer or fire department preference, rear-mount pumps may be powered by either a split-shaft transmission or by a power take-off. In either case, a driveshaft of appropriate length and size is connected between the transmission and the pump. Other than the location at the rear of the apparatus, the operation is the same as previously described for PTO and split shaft (mid ship transfer) drive pumps.

Pump Piping and Valves

The piping and valves attached to a pump are integral components of the fire pump system. The primary parts of the piping system are intake and discharge piping as well as pump drains and valves. NFPA® 1901 requires all components of the piping system be of corrosion resistant material. Most pipes are constructed of cast iron, brass, stainless steel, or galvanized steel and may include rubber hoses in certain applications. Many apparatus feature a combination of these materials. The piping system and the fire pump itself must be capable of withstanding a hydrostatic test of 500 psi (3 500 kPa) before being placed into service. In order to minimize pressure loss within the apparatus, all piping and hoses must be designed to run as straight as possible with a minimum number of bends or turns.

Intake Piping

Water may enter the fire pump either from piping that connects the pump to the onboard water tank or the piping that connects the pump to an external water supply. Initially, many fires are fought with water from the tank on board the apparatus. It is essential that the piping from the tank to the pump be large enough to allow for adequate streams for fire attack. According to NFPA® 1901 pumpers with a capacity of 500 gpm (2 000 L/min) or less should have piping capable of flowing 250 gpm (1 000 L/min). Pumpers with a capacity greater than 500 gpm (2 000 L/min) should be able to flow at least 500 gpm (2 000 L/min).

Many pumpers are equipped with tank-to-pump piping as large as 4 inches (100 mm) in diameter **(Figure 9.18)**. Mobile water supply units may feature multiple tank-to-pump lines. Modern pumps are equipped with check valves that prevent damage to the tank if the tank-to-pump valve opens inadvertently while water is being supplied to the pump under pressure, such as during a relay operation. The tank-to-pump valve must be maintained in proper condition, as a leak in this valve will not allow the pump to be primed if the tank is empty.

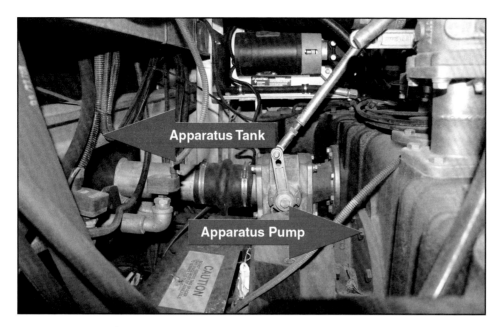

Figure 9.18 Tank-to-pump piping connects the water tank to the fire pump.

NOTE: If flow requirements will allow, refill the booster tank and keep it maintained as an emergency water supply during pumping operations. Air from the tank will be drawn back into the pump.

Fire apparatus pumps must be capable of being supplied from external pressurized and static sources. When using a static source, prime the pump by removing all or most of the air from the pump, lowering the atmospheric pressure within the pump casing. The primer is tapped into the pump at a high point on the suction side or the impeller eye and use a priming valve. Air trapped in the pump can prevent a successful drafting operation. Therefore, all intake lines in a centrifugal pump are normally located below the eye of the impeller and no part of the piping is above this point. The rare exception to this may be the tank to pump line where water is moving under the natural pressure of gravity.

The primary intake into the fire pump is through large-diameter piping and connections **(Figure 9.19)**. Intake piping is round in shape at the point where

Figure 9.19 Large diameter intake on pump panel.

the intake hose connects to it. As the piping nears the pump itself, it typically tapers to a square shape in order to eliminate the vortex that may occur in water that flows through circular piping. This vortex could introduce air into the pump. Midship pumps usually have a large intake connection on either side of the apparatus, whereas on front-mounted pumps the connection and piping extend from the lower portion of the pump.

Additional large-diameter intakes may be piped to the front or rear of an apparatus. However, due to the number of bends and length of the pipe, some of these may not allow the pump to supply its rated capacity. Unless they have been certified by the manufacturer to deliver rated capacity, front and rear intakes should be considered auxiliary intakes in the same manner as the pump panel mounted gated intakes. Pumps rated greater than 1,500 gpm (6 000 L/min) capacity may require more than one large intake connection at each location.

Additional intake lines, usually gated, are provided for use in relay operations, or when water is received through small diameter supply hose. Many of these intakes have 2½ inch (65 mm) hose couplings. The amount of flow that can be obtained is determined by the diameter of the pipe from the valve to the pump inlet and the straightness of the pipe routing. If 2½-inch (65 mm) pipe is used with 90 degree bends and T-fittings, the flow may be limited to 250 gpm (1 000 L/min). Whereas, if 3-inch (77 mm) pipe is used with a straighter piping route, a flow as high as 450 gpm (1 800 L/min) is possible through one of these intakes, which may also be used as auxiliary drafting points.

Discharge Piping

Based on NFPA® 1901, a sufficient number of 2½-inch (65 mm) discharge openings must be provided to flow the rated capacity of the pump **(Figure 9.20)**. As a minimum, all fire apparatus with a rated pump capacity of 750 gpm (3 000 L/min) or greater must be equipped with at least two 2½-inch (65 mm) discharges. Pumps rated less than 750 gpm (3 000 L/min) are required to have only one 2½-inch (65 mm) discharge. Discharges greater than 2½-inches (65 mm) in diameter may not be located on the pump operator's panel.

The apparatus may also be equipped with discharges smaller than 2½-inches (65 mm) in diameter. These discharges are commonly provided for use with preconnected attack lines. A minimum of 2-inch (50 mm) piping, valves, and elbows must be used to supply discharges where 1½-, 1¾-, or 2-inch (38 mm, 45 mm, or 50 mm) handlines are attached **(Figure 9.21)**.

Discharges are usually equipped with a locking ball valve that can be operated and locked in any position. When open, the valve should be locked to prevent movement. All valves should be designed and maintained so that they are easily operable at pressures of up to 250 psi (1 750 kPa).

When multiple attack lines that require different pressures are being operated, the driver/operator must set the engine discharge pressure to the highest level needed. Then each line requiring less pressure should have the valve partially closed and locked in position until the reduced flow through the valve is sufficient to provide the correct pressure for the hoseline. Water must be flowing through the lines in order to complete this operation, and individual line pressure gauges or flow meters must be used to ensure accuracy.

A tank fill line (or tank recirculating valve) should also be provided from the discharge side of the pump **(Figure 9.22)**. This allows the tank to be filled without making additional connections when the pump is being supplied from an external source. It also provides a means of replenishing the water tank on the apparatus. According to NFPA® 1901, apparatus equipped with tanks of less than 1,000 gallons (4 000 liters) must have a tank fill line of at least 1-inch

Figure 9.20 Based on NFPA® 1901, a sufficient number of 2½-inch (65 mm) discharge openings must be provided to flow the rated capacity of the pump.

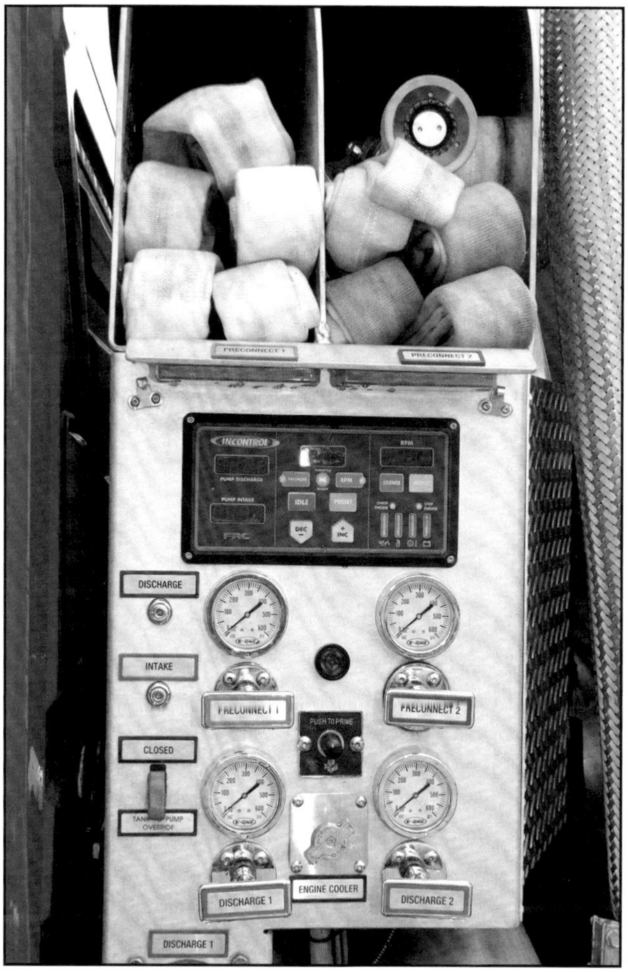

Figure 9.21 A typical preconnected attack line arrangement.

Figure 9.22 A driver/ operator connecting hose into the tank fill line.

(25 mm) in diameter. Tanks greater than 1,000 gallons (4 000 liters) must be provided with at least a 2-inch (50 mm) tank fill line. Recirculating lines are sometimes included in addition to the tank fill line.

On pumps not equipped with a thermal relief valve, the tank fill line can be used in conjunction with the tank-to-pump valve to circulate water through the pump to prevent overheating when no water is flowing. In a two-stage pump with the fill line coming off the first stage, overheating may still occur on the second-stage portion of the pump. The tank fill may be plumbed to the discharge header to capture water moving from both impellers, or a circulator valve may be used to help prevent the pump from overheating. The circulator valve is connected to the discharge side of the pump and enables water to be dumped into the tank or outside the tank onto the ground.

Some pumps are equipped with a booster line cooling valve (also called *a bypass valve*) that serves the same function as a circulator valve by diverting a portion of the discharge water into the tank. Circulator and booster line cooling valves are piped with small-diameter copper tubing with a very limited flow capability. These valves may not flow enough water to keep the pump cool during prolonged operations with intermittent flow or operations with very high pressures. For these instances, it may be necessary to discharge water through a waste or dump line. In order to help keep the engine from overheating, some pumps may be equipped with an engine cooler line that circulates tank water through a heat exchanger to aid in cooling the engine.

Valves

Valves control most of the intake and discharge lines from the pump. Valves must be constructed to be airtight and wear resistant **(Figure 9.23)**. Debris that is allowed to circulate through lines can cause damage to the valves, seals, and other pump components. Valve life may be extended by flushing the pump of debris.

The most common type of valve is the ball-type valve that permits the full flow of water through a line with a minimum friction loss. The most common actuators for ball-type valves are either push-pull handles or (T-handles) or quarter-turn handles. The push-pull valve handles on some pumps use a sliding gear tooth rack that engages a sector gear connected to the valve stem. This arrangement provides a mechanical advantage that makes the valve easier to operate under pressure as well as the setting of precise values of pressure when adjusting individual lines. The operating linkage may be adjusted so that the valves may be mounted remotely from the pump panel. The push-pull lever usually has a flat handle that can be used to lock the valve in any position by a 90-degree twist of the handle. The push-pull handle must be pulled straight out with the sides kept level. If this is not done, the shaft may bind, making the valve difficult to move or inoperable.

The quarter-turn handle has a simpler mechanical linkage with the handle mounted directly on the valve stem. The valve is opened or closed by a 90-degree movement of the handle. Modern versions of this handle lock by rotating the handle in a clockwise direction **(Figure 9.24)**. Some of the valves lock automatically when the handle is released, but the majority requires a positive action to lock the valve in position.

Figure 9.23 A discharge control valve from inside the pump compartment.

Figure 9.24 The push-pull lever has a flat handle that can be used to lock the valve in any position by a 90 degree twist of the handle.

Some apparatus may feature valves that are hydraulically, pneumatically, or electrically controlled. These valves use a ball-type valve that is operated by a toggle switch or touch screen on the pump panel. A visual display indicates the position of the valve as it opens or closes.

CAUTION
Driver/operators must ensure that intake valves are open or fully closed by the visual indicator on the pump panel.

Gate or butterfly valves are also used on fire apparatus. These are commonly used on large-diameter intakes and discharges. Gate valves are most commonly operated by a handwheel. Butterfly valves are most commonly operated by quarter-turn handles. Either may be equipped with hydraulic, pneumatic, or electric actuators, which are often used as remote operated dump controls on water tenders (tankers).

NFPA® 1901 requires that all intakes or discharges that are 3 inches (77 mm) or greater be equipped with slow acting valve controls. This feature prevents the valve movement from open to closed (or vice versa) in less than 3 seconds. This will minimize the risk of damage caused by water hammer when large volumes of water are being moved.

Pump Drains

Most pump connections are equipped with drain valves on the line side of the control valve **(Figure 9.25)**. On discharge fittings, drain valves provide a way for the driver/operator to drain the hose side of the valve after the discharge valve and nozzle are both closed. This is

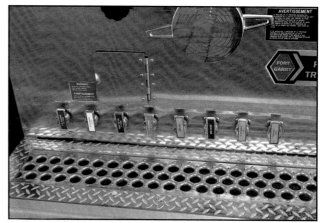

Figure 9.25 Each pump connection has its own drain valve.

useful when the hoseline has not been bled off by opening the nozzle. By using the drain valve, the line may be drained and the hose disconnected.

The bleeder valve on a gated intake serves another purpose. If a supply line is connected to the gated intake of a pump while the attack lines are being supplied from the tank, the changeover to the supply line can be made without interrupting the fire streams. Because the intake hose is full of air when it is dry, the water coming through the line would force air into the pump. This may cause a momentary loss of prime, as well as a fluctuation in nozzle pressure. By opening the bleeder valve on the line side of the intake valve, the air can be forced out of the hose and pass through the bleeder as the hose fills with water. When all the air has been evacuated from the line and the bleeder is discharging a steady stream of water, the bleeder valve can be closed, the intake valve opened, and the tank-to-pump valve closed. These actions should be conducted in order, making the transition with no interruption to the water flow.

Another purpose for pump and suction drains is to remove all the water from the system in climates where freezing may occur. In addition to the fact that ice will create a barrier to water flow, the expansion that occurs during freezing may cause damage to pump and piping components. Drains must be supplied at the lowest point on the pump and at the lowest point of each line connecting to it. These drains may also be connected to a master drain valve so that when operated, it will open the drains simultaneously. This drain should not be opened either when the pump is operating with pressure or with vacuum on the intake. If the valve is opened during these operations, the "O" ring used as a gasket to maintain an airtight connection may be damaged. Close all drains immediately after draining. Failure to close the drains may result in the inability to prime the pump during drafting operations.

It may be necessary to unwind and drain booster hose during freezing weather as simply opening the drain valve on the booster line supply piping will not drain the water from the hose. Water remaining in the hose may freeze, damaging the hoseline. Open a discharge valve to allow air to replace the draining water so that the vacuum will not hold water in the pump.

Some apparatus may be equipped with piping from the vehicle's air brake system to the booster reel or other hoseline. When the valve to this line is opened, compressed air discharges through the piping removing water from it.

Automatic Pressure Control Devices

The volume of water moving through the pump may change suddenly when a nozzle is closed rapidly. Firefighters operating a nozzle may be endangered when working with an unexpected and significant change in pressure. When a pump is supplying multiple attack lines, any sudden change in flow on one line can cause a pressure surge in another. Even the most alert driver/operator will be unable to compensate for sudden changes in flow to protect firefighters operating other attack lines. Automatic pressure regulation is essential to ensure the safety and effectiveness of personnel operating hoselines.

NFPA® 1901 requires some type of pressure control device to be part of any fire apparatus pumping system. This device must operate within three to ten seconds after the discharge pressure rises and restricts the pressure from exceeding 30 psi (210 kPa) above the set level. For relief valve systems, an indicator of system activation must be provided. For pumps that feature governor systems, there must be an indicator to show that the system is activated and identify whether it is controlling the engine speed or pump pressure. Except on apparatus equipped with automatic governors, a yellow indicator light located on the pump panel must illuminate when the pressure control system operates to control pressure in the pump. Some pressure relief valves are designed to expel excess water out of the pump. This must be done in such a way that does not expose the driver/operator or other firefighters to a pressurized water stream.

Relief Valves

The main feature of a relief valve is its sensitivity to pressure change and its ability to relieve excessive pressure within the pump discharge **(Figure 9.26)**. There are two basic concepts for pressure relief valves:

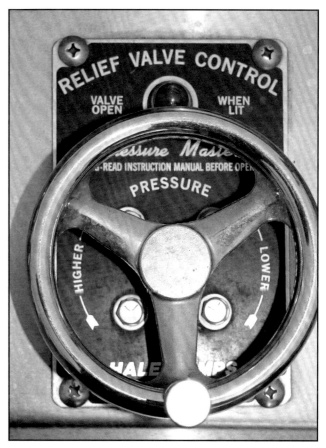

- **Those that relieve excess pressure on the *discharge side* of the pump**. This valve controls the pressure that is delivered to the hoseline nozzle from the pump.

- **Those that relieve excess pressure on the *intake side* of the pump**. An adjustable spring-loaded pilot valve bypasses water from the discharge to the intake chamber of the pump. Although only a small quantity of water is re-routed, this re-routing permits the pump to continue operation when pressure rises above the working, or set, pressure.

Although there are several types available, the most common relief valve uses a spring-controlled pilot valve. When the pump discharge pressure is lower than the pilot-valve setting, water flows from the pump discharge to the pressure chamber of the pilot valve. A diaphragm separates this pressure chamber from the pilot valve. Tension against the diaphragm is regulated by adjusting the handle of the pilot valve against the spring. As long as the hydraulic force in this chamber is less than the force of the spring, the pilot valve stays closed. The water is then transmitted back to the main valve chamber, and the main valve stays closed.

Figure 9.26 A pressure relief valve control device.

When the pump discharge pressure rises higher than allowed by the pilot-valve setting, the spring in the pilot valve compresses. This action allows the needle valve to move to the left, causing water to dump back into the pump intake. This action in turn reduces the pressure in the tube and behind the main valve. The hydraulic force on the small end of the main valve is now greater than that behind the main valve. As a result, the main valve opens and permits part of the water to return to the intake side, reducing discharge pressure. When the discharge pressure drops below the set pressure in the pilot valve, the pilot valve resets, pressure increases behind the large end of the main valve, and it closes.

A second type of relief valve, although equipped with a pilot valve, operates in a slightly different manner. When the pressure rises above the set pressure, the pilot valve moves, compressing its spring until the opening in the pilot valve housing is uncovered. Water flows through this opening and through the bleed line, and also into the pump intake. This flow reduces the pressure on the pilot valve side of the relief valve, allowing the higher pressure on the discharge side to force the valve open. Water flows from the discharge into the intake, relieving the excessive pressure **(Figure 9.27)**.

While discharge pressure relief valves are quick to react to overpressure conditions, they are somewhat slower to reset back to "all closed" positions. Therefore, it takes a short time for the pump to return to normal operation.

Intake pressure relief valves are intended to reduce the possibility of damage to the pump and discharge hoselines caused by water hammer when valves or nozzles are closed too quickly. The two basic types of intake pressure relief valves include:

- One that is supplied by the pump manufacturer and an integral part of the pump intake manifold.

- The second type is an add-on device that is screwed onto the pump intake connection **(Figure 9.28)**.

Some of these devices can be set by the driver/operator to allow a maximum amount of pressure into the fire pump. If the incoming pressure exceeds the set level, the valve activates and releases the excess pressure/water into the atmosphere until water has continued entering the pump at the pre-set level. It is generally recommended that the intake relief valves be set to open when the intake pressure rises more than 10 psi (70 kPa) above the necessary operating pressure.

Most screw-on intake pressure relief valves are also equipped with a manual shutoff valve that allows the water supply to the pump to be stopped if preferred. Bleeder valves on the intake pressure relief valve allow air to be bled off as an

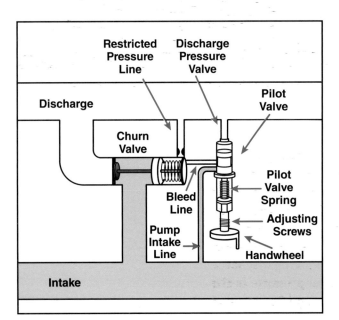

Figure 9.27 A relief valve relieves excessive water pressure.

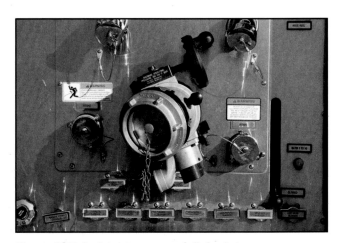

Figure 9.28 An intake pressure relief valve.

incoming supply hose is charged. This is particularly important when using devices in conjunction with large-diameter supply hose. A large amount of air pushes through these hoses until a solid column of water reaches the valve.

Pressure Governor

Pressure in a centrifugal pump may also be regulated by a mechanical or electronic governor that is pressure activated to adjust the engine throttle. The **pressure governor** is designed to regulate the engine speed to match the pump discharge requirements. When the pressure in the discharge piping of the pump exceeds the pressure necessary to maintain safe fire streams, the excessive pressure must be reduced. Because the speed of the impellers determines the pressure, and the engine speed determines the speed of the impellers, it is only necessary to reduce engine speed to reduce pressure.

Excessive pressure is generally caused by shutting down one or more operating hoselines. When excessive pressure builds up, a tube from the discharge side of the pump transmits the resulting pressure rise to a governing device, which then cuts back the throttle. A pressure governor device may be used in conjunction with a throttle control, and or pump discharge valves to control pressure to hoselines.

When drafting or pumping from the tank, the closed (draft) position is used; therefore, the water returns to the intake side of the pump. When pumping from a hydrant (external pressure source), the hydrant (or open) position is used so that the water is discharged onto the ground. The hydrant drain line discharging to the atmosphere can be run through a check valve to the tank to prevent water from continuously running on the ground.

Newer pumpers are often equipped with electronic governors. These devices use a pressure sensing element (pressure transducer) that is connected to the discharge manifold. The element controls the action of an electronic amplifier that compares the pump pressure to an electrical reference point. The element changes the throttle setting as needed by adjusting the amount of fuel supplied to the engine, bringing the pump to the preferred pressure. The governor will maintain any pressure set on the control above a specified setting and will return the engine to idle speed whenever the pressure drops below that point. The electronic governor also features **cavitation** protection by returning the engine to idle when intake pressure drops below 30 psi (210 kPa). These governors are accurate and quick to respond, eliminating the need for a discharge pressure relief valve.

Another advantage of the electronic governor is that when a discharge line is closed the engine rpm is adjusted, but the same discharge pressure is maintained on any lines still flowing. With a mechanical governor the same scenario would result in lower discharge pressure for all lines as the engine rpm is lowered.

NOTE: Driver/operators must be familiar with the specifications of electronic governors installed on their fire pumps. These devices may have slightly different cut-in or cut-off ranges. If the discharge pressure is reduced below a certain point for a specified period of time, the governor will return the pump to idle mode and cancel out the original pressure setting. The driver/operator must reselect the setting to resume pumping the discharge.

Pressure Governor — Pressure control device that controls engine speed, eliminating hazardous conditions that result from excessive pressures.

Cavitation — Condition in which vacuum pockets form due to localized regions of low pressure at the vanes in the impeller of a centrifugal pump, causing vibrations, loss of efficiency, and possibly damage to the impeller.

Priming Methods and Devices

The ability to initiate a successful drafting operation depends on creating a lower pressure within the pump and intake hose than exists in the atmosphere. This lower pressure will result in water being forced up into the intake hose and fire pump. Modern centrifugal fire pumps are unable to create this condition. A **priming device** is needed to create the vacuum that makes drafting possible. Primers fall into several categories including positive displacement, exhaust, vacuum, and air primers.

Positive Displacement Primers

Most modern pumpers use positive displacement primers. Small versions of both the rotary vane and rotary gear type positive displacement pumps are commonly in use. The theory behind these devices was outlined earlier in this chapter. Rotary vane primers require relatively high rpms as compared to rotary gear primers and can be driven by either mechanical means from the pump transfer gear case or by an electric motor. Although some apparatus feature primers that are driven off the transfer case of the transmission, an electric motor is the most popular means of powering rotary vane priming pumps, as they may be operated efficiently regardless of engine speed.

The primer pump inlet is connected to a control valve that is in turn connected to the fire pump. If there are high spots in the construction or mounting of the pump, the line from the priming pump may be connected to the main pump in several different locations. If the priming pump is driven electrically, the priming valve usually incorporates a switch into the valve. This design provides a single operation to prime the pump.

Many conventional primers use an oil supply or other type of fluid (**Figure 9.29**). The oil/fluid serves two purposes:

- As the pump wears, the clearance between the gears and the pump case increases and the pump loses efficiency.

- A thin film of oil/fluid is drawn into the pump and seals the gaps between the gears and the case.

- The oil/fluid also fills any irregularities in the housing caused sediment or debris.

- A coating of oil on the metal parts of the pump created by periodic operation of the primer will aid in the preservation of the pump.

Because the oil reservoir for the priming pump is often mounted higher than the pump itself, a vent hole is provided to break the siphon action as the tank drains. This vent must be checked frequently to ensure it is free of dirt and debris.

The ideal engine rpm for the transfer case, rear-driven primer operation depends on the construction of the primer, the gear ratio of the transfer case, and other features unique to a particular apparatus. The operator manual supplied by the fire pump manufacturer should specify the preferred engine speed (rpm) for priming but, in general, the range is between 1,000 to 1,200 rpm. Activate the primers with the engine at idle speed and then increase the throttle to the specified rpms. This will minimize wear on the mechanical clutch.

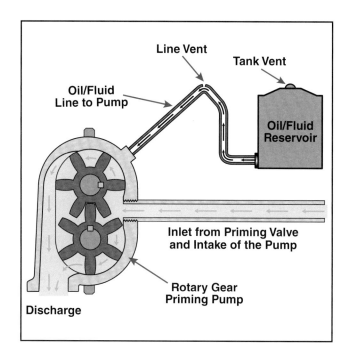

Figure 9.29 A primer uses oil/fluid to assist in drafting operations.

Oil-Less Primers

Most new pumpers are equipped with oil-less primers. These devices are constructed of materials that do not require lubrication; therefore, oil is not required in the priming process. Oil-less primers may also be installed into an older apparatus as an environmentally friendly initiative.

Exhaust Primers

Exhaust primers are generally found on skid-mounted pumps or older fire apparatus. This type of primer uses the same principle as a foam eductor. Exhaust gases from the vehicles engine are prevented from escaping to the atmosphere by an exhaust deflector. These gases are diverted to a chamber where their passing velocity creates a vacuum. This chamber is connected through a line and a priming valve to the intake of the pump. There the air is evacuated into the venturi chamber and then discharged along with the exhaust gas into the atmosphere. In order to create this vacuum, high engine rpms are required. Additionally, the exhaust primer requires a great deal of maintenance in order to remove the carbon deposits accumulated in the primer.

Vacuum Primers

The vacuum primer is a simple device that makes use of the vacuum already present in the intake manifold of any gasoline-driven engine. With gasoline-powered apparatus now a rarity in most fire departments, many driver/operators may not have the opportunity to work with or become familiar with this system. In order to prime the pump, a line is connected from the intake manifold of the engine to the intake of the fire pump with a valve connected in the line to control it. A float valve must be installed to prevent water from a primed pump from being drawn into the engine manifold. Because engine vacuum is greatest at near idle speed, the primer works best at low engine rpm.

Venturi Effect — Physical law stating that when a fluid, such as water or air, is forced under pressure through a restricted orifice, there is an increase in the velocity of the fluid passing through the orifice and a corresponding decrease in the pressure exerted against the sides of the constriction. Because the surrounding fluid is under greater (atmospheric) pressure, it is forced into the area of lower pressure.

Air Primers

Air primers are becoming an increasingly more popular method of priming pumps on modern fire apparatus. Virtually all pumpers are equipped with an air brake system using a compressor that is not needed for braking while the vehicle is parked and pumping. An air priming system uses the compressor to supply an airline to a jet pump that creates a **Venturi Effect** that primes the pump using no moving parts or lubricants **(Figure 9.30)**.

Pump Panel Instrumentation

The driver/operator must be familiar with all of the instrumentation located on the pump operator's panel. Some of the instrumentation is specific to operation of the fire pump and other gauges are duplicates of those found in the cab. NFPA® 1901 requires that all controls and instruments necessary to operate the pump are located on the pump operator's panel **(Figure 9.31)**. These include:

● Master pump intake pressure indicating device

● Master pump discharge indicating device

● Pumping engine tachometer

● Pumping engine coolant temperature indicator

● Voltmeter

● Pump pressure controls (discharge valves)

● Pumping engine throttle

● Primer control

● Water tank to pump valve

● Tank-fill valve

● Water tank level indicator

Most of the devices listed as indicators may be found as gauges or electronic indicators providing a digital display.

Although not specifically required by NFPA® 1901, a pumping engine fuel gauge is recommended and generally found on the pump operator's panel **(Figure 9.32)**. This feature allows the driver/operator to monitor fuel consumption during extended operations. An automatic transmission temperature gauge is also recommended for installation on the pump operator's panel. The driver/operator can help ensure that damage does not occur to the transmission by monitoring this gauge during pumping with the apparatus.

Master Intake and Discharge Gauges

The master intake and discharge gauges are the two primary gauges used by the driver/operator to determine the water pressure entering and leaving the pump. The master intake gauge (vacuum or compound gauge) is connected to the intake side of the pump and measures either positive pressure or a vacuum. This gauge is usually calibrated from 0 to 600 psi (0 to 4 200 kPa) of positive pressure and from 0 to 30 inches of mercury (vacuum) (0 to -100 kPa) on the negative side. This gauge provides a reading of the vacuum present at the intake of the pump during priming or when the pump is operating from draft.

Figure 9.30 An air priming system uses the compressor to supply an airline to a jet pump that creates a Venturi Effect. *Courtesy of Trident Emergency Products, LLC.*

Figure 9.31 A common pump operator's panel.

Figure 9.32 Gauges on the apparatus pump panel.

As the flow from the pump increases, the vacuum reading increases because more negative pressure is required to overcome the friction loss in the suction hose. When the vacuum reading approaches 20 inches (-70 kPa), the pump is nearing its capacity and is not able to supply additional lines.

The master intake gauge also provides a reading of the residual pressure when the pump is operating from a hydrant or is receiving water through a supply line from another pumper. Because the range of the vacuum scale is so small, even a slight error in the zero setting of the gauge can result in a large error in measuring the vacuum on the intake side of the pump.

A master pump discharge pressure gauge is also required on a pumper to reflect overall discharge pressure. The pump discharge pressure gauge registers the pressure as it leaves the pump, but before it reaches the gauges for each individual discharge line. External connections to these gauges must be provided to allow for calibrated gauges to be used during initial acceptance and service testing of apparatus.

Tachometer

The tachometer displays the engine speed in revolutions per minute. This information may provide an experienced driver/operator with a means to identify problems during a pumping operation. During acceptance testing, the rpm required to pump the rated capacity is determined and the information is recorded on an identification plate on the pump panel. A gradual increase in the amount of rpm required to pump the rated capacity indicates wear in the pump and possible need for repair.

Pumping Engine Coolant Temperature Indicator

The pumping engine coolant temperature indicator displays the temperature of the coolant in the engine that powers the fire pump. This may be the main vehicle engine, or in some cases, an auxiliary engine. Temperature information is an important indicator of engine performance, as an engine that operates too cool is not efficient and an operating temperature that is too high may result in damage to mechanical parts. Auxiliary cooling devices are provided for the lack of vehicle movement while the vehicle is engaged in pumping operations. These devices are explained later in this chapter.

Pumping Engine Oil Pressure Indicator

The pumping engine oil pressure indicator shows if an adequate supply of oil is being delivered to the critical areas of the engine that power the fire pump. This indicator does not measure the amount of oil in the crankcase; however, if this level is too low, the oil pump will be unable to maintain the proper amount of pressure. Normal operating oil pressures are specified in the manufacturer's maintenance manual, although the pressure for a particular engine may vary slightly. It is important that driver/operators are familiar with the reading expected for a particular apparatus. Any significant deviation from the normal oil pressure reading indicates an equipment malfunction.

Pump Overheat Indicator

The pump operator's panel may be equipped with an audible or visual indicator that warns the driver/operator when the pump will overheat. This may occur during prolonged periods of operation in which no water is discharged. Methods to prevent pump overheating are discussed earlier in this chapter as well as in Chapter 10, Operating Fire Pumps.

Voltmeter — Device used for measuring existing voltage in an electrical system.

Voltmeters and Ammeters

The **voltmeter** provides a relative indication of battery condition, and the **ammeter** indicates the status of the vehicle's alternator and charging system. Before the engine is started (with batteries turned on), the voltmeter indicates the top voltage available when the battery is fully charged, and measures the drop in voltage as electrical accessories are used.

Ammeter — Gauge that indicates both the amount of electrical current being drawn from and provided to the vehicle's battery.

Pump Pressure Indicators (Discharge Gauges)

Pump pressure indicators, commonly called *discharge gauges*, may be connected to the individual discharge outlets of the fire pump. These gauges must be connected to the outlet side of the discharge valve so that the pressure being reported is the pressure actually supplied to the hoselines after the valve. Pressure may be adjusted down for the overall pump discharge pressure as necessary. The gate valve must be adjusted each time the flow at the nozzle is changed. This readjustment is necessary because the pressure loss in the valve is determined by the amount of water flowing through it. If the nozzle is shut down on the hoseline being supplied, the individual pressure gauge for that discharge reads the same as the master pressure gauge because there is no flow through the valve to reduce the pressure. The gate valve should not be readjusted until water is flowing again.

Individual pressure gauges may also be supplied with master stream devices or the lines that supply them. These gauges are important in maintaining the proper pressure to produce an effective stream. When large flows are required, the friction loss is high in these supply lines, and the individual line gauge is the most accurate method of ensuring they are adjusted properly.

NFPA® 1901 allows flowmeter readouts to substitute for individual pressure discharge gauges. However, even with a flowmeter system in use, the apparatus is still required to have master intake and pressure gauges. Additional information regarding flowmeters may be found in Chapter 8, Fireground Hydraulic Calculations.

Pumping Engine Throttle

A pumping engine throttle must be contained on the pump operator's panel **(Figure 9.33)**. This device is used to increase or decrease the speed of the engine that powers the fire pump. An increase or decrease in engine speed will allow the driver/operator to control the amount of pressure that the fire pump supplies to the discharge. There are several types of throttles available, including a throttle knob (also called a *vernier*), that can be turned clockwise or counterclockwise to achieve the required pressure. Automatic throttle controls operated by a throttle switch or push button are commonly found on newer apparatus.

Figure 9.33 An example of two types of engine throttles.

Primer Control

The primer control is used to operate the priming device when the pump will draft from a static water supply **(Figure 9.34)**. This control is generally in the form of a push button, toggle switch, or pull lever. The function and operation of a priming device was previously detailed in this chapter.

Water Tank Level Indicator

This device displays the quantity of water held in the onboard water tank, allowing the driver/operator to anticipate the length of time attack hoselines may be operated until an external water source is needed. When engaged in interior fire fighting operations using only the onboard water tank for supply, it is critical to know when an external water source is needed. Interior crews must be withdrawn if the onboard supply is in danger of being exhausted before an external supply can be established.

The most common type of water level indicator uses a series of lights on the pump operator's panel. Sensors within the tank send signals that indicate the amount of water at increments of one quarter levels (¼, ½, ¾, full). These lights may be small LCD type lights mounted on the pump operator's panel or large lights mounted on the apparatus where they can be easily viewed from a distance by personnel operating at an incident **(Figure 9.35)**. Some apparatus, particularly older pumpers found in warmer climates, may be equipped with a site gauge that allows the driver/operator to view the water level through a clear tube. Newer apparatus are often equipped with a digital display indicating the water level in the onboard tank. During routine daily inspection, the driver/operator should verify the accuracy of the water level

Figure 9.34 A primer control.

Figure 9.35 Water tank level indicator on pump panel.

gauge by inspecting the fill opening to verify that the tank is full. If there is any question as to the level of water, the tank should be filled until it reaches the overflow point.

Foam Systems

If the pumper is equipped with a compressed air foam system (CAFS) or another foam system, the gauges and other controls related to this system are usually located on the pump operator's panel. Refer to Chapter 14 of this manual for additional information concerning built-in foam systems.

Auxiliary Cooling Devices

The primary function of an auxiliary cooling system is to control the temperature of coolant in the apparatus engine during pumping operations. Older apparatus usually contain one of two auxiliary coolers: either the marine or immersion type. The marine cooler is inserted into one of the hoses used in the engine cooling system so that the engine coolant must travel through it as it circulates through the system. The cooler features a number of small tubes surrounded by a water jacket that is connected to the discharge of the fire pump. When the pump is operating, water may be circulated through the water jacket of the auxiliary cooler. As coolant from the radiator passes through the tubes in the cooler, the colder water from the fire pump contacts the small metal tubes reducing the temperature of the coolant as it flows through. A valve is provided on the pump operator's panel to control the amount of water supplied to the auxiliary cooler from the pump.

The immersion type auxiliary cooler is mounted in a similar manner as the marine type, with the radiator coolant passing through the body of the cooler. In the immersion system, the water supplied by the fire pump passes through a coil or tubing mounted inside the cooler so that it is immersed in the coolant. As the colder water from the fire pump passes through the tubing some of the heat from the coolant is absorbed by the tubing and dissipated into the water supplied by the pump. This system is controlled by a valve at the pump operator's panel to regulate the amount of cooling chosen.

Both types of auxiliary coolers are designed so that the coolant in the radiator does not mix with the water from the fire pump so the engine coolant will not be contaminated.

Radiator Fill Valves

Older apparatus may feature a radiator fill valve that allows water from the pump to be circulated to the radiator in order to help cool the engine. This system causes the original coolant to become diluted and should be operated only in an emergency. The cooling system should be flushed and refilled with fresh coolant as soon as possible after this operation.

In extreme situations where a dramatic failure of a radiator hose or other cooling element has occurred while the pumper is supplying hoselines for interior fire fighting crews, a water stream may be directed at the engine to maintain some form of cooling for a very brief time while interior crews are withdrawn to safety. Once the crews are safe, the engine should be shut down immediately.

Chapter Summary

Because few water supply systems provide sufficient pressure to operate fire fighting hoselines and other appliances, most incidents require the fire department to increase the pressure available from the water system or draw a draft from a static water source.

In order to conduct safe and effective operations with fire department pumping apparatus, the driver/operator must know the operating theory as well as the capabilities of the apparatus, such as positive displacement, centrifugal pumps, foam systems, as well as any auxiliary pumping systems, that may be used in his or her department.

Review Questions

1. What are some different types of positive displacement pumps? (pp. 296-298)

2. What is the difference between pumping in the parallel position and the series position? (pp. 301-302)

3. What are the differences between a front-mount pump and a rear-mount pump? (pp. 308-312)

4. What are some main characteristics of intake piping and discharge piping? (pp. 312-316)

5. What is the purpose of automatic pressure control devices? (p. 318)

6. What are the main categories of primers? (pp. 322-324)

7. What are three examples of pump panel instrumentation? (pp. 324-329)

8. What are two types of auxiliary cooling devices? (p. 329)

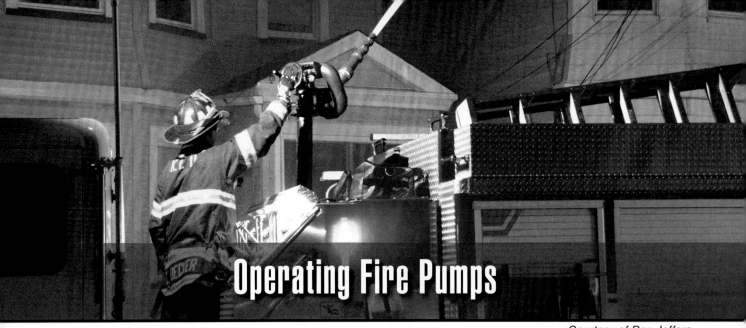

Operating Fire Pumps

Courtesy of Ron Jeffers.

Chapter Contents

chapter 10

Key Terms

NFPA® Job Performance Requirements

This chapter provides information that addresses the following job performance requirements of NFPA 1002, *Standard for Fire Apparatus Driver/Operator Professional Qualifications (2014).*

5.1.1, 5.2.1, 5.2.2, 5.2.4, 10.2.2

NFPA 1002, *Standard for Fire Apparatus Driver/Operator Professional Qualifications (2017).*

5.1.2, 5.2.3, 5.2.4, 5.2.5, 5.2.7, 10.2.2

Operating Fire Pumps

Learning Objectives

After reading this chapter, students will be able to:

1. Explain making the pump operational. (*NFPA 1002, 2014:* 5.1.1, 10.2.2 & *NFPA 1002, 2017:* 5.1.2, 10.2.2)

2. Summarize facts about operating from the water tank. (*NFPA 1002, 2014:* 5.1.1, 10.2.2 & *NFPA 1002, 2017:* 5.1.2, 10.2.2)

3. Explain considerations when operating from a pressurized supply source. (*NFPA 1002, 2014:* 5.1.1, 10.2.2 & *NFPA 1002, 2017:* 5.1.2, 10.2.2)

4. Summarize facts about operating from a static water supply source. . (*NFPA 1002, 2014:* 5.2.1, 5.2.2 & *NFPA 1002, 2017:* 5.2.3, 5.2.4, 5.2.5)

5. Describe actions taken for sprinkler and standpipe support. (*NFPA 1002, 2014:* 5.2.4 & *NFPA 1002, 2017:* 5.2.7)

6. Explain actions taken when troubleshooting pumping operation. (*NFPA 1002, 2014:* 5.1.1 & *NFPA 1002, 2017:* 5.1.2)

7. Engage and disengage a power take-off (PTO). (*NFPA 1002, 2014:* 5.2.1, 5.2.2, 5.2.4, Skill Sheet 10-1 & *NFPA 1002, 2017:* 5.2.4, 5.2.5, 5.2.7, Skill Sheet 10-1)

8. Engage and disengage a pump. (*NFPA 1002, 2014:* 5.2.1, 5.2.2, 5.2.4, Skill Sheet 10-2 & *NFPA 1002, 2017:* 5.2.4, 5.2.5, 5.2.7, Skill Sheet 10-2)

9. Perform pump operations from the apparatus water tank. (*NFPA 1002, 2014:* 5.2.1, Skill Sheet 10-3 & *NFPA 1002, 2017:* 5.2.4, Skill Sheet 10-3)

10. Make the transition from the apparatus water tank to an external pressurized water supply. (*NFPA 1002, 2014:* 5.2.1, Skill Sheet 10-4 & *NFPA 1002, 2017:* 5.2.4, Skill Sheet 10-4)

11. Operate from a pressurized water source. (*NFPA 1002, 2014:* 5.2.1, Skill Sheet 10-5 & *NFPA 1002, 2017:* 5.2.4, Skill Sheet 10-5)

12. Draft from a static water supply. (*NFPA 1002, 2014:* 5.2.1, 5.2.2, 5.2.4, Skill Sheet 10-6 & *NFPA 1002, 2017:* 5.2.3, 5.2.4, 5.2.5, 5.2.7, Skill Sheet 10-6)

13. Supply water to a sprinkler/standpipe system. (*NFPA 1002, 2014:* 5.2.4, Skill Sheet 10-7 & *NFPA 1002, 2017:* 5.2.7, Skill Sheet 10-7)

Chapter 10
Operating Fire Pumps

Case History

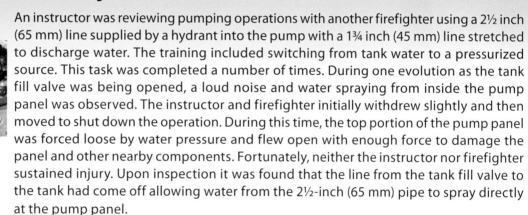

An instructor was reviewing pumping operations with another firefighter using a 2½ inch (65 mm) line supplied by a hydrant into the pump with a 1¾ inch (45 mm) line stretched to discharge water. The training included switching from tank water to a pressurized source. This task was completed a number of times. During one evolution as the tank fill valve was being opened, a loud noise and water spraying from inside the pump panel was observed. The instructor and firefighter initially withdrew slightly and then moved to shut down the operation. During this time, the top portion of the pump panel was forced loose by water pressure and flew open with enough force to damage the panel and other nearby components. Fortunately, neither the instructor nor firefighter sustained injury. Upon inspection it was found that the line from the tank fill valve to the tank had come off allowing water from the 2½-inch (65 mm) pipe to spray directly at the pump panel.

Driver/operators must wear full PPE even when operating at the pump panel in order to lessen the chance of injury should an event such as this occur. In addition, reacting quickly to shut down or modify operations when a problem is detected may help reduce the impact of mechanical problems.

Source: www.firefighterclosecalls.com/news/fullstory/newsid/30413/layout/no

After gaining an understanding of the operating theory behind fire pumps, the driver/operator must work to become proficient operating the fire pump. The following chapter contains information regarding the operation of a pump under a range of circumstances.

The driver/operator must first make the pump operational and then prepare to use at least one of three sources of water to supply the pumping operation. Information in this chapter details the use of the onboard water tank, pressurized water source, or a static water source to supply the pump. Pump operations at buildings equipped with automatic sprinkler and standpipe systems are also featured.

The instructional information provided is generic in nature in an effort to include the basic operating practices for many makes and models of fire pumps. Each manufacturer has certain guidelines with which you must become familiar. Consult the operator's manual for your assigned apparatus and model pump.

Making the Pump Operational

Making a fire pump operational, commonly referred to as "putting the pump into gear" begins after the apparatus is properly positioned and the parking brake has been set. Proper positioning for pumping apparatus was detailed in Chapter 4, Positioning Apparatus. Some apparatus have a feature that prevents the pump from throttling up or shifting into pumping gear if the parking brake has not been set. The operation of parking brakes was discussed in Chapter 3, Apparatus Safety and Operating Emergency Vehicles.

Most apparatus are designed so that the procedure for making the pump operational is performed entirely from the cab of the vehicle **(Figure 10.1)**. Several exceptions are explained later in this chapter. IFSTA recommends that the wheels be chocked every time the driver/operator exits the cab **(Figure 10.2)**. The placement of chocks provides an added measure of safety in the event the apparatus jumps into road gear or overrides the parking brake system.

The steps for engaging and disengaging a variety of pump drive systems are listed in **Skill Sheets 10-1** and **10-2**:

- Engage and disengage a power take off (PTO). **Skill Sheet 10-1**
- Engage and disengage a midship transfer pump. **Skill Sheet 10-2**

Figure 10.1 The driver/operator is performing in-cab pump activation procedures.

Figure 10.2 Every time the driver/operator exits the cab, IFSTA recommends chocking the wheels, which adds an added measure of safety in the event the apparatus jumps into road gear.

Operating from the Water Tank

Water supply from the onboard water tank is the sole source of supply for many incidents. In other cases, the driver/operator begins to operate with the water in the tank and then transitions to an external supply source. The driver/operator must be able to make the transition quickly and efficiently with no disruption to the incident operation. The following information describes operating from the onboard water tank and transitioning to an external pressurized water supply source. Information concerning drafting is explained later in this chapter.

Putting the Pump into Operation

When the fire pump has been made operational, the driver/operator is ready to operate the pump to generate sufficient pressure to create an effective fire stream. The initial water source is often the apparatus water tank. Upon exiting the cab and chocking the apparatus' wheels, the driver/operator then proceeds to the pump panel. While the specific steps may vary slightly from apparatus to apparatus, the common steps for performing pump operations from the apparatus water tank are described in **Skill Sheet 10-3**.

Another method for putting the pump into operation involves opening the appropriate discharges before you increase the discharge pressure by increasing engine speed:

- Open the tank-to-pump valve first.

- Open the discharges to the hoselines to be used **(Figure 10.3)**.

- Open the valves, and the hoselines begin to fill with water.

- Increase the throttle and the pressure in the hoselines will increase. If the nozzle is already open, the air will bleed off and you may set the discharge pressure accordingly. Otherwise, when hoselines are ready for water, open the appropriate discharges before the discharge pressure is developed.

- Reach the proper pressure only when water is flowing. Once the hoseline is opened, you may need to adjust the pressure accordingly.

While the pump is in operation, the driver/operator must perform the following:

- Monitor all gauges associated with the engine as well as the operation of the fire pump.

- Adjust the throttle until the desired flow rate is achieved if a flowmeter is in use. **(Figure 10.4)**.

During the fire attack, hoselines may operate intermittently. The pump may overheat if water is not flowing for an extended period of time, and the discharge pressure is maintained at a high level. In order to prevent

Figure 10.3 The driver/operator opening a hoseline discharge.

Figure 10.4 The driver/operator adjusting throttle.

Figure 10.5 The driver/operator opens the booster cooling valve to circulate water back into the tank.

this possibility, a means of moving water through the pump must be implemented. If the pump is equipped with a circulator, bypass, or booster cooling valve, it can be opened and set to circulate water back into the tank **(Figure 10.5)**.

This action provides some amount of cooling without wasting any water. The tank fill line may also be used to circulate water through the onboard tank in order to maintain cooling. The driver/operator must be aware that the tank fill line may be plumbed with a pipe large enough to cause pump cavitation when operating using the onboard tank:

- Sufficient cooling may be achieved by partially opening the valve.
- If the apparatus is so equipped, other measures include discharging water into the atmosphere or feeding a booster line back into the tank to circulate water.

NOTE: In order to partially open the tank fill valve and not create the potential for pump cavitation, some driver/operators open the valve the distance of their thumb to the pump panel with their hand on the valve control. You must:

- Monitor the water level in the onboard tank.
- Estimate the amount of time that water in the onboard tank will last based on rate of consumption.
- Ensure that personnel who are operating in dangerous areas are aware when the water level drops and are withdrawn before running out of water.
- Make a fairly accurate judgment of the duration of time a water supply will last based on the size of the tank and the approximate flow rate for specific hoselines, nozzles, and appliances. If the pump is equipped with a flowmeter, a reading of the amount of water flowed through the line may be available.

Transition to an External Water Supply

When operating at an incident requiring more water than is carried aboard the apparatus, it is necessary to transition to an external water supply before depleting the onboard tank. In the following section, the procedure for transitioning from an onboard water supply to an external source will be outlined. This commonly consists of a fire hydrant or another apparatus or static water source.

To begin the transition to external water, the driver/operator should:

- Connect the supply line into an appropriate intake of the fire pump **(Figure 10.6)**.
- Make the connection to an intake with a closed gate valve. The pump is already in operation. Air in the empty supply hose will enter the pump and may cause problems for the attack lines already being supplied.
- Open the bleeder valve on the gated intake so that air can escape ahead of the water supply. When the air has been purged from the bleeder and a steady stream of water drains from the valve, it may be shut. The water supply is now at the pump and ready for the transition.

Figure 10.6 The driver/operator is connecting the supply line to the fire pump intake.

With these steps completed, you are ready to transition from the apparatus tank to an external water source. The steps for transitioning to an external water source are listed in **Skill Sheet 10-4**.

Continue to adjust the discharge pressure by using the throttle until the intake gate valve is completely open. When this is complete, the pressure regulating devices may need to be adjusted again.

Operating from a Pressurized Supply Source

The two basic pressurized water supply sources that a driver/operator will encounter are a fire hydrant or supply hose from another pumper. With either of these sources, water enters the pump under pressure. As the discharge volume from the fire pump increases, the incoming pressure from the supply source may drop due to friction loss in the water system. If the discharge flow volume is increased too much, the intake pressure from the supply source may be reduced to a point that may damage the pump or water supply system.

Pumping at a low residual pressure (below 20 psi [140 kPa]) while being supplied by other apparatus is equally dangerous. This may cause the supply hose to collapse, interrupting the supply of water. It may also lead to cavitation of the pump.

NOTE: Cavitation is explained in greater detail later in this chapter.

Driver/operators should maintain a residual pressure of at least 20 psi (140 kPa) on their master intake gauge at all times during pumping operations. Water supply systems must maintain a residual pressure of at least 20 psi (140 kPa) within their mains for several reasons; contamination from sources outside the main may occur if the pressure in the main drops too low. In addition, overtaxing the water system may cause sediment and debris that has formed in older pipes to loosen, which could in turn damage the piping or reduce the water flow. Fire departments should maintain a working relationship with local water supply officials in order to ensure proper use and peak effectiveness of their system.

The remainder of the text in this section focuses primarily on hydrant operations. Chapter 12, Relay Pumping Operations, contains further information regarding receiving water from another pumper.

Figure 10.7 A pumper operating from a hydrant.

Operating from a Hydrant

Hydrant operations are basically the same whether a pumper supplies attack lines directly or supplies another pumper from the hydrant in a relay operation **(Figure 10.7)**. In either case, safe practices must be followed for the activities that take place.

Choosing a Hydrant

Several factors affect the choice of a hydrant. Safety and fire fighting needs may indicate that the closest hydrant to the fire may not be the most prudent choice. Depending on the constraints of the water supply system, the closest hydrant may be unable to supply the required volume of water and would require laying additional lines to another hydrant of greater capacity. Additionally, the hydrant may be too close to the fire creating a safety hazard for personnel and apparatus.

NOTE: Many water supply districts use a color-coded marking system to indicate the capacity of hydrants in their system.

In order to make an informed hydrant selection, a thorough knowledge of the water supply system is necessary. Hydrants served by large mains that are interconnected in a grid pattern receive their supply from several directions and usually have lesser amounts of sedimentation and deterioration. Typically the least desirable hydrants are those located on "**dead end mains**" that are served by smaller mains from only one direction. These hydrants generally have higher amounts of sediment and deterioration, which further reduce their capacity.

Once a hydrant has been selected, the pumper must be hooked to it without delay. The hydrant may be opened briefly and flushed of any accumulated debris before connecting the intake hose **(Figure 10.8)**. This action will ensure that the hydrant is operable and lessen the chance that debris may collect on the intake screen. The driver/operator and other firefighters should be proficient in making a smooth and efficient hydrant connection. Chapter 4, Positioning Apparatus, contains information regarding making hydrant connections.

Dead End Mains — Water main that is not looped and in which water can flow in only one direction.

Figure 10.8 Firefighter flushes debris from the hydrant water supply.

Making a Forward Lay

One of the most common ways for a pumper to be supplied with water from a hydrant is by making a **forward hose lay**. A forward lay consists of stopping at the hydrant, dropping the end of one or more supply hoselines at the hydrant, and then proceeding to the fire location **(Figure 10.9, p. 341)**. One potential problem of the forward lay depends on the distance from the hydrant to the fire. In a long lay with large flow demands, a pumper may need to be placed at the hydrant to make use of all available pressure. Another consideration is the amount of supply hose carried on the pumper. If the water supply pumper runs out of hose before it reaches the fire scene, it will be necessary to either bring in more hose and continue the forward lay or have the next arriving pumper lay from the first pumper to the fire and set up a relay pumping operation.

Once the lay has been made, the procedures used vary based on local policies. Some jurisdictions connect the line to the hydrant and work off hydrant pressure, while others await the arrival of a second pumper to hook up to the hydrant and supply the lines. In some cases, the second pumper is necessary due to flow requirements, elevation, or length of the hose lay.

Some departments use a four-way hydrant valve to aid the process of making a forward lay. This valve allows the original supply line that was laid by the first pumper to be immediately charged using hydrant pressure. The valve has a second discharge, usually 4½ or 5 inches (115 or 125 mm) in diameter, equipped with a shutoff valve. This allows a second arriving pumper, located at the hydrant, to be connected without interrupting the flow of water to the original supply line. The second pumper is then able to boost the pressure to the supply line using a second intake connection on the valve **(Figure 10.10, p. 342)**.

Forward Lay — Method of laying hose from the water supply to the fire scene

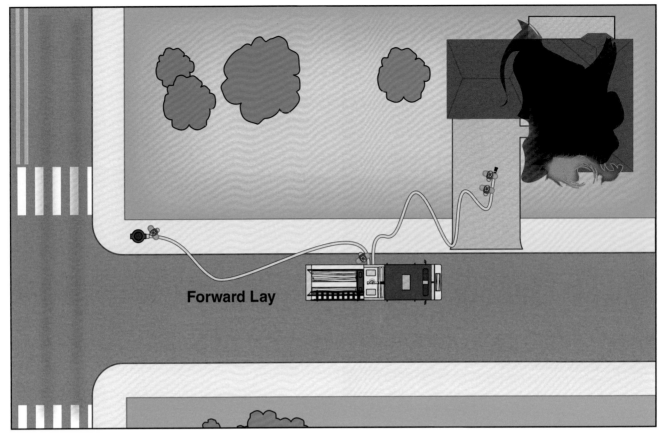

Figure 10.9 A forward lay is one of the most common ways for a pumper to be supplied with water from a hydrant.

The steps for the operation of a four-way valve:

- Connect the valve to the hydrant.
- Connect the original supply line, laid by the first pumper, to the supply line outlet.
- Open the hydrant. The clapper valve has operated to allow water to flow in the supply line.
- Connect the second pumper to the large diameter pumper intake connection on the four-way valve.
- Open the pumper intake valve. Open the four-way valve on the hydrant to supply the pump without interfering with the flow through the original supply line.
- Connect one of the pumper discharge outlets to the second intake of the hydrant valve.

NOTE: As the pressure in the pump builds, it overcomes the pressure from the hydrant that keeps the clapper valve open. When the pressure is high enough, the clapper valve closes. The original supply line is now being fed from the pump, not directly from the hydrant.

Attach gate valve(s) to unused hydrant discharges on dry barrel hydrants. This allows other connections to be made as the incident progresses without causing an interruption in the flow of the original line(s).

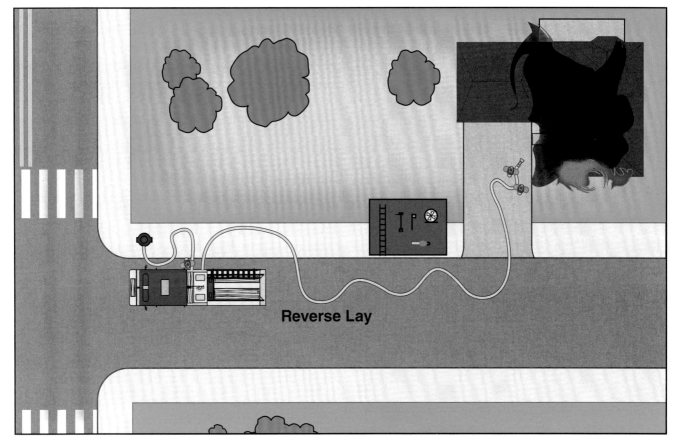

Figure 10.11 A reverse lay with equipment left at the scene as apparatus drive to the hydrant.

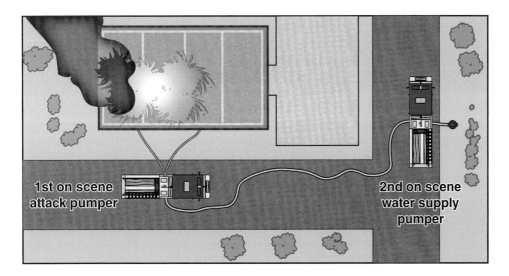

1st on scene attack pumper

2nd on scene water supply pumper

Figure 10.12 A two-pumper reverse lay operation.

from the pump intake. Pumpers built before 1991 may not be equipped with this feature. If water is allowed to enter the tank under pressure, the venting may not be adequate to allow the pressure to dissipate, resulting in damage to the tank. If the intake is equipped with a shutoff valve, it is acceptable to charge the intake line and bleed off the air while still pumping in water from the tank. Regardless of whether a particular apparatus is equipped with a check valve in the tank-to-pump line or a shutoff valve on the intake, the driver/operator should close the tank-to-pump valve after transitioning to an external water supply.

When the pump is full of water and the pressure in the system has stabilized with no water flowing, a reading of the pressure on the master intake gauge indicates the static pressure in the water supply system. The reading is important for estimating the remaining capacity of the hydrant as the water begins to move. The driver/operator should record the static pressure reading before he or she begins to pump. Some departments require the driver/operator to use a grease pencil to write the static pressure reading on the face of the intake gauge.

Putting the Pump in Service

Running a pump without water for a significant amount of time may cause the components to overheat and wear out faster, but the driver/operator may engage the pump before leaving the cab if it appears that water will be introduced within a few minutes. If the hydrant is inoperable, the pump drive system will need to be disengaged before the apparatus can be relocated. With the pump engaged and the apparatus wheels chocked, the driver/operator is ready to operate the pump panel. The steps for operating the pump from a pressurized water source are described in **Skill Sheet 10-5**.

When operating a two-stage pump, the driver/operator must set the transfer valve to the proper position before increasing the throttle to build the required discharge pressure. The selection is made based on the amount of water to be supplied. Even if only one line is initially put into operation, supply additional hoselines if the fire progresses. Initially placing the transfer valve in the series (pressure) position may dictate that the driver/operator reduces the throttle and subsequent discharge to hoselines if a changeover to parallel (volume) operation is required.

Figure 10.13 A driver/operator slowly opening the tank fill valve.

Pumps supplying a relay operation or master stream are usually used to supply large amounts of water, requiring the use of a parallel (volume) setting of the transfer valve. Exceptional circumstances include relay operations that require high pressure along the length of extended supply lines, to overcome elevation loss in a hose lay, or when supplying the upper floors of a high rise.

Open all valves slowly, especially when using large diameter hose **(Figure 10.13)**. The hose must be filled before pressure can be established. While observing the master intake and discharge gauges, the driver/operator should increase the engine rpm. If the master intake gauge drops below 20 psi (140 kPa), the throttle must not be increased any further because the pump may begin to cavitate. If there is adequate supply to continue to increase rpm, the throttle may be advanced until the required pressure and flow have been reached. The relief valve or governor may now be set.

NOTE: If the master intake gauge reaches 20 psi (140 kPa), the throttle must not be increased further due to risk of cavitation.

A driver/operator at the hydrant or in the middle of a relay operation may be located some distance from the fireground. At a distance, it may be difficult to determine how much water is being used or even if any lines are flowing. Several methods for preventing overheating are as follows:

- Establish a continuous minimum flow during intermittent use of water in fireground operations to keep the pump from overheating.

- Pull a length of the booster line or other small diameter line off the reel and fasten it to a sturdy object.

- Open the valve that supplies the booster reel and discharge water in a direction that will not interfere with the operation or damage other property. The booster line may also be directed back into the tank to circulate water continuously.

NOTE: During prolonged pumping operations, a bypass circulator may not provide sufficient cooling under some conditions and additional measures will be required to avoid overheating.

- Open a discharge drain valve **(Figure 10.14)**. Some may feature threaded outlets that allow a hose to be connected and routed away from the apparatus to a safe discharge point. This feature is especially important when attempting to prevent an accumulation of water during operations affected by freezing weather or on unstable ground. Open some drain valves before the valve is under pressure to avoid potential damage. Consult manufacturers' guidelines before operation.

Figure 10.14 A driver/operator opening a discharge drain valve.

- Partially open the tank-fill valve or tank-to-pump line. Even if the water tank becomes full and overflows through the tank vent, this result is preferable to the pump overheating. The driver/operator should create a flow sufficient to cool the pump without significantly diminishing the amount of water available for fire suppression.

Additional Water Available from a Hydrant

When a pumper is connected to a hydrant and is not discharging water, the pressure shown on the intake gauge is static pressure. When the pumper is discharging water, the intake gauge displays the residual pressure. The difference between the two pressures is used to determine how much more water the hydrant can supply. Several methods are available for making this determination:

- Percentage Method

- First-Digit Method

- Squaring-the-Lines Method

NOTE: The following calculations are used in the field and not theoretical calculations. Using the various methods may result in a slightly different answer. These methods do not provide precise answers for a full range of fireground conditions. However, under most circumstances, they are sufficiently reliable for fireground operations.

Percentage Method

To use the percentage method, first calculate the drop in pressure as a percentage. This may be accomplished by using the following formula:

Formula 10.1 (Customary & Metric) – Available Water from Hydrant Percentage Method

$$\text{Percent Drop} = \frac{(\text{Static} - \text{Residual})(100)}{\text{Static}}$$

Table 10.1 indicates how much more water is available from a hydrant and how many additional hoselines may be supplied. If the percentage is 10 or less, three additional lines with the same flow as the line being supplied may be added. For 11-15 percent, two lines may be added, and for 16-25 percent one line. When the result is over 25 percent, more water may be available, but not as much as is flowing through the first line.

Example 10.1 (Customary)

A pumper is supplying one line flowing 250 gpm. The static pressure was 70 psi and the residual pressure is reading 63 psi. Determine how many additional lines may be added.

$$\text{Percent Drop} = \frac{(\text{Static} - \text{Residual})(100)}{\text{Static}}$$

$$\text{Percent Drop} = \frac{(70 - 63)(100)}{70} = \frac{700}{70} = \mathbf{10}$$

Table 10.1 illustrates that a 10 percent drop means that three times the amount being delivered is available. This means that three additional lines flowing 250 gpm each may be added.

Example 10.1 (Metric)

A pumper is supplying one line flowing 1 000 L/min. The static pressure was 500 kPa and the residual pressure is reading 450 kPa. Determine how many additional lines may be added.

$$\text{Percent Drop} = \frac{(\text{Static} - \text{Residual})(100)}{\text{Static}}$$

$$\text{Percent Drop} = \frac{(500 - 450)(100)}{500} = \frac{5\,000}{500} = \mathbf{10}$$

Table 10.1 illustrates that a 10 percent drop means that three times the amount being delivered is available. This means that three additional lines flowing 1 000 L/min each may be added.

Table 10.1	
Additional Water Available at a Hydrant	
Percent Decrease of Pumper Intake Pressure	**Additional Water Available**
0-10	3 times amount being delivered
11-15	2 times amount being delivered
16-25	Same amount as being available
25 +	More water might be available, but not as much as is being delivered.

First-Digit Method

The first-digit method is a quick and easy way to calculate available water using psi and gpm. However, this method cannot be used with metrics.

Step 1: Find the difference in psi between static and residual pressures.

Step 2: Multiply the first digit of the static pressure by 1, 2, or 3 to determine how many additional lines of equal flow may be added. An explanation of how each number affects the outcome is detailed in the following list:

- If the psi drop is equal to or less than the first digit of the static pressure multiplied by one, three additional lines of equal flow may be added.

- If the psi drop is equal to or less than the first digit of the static pressure multiplied by two, then two additional lines of equal pressure may be added.

- If the psi drop is equal to or less than the first digit of the static pressure multiplied by three, then one additional line of equal flow may be added.

The following example illustrates the First-Digit Method.

Example 10.2

A pumper is supplying one line flowing 250 gpm. The static pressure was 65 psi, and the residual pressure reading is 58 psi. Determine how many lines may be added.

Difference in psi = Static Pressure — Residual Pressure

Difference in psi = 65 – 58 = **7 psi**

First Digit of Static Pressure x 1

6 x 1= 6

Seven is not less than six, but is less than 12 (2 x 6), so two more lines of at 250 gpm each may be added.

Squaring-the-Lines Method

When using the squaring-the-lines method, the driver/operator must note the static pressure of the water system before any pump discharges are open or know the usual static pressure in the water supply system under normal circumstances. Obtain this information from preplan documents or from previous experience.

You must also have a close idea of the volume of water initially flowed by the pumper. After establishing these figures, determine the additional amount of water available and square the number of lines currently flowing and multiply this by the original pressure drop. The following example illustrates this method.

NOTE: Table 10.2 shows the reasonable flow rates that may be assumed for various sized attack lines.

Example 10.3 (Customary)

A pumper connects to a hydrant that has a static pressure of 60 psi. When a 250 gpm handline is opened, the intake pressure drops to 52 psi. Determine how many more handlines flowing 250 gpm may be operated without lowering the residual pressure below 20 psi.

Difference in psi = Static Pressure — Residual Pressure

Difference in psi = 60 – 52 = **8 psi**

If a second 250 gpm line were added, the pressure drop would be as follows:

Multiplication Factor = (Number of Lines)^2

Multiplication Factor = 2^2 = **4**

Resultant Pressure Drop in System at the New Flow Rate = (Multiplication Factor) x (Original Pressure Drop)

Resultant Pressure Drop in System at the New Flow Rate = 4 x 8 = **32 psi**

If the pressure drop is 32 psi, the residual pressure in the system will be 28 psi. It would not be advisable to add a third hoseline under these conditions. Each time the flow rate is doubled, the pressure drop in the system is quadrupled. This is a simple and valuable fact for a driver/operator to use when performing quick mental calculations on the fireground.

Example 10.3 (Metric)

A pumper connects to a hydrant that has a static pressure of 420 kPa. When a 1 000 L/min handline is opened, the intake pressure drops to 365 kPa. Determine how many more handlines flowing 1 000 L/min may be operated without lowering the residual pressure below 140 kPa.

Difference in kPa = Static Pressure – Residual Pressure

Difference in kPa = 420 – 365 = **55 kPa**

Table 10.2
Assumed Flow Rates for Squaring-the-Lines Method

Hose Size in inches (mm)	Flow Rate in gpm (L/min)
1½ (38)	125 (500)
1¾ (45)	175 (700)
2 (50)	200 (800)
2½ (65)	250 (1 000)

If a second 1 000 L/min line were added, the pressure drop would be as follows:

Multiplication Factor = (Number of Lines)^2

Multiplication Factor = 2^2 = **4**

Resultant Pressure Drop in System at the New Flow Rate = (Multiplication Factor) x (Original Pressure Drop)

Resultant Pressure Drop in System at the New Flow Rate = 4 x 55 = **220 kPa**

If the pressure drop is 220 kPa, the residual pressure in the system will be 200 kPa. It would not be advisable to add a third hoseline under these conditions. Each time the flow rate is doubled, the pressure drop in the system is quadrupled. This is a simple and valuable fact for a driver/operator to use when performing quick mental calculations on the fireground.

Shutting Down the Hydrant Operation

All changes in flow should be made slowly and smoothly to avoid water hammer and pressure surges on water systems. Water hammer may carry enough force to damage hydrants and other equipment, and pressure surges may cause a water source to become unreliable.

NOTE: Some pumps may be equipped with pressure dump valves to protect the pump, piping, and valves. Set these devices at a point close to the intake pressure. When shutting down the water supply operation:

• Bring the engine rpms to idle gradually.

• Discontinue a pressure control device if in operation.

• Close valves in a slow and smooth motion. The apparatus fire pump should now be disengaged.

• Close the hydrant; operate the valve in the same slow and smooth manner to avoid possibility of water hammer and potential damage to the water supply system.

Pressure Differential
— Effect of altering the atmospheric pressure within a confined space by mechanical means. When air is exhausted from within the space, a low-pressure environment is created and replacement air will be drawn in; when air is blown into the space, a high-pressure environment is created and air within will move to the outside.

Operating from a Static Water Supply Source

All fire department pumpers should be capable of pumping water from a static water supply source. In most cases, this source is located some distance below the level of the fire pump. It is not possible to pull water into the pump. However, it is possible to evacuate some of the air inside the pump creating a **pressure differential** (partial vacuum), which allows atmospheric pressure acting on the surface of the water to force the water into the fire pump. In order to create this condition, an airtight, noncollapsible waterway (hard intake hose) must be used between the fire pump and the static water source. **Skill Sheet 10-6** lists the steps for setting up and drafting from a static water supply source.

Drafting Operations

In **Figure 10.15**, the pressure has been reduced inside the pump and intake hose to reduce the atmospheric pressure inside the pump and intake hose to 12.7 psi (86 kPa). With an atmospheric pressure at sea level of 14.7 psi (100 kPa), a partial vacuum of -2 psi (-14 kPa) is measured on the intake (compound) pressure gauge as 4 inches of mercury (Hg) (-13.6 kPa). This vacuum causes the water to rise 4.6 feet (1.4 m) into the intake hose from the surface of the water. The weight of water combined with the reduced air pressure acting on its surface creates a balance.

As the water begins to move through the pump, additional pressure losses are encountered. Any hose or appliance creates a certain amount of friction loss. The amount of friction loss is proportional to the amount of water moving through it. The inertia of water is an additional factor in friction loss. As water begins to move through a pump, a certain amount of energy is consumed in getting the water at rest to begin to move and increase its velocity sufficiently to supply the amount of water needed.

The amount of friction loss in the intake hose depends on the diameter and length of the hose as well as the intake strainer and any adapters in use. A hose with smaller diameter and greater length has higher friction loss, which allows less water at the pump **(Figure 10.16)**. Taking this into consideration, the diameter of intake hose may be increased for pumps with larger capacities. It is possible to increase the flow of a pump by using a larger diameter intake hose or adding additional intake hose. For example, a pumper rated at 750 gpm (3 000 L/min) is normally supplied with 4½ inch (115 mm) intake hose to attain the rated capacity. By equipping the pumper with 5-inch (125 mm) hose, the capacity of the pump can be increased to 820 gpm (3 300 L/min), if all other factors remain the same.

Atmospheric Pressure During Drafting Operations

The ability to overcome losses in pressure is limited to atmospheric pressure at sea level (14.7 psi [100 kPa] or 30 inches Hg). The inches of mercury measurement is used in drafting since the changes of pressure are so minute. This pressure decreases approximately 0.5 psi (3.5 kPa) or 1 inch of Hg for each 1,000 feet (300 m) of altitude gain. In a city located 5,000 feet (1 500 m) above sea level, the atmospheric pressure is 12.2 psi (85 kPa). Because the same atmospheric pressure of 14.7 (100 kPa) psi must overcome elevation pressure as well as any friction loss, increasing the height of the lift will decrease total pump capacity. A lift increased from 10 to 16 feet (3 m to 5 m) would require the vacuum to increase from 9 to 14 inches of mercury (Hg) (-30 to -50 kPa), which leaves 5 inches (-20 kPa) less to overcome any friction loss encountered. Considering the same 750 gpm (3 000 L/min) pumper used in the previous example, increasing lift to 16 feet (5 m) with 4½-inch (115 mm) intake hose would reduce the capacity of the pump to 585 gpm (2 350 L/min).

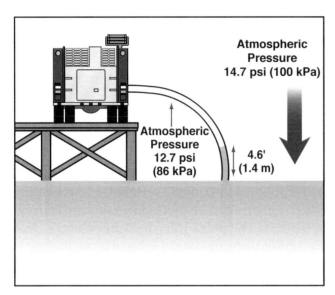

Figure 10.15 During drafting operations, creating a vacuum will cause the water to rise into the intake hose.

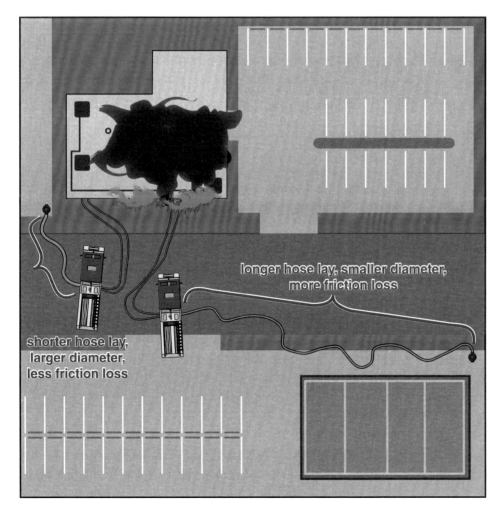

Figure 10.16 Hose lays will have less friction loss if they consist of hose with a large diameter and cover a short length.

With the pump moving water, the vacuum reading on the master intake gauge will provide an indication of the remaining capacity of the pump. Most pumps are able to develop a vacuum capacity of approximately 22 inches of mercury (Hg) (-75 kPa). Because compound gauges may not provide a completely accurate reading on the vacuum side, the driver/operator must acknowledge that any reading close to this point indicates that the pump is nearing the limits of its ability to supply water. An attempt to increase the discharge beyond this point may result in cavitation.

Cavitation During Drafting Operations

In theory, cavitation can be described as water being discharged faster than it is coming into the pump. This condition occurs when air cavities are created in the pump or bubbles pass through the pump. They move from the point of highest vacuum into the pressurized section where they collapse or fill with water.

The high velocity of the water filling these cavities causes a severe shock to the pump. In some cases of prolonged operation, damage to the pump may occur. During cavitation, the pressure drops below atmospheric and the boiling point of water drops to the point that the water changes to a vapor and creates a void composed of water vapor, or steam. As the vapor passes through the impeller of the pump, the pressure increases, the vapor condenses, and water rushes to fill the void. The temperature of the water, the height of the lift, and the amount of water being discharged affect the point at which cavitation begins.

There are a number of indicators that a pump is cavitating. The pressure gauge on the pump will fluctuate and hose streams may pulsate creating a distinctive popping or sputtering sound as the water leaves the nozzle. In cases of severe cavitation, the pump itself may make noises described as sounding like gravel is passing through the pump. The surest indication of cavitation may be a lack of reaction on the pressure gauge to increases in the throttle.

When a pump reaches the point of cavitation it is discharging all of the water that the atmospheric pressure or pressurized source can force into the intake. When water is discharged from the pump faster than it can be taken in, increasing the pump rpm will not increase the discharge pressure.

Cavitation may result when a pump has been equipped with inadequate piping from the water tank. In some departments, a pump is most often operated from its onboard water supply. Damage to the pump may occur from repeated attempts to pump more water from the tank than the piping allows to flow into the pump. This damage may be severe when the pump is operating at high pressures to supply long attack lines. Although cavitation can occur when operating from a hydrant system, it often occurs during drafting operations. The driver/operator must always be careful to keep discharge rates lower than intake.

Selecting the Drafting Site

The first consideration in establishing a drafting operation is site selection. If the purpose of the operation is to supply water to the fireground directly or through a relay, there may be little choice in the location. However, if the draft is being established to supply water tenders (tankers) for a shuttle operation, there may be several options. A site may be selected by:

- Amount of water
- Type or quality of water
- Accessibility of water

Amount of Water Available

The most important factor in choosing the draft site is the amount of water available. If the location features a static body of water such as a pool or lake, the size of the body becomes significant **(Figure 10.17)**. A backyard swimming pool containing 12,000 gallons (48 000 L) of water will not support a fire attack using master steams for any length of time. A small pond may not have a large standing capacity, but a rapid rate of replenishment may make it an effective source. A small stream may also prove a good source if the flow of water is moving rapidly.

In order for a pumper to approach its rated capacity using a traditional strainer, there must be at least 24 inches (600 mm) of water over the strainer **(Figure 10.18)**. It is also helpful to have at least 24 inches (600 mm) of water all around the strainer in order to avoid drawing foreign objects such as sand or gravel into the pump. In drafting operations with less than 24 inches (600 mm) of water above the strainer, it is more likely that floating debris such as branches or leaves may clog the strainer. Even a very high concentration of algae may prevent effective use of the strainer. In addition to clogging the strainer, small debris that enters the intake hose may collect on the pump intake screen. The rapid intake of water into the strainer may also cause a whirlpool that can result in allowing air into the intake hose, causing the pump to lose its prime. A floating object placed above the strainer, even something as simple as a beach ball or capped plastic jug, may lessen the chances of a whirlpool.

In order to draft from a swiftly moving shallow stream, a dam can be constructed using available material to raise the water level, or the bottom may be dug out to achieve greater depth. A floating strainer may also be used **(Figure 10.19)**. In using this device, the end of the intake hose floats on the surface, and water is drawn into the intake hose through a series of holes on the bottom of the strainer. Because water enters from the bottom, whirlpools are not a problem. In order for a floating strainer to work properly, it must float freely, unconstrained by the rigidity of the intake hose. Because the floating strainer takes in water only from one side, the pumper may not receive enough water to achieve its rated discharge capacity.

Figure 10.17 Driver/operators should know the available drafting sites in their jurisdiction.

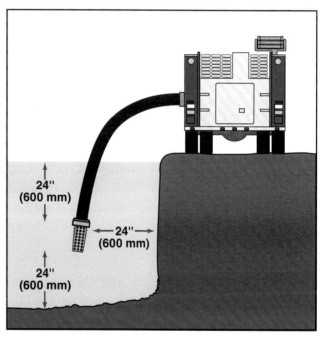

Figure 10.18 For a pumper to approach its rated capacity using a traditional strainer, there must be at least 24 inches (600 mm) of water around the strainer.

Figure 10.19 A floating strainer.

When using a portable tank or swimming pool for drafting operations, a low-level strainer is the appliance of choice. These strainers are designed to sit directly on the bottom of a tank or pool and allow water to be effectively drafted down to a depth of approximately 2 inches (50 mm) **(Figure 10.20)**. However, they may not be able to draft quantities to allow the pump to operate at its rated capacity.

In jurisdictions that may draft using ocean water, tidal movement must be considered. Locations acceptable for drafting during certain phases of tide may become unusable as the tide changes. Plan for and monitor tidal conditions during extended drafting operations.

Water temperature will also affect drafting operations. Water below 35°F (1.7°C) or above 90°F (32°C) may adversely impact the ability of the pump to reach capacity. In cold weather climates, the temperature of water several feet (meters) below the surface is often warmer than that closer to the surface. Heated water may be found in the vicinity of the discharges for power plant cooling towers or other industrial applications and should be avoided if possible.

Type and Quality of Water

Nonpotable Water — Water that has not been examined, properly treated, and not approved by appropriate authorities as being safe for consumption.

Although almost any type of water may be used for fire suppression, pumping nonpotable (untreated) water may be harmful to the pump. Using saltwater or a ground water supply in the vicinity of mining operations or other industrial plants may expose the pump to corrosion from the salt content or caustic chemicals that may be present in the ground water. Each time **nonpotable water** is pumped through the apparatus, the pump and piping should be thoroughly flushed with fresh water soon afterwards.

Dirty or sandy water may potentially cause serious problems **(Figure 10.21)**. Particles of sand and dirt too small to be blocked by the strainer may enter the pump where they can cause deterioration. As water passes through the eye of the impeller, the sand acts as an abrasive in the area between the clearance rings and the hub of the impeller. This abrasive effect increases the spacing, causing slippage from the discharge back into the intake and reducing the capacity of the pump.

Figure 10.20 Use a low-level strainer when drafting from a portable tank or swimming pool.

Figure 10.21 Dirty water at a drafting site may potentially damage the apparatus pump.

As dirty water passes through the pump, it is forced into the packing by discharge pressure. This action causes the packing to become contaminated by dirt and makes a good seal impossible. Without a good seal, air leaks result and the pump has a reduced ability to draft.

Accessibility

Accessibility to a water source is an important factor in selecting a drafting site. Because drafting is accomplished by evacuating air from the pump and allowing atmospheric pressure to push the water into it, a maximum of 14.7 psi (100 kPa) is available. Elevation pressure and friction loss in the intake hose must be overcome by this 14.7 psi (100 kPa). As the amount of lift required to reach the pump increases, the following effects occur:

- Elevation pressure increases

- Less friction loss can be overcome

- Capacity of the pump is decreased

All fire pumps meeting NFPA® and Underwriter's Laboratories Inc. requirements are rated to pump their capacity at 10 feet (3 m) of lift. If the lift is less, the capacity of the pump is higher; if the lift is greater, the capacity decreases. A pumper in good working order can lift water a maximum of 25 feet (7.5 m). However, all available atmospheric pressure is required to overcome this lift. As a result, the remaining capacity of the pump is of little value for fire suppression. To create an effective fire stream, a lift of no greater than 20 feet (6 m) is recommended. Working with this lift, the pump operates at about 60 percent of its rated capacity. When selecting a site for drafting, the lift must be kept as low as possible. It is more desirable to lay out an extra 100 feet (30 m) of supply line to set up at a draft location where the lift will be lower and more water can be supplied.

Other important variables to consider during draft site selection include the stability of the ground surface, the convenience of connecting hoselines, and the safety of the driver/operator. Preplanning potential drafting sites in a jurisdiction will identify any limitation or special considerations for specific areas. Advance preparation to secure the accessibility of strategic sites will aid in the efficiency of water supply operations. For additional information on static water supply sources, consult Chapter 11, Static Water Supply Sources.

Connecting to the Pump and Preliminary Actions

Once a suitable drafting site has been chosen, the driver/operator should move the apparatus toward that position. Use the following steps for connecting to the pump:

- Place the apparatus directly at the location from which the intake hose may be deployed.

- Set the parking brake and chock the wheels when the final position has been achieved.

- Follow local policies regarding the placement of traffic control devices or use of warning lights if the draft site is close to a roadway.

- Do not engage the pump until all connections are made, and it is ready to be put into operation.

- Park the vehicle short of the final drafting spot if the area around the actual drafting spot is limited as the intake hose and strainer are connected to the apparatus. Once they are connected, the driver/operator may slowly position the pumper at the final drafting point while other firefighters carry the hose and strainer, placing them in the desired position.

- Inspect the gaskets to be sure that they are in place and no dirt or gravel has accumulated inside the coupling. The strainer and the required lengths of intake hose must then be coupled and made airtight.

- Place each section of hose in line with the other before the coupling is turned. If the gaskets are in good condition and the coupling is connected properly, it should be possible to achieve an airtight connection with the couplings hand tight.

- Use, if necessary, a rubber mallet to make the connections tighter. Enough personnel must be available to connect the intake hose without placing it on the ground, as dirt may lodge in the couplings.

- Fasten a rope to the end of the strainer to aid in the handling of the hose and proper positioning of the strainer **(Figure 10.22)**.

Once the sections of intake hose are connected to the strainer, it is usually easier to connect the hose to the intake fittings by first putting the strainer into the water, then placing the apparatus into position. If an older, butterfly-type intake valve is normally connected to the pump intake, it is often removed before connecting the intake hose to the apparatus as this valve obstructs the waterway, reducing drafting capacity. Newer butterfly valves are less obtrusive, and keeping the valve in place will prevent the pump from draining which would make priming more time consuming.

Incorrect positioning of the intake hose may result in the formation of an air pocket that can prevent effective drafting. Routing intake hose over a high point, such as a fence or guard rail that is higher than the pump intake, may trap air in the hose.

With the design of certain strainers, rope may be used to suspend the strainer off the bottom by tying it to the pumper, a tree, or other fixed object. If the bottom slopes steeply from the water's edge, place a roof ladder in the water and lay the intake hose on it. Under extremely adverse conditions, a shovel or other flat metal object may be placed on the bottom to protect the strainer. Once the apparatus, intake hose, and strainer are in place, the driver/operator should follow the procedures detailed earlier in this chapter for making the pump operational.

Figure 10.22 Firefighter uses rope to lower suction hose into water.

Priming the Pump and Beginning Operation

When the pump has been made operational, priming the pump will begin the drafting operation. For two-stage pumps, the transfer valve must be in the parallel (volume) position. A pump in series (pressure) position may trap air that will need to be removed.

If the primer is a positive displacement pump that is driven by a transfer case, set the engine rpm according to the manufacturer's instructions. Most priming pumps are intended to work most effectively when the engine is set at a rate between 1,000 and 1,200 rpm. If the priming pump is driven by an electric motor the exact rpm is not critical; however, the rate should be sufficient to keep the alternator charging and prevent the loss of prime once the pump fills with water. If the apparatus features a vacuum-type primer, the engine rpm should be kept as low as possible without causing the engine to stall.

After the pump has been made airtight and the engine rpm set, operate the primer control. As the air is evacuated from the pump the master intake gauge will register vacuum reading. This reading should equal 1 inch of mercury (Hg) (-3.5 kPa) for 1 foot (300 mm) of lift required. The vacuum is measured from the surface of the water to the eye of the pump's impeller.

As the primer operates, the vacuum reading should increase as atmospheric pressure forces water into the intake hose. The hose will fill with water, the weight of which causes the intake hose to drop. When the body of the pump fills with water, the primer discharges water onto the ground under the apparatus. Initially the stream of water will be intermittent as the remaining air mixes with water as it is removed.

The priming action should not be halted until all air has been removed and a steady stream of water is discharged. As the pump fills with water, a pressure indication is displayed on the master discharge gauge.

The entire priming action typically requires 10 to 15 seconds from start to finish. However, when up to 20 feet (6 m) of intake hose lifting a maximum of 10 vertical feet (3 m), it may take as long as 30 seconds (45 seconds in pumps larger than 1250 gpm [5 000 L/min]) to accomplish this. If a prime has not been achieved in this time period, the priming attempt should be stopped and the problem traced. The most common inability to prime is an air leak that prevents the primer from developing enough vacuum to successfully draft water.

The most common cause of an air leak is an open drain or valve. If the pump is equipped with a circulator, shut it completely. Intake relief valves may also cause leaks. On older model apparatus, the valve may be equipped with a shut off. On newer models, a threaded intake relief discharge may be present, requiring that it be capped before another attempt at priming is made.

Other sources for potential leaks are the gaskets on the couplings of the intake hoses. The ears on each coupling may require a few hits with a rubber mallet to ensure they are airtight **(Figure 10.23)**.

If the previous measures are taken and priming is still not possible, the following list of potential problems may be reviewed:

Figure 10.23 Firefighter uses rubber mallet to tighten suction hose connections.

- Insufficient fluid in the priming reservoir
- Engine speed (rpm) is too low
- Lift is too high
- A high point in the intake hose is creating an air pocket

After successfully priming the pump, the throttle setting should slowly be increased before attempting to open any discharges. Increasing the throttle setting is required to raise the pressure to between 50 and 100 psi (350 kPa and 700 kPa). Open the desired discharge valve slowly while observing the discharge pressure. If the pressure drops below 50 psi (350 kPa), pause for a brief time to allow it to stabilize before opening the valve further. Opening the valve too quickly may cause air to enter the pump causing a loss of prime.

If the pressure continues to drop, momentarily operating the primer may eliminate any small pockets of air still trapped in the pump and restore the pressure to its point. Once water begins to flow, the discharge gauge may fluctuate due to air trapped in the pump and hose. This effect will stabilize once full flow is established. The driver/operator should not attempt to set the discharge pressure to the desired value until water is flowing and the gauge is stabilized. If the discharge hoselines are not ready for water, another discharge or booster line may be opened, allowing water to discharge back to the source.

Constant movement of water through the pump is required in order to prevent overheating. This flow is also important to maintain the vacuum that the primer has established in the pump. Without moving water, even a very small air leak may result in a loss of vacuum. As previously mentioned, even flowing a booster line back into the static source during the entire time the pump is drafting will help prevent loss of prime should other flow requirements cease. If the apparatus priming device fails to operate, it may be possible to use water from the vehicle's onboard tank to achieve a prime. Once the desired pressure has been established and hoselines are in service, set the relief valve or pressure governor.

NOTE: If all the water from the booster tank is lost and the tank-to-pump valve does not seal, establishing prime will be difficult.

Establishing a prime can sometimes be done by using the tank water to fill the pump and intake hose sufficiently to allow a prime to be achieved. This method will be successful only if an adequate seal is established when the tank-to-pump valve is closed. If this valve does not seal properly and all the water from the onboard tank is used, the driver/operator will not be able to establish a prime. A jet siphon is another method that may be used to employ a Venturi effect to achieve water movement during drafting operations.

Operating the Pump from Draft

Operating from draft is demanding for the apparatus and driver/operator alike. This operation requires diligent monitoring of the gauges associated with the pump as well as the engine. The engine temperature gauge must be kept within the normal operating range, using the auxiliary cooler as necessary. Any deviation from the normal engine temperature is a sign that another pumper may need to be brought in to continue the drafting operation.

Several types of problems may occur during drafting operations. They fall into the following general categories:

- **Air leak on the intake side of the pump** — The most common source of problems while operating at draft. If the discharge pressure gauge begins to fluctuate with a corresponding loss of vacuum on the intake gauge, air is most likely coming into the pump along with the water. The intake hose couplings should be re-checked for tightness. Even though they were initially tight enough to establish the draft, vibration over time may have caused them to loosen.

- **Whirlpool allowing air to enter the pump** — If there is not enough water above the drafting strainer, a whirlpool may be allowing air to enter the pump. This may be corrected by placing a beach ball or other floating object above the strainer. A floating dock strainer may also be used in areas of shallow water where whirlpooling may be a problem.

- **Air leakage due to defective pump packing** — If the onboard water tank is empty, the tank-to-pump line may be a source of leakage. Additionally, all drains and intake openings should be re-checked for leakage.

NOTE: Strainers should be flow tested before being deployed at an incident. Many are not capable of flowing up to the maximum capacity of the pump.

CAUTION
Damaged or leaking tank-to-pump valves may lead to the inability to achieve or maintain a draft.

Defective pump packing may also cause air leakage. If there is an excessive amount of water leaking from the packing, in a steady stream instead of dripping, the packing may be the cause. If this is the case, nothing can be done to remedy the situation while the pump is operating. If the problem becomes severe enough to cause the pump to lose its prime, the pumper will have to be removed from service and replaced with another pumper.

While the pump is operating, a gradual increase in the vacuum may be noted with no change in the flow rate. This is an indication that a blockage is developing. A blockage often occurs after a pump has been operating at a high rate of discharge, which creates a maximum velocity of water entering the strainer. In extreme cases, the pump may go into cavitation, resulting in a fluctuation and gradual decrease of the discharge pressure. An immediate solution is to decrease the engine rpm until the pressure drops. A drop in pressure indicates that the flow has decreased below the point of cavitation.

Because operating at this reduced pressure may not be sufficient to maintain the desired flow, the driver/operator should attempt to clear the blockage and return to normal operation. The most common place for a blockage to occur is in the strainer. If the strainer can be reached easily, leaves or other debris may be removed by hand or by using a booster line to spray the debris out of the way. If these methods are unsuccessful, the pump may be back-flushed in an attempt to clear the debris.

Blockage may also occur against the strainer located at the intake of the pump. In this case, the pumping operation must be discontinued while the intake hose is removed to access and clear the strainer.

Equipment problems may also lead to a blockage. Because the intake hose is operating under a vacuum, the inner liner can become detached from the hose itself and collapse, blocking a portion of the waterway. This may not be immediately apparent upon investigation, as the liner may return to its original position when the hose is disconnected and the vacuum is broken.

Attempting to exceed the capacity of the pump will also lead to cavitation accompanied by a high reading on the vacuum gauge. Cavitation may occur well below the rated capacity of the pump if a high lift is involved in the drafting operation. The actual capacity of the pump is determined in a given scenario by the diameter and length of the intake hose, the strainer design, and the vertical lift.

Shutting Down the Operation

When preparing to shut down a drafting operation, slowly decrease the engine speed to idle, take the pump out of gear, and allow the pump to drain. After the pump has been drained and the connections removed, operate the positive displacement primer for several seconds until primer oil or fluid comes out of the discharge from the priming pump. This action will aid in lubrication of the priming pump. The fire pump should then be thoroughly flushed when a supply of fresh water is available, unless the pumping operation was conducted using a very clean static water supply.

Sprinkler and Standpipe Support

Fixed fire suppression systems are an integral part of the fire protection features of many buildings. The driver/operator is responsible for providing adequate support to these systems during fireground operations. These suppression systems commonly consist of the automatic sprinkler and standpipe systems detailed in the following sections.

NOTE: The steps for supplying water to both automatic sprinkler and standpipe systems are listed in **Skill Sheet 10-7**.

Supporting Automatic Sprinkler Systems

Properly installed and maintained fire sprinklers have a proven history of providing reliable protection to many types of occupancies. Sprinkler systems are designed to support the flow of a specified number of fire sprinklers based on the hazard being protected. Most fires are controlled by the activation of relatively few sprinklers. As a result, the automatic water supply for a sprinkler system is designed to supply only a fraction number of the total fire sprinklers at any given time. During sprinkler activation for a fire, the fire department must be prepared to augment the water supply to the sprinkler system based on local policy. This may include compensating for obstructed or inadequate water supply or improperly closed valves.

The installation of all occupancies with automatic sprinkler systems should be identified in preincident planning. The location of the fire department connection (FDC) as well as the closest hydrant or static water supply should also be identified **(Figure 10.24)**. Specific requirements for pump pressure at each building should be noted per local policy.

Although each jurisdiction may adopt policies and guidelines to suit unique conditions, a general procedure should require preparations to be made for the immediate supply of the FDC at all sprinklered occupancies where there is a fire with sprinkler activation. The fire department connection may consist of a Siamese with at least two 2½-inch (65 mm) female connections connected to a clappered inlet, or one large diameter sexless connection. As water flows into the system, it first passes through a check valve that prevents water flow from the sprinkler system back into the FDC. However, it does allow water from the FDC into the sprinkler system as long as it is supplied at a pressure greater than that holding the check valve closed.

Depending on local policy, the first arriving or other first alarm engine company should locate the FDC and nearest suitable hydrant, or water supply. If there is any indication of a fire, the appropriate hoselines should be connected to the FDC and the pumper should establish water supply at the hydrant, making all appropriate connections.

Figure 10.24 A pumper crew checking the location of the FDC against the prefire plan.

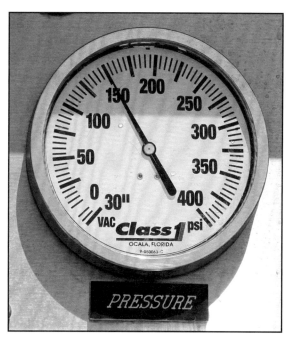

CAUTION
When interior attack crews are operating hoselines from a combination sprinkler/ standpipe system with sprinklers flowing, the pressure supplied to the FDC should be based on a safe operating pressure for the interior crews.

It is advisable to confirm the presence of actual fire conditions before a pumper begins to flow water to the FDC. It is possible that a sprinkler system has malfunctioned or been tampered with, causing the activation of a sprinkler head.

If the sprinkler system is to be supplied at the FDC, the driver/operator should slowly develop the amount of pressure required to supply the system, after the need to supply the system has been confirmed. Multistage pumps should be operated in parallel (volume) position. Depending on the policies of a jurisdiction, the suggested discharge pressure may be printed on a plate at the FDC, or contained in preincident planning information. If no specific information is available, the general guideline is to discharge 150 psi (1 050 kPa) into the FDC **(Figure 10.25)**.

NOTE: If this general rule is used, the driver/operator should attempt to obtain accurate information to determine the nozzle type, elevation loss, and friction loss involved in fire attack. Reports from the interior attack team may provide this information.

Figure 10.25 When specific information is unavailable, driver/operators should pump 150 psi (1 050 kPa) into the FDC when supporting automatic sprinkler systems.

As soon as practical, firefighters should be sent to check the sprinkler control valves. Closed valves should be opened, except in cases where it is known that they control an area of the building where the sprinkler system is undergoing construction or renovation. Opening valves under these circumstances may cause a severe loss of water to the system. If a stationary fire pump supplies the sprinkler system, firefighters should also ensure that it is operating. Sprinkler control valves are often located in the fire pump room making it efficient for one team of firefighters to accomplish both tasks.

Supporting Standpipe Systems

Standpipe systems allow for quicker access to water supply for attack hose-lines in multi-floor or single floor buildings with large floor areas. Fire attack teams may connect to the 2½ inch (65 mm) or 1½ inch (38 mm) connections located at strategic points on each floor. Fire attack crews should bring attack lines with them to initiate standpipe operations. House hose installed at the standpipe connection may be unlined, single-jacket hose designed for occupant use. It has not been manufactured or tested to the same standard as fire department hose.

Standpipe systems may be wet or dry, depending on the fire code requirements for a particular occupancy. Some wet pipe systems contain water under pressure and may be used as soon as a hoseline is stretched and the valve is opened. A dry pipe system must be charged with water from the occupancy's water supply, stationary fire pump, a fire department pumper, or a combination of the sources. The fire department should always support the FDC to ensure adequate flow and pressure is provided for fire fighting operations. All FDCs should be clearly marked to prevent the driver/operator from confusing which system is being supplied **(Figure 10.26)**. Some FDCs are combined to supply both an automatic sprinkler and standpipe system. Both wet and dry systems should be supplied by a fire department pumper to supplement the system's water supply.

Figure 10.26 Clearly marked FDCs provide necessary information to driver/operators at the scene of an emergency.

The hose lays previously detailed for use in supplying a fire department connection for sprinkler systems apply to standpipes as well. Pump discharge pressure will depend on the following variables:

- Pressure loss (25 psi [175 kPa]) for flows exceeding 350 gpm (L/min) in the standpipe

- Friction loss in the hose lay from the pumper to the fire department connection

- Friction loss in the hose on the fire floor

- Nozzle pressure for the type of nozzle in use
- Elevation pressure due to the height of the building

Generally, the friction loss in the standpipe is small unless the flow is very large, such as when two 2½ inch (65 mm) lines are being supplied from the same riser. Allowance must also be made for the pressure losses in the FDC and pipe bends. The driver/operator should be familiar with the hose and nozzles in use for standpipe operations in the jurisdiction. This information will allow for a more accurate hydraulic calculation. Chapter 7, Theoretical Pressure Calculations and Chapter 8, Fireground Hydraulic Calculations, contain detailed information regarding these calculations.

Add approximately 5 psi (35 kPa) for each floor above the fire department connection that will have operating fire streams. Consider friction loss for the attack line(s), standpipe piping, and layout from the pumper to the standpipe connection. These calculations can become complex and are not practical to compute under fireground conditions. Fire departments should have a planned pump discharge pressure, or develop a rule-of-thumb for each building in the area equipped with a standpipe.

CAUTION
Do not use pump discharge pressures in excess of 185 psi (1 300 kPa) unless the standpipe system, hose, and appliances have been designed to function under high pressures.

When a standpipe system is known to be equipped with **pressure-reducing valves**, the elevation pressure used must be based on the total height of the standpipe or zone being used. If the pressure at a particular valve is less than that for which the valve was adjusted, the result will be inadequate pressure for attack hoselines.

Pressure-Reducing Valve — Valve installed at standpipe connection that is designed to reduce the amount of water pressure at that discharge to a specific pressure, usually 100 psi (700 kPa).

Vandals may tamper with the valves in a dry standpipe system, leaving them in the open position. Firefighters should be aware of this possibility and should check for open valves during incidents. When the standpipe is charged, water will be discharged at all the points where caps are off and the valve is open. A large number of discharge points will greatly reduce the amount of water available for fire suppression efforts.

When a dry standpipe system is charged, there will be a time delay as water fills the system and expels the air. Trapped and compressed air may be released under high pressure when a valve is opened.

NOTE: Many manual standpipe systems are designed to be pumped at a pressure of 150 psi (1 050 kPa) at the FDC.

Some standpipes may require adaptation in order to be used. For example, if the FDC is found to have a frozen swivel on a 2½ inch (65 mm) connection, a double male adapter with a double female adapter can be added to the con-

Figure 10.27 A firefighter attaches a hose with double male/double female adapter to a FDC with a "frozen" female swivel.

nection to provide movement **(Figure 10.27)**. If the fire department connection has been vandalized or access blocked, a standpipe connection on the first floor will offer a way to provide some support to the system by using a double female connector and pumping into the system. An aerial device may be used to create an external standpipe by employing its pre-piped water-way or running hose up an aerial ladder. This tactic commits the use of an aerial device to this task for the duration of the incident. An external standpipe may also be created by hoisting up, or rolling hose down the outside of a building, securing it inside every two or three floors. Supply hose can also be stretched up the interior stirs to take the place of a standpipe system. This is often a time-consuming and labor-intensive task, usually used as a last resort. IFSTA's **Fire Protection, Detection, and Suppression Systems** manual contains additional details on operations at buildings featuring automatic sprinklers and standpipes.

Troubleshooting

The driver/operator must be prepared to efficiently troubleshoot and correct a variety of issues that may affect the ability of the pumper to deliver the necessary pressure or volume of water at an incident. Immediately upon any indication that water supply or pumping ability may be unattainable or interrupted, you must notify the officer or Incident Commander. Appropriate decisions may then be made to ensure operational safety and effectiveness.

The driver/operator should use a logical process to trace the problem back to its source and then attempt to troubleshoot the problem. For example, if you increased the throttle and opened the appropriate valves but the pump would not develop pressure, the logical steps would be to ensure that the pump was properly engaged. The indicator light on the pump panel and in the cab should be illuminated, and the transfer valve should be properly placed with the transmission in the appropriate gear. The speedometer may also register a speed above zero mph (km/h).

Another problem may occur when water supply to the apparatus is inter-rupted. One of several problems may need to be addressed if a charged supply line suddenly loses water. You will need to determine the source of the problem by following logical steps back to the source. You may need to ask other fire-fighters to help determine the source of the problem; for example, the supply line may have burst or a vehicle may have parked on it. If the line is intact, the source may be compromised; a hydrant or water main may have failed, or a portable folding tank or tender may need to be replenished.

The driver/operator experiencing a pump or supply failure may also enlist the help of another driver/operator if available in order to gain a fresh perspective in search of the cause and solution to a problem. A flowchart and **Table 10.3, p. 368**, at the end of this chapter, contain additional information regarding operating the pump and troubleshooting during pumping operations.

Chapter Summary

Driver/operators must have the ability to operate fire pumps under challenging fireground conditions. The ability to make the pump operational, trouble-shoot, and correct problems that may develop are vital to the success of any fire attack. As well, the driver/operator must be able to supply the required attack lines for fire suppression. Choosing the best water supply source with options ranging from the onboard tank to pressurized hydrants and static water sources will enable the driver/operator to supply other pumpers, the sprinkler, or standpipe system in an occupancy or attack lines.

Review Questions

1. What two items need to be done before making a fire pump operational? (p. 336)

2. What actions should be taken by the driver/operator when transitioning to an external water supply? (p. 338)

3. What are the methods used to determine how much more water a hydrant can supply? (p. 347)

4. What factors should be considered when selecting a drafting site? (p. 355)

5. What factors affect pump discharge pressure in hose lays for use in supplying a fire department connection for standpipes? (pp. 364-365)

6. What are some problems that may need to be addressed if a supply line that was charged suddenly loses water? (p. 366)

Table 10.3
Troubleshooting During Pumping Operations
Problems Common to all Types of Operation

Problem	Symptoms	Probable Cause	Possible Solutions
Unable to get a reading on the pressure gauge when the pump is put in service.	Green light indicating that the pump shift transfer is complete is not illuminated.	Pump drive system is not fully engaged.	Check the position of the shift transfer control. If it is in the proper position, release the transfer control, allow the gears to turn, then operate it again. Automatic transmission: repeat pump shifting procedure to ensure power transfer to pump operation.
	Green light is on, no mph (km/h) reading registers on the speedometer. the proper gear. Automatic	Vehicle clutch is not engaged.	Check the remote clutch control on the pump operator's panel.
		Road transmission is not in position for pump operation. transmission selector is in wrong position.	Check the shift lever: lock it in the proper
	Speedometer reading is normal for pump operation. All indications are correct and rpm reading is as specified.	There is no water in the pump.	Check the water supply. Ensure that all applicable valves are open. Primer pump may need to be operated to eliminate air in the main pump.
		Gauge is defective. Pressure may be there but not reading on the master pressure gauge.	Check the shutoff (snubber) dampening valve associated with the gauge. Open the gate valve to one of the capped discharge outlets and look for pressure reading on the individual line gauge. Open an uncapped discharge outlet from the pump to see if water is discharged under pressure.
Pump will not develop sufficient pressure.	The rpm reading on the tachometer is normal when compared with the UL plate.	Two-stage pump: • Pump transfer valve is in the wrong position.	The transfer valve should be in the SERIES or PRESSURE position anytime more than 200 psi (1 400 kPa) is needed.
		• Swing check valve may be leaking if the pump is in the SERIES position.	Set the discharge pressure to 50 psi (350 kPa), change from PARALLEL to SERIES, and listen for the metallic sound of the valve operating. If it is blocked, remove the strainer from the large intake and attempt to clear the valve seat of any debris.
		• The transfer valve has not completed its travel and is only partially operated.	Check all mechanical and electrical indications as well as observing pressure gauge readings as the valve is operated. Use the manual override controls to complete the operation of the valve. It may be possible to assist the action of the valve mechanically if the power transfer mechanism is faulty.
		Automatic transmission: transmission not staying in pumping gear lockup and is downshifting as load increases.	Remove pump from service and repair or adjust so apparatus will operate in correct pumping gear.

Problems Common to all Types of Operation

Problem	Symptoms	Probable Cause	Possible Solutions
Pump will not develop sufficient pressure.	The rpm reading on the tachometer is normal when compared with the UL plate.	Wear on the clearance rings inside the pump may cause excessive slippage.	Take the pumper out of service until it can be repaired.
	Relief valve is operating and the indicator light is on.	Relief valve pressure adjustment is set too low.	Increase the operating pressure of the relief valve by turning the adjustment control clockwise until it closes.
	The indicator light shows that the relief valve is closed.	The relief valve may be stuck open or may not be properly seated, allowing water to bypass back to the intake.	Turn the relief valve operating control to the OFF position.
			Increase the setting of the adjustment control to maximum clockwise position.
			Exercise the valve by rapidly turning the control valve on and off or alternately increasing and decreasing the pressure adjustment control to cause the valve to operate.
	Engine rpm cannot be raised to the value required as determined by the UL plate, even at full throttle. Tachometer reading is low, pressure gauge reading is too low.	Flow requirements may be exceeding the capacity of the pump.	The capacity of the pump in the SERIES or PRESSURE position is limited to 50 percent of its rated capacity at 250 psi (1 700 kPa) and 70 percent at 200 psi (1 400 kPa) net pump pressure.
		Throttle linkage may have slipped or be stuck.	Check the action of the linkage. It may be possible to override the action of the throttle by using the accelerator or hand throttle in the cab or by manually operating the linkage at the carburetor.
		Severe engine overheating can reduce the power available to drive the pump.	Check the engine temperature gauge. Adjust the auxiliary cooling valve to maintain the proper operating temperature.
			Check the level of the coolant in the radiator. If it is too low and the water that is being pumped is clean and pure, open the radiator fill valve to bring the coolant up to the proper level.
		Reduced engine power.	If additional pressure is essential, use another pumper. Take the unit out of service until it can be repaired.
The pump is unable to supply its rated capacity.	The rpm reading on the tachometer is normal when compared to the UL plate.	Two-stage pump: • Transfer valve is in the wrong position.	The transfer valve should be in the PARALLEL or VOLUME position anytime 50 percent or more of the capacity of the pump is needed.
		• The swing check valve is not opening completely.	Remove the strainer from the large intake opening on each side of the pump. Make sure that the valve swings freely by inserting a rod and pushing on the face of the valve.

Problem	Symptoms	Probable Cause	Possible Solutions
The pump is unable to supply its rated capacity.	The rpm reading on the tachometer is normal when compared to the UL plate.	Two-stage pump: • The swing check valve is not opening completely.	Remove the strainer from the large intake opening on each side of the pump. Make sure that the valve swings freely by inserting a rod and pushing on the face of valve.
	The intake gauge registers or has a positive pressure indicated.	Blockage in the waterways of the pump. An object lodged inside the impeller can reduce the capacity.	Thoroughly back-flush the pump by connecting a supply line to the highest discharge outlet and opening the large intake fittings.
		Wear in the pump, usually the clearance rings or relief valve, allowing slippage from the discharge back to the intake.	Remove the pumper from service until it can be repaired.
	The intake compound gauge is registering a high vacuum, and the discharge pressure gauge is fluctuating (cavitation).	Blockage of the strainer at the intake fitting of the pump.	Disconnect the intake line and clean any accumulated debris from the strainer.
		Inadequate water supply or supply lines.	Connect an additional supply line to the intake of the pump.
			Reduce the amount of discharge lines being supplied.
			Lower the discharge pressure to reduce the amount of water flowing through the lines.
	Unable to develop enough engine rpm at full throttle to supply the rated capacity.	See items listed under "Pump will not develop sufficient pressure with low engine rpm."	
Pump overheating while in operation.	Pump overheating warning light or physical observation.	Inadequate flow through the pump while operating under pressure.	Open the booster cooling valve or set the circulator valve to TANK or SPILL position as appropriate.
			Open the tank fill valve if it is connected to the discharge side of the pump.
			Use the booster line to maintain a minimum flow of water while pumping.
		Excessive throttle on relief valve-equipped pumps.	Reduce engine rpm.
Relief valve is inoperative or slow acting.	Pressure surges are excessive when individual hoselines are shut down.	Strainer in the pressure line to the pilot valve is dirty.	Open the flush line while pumping clean water to back-flush the in-line strainer.
			Remove the strainer element and wash in clear water.
		Relief valve is corroded or dirty.	If the relief valve is equipped with a shut-off, set the discharge pressure on the pump to 150 psi (1 050 kPa), set the relief valve adjustment control to minimum and alternately turn the valve off and on for 60 seconds. If no control valve is provided, set the pump pressure to 150 psi (1 050 psi) and cause the relief valve to operate by cranking the adjustment control in and out rapidly.

Problems Common to all Types of Operation			
Problem	**Symptoms**	**Probable Cause**	**Possible Solutions**
Relief valve is inoperative or slow acting.	Pressure surges are excessive when individual hoselines are shut down.	Defective relief valve	Dismantle the valve and clean all working parts, replacing all defective items as needed.
Operating from the Tank			
Unable to establish an adequate operating pressure or a loss of pressure occurs when the first discharge valve is opened.	Pressure increases with the engine rpm up to a point, then holds steady or fluctuates.	Some air is trapped in the pump as it fills with water.	Operate the primer until all of the air is removed from the pump. Transfer the pump from SERIES to PARALLEL and back several times while flowing water.
			If only small lines are being supplied, opening the pump to tank valve and increasing the velocity of the water through the pump for a short time may remove the rest of the air.
		Automatic transmission: • Intermittent transmission slippage.	Adjust transmission.
		• Low transmission fluid level.	Increase fluid level.
		• Transmission not remaining in correct pumping gear.	Adjust transmission.
Fluctuation of the pressure gauge and a reduction of discharge pressure when additional lines are put in service.	High vacuum reading on the intake compound gauge.	The tank-to-pump valve may not have been fully opened or has vibrated to a partially CLOSED position.	Check the tank-to-pump valve and lock it in the OPEN position if the valve has a locking mechanism.
		Tank-to-pump piping may be too small to supply the amount of water required by the hoselines in service.	Shut down one of the hoselines if fire-ground conditions permit.
			Reduce the discharge pressure until fluctuations stop and pressure gauge begins to drop.
While pumping, the discharge pressure drops to a very low value and water supply is interrupted.	Compound gauge on the intake reads 0 or fluctuates. Engine speed increases.	An air leak in the pump.	Check all caps and valves on the intake side of the pump.
	Water gauge reads empty.	The water supply from the tank is exhausted or nearly so.	Reduce the pressure until the gauge becomes steady and flow resumes.
			Arrange for another water supply as soon as possible.
Operating from Draft			
The suction line collapses when the discharge valve to a hoseline is opened.	The intake pressure drops to less than 0. Discharge pressure also drops.	Kinks in suction lines can cause excessive friction loss when the water begins to move.	Rearrange the suction line to eliminate any kinks or restrictions.

Operating from a Hydrant			
Problem	**Symptoms**	**Probable Cause**	**Possible Solutions**
The suction line collapses when the discharge valve to a hoseline is opened.	The intake pressure drops to less than 0. Discharge pressure also drops.	Suction line may be too small for the amount of flow needed.	3-inch (77 mm) suction hose can supply approximately 500 gpm (2 000 L/min), but gated 2½-inch (65 mm) intake fittings may limit the flow to less that 300 gpm (1 200 L/min). If 2½- or 3-inch (65 mm) or 77 mm) suction line is used, it should be brought into the large intake, either through a suction siamese or bell reducer.
	Water coming out of the ground around the barrel of the hydrant.	Hydrant not fully opened.	Turn the hydrant wrench in a counter-clockwise direction until it reaches the limit of its travel.
While supplying water, the suction line collapses and the pump begins to cavitate.	Intake pressure drops to less than 0. Discharge pressure fluctuates and decreases.	Additional water being demanded by the hoselines that are being supplied.	Reduce the number of hoselines in service or the flow settings on the nozzles.
			Reduce the discharge pressure on the pump by reducing the throttle setting until cavitation stops.
		Additional demands on the water system may have reduced the residual pressure in the system.	Decrease the amount of water being used by changing the nozzle settings or taking attack lines out of service.
			Obtain a supplementary supply from another hydrant, a relay, or from a water shuttle.
Operating from Draft			
Pump will not prime.	Unable to get water into the pump through the hard suction hose. No vacuum reading is registered on the intake compound gauge.	Drain valve left open.	Check the master drain valve to make sure it is fully closed. Check the individual drain valves for governor, auxiliary cooler, and so on.
		Intake valves left open or caps not airtight.	Tighten caps on large suction fittings that are not being used.
			Make sure the tank-to-pump valve is closed if the tank is empty.
		Booster line cooler valve or circulator valve left in OPEN position (Barton American pump).	Shut the booster line cooling valve.
			Put the circulator valve in the Vertical position, between the TANK and SPILL settings.
		Intake relief valve may be leaking.	If the relief valve is equipped with a shut-off valve, close it. If it has fire hose threads on the discharge opening, put a cap on it.
		Suction hose connections are not airtight.	Listen for air leaks at each connection. Tighten with a rubber mallet if any connection appears to be leaking.

Problem	Symptoms	Probable Cause	Possible Solutions
Pump will not prime.	Unable to get water into the pump through the hard suction hose. No vacuum reading is registered on the intake compound gauge.	Suction hose connection to the floating strainer not airtight.	Tighten the coupling with a rubber mallet or a spanner wrench.
		Pump packing is too loose and leaking air.	Take pumper out of service until the packing can be adjusted or the pump repacked.
		Not operating the primer long enough to get rid of the air.	A typical fire pump requires 15 seconds to prime through 20 feet (6 m) of suction hose but may take as long as 30 seconds to prime completely.
		Tank-to-pump valve not sealing with an empty tank.	Partially fill tank (temporary). Repair valve (permanent).
			Engage the pump, build up 100 psi (700 kPa), and discharge water from the booster line. While keeping the end of the suction hose submerged, take the cap off the end and install the strainer. Slowly close the tank-to-pump valve while continuing to flow water from the booster line. The pump is now primed.
		Engine rpm is too low.	The engine rpm should be as specified in the manufacturer's instructions but is usually 1,000 to 1,200 rpm.
		No oil in the reservoir for the priming pump.	A supply of oil should be carried on any pumper that uses oil for priming. If this is the case, oil can be put in the reservoir to replenish the supply.
			If the regular priming oil is not available, putting water in the reservoir may enable the primer to operate, but it should be thoroughly cleaned out and a supply of oil put in at the first opportunity.
	The electric motor will not operate to drive the primer.	A bad battery or a poor connection between the cable and battery terminals.	Inspect the battery terminals. If they are corroded, it may be possible to loosen the fastening and clean the terminal sufficiently to run.
	Very little air is being discharged from the primer.	Defective primer.	If the primer will not operate for mechanical reasons, the pump can be primed by connecting the hard suction hose to the pump and installing the cap on the end of the hose, then submerging the hose under water. Open the tank-to-pump valve, allowing the suction hose to fill with water as well as the pump.
The pump loses its prime when the first discharge valve is opened and water begins to flow.	The discharge pressure gauge drops sharply.	Valve may have been opened too rapidly.	Carefully observe pressure gauge while slowly opening the discharge valve. If the pressure begins to drop suddenly, pause and allow it to stabilize before continuing.

Problem	Symptoms	Probable Cause	Possible Solutions
The pump loses its prime when the first discharge valve is opened and water begins to flow.	The discharge pressure gauge drops sharply.	The pump was not completely primed and still had some air trapped in it when the primer was released.	Allow the primer to continue to operate until a steady stream of water is discharging from it before closing the priming valve.
			If pressure drops suddenly while opening a discharge valve, operate the primer momentarily to remove any remaining air from the pump.
		The pump may not be turning fast enough to sustain the prime when water begins to flow.	Adjust the discharge pressure to 75 psi (525 kPa) or more before opening the discharge valve.
		The priming valve can stick causing air to leak into the pump.	Check the priming valve control to see that it is in the CLOSED position. Exercise the valve to clear any debris from the valve seat.
		Rock or debris in impeller.	Take pumper out of service until it can be repaired.
	The reading on the pressure gauge drops sharply and the intake gauge returns to the 0 reading.	A high spot in the suction line has trapped a quantity of air when the pump was primed. This air has been drawn into the pump when the water began to move through the suction hose.	Attempt to eliminate the high spot by moving the suction hose and prime the pump again.
			If the high spot cannot be eliminated, it may be possible to scavenge the air from the suction hose by operating the primer again each time the pressure begins to drop.
The pump loses its prime during the course of a pumping operation.	The pump loses it prime when all nozzles are closed and no water is flowing.	An air leak on the intake side of the pump.	Check all connections to see that they are airtight.
		The packing may be mis-adjusted, allowing air to leak into the pump around the shaft.	Open a discharge outlet and allow water to flow at all times to maintain a higher vacuum reading in the intake side of the pump. If the problem becomes acute, take the pumper out of service until it can be repaired.
	The pump loses its prime when it is operating near its maximum capacity. The vacuum reading on the intake gauge is near 0 and is fluctuating.	A whirlpool over the strainer is allowing air to get into the pump through the suction hose.	Put a board or other object over the whirlpool to break up the whirling motion and stop the air from getting into the suction hose.
		Air leak on the intake side of the pump.	Check all connections.
The pump goes into cavitation when the flow increases.	The intake gauge registers more than 22 inches (559 mm) of vacuum, the pressure gauge fluctuates and decreases reading.	The flow exceeds the capacity of the pump at the lift that is required.	The capacity of the pump decreases as the lift increases. At a 20-foot (6 m) lift, the capacity of the pump is only 60 percent of what it would be with a 10-foot (3 m) lift.

Operating from Draft			
Problem	**Symptoms**	**Probable Cause**	**Possible Solutions**
The pump goes into cavitation when the flow increases.	The intake gauge registers more than 22 inches (559 mm) of vacuum, the pressure gauge fluctuates and decreases reading.	The suction line may be partially blocked.	Debris blocking the strainer on the suction hose. Clean the strainer manually.
			Debris is trapped in the strainer at the intake of the pump. Shut down the pump, remove the suction hose and clear the strainer.
		Inner rubber liner of suction hose has become separated from hose. The result is restriction caused by the "bubble" of inner liner.	The suction hose can collapse. It will have to be replaced if the reduced capacity is unacceptable.
			Replace suction hose.
Operating in Relay			
Intake supply line collapses when the throttle setting is increased to establish the initial discharge pressure as required.	The intake pressure gauge reading is negative, that is, reading vacuum instead of pressure.	The dump line or uncapped discharge used to waste water while establishing the relay may still be open.	Close the valve to any uncapped discharge or dump line.
			If the pumper is operating as the terminal unit in a relay, adjust the valve on the dump line to bring the residual pressure at the intake of the pump to 50 psi (350 kPa).
		The terminal pumper may be attempting to take more water from the relay than it can supply.	Notify the water supply officer that the relay is unable to supply the amount of water being called for so that additional supply lines can be put in service.
			Reduce the discharge pressure until the intake gauge registers a positive reading.
While the relay is operating, the intake pressure increases above 50 psi (350 kPa).	The intake pressure gauge is reading above 50 psi (350 kPa) and the discharge pressure also increases accordingly.	Changes in flow of the attack line cause the friction loss to decrease and the residual pressure to increase.	No action is necessary unless the pressure increase becomes dangerous. Minor variations are to be expected in a relay and frequent adjustments are undesirable.
While the relay is operating, the intake pressure increases dangerously.	Intake pressure gauge is reading above 150 psi (1 050 kPa), the discharge pressure is above 200 psi (1 050 kPa).	Hoselines have been shut down with no corresponding dumping of excess water.	Open the uncapped discharge or dump line until the intake residual pressure returns to 50 psi (350 kPa).

Courtesy of Bill Eckman.

OPERATING A PUMPER FROM THE TANK ON THE APPARATUS
Step 1: Positioning the Apparatus

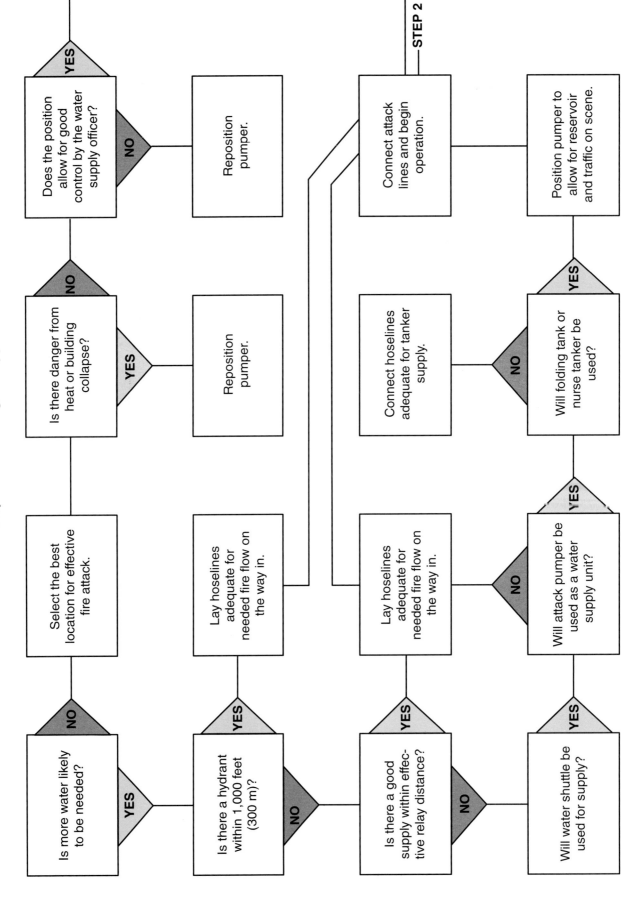

OPERATING A PUMPER FROM THE TANK ON THE APPARATUS
Step 2: Put Pump in Service and Establish Operating Pressure

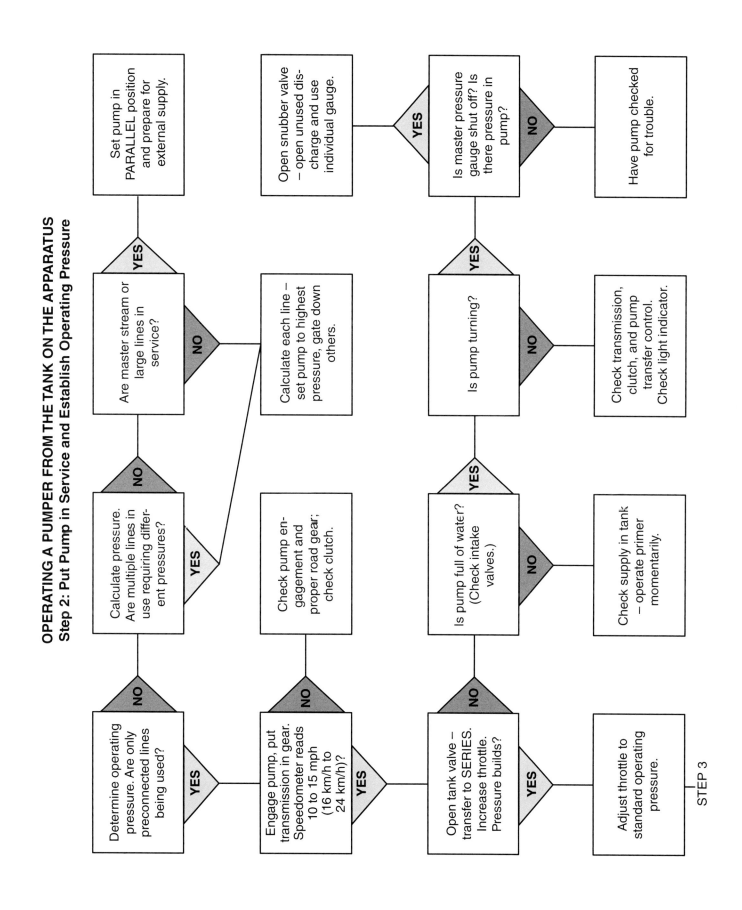

OPERATING A PUMPER FROM THE TANK ON THE APPARATUS
Step 3: Maintaining Good Operating Pressure

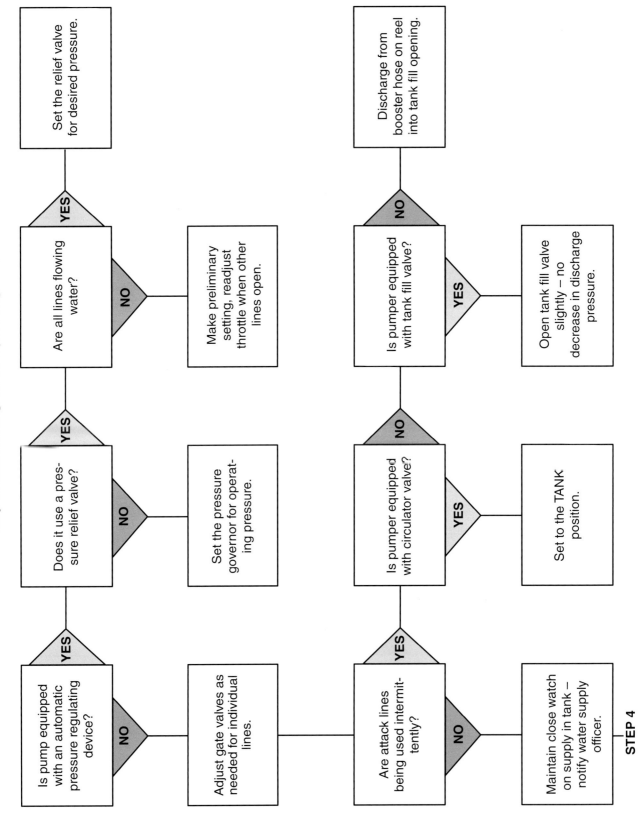

Is pump equipped with an automatic pressure regulating device?

— YES → Does it use a pressure relief valve? — YES → Are all lines flowing water? — YES → Set the relief valve for desired pressure.

Does it use a pressure relief valve? — NO → Set the pressure governor for operating pressure.

Are all lines flowing water? — NO → Make preliminary setting, readjust throttle when other lines open.

Is pump equipped with an automatic pressure regulating device? — NO → Adjust gate valves as needed for individual lines.

Adjust gate valves as needed for individual lines. → Are attack lines being used intermittently? — YES → Is pumper equipped with circulator valve? — NO → Is pumper equipped with tank fill valve? — NO → Discharge from booster hose on reel into tank fill opening.

Is pumper equipped with circulator valve? — YES → Set to the TANK position.

Is pumper equipped with tank fill valve? — YES → Open tank fill valve slightly – no decrease in discharge pressure.

Are attack lines being used intermittently? — NO → Maintain close watch on supply in tank – notify water supply officer.

STEP 4

OPERATING A PUMPER FROM THE TANK ON THE APPARATUS
Step 4: Making the Transition to an External Supply

Will the supply be from a hydrant or another pumper under pressure?

YES → Connect supply line to gated intake – bleed off air trapped in hoseline – open intake valve slowly while closing tank valve. → Has the discharge pressure changed from set pressure?

NO (from "Will the supply...") → Will external supply require drafting or folding tank operation?

Has the discharge pressure changed from set pressure?

YES → Readjust throttle as needed – reset relief valve or pressure governor.

NO → As soon as a good supply is available, open tank fill valve slightly to fill tank – do not take enough to limit fire flow. → **STEP 5**

Will external supply require drafting or folding tank operation? → Is the pumper equipped with a gated large suction inlet?

Is the pumper equipped with a gated large suction inlet?

YES → Connect large suction hose with gate closed. Use floating or low level strainer and make all connections airtight. → Open suction valve while closing tank valve. Operate primer as needed. Has discharge pressure changed from the set point?

NO → Fire flow will be interrupted while connections are made and draft procedures followed.

Open suction valve while closing tank valve. Operate primer as needed. Has discharge pressure changed from the set point?

YES → Readjust throttle as needed – reset relief valve or pressure governor.

NO → As soon as a good supply is available, open tank fill valve slightly to fill tank – do not take enough to limit fire flow.

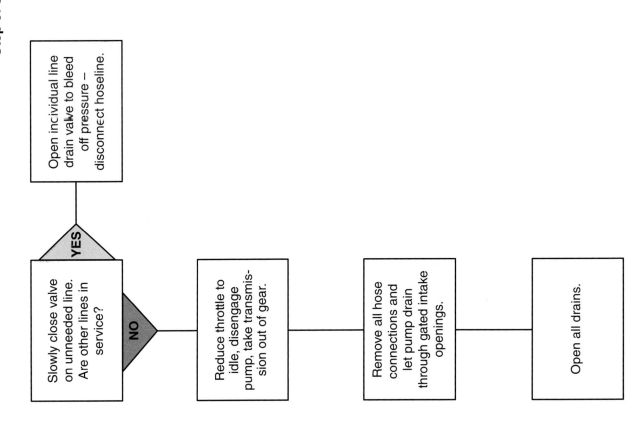

OPERATING FROM A HYDRANT
Step 1: Positioning the Pumper and Connecting to the Hydrant

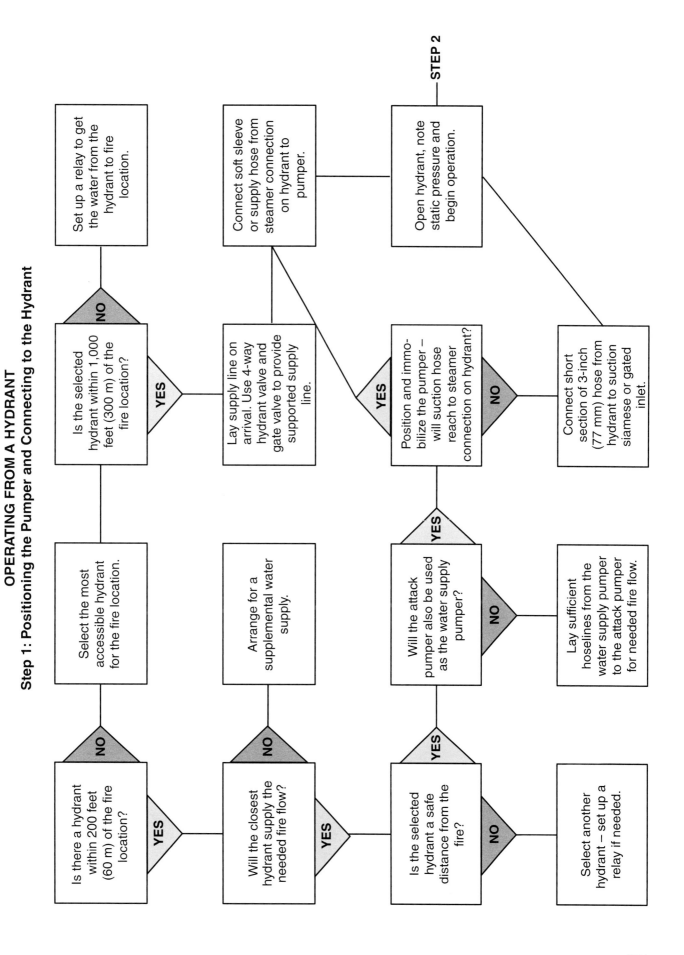

OPERATING FROM A HYDRANT
Step 2: Putting the Pumper in Service

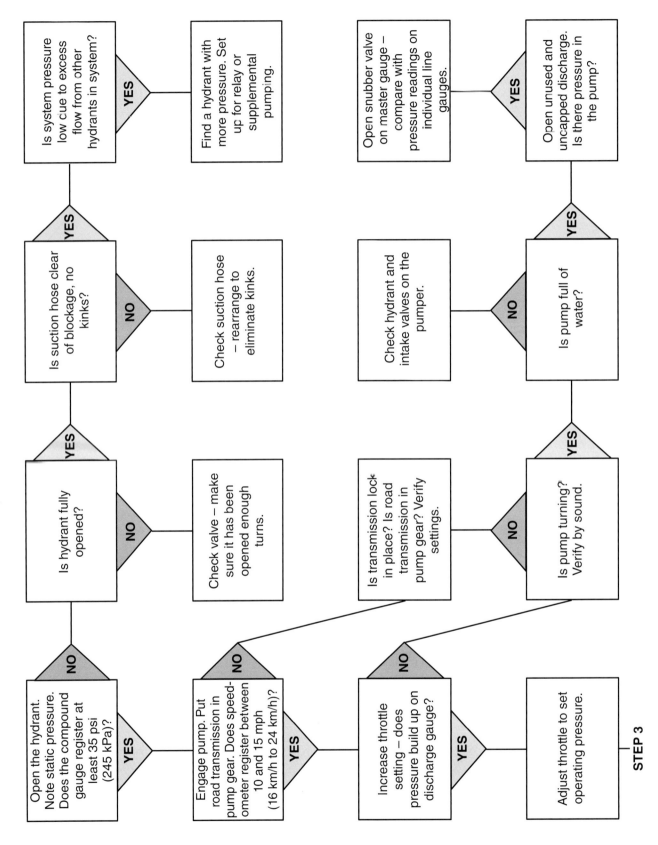

Open the hydrant. Note static pressure. Does the compound gauge register at least 35 psi (245 kPa)?

YES → Is hydrant fully opened?

NO → Check valve – make sure it has been opened enough turns.

Is hydrant fully opened?

YES → Is suction hose clear of blockage, no kinks?

NO → Check suction hose – rearrange to eliminate kinks.

Is suction hose clear of blockage, no kinks?

YES → Is system pressure low cue to excess flow from other hydrants in system?

YES → Find a hydrant with more pressure. Set up for relay or supplemental pumping.

Engage pump. Put road transmission in pump gear. Does speed-ometer register between 10 and 15 mph (16 km/h to 24 km/h)?

NO → Is transmission lock in place? Is road transmission in pump gear? Verify settings.

Check hydrant and intake valves on the pumper.

YES → Is pump turning? Verify by sound.

NO → Is pump full of water?

Is pump full of water?

YES → Open unused and uncapped discharge. Is there pressure in the pump?

YES → Open snubber valve on master gauge – compare with pressure readings on individual line gauges.

Increase throttle setting – does pressure build up on discharge gauge?

NO → Is pump turning? Verify by sound.

YES → Adjust throttle to set operating pressure.

STEP 3

OPERATING FROM A HYDRANT
Step 3: Maintain Operating Pressure

Observe compound gauge while opening discharge valves – does incoming pressure drop more than 25 percent?

→ **YES** → Notify water supply officer that more than 50 percent of the available water is being used.

→ **NO** → **Is engine temperature at or below the normal operating point?**

→ **NO** → Open auxiliary cooling valve far enough to maintain normal operating temperature of the engine.

→ **YES** → **Is the pump equipped with an automatic pressure control device?**

→ **NO** → Closely observe master pressure gauge – adjust throttle to maintain set pressure.

→ **YES** → **Does pump have pressure relief valve?**

→ **NO** → Set the pressure governor according to manufacturer's instructions.

→ **YES** → **Are all discharge hoselines flowing at a maximum flow rate?**

→ **NO** → Make preliminary adjustment of relief valve – adjust throttle when additional lines are put in service.

→ **YES** → **Adjust relief valve to be closed at pressure set point. Does indicator light show valve to be closed?**

→ **NO** → Readjust pressure set control while observing pressure gauge to determine relief valve position.

→ **YES** → **Does indicator show the relief valve opening when lines are shut down?**

→ **NO** → Check relief valve shutoff controls, mechanical as well as hydraulic.

→ **YES** → **Are attack lines being opened and closed intermittently and frequently?**

→ **YES** → Set circulator valve to SPILL position or set small hoseline to discharge continuously under vehicle.

→ **NO** → **STEP 4**

OPERATING FROM A HYDRANT
Step 4: Operating Practices

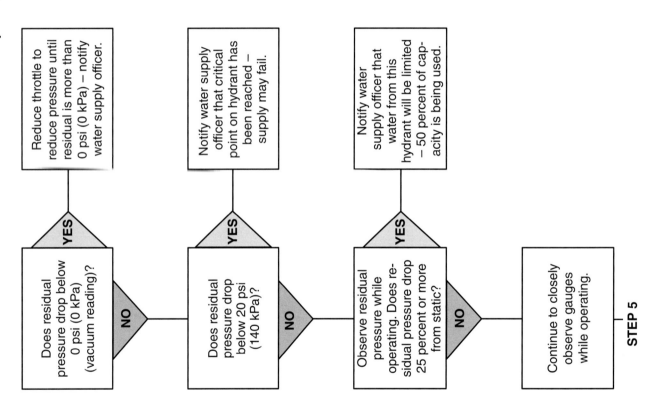

Does residual pressure drop below 0 psi (0 kPa) (vacuum reading)?

YES → Reduce throttle to reduce pressure until residual is more than 0 psi (0 kPa) – notify water supply officer.

NO ↓

Does residual pressure drop below 20 psi (140 kPa)?

YES → Notify water supply officer that critical point on hydrant has been reached – supply may fail.

NO ↓

Observe residual pressure while operating. Does residual pressure drop 25 percent or more from static?

YES → Notify water supply officer that water from this hydrant will be limited – 50 percent of capacity is being used.

NO ↓

Continue to closely observe gauges while operating.

STEP 5

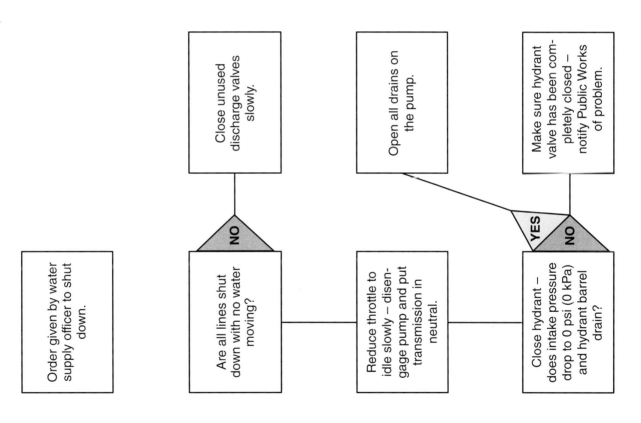

Order given by water supply officer to shut down.

Close unused discharge valves slowly.

NO

Are all lines shut down with no water moving?

Reduce throttle to idle slowly – disengage pump and put transmission in neutral.

Open all drains on the pump.

YES

NO

Close hydrant – does intake pressure drop to 0 psi (0 kPa) and hydrant barrel drain?

Make sure hydrant valve has been completely closed – notify Public Works of problem.

OPERATING FROM DRAFT
Step 1: Positioning, Connecting, and Priming the Pumper

STEP 2

Adjust throttle to attain desired operating pressure.

Open discharge valve while observing gauge and adjusting throttle. Does pressure gauge drop below 50 psi (350 kPa)?

NO / **YES**

Operate primer control momentarily until pressure increases above 50 psi (350 kPa). Continue to open discharge valve.

Check electrical and mechanical controls — operate manual override.

YES / **NO**

Check controls — operate manual override.

Engage pump and set transmission — increase throttle. Does discharge pressure go above 50 psi (350 kPa)?

NO / **YES**

Does pump prime? Is water discharged from primer or pressure built up within 30 seconds.

YES / **NO**

Is primer operating? (sound of pump turning with rotary primer or engine running rough when vacuum primer operated).

NO / **YES**

Select a better draft location or reposition the pumper.

Check transmission and pump shift control. Has pump transfer completed? Is green light on?

NO / **YES**

Operate primer. Does suction hose drop as it fills with water?

YES / **NO**

Check all suction hose connections, drains, and inlet or discharge outlets for air leaks.

Select draft site. Position and immobilize pumper. Is total lift less than 20 feet (6 m)?

NO / **YES**

Can the water be reached with 20 feet (6 m) of hard suction hose?

NO / **YES**

Connect suction hose with airtight connections. Is strainer float type or 24 inches (600 mm) below surface of the water?

YES / **NO**

Dam stream or dig out for greater depth.

OPERATING FROM DRAFT
Step 2: Putting the Pumper in Service

Calculate required pressure. Is the set pressure less than 250 psi (1 750 kPa)?

YES → Call for relay pumpers or additional hoselines to reduce needed pressure.

NO → Has the transfer valve completed its travel? (pressure light is on or manual indicator observation)

NO → Operate manual override controls or transfer back to volume – then to pressure.

YES → Set the transfer control to PRESSURE position. Adjust throttle. Can the desired pressure be attained?

Is the required flow 50 percent or more of the rated capacity or is it a single-stage pump?

YES → Set the transfer control to PRESSURE position. Adjust throttle. Can the desired pressure be attained?

NO → Check tachometer. Is rpm indicated correct for pressure needed per UL test plate?

NO → Check travel of throttle – try using throttle in cab or accelerator to get correct rpm.

YES → Is transmission lock in place? Is road transmission in pump gear?

YES (desired pressure attained) → Open discharge valves and adjust throttle. Can the desired pressure be attained?

NO → Does compound gauge indicate more that 20 inches (500) of vacuum?

YES → Check for excess flow rate or for blockage in strainer or suction hose.

NO → Is transmission lock in place? Is road transmission in pump gear?

Does compound gauge indicate more that 20 inches (500) of vacuum?

NO → Is pump cavitating? Pressure should drop immediately when rpm drops.

YES → Reduce rpm to the threshold of cavitation. Pressure will decrease with rpm change.

Is transmission lock in place? Is road transmission in pump gear?

NO → Slowly shut down pump. Put transmission in pump gear — repeat process.

Open discharge valves and adjust throttle. Can the desired pressure be attained?

YES → Set operating controls to maintain pressure.

STEP 3

OPERATING FROM DRAFT
Step 3: Maintain Operating Pressure

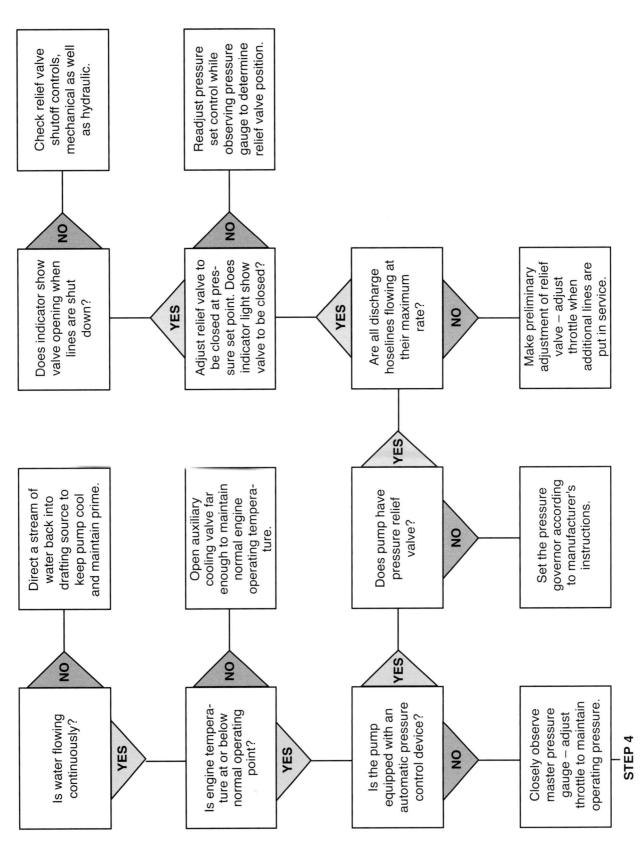

Is water flowing continuously? → NO → Direct a stream of water back into drafting source to keep pump cool and maintain prime.

YES ↓

Is engine temperature at or below normal operating point? → NO → Open auxiliary cooling valve far enough to maintain normal engine operating temperature.

YES ↓

Is the pump equipped with an automatic pressure control device? → NO → Closely observe master pressure gauge – adjust throttle to maintain operating pressure. → STEP 4

YES ↓

Does pump have pressure relief valve? → NO → Set the pressure governor according to manufacturer's instructions.

YES ↓

Are all discharge hoselines flowing at their maximum rate? → NO → Make preliminary adjustment of relief valve – adjust throttle when additional lines are put in service.

YES ↓

Adjust relief valve to be closed at pressure set point. Does indicator light show valve to be closed? → NO → Readjust pressure set control while observing pressure gauge to determine relief valve position.

YES ↓

Does indicator show valve opening when lines are shut down? → NO → Check relief valve shutoff controls, mechanical as well as hydraulic.

388   Chapter 10 • Operating Fire Pumps

OPERATING FROM DRAFT
Step 4: Shutting Down

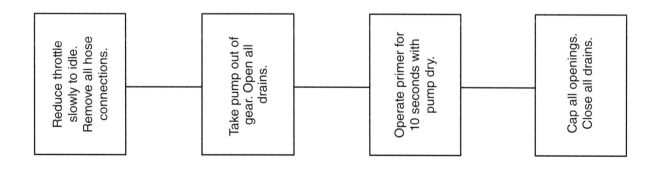

Reduce throttle slowly to idle. Remove all hose connections.

Take pump out of gear. Open all drains.

Operate primer for 10 seconds with pump dry.

Cap all openings. Close all drains.

NOTE: The information contained in this skill sheet provides sound, generic advice for engaging and disengaging a PTO for an apparatus with an automatic transmission. Follow manufacturer's instructions for apparatus with a manual transmission.

While many of the basic principles are the same for all makes and models of pumps and apparatus, each manufacturer's equipment has special nuances with which the driver/operator must be familiar. For that reason, the driver/operator should always consult the operator's manual for the apparatus and pump being operated. Remember to always follow manufacturer's recommendations and department standard operating procedures (SOPs).

Engaging the Pump

Step 1: Bring the apparatus to a full stop, and set the parking brake. Secure vehicle with wheel chocks if not in a pump and roll application.

Step 2: Place the drive transmission into neutral or leave in drive, depending on the manufacturer's instructions.

Step 3: Operate the PTO control. This may be a lever, push-pull control, or other type switch located in the cab.

Step 4: Place the drive transmission into the gear recommended by the manufacturer. Most PTO applications will require leaving the vehicle in neutral.

    a. Once the PTO has been properly activated and the pump is engaged, an indicator light on the dashboard should light. This signals that the pump is operational. If this light does not illuminate, repeat the procedure.

    b. Excessive engine rpms may result in dangerous pump pressures.

Step 5: Release the parking brake (pump and roll only).

Disengaging the Pump

Step 1: Use the throttle control to reduce the engine to idle speed.

Step 2: Set the parking brake.

Step 3: Place the drive transmission into the gear recommended by the manufacturer.

Step 4: Operate the PTO control in the direction opposite of that used to engage the pump.

NOTE: The PTO should now be deactivated and the pump should not be in gear. The pump indicator light should not be illuminated. If it is still lit, repeat the procedures

Step 5: Once the PTO is disengaged, resume normal operations.

NOTE: The information contained in this skill sheet provides sound, generic advice for engaging and disengaging a midship transfer pump for an apparatus with an automatic transmission. Follow manufacturer's instructions for apparatus with a manual transmission.

While many of the basic principles are the same for all makes and models of pumps and apparatus, each manufacturer's equipment has special nuances with which the driver/operator must be familiar. For that reason, the driver/operator should always consult the operator's manual for the apparatus and pump being operated. Remember to always follow manufacturer's recommendations and department standard operating procedures (SOPs).

Engaging the Pump

Step 1: Bring the apparatus to a full stop.

Step 2: Shift the transmission into neutral.

Step 3: Set the apparatus parking brake.

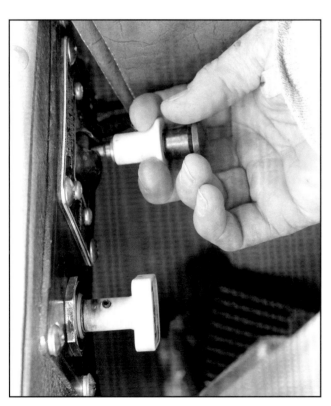

Step 4: Operate the pump shift control to transfer power from the drive axle to the pump drive.

NOTE: If the driver/operator must leave the cab to perform this step, he or she should secure the vehicle with wheel chocks prior to engaging the pump.

Step 5: Shift the transmission into the appropriate gear for pumping.

NOTE: A pump indicator light should illuminate to signify to the driver/operator that the apparatus is ready to pump.

Disengaging the Pump

Step 1: Use the throttle control to reduce the engine speed to idle.

Step 2: Shift the transmission into neutral.

NOTE: The pump indicator light should not be illuminated. If it is still lit, repeat the procedure.

Step 3: Operate the pump shift control to transfer power from the pump drive to the drive axle.

NOTE: Remember to always follow manufacturer's recommendations and department standard operating procedures (SOPs).

Step 1: Position the apparatus in a safe position, and immobilize it by setting the parking brake and chocking the wheels.

Step 2: Make the fire pump operational.

Step 3: Open the tank-to-pump valve fully.

Step 4: (Multistage pump) Set the transfer valve to the proper position. SERIES (PRESSURE) position (generally).

Step 5: Increase the engine rpm using the hand throttle or pressure governor (must be in correct mode).

Step 6: Observe the master pressure gauge as the throttle/ pressure governor is being advanced.

    a. If the pump is normally full of water, the master pressure gauge should start to rise as soon as the rpm is increased. Use primer as dictated by local SOPs to evacuate air.

    b. If the pump has been drained of water, it will be full of air. The air has to be forced out of the pump by the water as it enters before discharge pressure can build. At least one of the discharge valves or the tank fill line must be open before the air can escape and the pump can fill with water.

NOTE: If the master pressure gauge still fails to register a reading, the pump may not be in the proper gear. Immediately decrease the engine speed and return to the apparatus cab and verify that the transmission is in the proper gear or that the pump shift transfer has been made. (Pressure governors usually will not operate and show an error if the pump is not engaged.)

Step 7: If none of the attack lines are ready to be charged by the time the pump pressure has built up, allow water to circulate using one of the following methods.

    a. Pull some of the booster line off the reel, securely tie off the nozzle to a solid object, open the valve that supplies the booster reel, and discharge water in a direction that will not harm people or damage property.

    b. Open a discharge drain valve.

    c. Partially open the tank fill valve or pump-to-tank line.

    d. Use a bypass or circulator valve if the apparatus is so equipped.

10-3
Perform pump operations from the apparatus water tank.

SKILL SHEETS

Step 8: Initiate waterflow if the hoselines are ready for water when the pressure is set. Open the discharge valve slowly, locking in the OPEN position.

Step 9: Set the relief valve/or ensure pressure governor is in the correct mode.

Step 10: Prevent overheating by maintaining water movement through the pump.

Use the tank fill line to circulate water through the booster tank.

Step 11: Monitor the water level in the tank.

    a. Notify the officer in charge of the amount of water remaining in the tank.

    b. Estimate the amount of time water will last at present rate of consumption.

SKILL SHEETS

10-4

Make the transition from the apparatus water tank to an external pressurized water supply.

NOTE: Always follow manufacturer's recommendations and department standard operating procedures (SOPs).

Step 1: Position the apparatus in a safe position, and immobilize it by setting the parking brake and chocking the wheels.

Step 2: Engage the pump.

Step 3: Open the tank-to-pump valve.

Step 4: Set the transfer valve to the SERIES (PRESSURE) position (if necessary).

Step 5: Open discharge(s) and increase the throttle setting to obtain the desired pressure, priming (if necessary).

Step 6: Set the relief valve or pressure governor.

Step 8: As soon as an adequate supply of water is available, divert enough of it through the tank fill line to replenish the supply in the tank.

Step 7: When an external supply becomes available, open the intake valve while adjusting the throttle to avoid a pressure surge.

    a. If using a pressure governor, switch to "rpm" mode and ensure air is bled from the supply line before opening intake and switch back to "pressure" mode.

    b. Adjust throttle to maintain discharge pressure.

    c. Position tank-to-pump valve per local SOPs.

NOTE: Always follow manufacturer's recommendations and department standard operating procedures (SOPs).

Step 1: Position the apparatus in a safe position, and immobilize it by setting the parking brake and chocking the wheels.

Step 2: Make hydrant connections, open intakes, and bleed air pressure as needed.

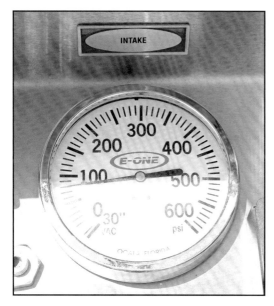

Step 3: Note the static pressure in the water system by reading the master intake. Check this pressure after the pump is full of water and after pressure in the system has stabilized.

Step 4: Multistage pump: Set the transfer valve to the proper position. SERIES (PRESSURE) position (generally).

Step 5: Increase the engine rpm, using the hand throttle/ pressure governor (ensure in "pressure").

Step 6: Observe the master pressure gauge as the throttle is being advanced.

a. If the pump is normally full of water, the master pressure gauge should start to rise as soon as the rpm is increased. Use primer as dictated by local SOPs to evacuate air.

b. If the pump has been drained of water, it will be full of air. The air has to be forced out of the pump by the water as it enters before discharge pressure can build. At least one of the discharge valves or the tank fill line must be open before the air can escape and the pump can fill with water.

Step 7: If none of the attack lines is ready to be charged by the time the pump pressure has built up, allow water to circulate.

a. Partially open the pump-to-tank line.

b. Remove air trapped in the pump and piping.

c. Establish a stable pressure.

Step 8: If the hoselines are ready for water when the pressure is set, initiate waterflow. Open the discharge valve slowly.

Step 9: Set the automatic pressure-regulating device for the operating pressure or verify pressure governor into the correct mode.

Step 10: Monitor the pump temperature to prevent overheating, using one of the following methods as appropriate:

a. Disengage fire pump if possible.

b. Use a bypass or circulator valve if the apparatus is so equipped.

c. Partially open the tank fill valve.

d. Discharge water to atmosphere by hoseline or outlet.

Step 1: Select the drafting site, ensuring that there is an adequate water depth and water quality and that the location is accessible and stable.

Step 2: Ensure that apparatus will operate on an improved surface.

Step 3: Position the apparatus to allow connection of hard intake hose.

CAUTION: Any personnel working near the edge of bodies of water are required to wear a personal flotation device (PFD).

Step 4: Assemble hose and strainers.

Step 6: Connect the strainer to the end of the intake hose.

Step 7: Tie the guide rope to the strainer securely.

Step 5: Connect the sections of intake hose.
   a. Align each section of hose before turning it.
   b. Hand tighten connections.
   c. Use a rubber mallet as necessary to make connections airtight.

Step 8: Connect intake hose to apparatus, ensuring all connections are tight.

Step 9: Place the intake hose and strainer into the water slowly to avoid stirring up the sediment and dirt in the water.

Step 10: Place pump in gear. Operate primer until waterflow is established (operate no longer than manufacturer recommendations).

Step 11: Operate pump/pressure governor in correct mode.

Step 1: Position the pumper as close to the water supply as possible; establish water supply per local SOP. Chock wheels when vehicle is parked.

Step 2: Attach water supply to the FDC.

    a. Remove FDC cap.

    b. Spin inlet swivel connections to make sure that they turn freely.

    c. Check FDC inlets for gaskets, obstructions, and to make sure that clappers work freely.

    d. Attach appropriate-sized lines to supply the FDC (1¾-inch [45 mm] hose for 1½-inch [38 mm] FDC, 2½-inch [65 mm] FDC require at least one 3-inch [77 mm] or two 2½-inch [65 mm] lines). Some FDC may be adapted for LDH support.

NOTE: One line may be attached first and charged, and a second line added (attach left side first), or both lines may be connected prior to charging.

Step 3: Note the static pressure in the water system by reading the master intake after the pump is full of water and after pressure in the system has stabilized.

Step 4: Charge lines to the FDC to the required appropriate for sprinkler/standpipe support (100 psi [700 kPa] for 1½-inch [38 mm] FDC or 150 psi [1 050 kPa] for 2½-inch [65 mm] FDC unless otherwise stamped).

NOTE: For standpipe support, determine pump pressure based on nozzle pressure, friction loss in attack lines, appliances, and the standpipe system itself. In addition, factor in elevation loss or gain.

Step 5: Operate pump and/or pressure governor in correct mode.

Step 6: Troubleshoot problems as they arise, using one of the following techniques as necessary:

    a. FDC connection has a frozen swivel – Use a double male with a double female.

    b. FDC unusable because of vandalism – Charge the first-floor standpipe riser by attaching a double female to a hose valve at the first-floor level.

    c. Single-riser building where the standpipe is totally unserviceable – Use standpipes in adjacent buildings to protect exposures.

    d. If you cannot develop pressure, check that all outlets are closed, except the one being used.

Static Water Supply Sources

Chapter Contents

Key Terms

NFPA® Job Performance Requirements

This chapter provides information that addresses the following job performance requirements of NFPA 1002, *Standard for Fire Apparatus Driver/Operator Professional Qualifications (2014)*.

5.2.1, 5.2.2, 10.2.1, 10.2.2, 10.2.3

NFPA 1002, *Standard for Fire Apparatus Driver/Operator Professional Qualifications (2017)*.

5.2.3, 5.2.4, 5.2.5, 10.2.1, 10.2.2, 10.2.3

Static Water Supply Sources

Learning Objectives

After reading this chapter, students will be able to:

1. Explain the principles of lift. (*NFPA 1002, 2014:* 5.2.1 & *NFPA 1002, 2017: 5.2.4*)

2. Summarize considerations when drafting from a natural static water supply source. (*NFPA 1002, 2014:* 5.2.1, 10.2.1, 10.2.2, 10.2.3 & *NFPA 1002, 2017:* 5.2.3, 5.2.4, 10.2.1, 10.2.2, 10.2.3)

3. Describe types of artificial static water supply sources. (*NFPA 1002, 2014:* 5.2.1 & *NFPA 1002, 2017:* 5.2.3, 5.2.4)

4. Dam a stream with a ladder and salvage cover. (*NFPA 1002, 2014:* 5.2.1, 5.2.2, Skill Sheet 11-1 & *NFPA 1002, 2017:* 5.2.4, 5.2.5, Skill Sheet 11-1)

Chapter 11
Static Water Supply Sources

Case History

Firefighters participated in a training exercise that included the setup and use of portable folding water tanks. While attempting to remove a portable tank from the apparatus, a retaining strap came loose before the firefighters had control of the tank. This resulted in one of the firefighters being struck in the head by the falling tank. The firefighters were wearing full PPE and no injuries were reported.

Proper use of PPE is essential to safety during all fireground tasks, including training. In addition, familiarity with the manner in which equipment is mounted on apparatus will save time and enhance safety during training and fire fighting operations.

Source: *www.firefighterclosecalls.com/news/fullstory/newsid/47808/layout/no*

Static water supply sources may need to be used for fire suppression operations for a variety of reasons. Rural areas often do not have a municipal water supply. Even suburban and urban locations that feature a fully functional municipal system may not have sufficient distribution capabilities to provide water for fire fighting operations in addition to their service area. When factoring in the potential for tornadoes, earthquakes, or other incidents that may render municipal systems inoperable, it becomes apparent that alternate water supply sources may be required fairly routinely.

Static water sources, such as lakes, rivers, oceans, cisterns, pools and portable tanks, may be available within a jurisdiction for fire suppression use. Whether they are considered a primary or auxiliary source for an area, the driver/operator must be able to evaluate their potential usability for pumping operations.

The following chapter explains the factors that determine the usability and reliability of these sources. The procedure for determining the net pump discharge pressure required when pumping from a static source is also examined in this chapter.

Principles of Lift

Raising water from a static source, or drafting, requires the driver/operator to understand basic principles of lift. *Lift* is the difference in elevation between the surface of the static water supply and the center of the pump intake. In

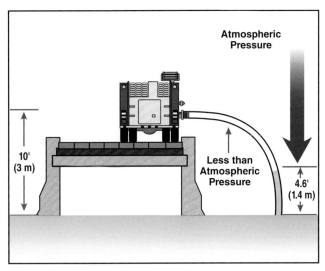

Figure 11.1 Pressure in the intake hose is less than atmospheric pressure, which forces water to rise inside the hose.

order to establish a draft, air must be exhausted from the intake hose and fire pump. During the process of drafting, the priming device exhausts the air from the intake hose and fire pump creating a pressure difference between the inside of the pump, the intake hose, and the atmosphere **(Figure 11.1)**. The pressure in the intake hose and in the pump drops lower than the atmospheric pressure. This results in water being forced into the hose and pump because of the partial vacuum created in the pump. A total vacuum is impossible to create using fire service equipment.

Because the pressure outside the intake hose is higher than the pressure in the hose, water is forced in and continues to rise until the pump is full of water or the pressure within the pump and intake hose equals atmospheric pressure. The maximum height of the lift is affected by the angle of the intake hose, by the amount of negative pressure (vacuum) that the priming device can produce, and the existing atmospheric pressure. If the water does not rise to the level of the pump intake, drafting will not be possible.

Theoretical Lift

If a fire department pumper were capable of creating a total vacuum, water could be raised by atmospheric pressure to a height in accordance with that pressure. This **theoretical lift** would decrease as altitude above sea level increases. For every 1,000 feet (300 m) of altitude, the atmospheric pressure decreases by approximately 0.5 psi (3.5 kPa). Because a total vacuum is not attainable using a fire department pumper, the maximum lift at a given altitude will be less than the theoretical lift.

Theoretical lift can be calculated by determining the actual atmospheric pressure of an area and multiplying that number by the water's pressure per square foot (kPa) while it is in the intake hose.

A total vacuum is not attainable using a fire department pumper, meaning that pumpers cannot be expected to draft water that is located 33.9 feet (10 m) below the level of the pump. Concepts of lift as they relate to fire fighting operations are detailed in the following sections.

Maximum Lift

In the fire service, **maximum lift** is defined as the greatest height to which any amount of water may be raised through an intake hose to the pump. Variables affecting maximum lift include the atmospheric pressure, the condition of the fire pump and primer, and the intake hose, gaskets, and all valves. In most circumstances, maximum lift is approximately 25 feet (7.5 m) **(Figure 11.2)**. As the point of maximum lift is approached, all available atmospheric pressure is used to overcome the gravity pressure affecting the lift. As a result, the volume of water available for the fire pump may be too low to be of value in fire suppression. In addition, the condition and strength of the motor driving the fire pump may affect the ability to achieve maximum lift and delivery of the required amount of water.

To determine the maximum lift that a pumper can achieve using the customary system of measurement, the vacuum reading — in inches of mercury at the intake gauge — is read and multiplied using **Formula 11.1 (Customary)**.

NOTE: Making a field calculation will require the use of a specialized gauge that displays accurate vacuum readings. A larger portion of the gauge is used to read negative pressure.

Formula 11.1 (Customary): Determining Maximum Lift

L= 1.13 Hg

Where:

L = Height of lift in feet (ft)

1.13 = A constant

Hg = Inches of Mercury

Example 11.1 (Customary)

Determine the maximum height to which water will be lifted when the intake gauge reads 14 Hg (Inches of Mercury).

L = 1.13 Hg

L= 1.13 (14) = **15.82 ft (app. 16)**

To determine the maximum lift that a pumper can achieve in the metric system of measurement, the vacuum reading in millimeters of mercury (mm of mercury) at the intake gauge is read and multiplied using **Formula 11.1 (Metric).**

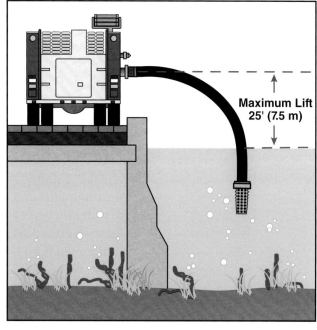

Figure 11.2 Maximum lift is normally 25 feet (7.5 m), but it may vary based on the atmospheric pressure.

Formula 11.1 (Metric): Determining Maximum Lift

L = 0.013 56 Hg

Where:

L = Height of lift in meters (m)

0.013 56 = A constant

Hg = Millimeters of Mercury

Example 11.1 (Metric)

Determine the maximum height to which water will be lifted when intake gauge reads 250 mm of mercury:

L = 0.013 56 Hg

L = (0.013 56) (250) = **3.39 m (app 3.4)**

Dependable Lift — Height a column of water may be lifted in sufficient quantity to provide a reliable fire flow. Lift may be raised through a hard suction hose to a pump, taking into consideration the atmospheric pressure and friction loss within the hard suction hose; dependable lift is usually considered to be 14.7 feet (4.5 m).

Dependable Lift

The driver/operator should have an understanding of theoretical and maximum lift. Generally, you will be more concerned with the concept of **dependable lift** — the height a column of water may be lifted in sufficient quantity to provide a reliable fire flow. After factoring in the surrounding atmospheric pressure and friction loss in the intake hose, every fire pump that is operating properly should have a dependable lift of at least 14.7 feet (4.5 m). **Tables 11.1 a** and **b** list minimum discharges that can be expected from a pumper operating at draft with various lifts.

All fire department pumping apparatus are rated when drafting with a minimum lift of 10 feet (3 m) from the center of a pump intake to the surface of water through 20 feet (6 m) of hard intake hose. A strainer is submerged at least 2 feet (600 mm) in a water depth of at least 4 feet (1.2 m). As the lift or friction loss in hard intake hose is increased, the water supply capability of the pump decreases. The pump may only deliver about 70 percent of its capacity if lift is increased by 5 feet (1.5 m), to a 15-foot lift (4.5 m), and 60 percent at a 20 foot (6 m) lift.

Table 11.1a (Customary)
Discharge at Various Lifts

Rated Capacity, Pump		500 gpm		750 gpm		1000 gpm		1250 gpm	1500 gpm		
Intake Hose Size (inches)		4	4½	4½	5	5	6	6	6	Dual 5	Dual 6
Lift in Feet	20' Intake Hose (Two Sections) 4	590	660	870	945	1160	1345	1435	1735	1990	2250
	6	560	630	830	905	1110	1290	1375	1660	1990	2150
	8	530	595	790	860	1055	1230	1310	1575	1810	2040
	10	500	560	750	820	1000	1170	1250	1500	1720	1935
	12	465	520	700	770	935	1105	1175	1410	1615	1820
	14	430	480	650	720	870	1045	1100	1325	1520	1710
	16	390	430	585	655	790	960	1020	1225	1405	1585
	30' Intake Hose (Three Sections) 18	325	370	495	560	670	835	900	1085	1240	1420
	20	270	310	425	480	590	725	790	955	1110	1270
	22	195	225	340	375	485	590	660	800	950	1085
	24	65	70	205	235	340	400	495	590	730	835

NOTES:

1-Net pump pressure is 150 psi. Operation at a lower pressure will result in an increased discharge; operation at a higher pressure, a decreased discharge.

2-Data based on a pumper with ability to discharge rated capacity when drafting at not more than a 10-foot lift. Many pumpers will exceed this performance and therefore will discharge greater quantities than shown at all lifts.

CONDITIONS: Operating at Net Pump Pressure of 150 psi; Altitude of 1000 feet; Water Temperature of 60°F; Barometric Pressure of 28.94" Hg (poor weather conditions).

Table 11.1b (Metric)
Discharge at Various Lifts

Rated Capacity, Pump		2 000 L/min		3 000 L/min		4 000 L/min		5 000 L/min	6 000 L/min		
Intake Hose Size (mm)		100	115	115	125	125	150	150	150	Dual 125	Dual 150
Lift in Meters	1.2	2 233	2 498	3 293	3 577	4 391	5 091	5 432	6 568	7 532	8 517
	1.8	2 119	2 385	3 142	3 426	4 201	4 883	5 205	6 283	7 532	8 139
	2.4	2 006	2 252	2 990	3 255	3 994	4 656	4 959	5 962	6 851	7 722
6 m Intake Hose (Two Sections)	3.0	1 893	2 120	2 839	3 104	3 785	4 428	4 732	5 678	6 511	7 325
	3.7	1 760	1 968	2 650	2 915	3 539	4 183	4 449	5 337	6 113	6 889
	4.3	1 628	1 817	2 451	2 725	3 293	3 956	4 163	5 016	5 754	6 473
	4.9	1 476	1 628	2 214	2 479	2 990	3 634	3 861	4 637	5 318	6 000
9 m Intake Hose (Three Sections)	5.5	1 230	1 400	1 874	2 120	2 536	3 161	3 407	4 107	4 694	5 375
	6.1	1 022	1 173	1 608	1 817	2 233	2 744	2 990	3 615	4 202	4 807
	6.7	738	852	1 287	1 419	1 836	2 233	2 498	3 028	3 596	4 107
	7.3	246	265	776	890	1 287	1 514	1 874	2 233	2 763	3 161

NOTES:

1-Net pump pressure is 1 000 kPa. Operation at a lower pressure will result in an increased discharge; operation at a higher pressure, a decreased discharge.

2-Data based on a pumper with ability to discharge rated capacity when drafting at not more than a 3 meter lift. Many pumpers will exceed this performance and therefore will discharge greater quantities than shown at all lifts.

CONDITIONS: Operating at Net Pump Pressure of 1 000 kPa; Altitude of 300 meters; Water Temperature of 15.5°C; Barometric Pressure of 735 mm Hg (poor weather conditions).

Determining Net Pump Discharge Pressure

Net pump discharge pressure must account for all factors that contribute to the amount of work required by a pump to produce a fire stream. When at draft, net pump discharge pressure is the sum of the pump discharge pressure and the intake pressure correction that takes into account the friction loss in the intake hose and the height of the lift. These allowances are listed in **Tables 11.2 a** and **b, p. 408**. **Formula 11.2** shows how to calculate pressure correction.

Formula 11.2 (Customary): Pressure Correction

$$PC = \frac{\text{Lift} + \text{Total Intake Hose Friction Loss}}{2.3}$$

Where:

PC = Pressure Correction in pounds per square inch (psi)

Lift = Required Lift in feet (ft)

Total Intake Hose Friction Loss = Number taken from Table 11.2

2.3 = A constant

Table 11.2a (Customary)
Allowances for Friction Loss in Intake Hose

Rated Capacity of Pumper gpm	Diameter of Intake Hose in Inches	For 10 ft. of Intake Hose	Allowance (feet) for Each Additional 10 ft. of Intake Hose
500	4	6	plus 1
	4½	3½	plus ½
750	4	7	plus 1½
	5	4½	plus 1
1000	4½	12	plus 2½
	5	4½	plus 1½
	6	4	plus ½
1250	5	12½	plus 2
	6	6½	plus ½
1500	6	9	plus 1
1500	4½ (dual)	7	plus 1½
1500	5 "	4½	plus 1
1500	6 "	2	plus ½
1750	6	12½	plus 1½
1750	4½ (dual)	9½	plus 2
1750	5 "	6½	plus 1
1750	6 "	3	plus ½
2000	4 ½ "	12	plus 1½
2000	5 "	8	plus 1½
2000	6 "	4	plus ½

NOTE: The allowance computed above for the capacity test should be reduced by 1 psi for the allowance on the 200-psi test and by 2 psi for the allowance on the 250-psi test.

Table 11.2b (Metric)
Allowances for Friction Loss in Intake Hose

Rated Capacity of Pumper L/min	Diameter of Intake Hose in mm	For 3 m of Intake Hose	Allowance (feet) for Each Additional 3 m of Intake Hose
2 000	100	1.8	plus 0.3
	115	1.1	plus 0.15
3 000	115	2.1	plus 0.45
	125	1.4	plus 0.3
4 000	115	3.7	plus 0.75
	125	2.4	plus 0.45
	150	1.2	plus 0.15
5 000	125	3.8	plus 0.61
	150	2	plus 0.15
6 000	150	2.7	plus 0.3
	115 (dual)	2.1	plus 0.45
	125	1.4	plus 0.3
	150	0.6	plus 0.15
7 000	6	3.8	plus 0.45
	115 (dual)	2.9	plus 0.61
	125	2	plus 0.3
	150	0.9	plus 0.15
8 000	115	3.7	plus 0.75
	125	2.4	plus 0.45
	150	1.2	plus 0.15

NOTE: The allowance computed above for the capacity test should be reduced by 7 kPa for the allowance on the 1 350 kPa test and by 14 kPa for the allowance on the 1 700 kPa test.

Example 11.2 (Customary)

What is the intake pressure correction on a 1,250 gpm pumper that is conducting a drafting operation where the required lift is 8 feet? It is using 20 feet of 5-inch intake hose.

$$PC = \frac{Lift + Total\ Intake\ Hose\ Friction\ Loss}{2.3}$$

Lift = 8

Total Intake Hose Friction Loss = (12.5 + 2) from Table 11.2

$$PC = \frac{8 + (12.5 + 2)}{2.3} = \textbf{9.78 psi (app. 10)}$$

Formula 11.2 (Metric): Pressure Correction

$$PC = \frac{Lift + Total\ Intake\ Hose\ Friction\ Loss}{0.1}$$

Where:

PC = Pressure Correction in kilopascals (kPa)

Lift = Required Lift in meters (m)

Total Intake Hose Friction Loss = Number taken from Table 11.2

0.1 = A constant

Example 11.2 (Metric)

What is the intake pressure correction on a 5 000 L/min pumper that is conducting a drafting operation where the required lift is 2 meters? It is using 6 meters of 125 mm hose.

$$PC = \frac{Lift + Total\ Intake\ Hose\ Friction\ Loss}{0.1}$$

Lift = 2

Total Intake Hose Friction Loss = (3.8 + 0.61) from Table 11.2

$$PC = \frac{2 + (3.8 + 0.61)}{0.1} = \textbf{64.1 kPa (app. 65)}$$

Upon completing this correction, the net pump discharge pressure at draft may be calculated by using **Formula 11.3.**

Formula 11.3 (Customary and Metric): Net Pump Discharge Pressure at Draft

$NPDP_{Draft} = PDP + PC$

Where:

$NPDP_{Draft}$ = Net Pump Discharge Pressure at Draft (psi or kPa)

PDP = Pump Discharge Pressure (psi or kPa)

PC = Intake Pressure Correction

Example 11.3 (Customary)

A 1,000 gpm pumper operating from draft has a pump discharge pressure of 120 psi. The required lift is 9 feet through 20 feet of 5-inch intake hose. Calculate the net pump discharge pressure.

$$PC = \frac{Lift + Total\ Intake\ Hose\ Friction\ Loss}{2.3}$$

Lift = 9

Total Intake Hose Friction Loss = (4.5 + 1.5) from Table 11.2

$$PC = \frac{9 + (4.5 + 1.5)}{2.3} = \textbf{6.52 psi}$$

$NPDP_{Draft} = PDP + PC$

$NPDP_{Draft} = 120 + 6.52 = \textbf{126.52 psi (app. 125)}$

Natural Static Water Supply Sources

Driver/operators may be required to draw from natural or artificial static water sources. The following sections explain the attributes of each as they apply to fire suppression water supply.

Natural static water supply sources include lakes, ponds, streams, rivers, and oceans. Through preincident planning, you should become familiar with all potential drafting sources within your jurisdiction and surrounding jurisdictions to which you may respond, including your approach and departure routes and potential drafting sites. A review of response history may help to determine which sites have proven satisfactory during past incidents. This information will expedite water supply operations during incidents. When evaluating a potential water supply source, first determine its adequacy and accessibility.

Adequacy of Natural Static Water Supply Sources

When considering a major lake or river, the adequacy of the source is generally not a major problem. Driver/operators must realize that smaller natural sources may be more susceptible to fluctuations in adequacy during periods of drought than larger bodies of water. Before committing apparatus to a location, you should observe and evaluate current conditions.

Accessibility of Natural Static Water Supply Sources

A major factor in determining the usability of a static water supply source is the ability of fire apparatus to access and set up an effective drafting operation at the site. Driver/operators must be able to evaluate conditions that affect water source accessibility. Many different problems may impede access including:

• Inability to position the pumper close enough to the water

• Wet/soft ground approaches

• Inadequate depth of the water source

• Silt or debris laden water

• Freezing weather

• Swift water

Inability to Position the Pumper

Pumpers may not be able to reach the water in all areas. These environments may include:

- Bridges too high above the surface of the water
- Bridges unable to support the weight of apparatus
- Very high banks around a water source
- Terrain surrounding a water source that will not permit apparatus to reach the water with intake hoses
- Physical barriers such as walls or concrete highway lane separators

Fire departments can ensure access at particular sites by using preincident planning and a proactive approach to creating and maintaining favorable conditions. Many communities feature public boat launches that provide excellent drafting access **(Figure 11.3)**. In some jurisdictions, fire departments oversee construction of gravel drives and dry hydrants to create adequate water supply availability. Brush and tree limbs may need to be cleared and maintained in order to ensure access at some potential drafting sites. Local bridges suitable for drafting points with sufficient weight limits should be noted on preplans and familiar to all driver/operators.

Figure 11.3 Driver/operators should be aware of their community's drafting sites, such as public boat launches.

In certain locations, where fire apparatus cannot make the required approach, it may be necessary to position portable pumps at the supply source if it is the only site available. These pumps may supply a fire department pumper that can then supply a relay or water shuttle operation. Floating pumps placed in an adequate water source can develop and maintain a flow of up to 500 gpm (2 000 L/min). Fire boats are also used to supply land based pumpers from fresh or salt water sources.

In addition, some jurisdictions employ a water eductor that allows the utilization of static water supplies that are located a modest distance from a fire apparatus. By using a hoseline to create a Venturi effect, water from a static supply is forced to the pumper.

Wet or Soft Ground Approaches

Weather conditions may create unsafe and unusable approaches around what is normally a favorable static water supply location. Rain-soaked ground may not support the weight of heavy pumping apparatus. Vehicles may become stuck or unstable in mud and soft ground. Operating apparatus on unstable terrain is dangerous and may result in a rollover. Wet ground that initially supports the weight of a pumper may, over time, settle and mire the apparatus requiring a tow truck to free the vehicle.

In cold weather climates, driver/operators must consider that after traversing frozen ground to arrive at a drafting site, thawing may occur from an increase in air temperature, or immediately around the apparatus from the heat of the vehicle's exhaust. The apparatus may begin to sink in the softened ground. If pumping operations are ongoing, the apparatus should continue to provide water if possible. Arrangements for a tow truck may be made to free the apparatus after the incident has been stabilized.

Even when weather is not a contributing factor, driver/operators must be aware that some terrain may not support the weight of a fire apparatus. Marshy ground or areas of high sand content may be too soft.

Inadequate Depth for Drafting

Static water sources must be of sufficient depth in order to be useful for drafting operations. Although lesser depths may be suitable, 2 feet (600 mm) of water all around a barrel-type strainer is generally considered the minimum for that type of equipment. Floating strainers may be used for water as shallow as 1 foot (300 mm). Low-level strainers are most commonly used to draft from portable water tanks. These devices may draw water as shallow as 1 to 2 inches (25 to 50 mm), but generally will not provide the flow required to reach the capacity of the pumping apparatus.

In small, fast-running streams, a ladder and salvage cover may be configured to create a dam that will raise the level of the water to allow drafting operations. This method may also be applied in other cases where water needs to be diverted or recycled. See **Skill Sheet 11-1** for the steps to construct a makeshift dam.

Silt and Debris

The presence of silt or other waterborne debris may create several problems during drafting, including:

- Clogging of the strainer, resulting in reduced water intake
- Damaging or seizing up fire pumps
- Clogging fog stream nozzles

When drafting from a natural water supply source, it is especially important that all intake hoses have a strainer attached and supported so that it does not rest on or near the bottom of the supply source. A ladder may be used to achieve this position **(Figure 11.4)**. Bring the intake hose and strainer through rungs of the ladder near the bottom, based on the steepness of the bank. A piece of rope or webbing preattached can also help secure and position the strainer. This procedure should ensure that the strainer is positioned horizontally to the bottom of the supply source. If an adequate draft cannot be established due to clogging at the strainer, **back flushing** with tank water may help to dislodge the debris.

In order to help avoid problems with silt and debris, jurisdictions may install dry hydrants at favorable drafting locations **(Figure 11.5)**. Although they may restrict the volume of water that can be drafted, a dry hydrant allows for more efficient access to a natural supply source through a pre-piped installation. When properly installed and maintained, approaches to the site will be safer and problems with debris will be minimized. For more information regarding dry hydrants, refer to Chapter 4, Positioning Apparatus.

Regardless of the method of intake, any operation that draws salt or dirty water into the pump requires flushing the pump with clean, fresh water after the pumping operation is completed This action will help prevent corrosion

Back Flushing — Cleaning a fire pump or piping by flowing water through it in the opposite direction of normal flow.

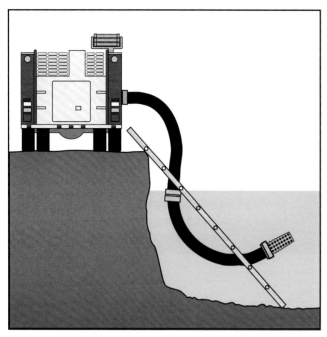

Figure 11.4 Driver/operators should take precautions so that intake strainers do not come in contact with the bottom of the water source.

Figure 11.5 Dry hydrants at predetermined static water supply sources may help expedite drafting operations.

of the pump and associated components and will remove any debris that may clog piping, strainers, or nozzles from the system.

NOTE: Many dry hydrants are installed in secluded rural areas and are subject to vandalism. Local fire departments should conduct regular inspections of these locations in order to ensure usability.

Freezing Weather

On larger bodies of water surface, freezing can make access time consuming and difficult, while shallow bodies of water may freeze to near bottom, making them useless for drafting operations. Some methods for gaining access to static water supplies during freezing weather include:

- Fill barrels with environmentally friendly antifreeze. Float barrels on the water before temperatures drop below freezing. Allow them to freeze in place. Knock out the top and bottom of the barrel to provide an access point for the intake hose and strainer.

- Set wooden plugs or plastic garbage cans in a location and allow them to freeze in place. If a drafting operation is required, the plug or barrel may be driven through the ice, creating a hole. (See *auger* mentioned below.)

These methods require proactive fire department approach as well as approval from a local or state agency with regulatory authority over the water source. In cases where there are no provisions for quick access through the ice, it may be necessary to cut a hole for the intake hose and strainer. Most fire departments use a chain saw, power **auger**, axe, or a combination of tools to breach the ice. Firefighters operating on the ice should use extreme caution to be sure that the strength of the ice will not be unduly compromised by their

Auger — Tool for boring (drilling) holes in floors and other solid barriers including ice.

Figure 11.6 Firefighters should maintain situational awareness when performing ice cutting operations.

weight and cutting activities **(Figure 11.6)**. Firefighters may also deploy a ground ladder across the ice to help distribute their weight. Provisions for making an ice rescue should be available at the scene before any firefighters begin work on the ice.

> **WARNING!**
> Regardless of the assumed depth, all firefighters working in close proximity to bodies of water must wear personal flotation devices and use safety lines.

Swift Water

Attempting a drafting operation using swiftly flowing water can be difficult and dangerous. Strong currents often make it difficult to keep the strainer submerged below the surface of the water. Firefighters working near the water's edge trying to control an intake hose in these conditions are in danger of being thrown into the water.

> **WARNING!**
> Regardless of the assumed depth, all firefighters working in close proximity to bodies of water must wear personal flotation devices and use safety lines.

Artificial Static Water Supply Sources

Artificial static sources often provide reliable sources for drafting operations. In many cases, these sources have been located and constructed specifically for fire protection purposes. Common artificial static water supply sources include:

- Cisterns
- Private water storage tanks
- Ground reservoirs
- Swimming pools
- Agricultural irrigation systems

Cisterns

A **cistern** is an underground water storage receptacle that is usually found in an area not serviced by a hydrant system **(Figure 11.7)**. Cisterns typically receive their water from a well or rainwater runoff. Although most often used for domestic or agricultural purposes, some are specifically constructed and placed for fire department use. Some suburban and urban jurisdictions have cisterns in strategic locations to act as a backup water supply system.

Although they may vary in size, cisterns typically range from 10,000 to 100,000 gallons (40 000 to 400 000 L). This supply may be accessed by removing a utility cover that allows the use of an intake hose and strainer. Other cisterns may feature a dry hydrant connection that allows for more rapid set up of drafting operations. In order to ensure usability in freezing weather, the intake strainer of the dry hydrant set up must be located below the frost line.

Private Water Storage Tanks

Large residential, industrial, or agricultural locations may feature private water storage tanks. These tanks may range in size from several hundred to tens of thousands of gallons of water. These tanks may be stored at ground level or elevated (technically an elevated tank is not a static source as it has elevation pressure at the outlet).

Firefighters should be aware of the capacity of private water supply tanks in their jurisdiction, but should not be confident of their availability unless they are routinely monitored by the fire department. The fire department may require the owner to equip these tanks with appropriate connection points for fire department use.

Cistern — Water storage receptacle that is usually underground and may be supplied by a well or rainwater runoff.

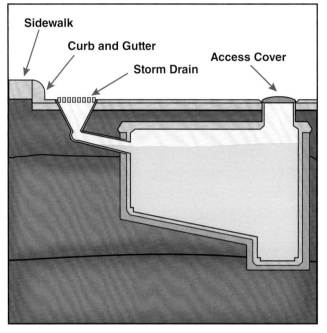

Figure 11.7 Driver/operators should be aware of the locations of cisterns in their jurisdiction.

Ground Reservoirs

Ground reservoirs are artificial installations that have similar characteristics as a pond or lake **(Figure 11.8, p. 416)**. They may be found on large commercial or industrial properties as well as municipal water treatment facilities. These reservoirs typically contain many millions of gallons (liters) of water. Ground reservoirs may be more accessible to fire apparatus than natural bodies of water because of their installation at a working facility. Often, improved roads lead to the water's edge, and dry hydrants may be installed for facility personnel or firefighters to use for water supply. A district with dry hydrants should have a maintenance policy in place.

NOTE: Driver/operators should be aware of the policy in their jurisdiction that assigns responsibility for annual back flushing or other maintenance of dry hydrants.

Swimming Pools

Swimming pools may provide a ready source of water for drafting operations. However, access to some pools may be difficult due to their backyard location and the presence of fences **(Figure 11.9, p. 416)**. Fire departments that may use

Figure 11.8 Ground reservoirs are typically more accessible than lakes.

Figure 11.9 Fences may hinder fire department access to swimming pools.

swimming pools as a static water supply source should preplan operations for accessibility and minimization of property damage. If the fire apparatus is unable to position close enough to conduct drafting operations, portable or floating pumps may be used to supply water to the apparatus.

When conducting preincident planning the accessibility and capacity of any swimming pools considered for fire protection should be determined. A typical residential swimming pool may contain adequate water supply for a fire in a single family dwelling. However, the supply would not be sufficient to conduct an extended operation. Furthermore, driver/operators must consider that swimming pools may be partially or completely drained during winter months. In some jurisdictions, fire departments that use a pool for water supply are responsible for refilling it and repairing any damage caused as by fire department operations. The capacity of a pool can be determined by using one of the following formulas:

Square/Rectangular Pools

Formula 11.4 (Customary): Square/Rectangular Pool Capacity

$$C = 7.5 \times L \times W \times D$$

Where:

C = Capacity in gallons

7.5 = Number of gallons per cubic foot

L = Length in feet (ft)

W = Width in feet (ft)

D = Average depth in feet (ft)

Example 11.4 (Customary)

Calculate the volume capacity of a swimming pool that is 40 feet wide, 100 feet long, and has an average depth of 6 feet.

C = 7.5 x L x W x D

L = 100

W = 40

D = 6

C = (7.5)(100)(40)(6) = **180,000 gallons**

Formula 11.4 (Metric): Square/Rectangular Pool Capacity

C = 1 000 x L x W x D

Where:

C = Capacity in liters

1 000 = Number of liters per cubic meter

L = Length in meters (m)

W = Width in meters (m)

D = Average depth in meters (m)

Example 11.4 (Metric)

Calculate the volume capacity of a swimming pool that is 12 meters wide, 30 meters long, and has an average depth of 2 meters.

C = 1 000 x L x W x D

L = 30

W = 12

D = 2

C = (1 000)(30)(12)(2) = **720 000 liters**

Round Pools

Formula 11.5 (Customary): Round Pool Capacity

C = 7.5 x π x r² x D

Where:

7.5 = Number of gallons per cubic foot

π = Pi, 3.14

r = Radius (½ the diameter) in feet (ft)

D = Average Depth in feet (ft)

Example 11.5 (Customary)

Calculate the volume capacity of a swimming pool that is 24 feet in diameter with an average depth of 4 feet.

C = 7.5 x π x r² x D

r = 12

D = 4

C = (7.5)(3.14)(12)² (4) = **13564.8 gallons (app. 13,500)**

Formula 11.5 (Metric) — Round Pools Capacity

$C = 1\ 000 \times \pi \times r^2 \times D$

Where:

C = Capacity in liters

1 000 = Number of liters per cubic meter

π = Pi, 3.14

r = Radius (½ the diameter) in meters (m)

D = Average Depth in meters (m)

Example 11.5 (Metric)

Calculate the volume capacity of a swimming pool that is 8 meters in diameter with an average depth of 1.3 meters.

$C = 1\ 000 \times \pi \times r^2 \times D$

r = 4

D = 1.3

$C = 1\ 000 \times \pi \times r^2 \times D$

$C = (1\ 000)(3.14)(4)^2(1.3) = \textbf{65 312 liters (app. 65 000)}$

Large indoor or outdoor pools that have been preplanned as a potential static water supply source may be equipped with connections similar to a dry hydrant for quick fire department hook-ups. The connection should be identified in preplans and clearly marked along with instruction for opening any valves that may be necessary to operate the connection. Flush fire department pumpers with clear water after drafting from a swimming pool in order to remove damaging chlorine residue from the pump and piping.

WARNING!
Using an internal combustion engine indoors creates a danger of carbon monoxide poisoning to the occupants of the building.

Agricultural Irrigation Systems

Agricultural irrigation systems in some jurisdictions may flow in excess of 1,000 gpm (4 000 L/min) and may function as a potential water source for fire protection. Irrigation systems generally supply water via open canals and portable pipes. Open canals running through a property may feature several sites suitable for drafting by fire department pumpers. Portable pipes may also be accessible to pumpers, but connections may require specially threaded adapters or other tools to operate the system.

Chapter Summary

Driver/operators must be able to access an adequate water supply with which to supply pumping apparatus for fire suppression operations. While many locations feature pressurized water systems with hydrants supplying water for fire protection, other jurisdictions may have static water sources as a backup or primary source for fire fighting. Typical static water supply sources include natural bodies of water such as lakes, ponds, or oceans, as well as artificial installations like cisterns, swimming pools, or ground reservoirs.

Local fire departments must preplan the location, accessibility and capacity of the sources they intend to use. Driver/operators must familiarize themselves with these preplans as well as the methods of achieving an adequate water supply during various weather conditions and levels of supply.

Review Questions

1. What is meant by theoretical lift, maximum lift, and dependable lift? (p. 404)

2. What are some factors that must be considered when drafting from a static natural water supply source? (p. 410)

3. What are some examples of artificial static water supply sources? (p. 414)

Step 1: Spread the salvage cover flat on the ground. If the ladder is longer than the salvage cover, two salvage covers may be used.

Step 2: Lay the ladder down on one of the long sides of the salvage cover(s).

Step 3: Grab the salvage cover and begin to roll the ladder with the salvage cover, wrapping the beams.

Step 4: Roll the ladder until there is approximately 4 feet (1 m) of cover remaining on the ground that is free to form a flap.

Step 5: Place the ladder wrapped with a salvage cover to an area where the stream or ground is flat.

NOTE: This will allow the most contact with the bottom of the ladder. The ladder may need to be angled in the stream to make contact with the sides of the banks.

Step 6: Stretch the free flap upstream, and secure it to the ground.

NOTE: The more secure this section is, the less water will escape under the dam.

Step 7: Tuck in the ends of the salvage cover and adjust as necessary to limit excessive leakage.

Step 8: Support the middle of the down stream side of the ladder with a straight pry bar, rod, or post as the weight of the water may push the dam over. If using as a water diversion, support the ladder on both ends.

Relay Pumping Operations

Chapter Contents

chapter 12

Key Terms

NFPA® Job Performance Requirements

This chapter provides information that addresses the following job performance requirements of NFPA 1002, *Standard for Fire Apparatus Driver/Operator Professional Qualifications (2014).*

> 5.2.2

NFPA 1002, *Standard for Fire Apparatus Driver/Operator Professional Qualifications (2017).*

> 5.2.5

Relay Pumping Operations

Learning Objectives

After reading this chapter, students will be able to:

1. Describe relay apparatus and equipment. (*NFPA 1002, 2014:* 5.2.2 & *NFPA 1002, 2017:* 5.2.5)

2. Explain relay pumping operational considerations. (*NFPA 1002, 2014:* 5.2.2 & *NFPA 1002, 2017:* 5.2.5)

3. Summarize general guidelines for relay operations. (*NFPA 1002, 2014:* 5.2.2 & *NFPA 1002, 2017:* 5.2.5)

4. Describe the open relay method. (*NFPA 1002, 2014:* 5.2.2 & *NFPA 1002, 2017:* 5.2.5)

5. Summarize facts about the closed relay method. (*NFPA 1002, 2014:* 5.2.2 & *NFPA 1002, 2017:* 5.2.5)

6. Operate in an open relay. (*NFPA 1002, 2014:* 5.2.2, Skill Sheet 12-1 & *NFPA 1002, 2017:* 5.2.5, Skill Sheet 12-1)

7. Operate in a closed relay. (*NFPA 1002, 2014:* 5.2.2, Skill Sheet 12-2 & *NFPA 1002, 2017:* 5.2.5, Skill Sheet 12-2)

Chapter 12
Relay Pumping Operations

Courtesy of Ron Jeffers.

Case History

While engaged in a relay pumping exercise, a fire department pumper was connected to a pressurized water source. Upon closing the intake valve on the pumper, the hydrant valve failed with a large portion of the gate forcefully ejected from the hydrant. After investigating the incident, the fire department determined that the hydrant gate was part of the equipment assigned to a reserve piece of apparatus. Although its exact age was unknown, it was thought to be more than 20 years old.

This fire department subsequently inspected all similar gates for potential defects and removed four others from service. All appliances should be regularly and carefully inspected for signs of wear or defect based on manufacturers' recommendations.

Source: *www.firefighterclosecalls.com/news/fullstory/newsid/47752/layout/no*

Driver/operators may find that the water source is remote from the fire scene during some incidents. In these instances, relay pumping may have to be employed. A relay pumping operation consists of a pumper positioned at the water supply source that is used to pump water under pressure through one or more supply lines to another pumper connected further down the supply line(s). This pumper boosts the pressure to supply the next pumper and so on until water reaches the attack pumper. In order to be effective, relay operations require preplanning, training, and coordinating of all participants. The following chapter describes the components of a relay operation, factors that influence the effectiveness of relay pumping, and various methods for establishing a relay operation.

Relay Apparatus and Equipment

Depending on local policy and equipment availability, a variety of apparatus, hose, and equipment may be used to establish a relay pumping operation. Most commonly, driver/operators of fire department pumpers lay the supply hose and participate in the **relay operation**. However, any type of apparatus equipped with an adequately sized pump can be used for relay pumping.

The following terms are used throughout the chapter to describe the various positions and apparatus within a relay pumping operation **(Figure 12.1, p. 426)**:

Relay Operation — Using two or more pumpers to move water over a long distance by operating them in series; water discharged from one pumper flows through hoses to the inlet of the next pumper, and so on. *Also known as* Relay Pumping.

- **Water supply pumper** — Pumper that takes water from a hydrant or static source and pumps it under pressure to the next apparatus in the relay pumping operation. Water supply pumpers should be the apparatus with the largest pumping capacity. Some jurisdictions refer to water supply pumpers as *source pumpers.*

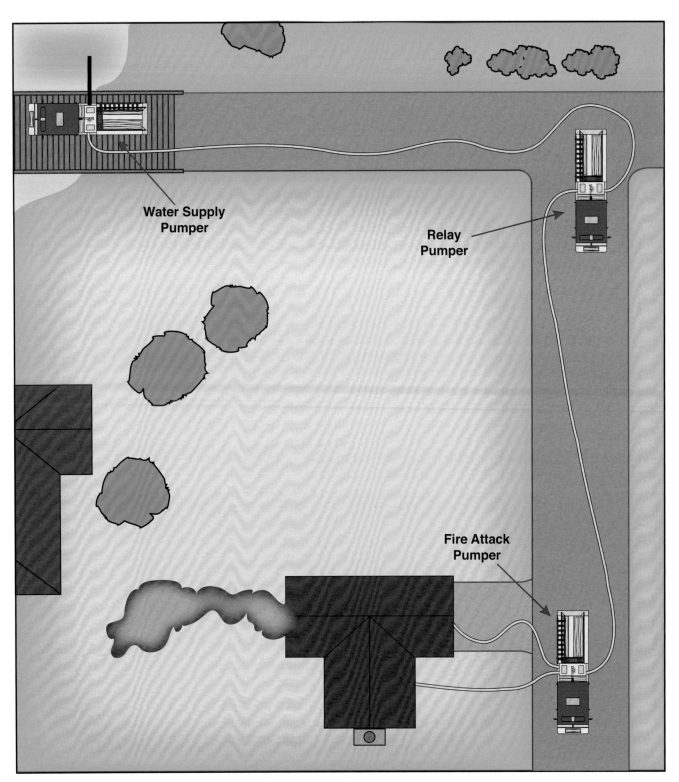

Figure 12.1 Apparatus are named based on their role within a relay pumping operation.

NOTE: A smaller pumper must sometimes be used as a water supply pumper due to the order of apparatus arrival. If possible, avoid this action as it will limit the overall fire flow for the incident.

- **Relay pumper** — Pumper or pumpers connected within the relay that receive water from the source pumper or another relay pumper, raises the pressure, and then supplies water to the next apparatus. This pumper may be of smaller capacity due to its ability to use the acquired energy of previous pumpers in the relay.

- **Fire attack pumper** — Pumping apparatus located at the fire scene that receives water from the relay and is responsible for supplying the attack lines and appliances required for fire suppression.

Some fire departments, especially those that have occasion to make many long hose lays, employ hose **tenders** to assist in relay pumping operations **(Figure 12.2)**. Hose tenders may be equipped with a fire pump that allows the apparatus to participate in the pumping operation once the supply line is laid. It is possible for a hose tender to carry a mile or more of **large diameter hose (LDH)**. This hose may be packed on a traditional hose bed or wound on a mechanically operated reel. Most hose tenders are equipped with a wide assortment of valves, manifolds, and other appliances for use in relay pumping operations.

NOTE: LDH is commonly divided into attack and supply line categories. Each category of hose will have different working pressure limitations. Driver/operators should be aware of the type of hose carried on their apparatus and its capabilities.

Tender — Term used within the Incident Command System for a mobile piece of apparatus that has the primary function of supporting another operation; examples include a water tender that supplies water to pumpers, or a fuel tender that supplies fuel to other vehicles.

Large Diameter Hose (LDH) — Relay-supply hose of 3½ to 6 inches (90 mm to 150 mm) in diameter; used to move large volumes of water quickly with a minimum number of pumpers and personnel.

Figure 12.2 Hose tenders can assist relay pumping operations that require large lengths of supply hose. *Courtesy of Ron Jeffers.*

Relay Pumping Operational Considerations

Several considerations apply to all relay pumping operations. Basically, the need for relay pumping is determined by the amount of water required at an incident and the distance between the incident scene and the water source.

At some incidents, a relay operation must supply the total volume of water required to perform fire suppression. In others, relay operations may be used to supplement a municipal water supply. The amount of water required will have a major impact on the design of the relay system.

The distance of the relay is the second important consideration. The longer the hose lay, the more friction loss will be encountered. As explained in previous chapters, friction loss is directly affected by the amount of water being flowed, the diameter of the hose, and the distance between pumpers. If the amount of flow through a relay operation needs to be increased, depending on the size of the supply hose and fire flow requirements, at least one of three conditions must be met:

- The diameter of the supply hose or the number of hoselines must be increased.

- The pump discharge pressure of the pumpers involved in the relay must be increased.

- More pumpers must be added to the relay to overcome friction loss or elevation.

Certain factors limit the options available at particular incidents. It is impractical to replace an existing layout of supply hose with a larger diameter hoseline, shut down the existing layout, and then restart the operation using the larger hose. It is more conceivable that pumpers or hose tenders not already in use could lay an additional hoseline between the relay pumpers. This line could be connected and used to supplement the flow already being supplied.

Pumpers in the relay operation could increase their pump discharge pressure. However, this action will not necessarily increase the volume of water through the system. Centrifugal pumps are rated to pump at their maximum volume capacity at 150 psi (1 050 kPa) at draft. When pumping at pressures higher than 150 psi (1 050 kPa), the volume capability of the pump is reduced proportionately. Depending on the length of the hose lay and the volume of water flowed, a point will be reached where increased pressure will not increase the volume. The driver/operator must consider the limitations of the hose when increasing discharge pressure. At no time should discharge pressures exceed the pressure at which hose or appliances have been service tested.

Elevation pressure may also factor into some relay pumping operations. If the water supply must be pumped uphill, the pressure loss on the lay is greater than simple friction loss. For downhill pumping, the reverse holds true. Elevation pressure is not affected by the amount of water being moved, only by the topography.

Increasing flow during a relay operation may be accomplished by placing additional pumpers in the system. This will shorten the length of hose each pumper must supply and allow pumpers to operate at lower pressures and maximum flows within the relay operation. If relay inline valves were not placed in the hose lay from the outset, this evolution will require the shutdown of the water supply until the new apparatus are added.

Relay operations may use LDH to supply a low flow rate where the distance between each pumper exceeds the length of supply hose carried on each pumper. It may become necessary to use additional pumpers to lay more hose but not take part in pumping operations. Using Table 12.1, the driver/operator can determine the distance that a particular flow rate may be pumped through a specified hose diameter.

Tables 12.1 a and **b** contain built-in consideration for the 20 psi (140 kPa) residual pressure that should be maintained at the next pumper in the relay.

Table 12.1a (Customary)
Maximum Waterflow Distance Per Pumper

Flow in gpm	Hose size in inches						
	One 2½	One 3	One 4	One 5	Two 2½	One 2½ & One 3	Two 3s
250	1,440 ft	3,600 ft	13,200 ft	33,000 ft	5,760 ft	9,600 ft	14,400 ft
500	360 ft	900 ft	3,300 ft	8,250 ft	1,440 ft	2,400 ft	36,000 ft
750	160 ft	400 ft	1,450 ft	3,670 ft	640 ft	1,050 ft	1,600 ft
1000	90 ft	225 ft	825 ft	2,050 ft	360 ft	600 ft	900 ft
1250	50 ft	140 ft	525 ft	1,320 ft	200 ft	375 ft	500 ft

Table 12.2b (Metric)
Maximum Waterflow Distance Per Pumper

Flow in L/min	Hose size in mm						
	One 65	One 77	One 100	One 125	Two 65s	One 65 & One 77	Two 77s
1 000	440 m	1 100 m	4 260 m	9 420 m	1 770 m	2 980 m	4 670 m
2 000	110 m	275 m	1 070 m	2 360 m	443 m	740 m	1 160 m
3 000	40 m	122 m	470 m	1 050 m	200 m	330 m	520 m
4 000	28 m	69 m	270 m	590 m	110 m	180 m	290 m
5 000	18 m	44 m	170 m	380 m	70 m	120 m	190 m

The figures in the charts were based on a discharge pressure of 200 psi (1 400 kPa) for 2½ and 3-inch (65 and 77 mm) hose and 185 psi (1 300 kPa) for 4- and 5-inch (100 and 125 mm) hose.

As previously mentioned, fire department pumpers are rated to flow their maximum volume at 150 psi (1 050 kPa), 70 percent of their maximum at 200 psi (1 400 kPa), and 50 percent of their maximum at 250 psi (1 750 kPa) at draft.

Because the referenced tables are based on discharge pressures of 185 and 200 psi (1 300 and 1 400 kPa), the following are the minimum pump capacities that must be used to achieve the flows/ distances on the tables:

- 750 gpm (3 000 L/min) pumper — 250 and 500 gpm (1 000 and 2 000 L/min) flows

- 1,250 gpm (5 000 L/min) pumper — 750 gpm (3 000 L/min) flow
- 1,500 gpm (6 000 L/min) pumper — 1,000 gpm (4 000 L/min) flow
- 1,750 gpm (7 000 L/min) pumper — 1,250 gpm (5 000 L/min) flow

If distances shorter than those on the chart are encountered, it will be possible to use smaller capacity pumpers or remove one or more pumpers from the relay.

Using the numbers in Tables 12.1 a and b, the number of pumpers needed to relay a specific amount of water may be determined by using the following formula:

Formula 12.1 (Customary and Metric) — Relay Distance

$$P = \frac{R}{D} + 1$$

Where:

P = Total number of pumpers needed

R = Relay distance

D = Distance from Tables 12.1 a or 12.1 b

NOTE: When using this formula all answers must be rounded UP to the nearest whole number. An answer of 3.2 would be rounded to 4, meaning 4 pumpers are required for relay operations.

Example 12.1 (Customary)

Using a single 3-inch supply line, how many pumpers will be needed to supply 1,000 gpm to a fire scene that is 1,000 feet from the water source **(Figure 12.3)**?

$$P = \frac{R}{D} + 1$$

R = 1000

D = 225 from Table 12.1a

$P = \frac{1000}{225} + 1 = $ **5.44 pumpers needed (Round up to 6)**

Example 12.1 (Metric)

If a single line of 77 mm hose is used, how many pumpers will be needed to supply 4 000 L/min to a fire scene that is 300 meters from the water supply source?

$$P = \frac{R}{D} + 1$$

R = 300

D = 69 from Table 12.1b

$P = \frac{300}{69} + 1 = $ **5.35 pumpers needed (Round up to 6)**

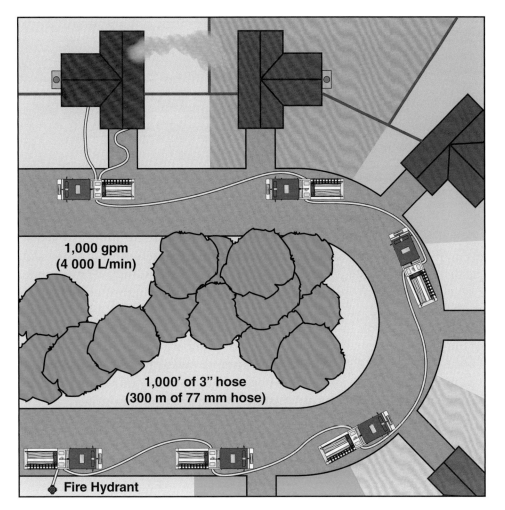

1,000 gpm
(4 000 L/min)

1,000' of 3" hose
(300 m of 77 mm hose)

Fire Hydrant

Figure 12.3 *Example 12.1 (Customary and Metric)*

Example 12.2 (Customary)

If two 3-inch hoselines are used, how many pumpers are required to supply 750 gpm to a fire scene that is 2,000 feet from the water source (**Figure 12.4, p. 432**)?

$$P = \frac{R}{D} + 1$$

R = 2000

D = 1600 from Table 12.1a

$P = \frac{2000}{1600} + 1 =$ **2.25 pumpers needed (Round up to 3)**

Example 12.2 (Metric)

If two lines of 77 mm hose are used, how many pumpers will be needed to supply 3 000 L/min to a fire scene that is 600 meters away from the water source?

$$P = \frac{R}{D} + 1$$

R = 600

D = 520 from Table 12.1b

$P = \frac{600}{520} + 1 =$ **2.15 pumpers needed (Round up to 3)**

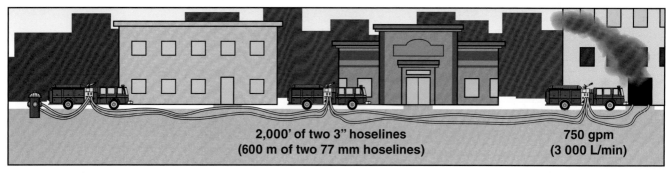

Figure 12.4 *Example 12.2 (Customary and Metric)*

2,000' of two 3" hoselines
(600 m of two 77 mm hoselines)

750 gpm
(3 000 L/min)

When relaying long distances, the hose lays between each pumper should be as equalized as possible. In cases where multiple diameters of hose are used, the distances between pumpers must be adjusted accordingly. For example, if several pumpers are setting up a relay of 1,000 gpm using 5-inch hose, each pumper can be placed 2,050 feet apart. If a pumper carrying 3-inch supply hose lays dual supply lines as part of the operation, its portion of the lay must be limited to 900 feet. In metrics, if several pumpers are setting up a relay of 4 000 L/min using 125 mm hose, each pumper can be placed 590 m apart. If a pumper carrying 77 mm supply hose lays dual supply lines as part of the operation, its portion of the lay must be limited to 290 m.

Several considerations apply to all relay pumping operations. Basically, the need for relay pumping is determined by the amount of water required at an incident and the distance between the incident scene and the water source.

General Guidelines for Relay Operations

Regardless of the type of relay used for a particular incident, driver/operators must be familiar with the basic guidelines for setting up, operating, and shutting down relay operations. Safe and efficient operations depend on coordination and communication, as well as proper planning.

Putting a Relay into Operation

A relay pumping operation begins with the largest capacity pumper working from the water source. When drafting from a static source, this pumper may need to develop a higher pump discharge pressure than the other pumpers in the relay operation. The increased pump discharge pressure compensates for the energy lost due to friction loss in the suction hose as well as the energy required to overcome the height of the lift. The source pumper does not have the residual pressure at the intake that the relay pumpers receive that aids in preventing pump cavitation. For their own safety and the efficient operation of the system, all personnel involved in the relay operation must understand that the overall capacity of the system is determined by the smallest pump and the smallest diameter of hose used in the relay.

Once the water supply has been established, the source pumper should open a discharge or allow water to discharge through a dump line until the first relay pumper is ready for water **(Figure 12.5)**. Failure to keep water moving through the pump when using a static water supply may result in loss of prime or overheating the pump, either of which would delay the operation. Open the tank fill to move water by overflowing the tank.

The relay pumper should be waiting for water with a dump line or discharge open and the pump out of gear. When the source and relay pumpers are ready, the discharge supplying the hoseline on the source pumper is opened while the valve on the **dump line** is closed in a coordinated action. Open the discharge to the supply line slowly to prevent a sudden loss of water from the pump, which may result in a loss of prime if pumping from draft. Water begins to flow from the source pumper to the relay pumper, and the desired pressure is built. As water fills the supply line, air will be forced through the relay pump and out the open dump line. When a steady flow of water begins to issue from the dump line, the pump on the relay pumper may be engaged.

NOTE: The relay pumper may engage the pump before receiving water from the source pumper if water is circulated from the onboard tank through the pump, or if the delay in receiving water from the source pumper is very brief.

It is advisable for driver/operators to maintain an intake pressure of 20 to 30 psi (140 to 210 kPa) as a relay pumper. Once the pump discharge pressure on the relay pumper has reached the desired pressure, with water being discharged, no further adjustments should be required. Follow the same procedure for each successive relay pumper in the operation. The first relay pumper opens the discharge valve supplying the relay or attack pumper on a coordinated basis. Conduct this process while observing the intake pressure gauge to maintain intake pressure within the desired range of 20 to 30 psi (140 to 210 kPa) residual pressure. The next relay pumper follows the same initial actions as the first. Following this process, long relay operations may be completed efficiently with a minimum of delay.

Figure 12.5 Opening a discharge will keep water moving through the pump, which will help prevent the pump from overheating.

As water begins to reach each pumper, the driver/operator should **bleed** any air from the line before opening the intake valve. Bleed the air by opening a discharge. Once the air is vented, you may open the necessary discharge valves.

Operating the Relay

Once the relay operation is flowing water at the desired pressure, the driver/operator of the attack pumper should set the pressure governor at an appropriate level. These devices serve an important role in the safety of a relay operation because of the cumulative effect of pressure increases when changes in flow occur. Apparatus equipped with pressure governors should be set in the pressure mode when acting as the attack pumper and in the rpm mode while working as a relay pumper.

Pressure Governors

When operating in the "RPM" mode, the throttle may be set and the corresponding engine rpm will be maintained by the pressure governor. If, while operating in this mode, the pressure increases beyond a preset range, the governor will reduce engine rpm to limit the increase in pressure. Operating in the pressure mode will allow the regulator to attempt to maintain a specific pump pressure by adjusting engine rpm as required.

For relay pumpers equipped with an adjustable intake relief valve, they should be set to 10 psi (70 kPa) above the static pressure of the water system to which it is attached or 10 psi (70 kPa) above the discharge pressure of the previous pumper in the relay. This valve should never be set to discharge at a rate above the safe working pressure of the hose.

Attack pumpers equipped with an adjustable intake relief valve should be set between 50 and 75 psi (350 and 525 kPa) to establish a stable operating condition. If an attack line is shut down, or the amount of discharge changes, the friction loss in the supply line decreases and the residual pressure increases. The intake relief valve will operate, allowing water to dump from the intake. When this occurs, the flow through the supply line and the pressures in the relay return to their original settings. Increases in demand by the attack pumper will cause reduced residual pressure, and the valve will close. Water will cease dumping, and again the pressure will stabilize at the original setting. Pumps equipped with automatic pressure governors will automatically make this compensation with an internal relief valve operating in the pressure mode.

The driver/operator of the attack pumper should expect small variations in pressure during relay pumping operations. You should not attempt to correct minor fluctuations as long as the intake pressure does not drop below 20 psi (140 kPa). Constantly modifying pressure settings in an attempt to achieve an exact pressure will affect other pumpers in the relay. Frequent changes may result in constantly varying pressures and driver/operators overcompensating for pressure changes that may be delayed in long relay operations.

NOTE: During long relay operations smaller capacity pumps may require higher residual pressures as the relay operation stabilizes.

Like all fireground operations, relay pumping requires the use of effective, clear communication for success. While working in the operation, you must be aware of the actions of the other units in order to coordinate their efforts safely and efficiently. Radios can be effective for this operation but may be hampered by, or create, an excessive volume of radio traffic. If additional radio frequencies are available, one may be assigned specifically for the relay operation, thus freeing the fireground channel for fire attack use. Once operations have been established and the water supply is flowing, there should be need for very little further communication. In some cases, firefighters may be sent between apparatus to act as messengers if no other method of communication is available.

Shutting Down the Relay

When the need for relay pumping has ended, the operation should be discontinued from the fire scene first. If done in reverse with relay pumpers still operating, they may run their pumps dry in a high rpm condition and risk cavitation. Beginning with the attack pumper and coordinating with the other pumpers in the relay, each driver/operator should slowly decrease the throttle, open the dump line valve, and then disengage the pump. Close all valves slowly to prevent water hammer at any point in the system. This method provides for the refilling of onboard water tanks of the apparatus involved in the relay.

NOTE: To maintain safety for all personnel, clear communications between each driver/operator and the Water Supply Officer is important. Use standardized terminology throughout the operation for consistency.

Open Relay Method

During relay pumping operations, the open relay method may be employed to provide an alternate water supply system. This method consists of deploying portable folding drop tanks at each intake for pumpers in the relay operation. See **Skill Sheet 12-1** for steps to operate in an open relay. Operating from portable folding drop tanks eliminates the pressure surges and inconsistent supply sometimes found in closed relays. Additionally, this method requires no adapters or other appliances to connect intake hoses in the system. Driver/operators must be sure to place the hard sleeve and supply hoses at opposite ends of the portable folding drop tank in order to avoid turbulence.

Closed Relay Method

Each fire department, as well as neighboring departments that conduct joint operations, should have a standard policy for the use of relay pumping. These operations should be practiced within the department and jointly between mutual aid partners on a regular basis. See **Skill Sheet 12-2** for the general steps for operating in a closed relay.

In some areas, regional organizations have formulated procedures that include the setup of relay pumping operations by an Incident Commander. Upon request, a predetermined task force assignment is dispatched to initiate a relay pumping operation. These units set up a relay water supply operation independent of other companies already operating at the scene. To attain maximum proficiency, these relay task force units must train together and have compatible equipment.

Depending on the preferences of local jurisdictions, a variety of hose diameters may be used to complete relay pumping operations. When using medium diameter hose (MDH), 2½ or 3 inches (65 or 77 mm) in diameter, generally multiple hoselines are laid. Large diameter hose (LDH), 4 or 5 inches (100 mm or 125 mm) in diameter, often requires only one supply line to meet fireground requirements.

A wide variety of appliances, such as pressure relief valves, may be used to complete relay pumping operations. Driver/operators should refer to NFPA® 1962 for further information regarding the placement of relief devices. Sometimes referred to as *relay relief valves*, these appliances are intended to enhance firefighter safety and reduce the possibility of damage to the pump and other water supply components that may be caused by water hammer when valves are operated too quickly or intake pressures rise dramatically.

There are two basic types of intake pressure relief valves. One type, supplied by the pump manufacturer, is an integral part of the pump intake manifold. The second type is an add-on device that is screwed onto the pump intake connection. In some cases, these devices are preset to allow a predetermined amount of pressure into the fire pump. If the incoming pressure exceeds the preset level, the valve opens and dumps the excess pressure/water until water is entering the pump at the correct pressure.

Many of the screw-on intake pressure relief valves are also equipped with a gate valve that allows the water supply to the pump to be shut off. Bleeder valves on the intake pressure relief valve allow air to bleed off as the incoming supply hose is charged. This is especially important with the large amount of air pushed through large diameter supply hose as it is being filled with water.

The introduction of a large amount of air into the pump may cause a loss of discharge pressure, possible water hammer, and air at the nozzle possibly shutting down the operation. Bleeder valves may be located directly on the intake piping to the pump itself. Driver/operators must remember that when operating from draft, the bleeder valve must be closed if the intake hose is connected to an inlet with a manual shutoff valve.

Relay pumping operations that require the use of later arriving companies to achieve the required flow can set up an initial operation of lesser volume and greater spacing with inline relay valves placed in the relay line awaiting the arrival of incoming pumpers. An inline relay valve is placed along the length of a supply hose that permits a pumper to connect to the valve to boost pressure in the hose. These valves will allow later arriving pumper to tie into the relay and boost pressure and volume after it has already started flowing, without interrupting the water supply.

During LDH relay operations that must supply more than one attack pumper, a discharge manifold may be used to break down the LDH into two or more hoselines that may then be connected to different pumpers. Several different designs are available for discharge manifolds. Typically they feature one LDH inlet and a combination of MDH and LDH discharges. If multiple smaller lines are in use to supply the relay, each line may be used to support a different attack pumper based on the fire flow requirements of the incident.

Chapter Summary

Relay pumping operations may need to be employed wherever a water supply is too far distant to allow for a single pumper to draw from the static or pressurized source and provide effective fire streams. Relay pumping may be used anywhere pressurized water systems are insufficient for the flow required at a fire scene. Using hydrants from a greater distance to draw from a different main is often required at large fires. The prospect of driver/operators in any jurisdiction conducting a relay pumping operation reinforces the need for preplanning, familiarity with the necessary equipment, and training to achieve this water supply operation safely and efficiently.

Review Questions

1. What are source pumpers, relay pumpers, and fire attack pumpers? (pp. 426-427)

2. What determines the need for relay pumping? (p. 427)

3. What determines the overall capacity of a relay pumping system? (p. 432)

4. What is the open relay method? (p. 435)

5. What is the purpose of relief valves? (p. 435)

NOTE: Adjustments in flow may be necessary as the incident progresses. This skill sheet provides general steps for operating in an open relay. Always follow the SOPs of the jurisdiction. This method is often used in conjunction with mobile water supply apparatus shuttling water.

Step 1: Position the attack pumper.

Step 2: Set up a portable tank from which the attack pumper drafts.

Step 3: For maximum waterflow, lay hose from source pumper to portable tank. Secure the supply hose.

Step 4: Source pumper supplies water (through the relay pumpers, if applicable) into the portable tank.

Step 5: Once sufficient water is in the portable tank, the attack pumper driver/operator can draft from the portable tank, refill apparatus water tank, and continue operations.

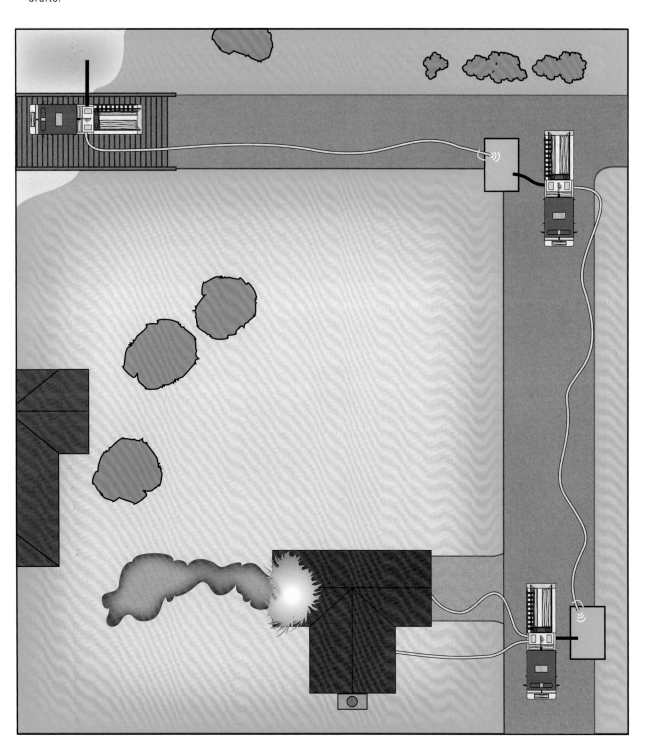

SKILL SHEETS

NOTE: This skill sheet provides general steps for operating in a closed relay. Always follow the SOPs of the jurisdiction.

Step 1: Personnel decide whether to utilize a forward or reverse lay.

Step 2: The driver/operator positions the attack pumper at the fire.

Step 3: The driver/operator of the next pumper connects to forward laid hose or continues the reverse lay.

Step 4: The driver/operators continue to lay hose until the water source is reached. This may require multiple pumping apparatus.

Step 5: The driver/operator connects the source pumper to the pressurized water source or establishes a draft.

Step 6: Once a water supply is established, the driver/operator of the source pumper communicates with the operator of the next pumper advising that water is ready.

Step 7: Once both operators acknowledge that they are prepared, the driver/operator of the source pumper pumps water to the next pumper in line. The IC determines the flow and the operator of the source pumper begins pumping available water within pump capabilities.

Step 8: The driver/operator of the receiving pumper should ensure that air is bled from the hoseline as it approaches the pump.

Step 9: Once the next pumper has water, the driver/operator notifies the next in line that water is ready to be sent.

Step 10: Driver/operators should continue Steps 7-9 for all relay pumpers until water reaches the attack pumper.

Step 11: The driver/operator should set the attack pumper's relief valve or electronic pressure governor as required.

Step 12: Driver/operators must ensure that all pumpers maintain a minimum of 20 psi (140 kPa) residual intake pressure.

Step 13: The driver/operator of the attack pumper should request more or less pressure as needed.

   a. Pressure decreases should begin at the attack pumper, and all driver/operators of relay pumpers should back off accordingly.

   b. Pressure increases begin at the source pumper until the capacity of the pump is reached.

   c. Driver/operators should balance the pressure supplied by each truck so that a truck is not pushing water through others (balancing work).

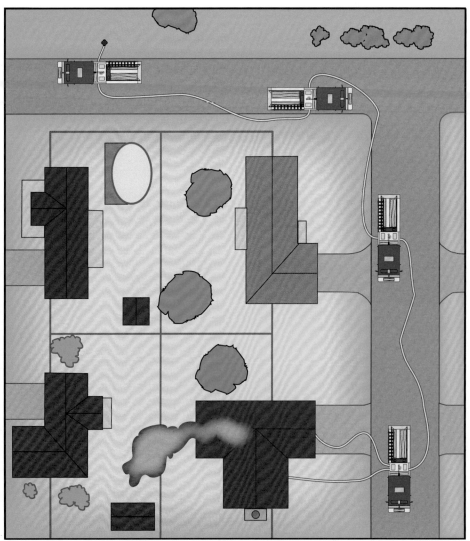

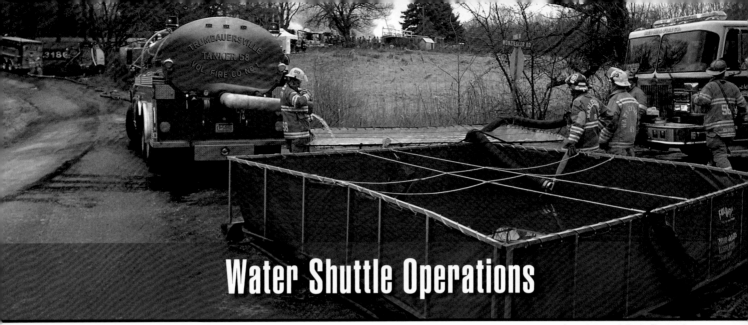

Courtesy of Bob Esposito.

Water Shuttle Operations

Chapter Contents

Key Terms

NFPA® Job Performance Requirements

This chapter provides information that addresses the following job performance requirements of NFPA 1002, *Standard for Fire Apparatus Driver/Operator Professional Qualifications (2014)*.

10.1.1, 10.2.1, 10.2.2, 10.2.3

NFPA 1002, *Standard for Fire Apparatus Driver/Operator Professional Qualifications (2017)*.

5.2.3, 10.1.1, 10.2.1, 10.2.2, 10.2.3

Water Shuttle Operations

Learning Objectives

After reading this chapter, students will be able to:

1. Identify water shuttle apparatus. (*NFPA 1002, 2014 and 2017:* 10.2.3)

2. Summarize considerations taken for the setup of a water shuttle. (*NFPA 1002, 2014 and 2017:* 10.2.1)

3. Describe fill site operations. (*NFPA 1002, 2014:* 10.2.1 & *NFPA 1002, 2017:* 5.2.3, 10.2.1)

4. Distinguish among dump site operational methods. (*NFPA 1002, 2014 and 2017:* 10.2.2, 10.2.3)

5. Explain methods of evaluating tender performance. (*NFPA 1002, 2014 and 2017:* 10.1.1, 10.2.2, 10.2.3)

6. Verify operational readiness of mobile water supply apparatus. (*NFPA 1002, 2014 and 2017:* 10.1.1, Skill Sheet 13-1)

7. Operate at a fill site as part of a water shuttle operation. (*NFPA 1002, 2014 and 2017:* 10.2.1, Skill Sheet 13-2)

8. Operate at a portable water tank dump site as part of a water shuttle operation. (*NFPA 1002, 2014:* 10.2.2, 10.2.3, & *NFPA 1002, 2017:* 5.2.3, 10.2.2, 10.2.3, Skill Sheet 13-3)

9. Establish, operate, and shut down a multiple portable tank water shuttle dump site. (*NFPA 1002, 2014:* 10.2.2, 10.2.3, & *NFPA 2017:* 5.2.3, 10.2.2, 10.2.3, Skill Sheet 13-4)

Chapter 13
Water Shuttle Operations

Case History

A rural volunteer fire department engaged in a training evolution to practice water shuttle operations. The scenario consisted of drafting from a static source to fill tenders that would in turn make a water shuttle run to supply portable folding tanks at a dump site. The source pumper supplied a 5-inch (125 mm) LDH equipped with a manifold appliance. The manifold was used to control the flow of water to a pair of 2½ inch (65 mm) hoselines being used to supply water to the tenders.

When the onboard tank of a tender was full, the order was given for the firefighter stationed at the manifold to close the valves. The firefighter slowly closed both valves simultaneously while leaning over the appliance. When the valves were approximately halfway closed the manifold ruptured, splitting in two, with the top portion striking the firefighter in the upper thigh and lower abdomen regions. The firefighter, who was wearing full PPE, was lifted off the ground and rendered unconscious. After being airlifted to a hospital, it was determined that the firefighter suffered severe bruises and lacerations, but no internal injuries.

Manifolds, as well as all fire department appliances, must be maintained in accordance with the manufacturer's recommendations. The proper adjustment and periodic testing of pressure relief valves on these devices is of the utmost importance. Firefighters should be taught to never stand directly over appliances and to always wear full PPE during these operations.

Water shuttle operations are used to provide water supply to incident scenes where relay pumping is not a viable option. In a water shuttle operation, mobile water supply apparatus (tenders or tankers depending on local vocabulary) deliver their load of water to the incident scene, dump it into portable tanks, travel to a fill site, reload, and then return to the incident scene to dump another load of water (**Figure 13.1, p. 444**). During some incidents, several water tenders may make multiple round trips to keep the scene supplied with water.

NOTE: Any apparatus with an onboard water tank may be used to deliver water to an incident. However, mobile water supply apparatus are designed, built, and operated specifically for this purpose.

Generally, relay pumping or tanker shuttle operations are the primary methods of providing water supply to points remote from a water source. There are several tactical differences between the two methods. Relay pumping usually provides a more reliable supply of continuous water with the use of fewer apparatus, but it is more labor intensive to take up when an incident is terminated.

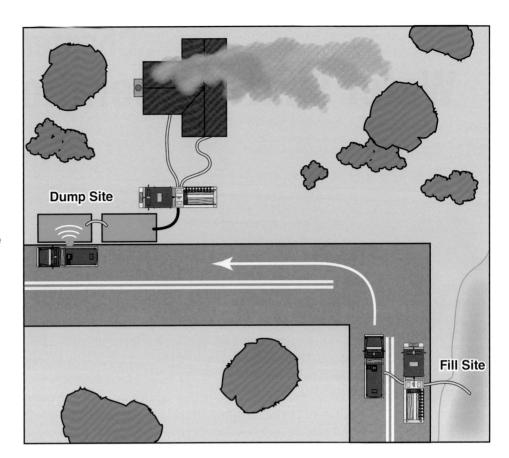

Figure 13.1 Water shuttle operations consist of water tenders delivering water from the fill site to the dump site.

Fill Site — Location at which tankers/tenders will be loaded during a water shuttle operation.

Dump Site — Location approved for water shuttle apparatus to discharge their water for other apparatus to draw during incident operations.

Safety is also a major consideration. See **Skill Sheet 13-1** for the steps to verify the operational readiness of your mobile water supply apparatus. Once relay pumping is set up, there are no moving pieces of apparatus. Other than the possibility of a hose failure, there is little danger involved with the system. A shuttle operation relies on the constant movement of apparatus at the **fill** and **dump sites**, as well as on the route between the two locations. With the movement of multiple pieces of apparatus, the chance of a collision increases.

The most favorable aspect of a water shuttle operation is the ease with which it is terminated when the incident is concluded. Often, a few portable tanks and appliances are the only equipment that must be picked up. Take-up from a relay operation may involve repacking a considerable amount of supply hose.

The decision to use a relay pumping operation or a water shuttle operation may be based on the distance to the water supply, the required fire flow, and the type of equipment a particular jurisdiction uses. The jurisdiction's policies and training are also a consideration in the type of operation used. In some cases, an incident may begin with a water shuttle operation for the sake of expediency and then transition to a relay as supply lines are laid. This operation requires coordination to avoid interfering with the shuttle route as supply lines are laid.

The following chapter explains the major components of a water shuttle operation: the fill site, the shuttle route, and the dump site. The types of apparatus used in a shuttle operation, as well as the methods used to calculate the effectiveness of the operation, are also explained in the upcoming sections.

Although local jurisdictions may practice specific water shuttle procedures that differ slightly from those detailed in this text, the methods outlined in this manual allow fire departments to achieve the optimum benefit from the referenced resources. Individual jurisdictions must adjust their procedures based on local equipment, conditions, and training.

Water Shuttle Apparatus

The two primary types of apparatus associated with water shuttle operations are water tenders and pumpers. Each serves a specific role in achieving water supply.

Pumpers

With the exception of operations that feature a vacuum tanker (described later in the chapter) or the use of a hydrant, most water shuttles require at least two pumpers for water supply. A pumper located at the water source (fill site) is generally referred to as the *fill site pumper* and has the responsibility of filling water tenders (**Figure 13.2**). For large-scale operations, this function may require two or more fill site pumpers to maintain an adequate supply to the fire scene.

NOTE: In order to fill at maximum capacity, a pumper is usually required at the hydrant.

Another pumper is located near the fire scene and is used to draft water from portable tanks that are filled by water tenders making shuttle runs to and from the fill site. This location is commonly called the *dump site,* and the dump site pumper is assigned to this operation (**Figure 13.3**). Depending on the distance from the fire scene and the particulars of the operation, the dump site pumper may also operate as the attack pumper or it may relay water to the attack pumper. (This concept is discussed in greater detail later in this chapter.)

Fill site pumpers operating from static water sources and dump site pumpers must be equipped with hard intake hose and strainers in order to conduct drafting operations. In accordance with NFPA® 1901, water tenders must be designed to be filled at a rate of at least 1,000 gpm (4 000 L/min) so that pumpers assigned to the fill site must be rated at that capacity or greater.

Figure 13.2 A fill site pumper is responsible for filling tenders in water shuttle operations.

Figure 13.3 The dump site pumper drafts water from a portable water tank.

Water Tenders

Each department must choose the appropriate capacity of their tender(s) based on local water supply availability, road conditions, and bridge height and weight restrictions. Vehicle weight restrictions generally limit single rear axle apparatus to a maximum capacity of 2,000 gallons (8 000 L). However, the single axle apparatus carrying this load must be designed to carry the weight. For apparatus with a capacity greater than 2,000 gallons (8 000 L), tandem rear axles, tri-axles, or semi-trailers are required. Many jurisdictions employ tenders of significant capacity to fulfill their water supply requirements.

Water tenders that are used only for shuttle operations do not require a fire pump if they are equipped with a suitable dumping system. However, many fire departments choose to equip their water tenders with a pump of some capacity. Tenders featuring pumps of 750 gpm (3 000 L/min) or greater rating are often called **pumper/tenders (Figure 13.4)**.

NOTE: In order to be considered a tender under NIMS typing, an onboard or portable fire pump is required.

Some fire departments operate vacuum tenders to improve water shuttle efficiency **(Figure 13.5)**. There is no need for a separate pumper at the fill site if you are using a vacuum tender. The vacuum tender is able to self-fill from a static water source at a rate of up to 2,000 gpm (8 000 L/min) with a lift of up to 22 feet (6.5 m). These apparatus are also capable of discharging its water tank at a rate up to 1,750 gpm (7 000 L/min).

As discussed in Chapter 3, Operating Emergency Vehicles, fire departments that choose to convert other types of tank trucks to mobile water supply apparatus must be aware of the weight limits and tank characteristics of these vehicles as they relate to carrying water for fire suppression. Local jurisdictions must be sure that their apparatus meet the requirements of NFPA® 1901 *Standard for Automotive Fire Apparatus*.

The success of a water shuttle operation depends on its efficiency. The variables that can be controlled through equipment and training to increase efficiency are filling and dump times. The other components of a water shuttle operation, such as response time and travel time of the shuttle, are not gener-

Figure 13.4 Pumper/tenders have large water tanks and the ability to pump at 750 gpm (3 000 L/min) or greater. *Courtesy of Ron Jeffers.*

Figure 13.5 Vacuum tenders improve water shuttle efficiency.

ally controllable for the fire department. Any attempt to "make up time" by driving faster than recommended during road travel is unsafe and may lead to an incident involving mobile water supply apparatus that may result in property damage, injury, and death to firefighters and civilians. Faster water shuttle operations are achieved by efficient filling and dumping operations, not speeding. When designing or purchasing water tenders for shuttle operations, the filling and dumping capabilities are of prime importance. Apparatus that use medium diameter supply hose for filling should have at least two external fill connections piped directly to the tank **(Figure 13.6)**. If LDH is used, one fill connection is generally sufficient **(Figure 13.7)**.

Figure 13.6 Apparatus using MDH to fill the water tank should have multiple direct-fill connections.

With LDH in wide use throughout the fire service, a single line is often used as a fill line for water tenders. This larger diameter hose may actually provide little advantage in a fill operation. After filling the initial tender the LDH will remain partially filled with water during each subsequent fill operation. This hose is extremely heavy and may be difficult to handle, thus any advantage gained by a shorter filling time may be lost in longer handing times. An alternative may be to use a 3-inch (77 mm) hose for each tank fill with quarter turn connectors.

Some apparatus may be designed with inlets that fill the tank from the top or bottom **(Figures 13.8 a and b, p. 448)**. Hydraulically, either design has little effect on usability. However, top tank fill inlets should be placed so that the hose may be connected easily from the ground. Fixed piping should carry the water from the inlet to the tank. It is preferable to have an "air gap" in the fill piping to avoid pressurizing the vehicle's onboard water tank.

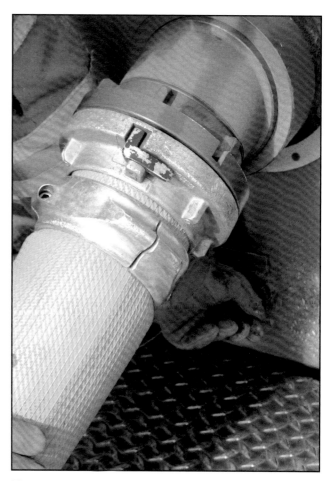

Figure 13.7 In most circumstances, only one LDH intake is necessary to fill the water tank.

CAUTION
Filling through the tops of tanks is dangerous and should be discouraged.

Figure 13.8a An apparatus with a tank inlet located near the bottom of the tank.

Figure 13.8b An apparatus with a tank inlet located near the top of the tank.

NFPA® 1901 requires that water be capable of being dumped from the left, right, and rear of the apparatus **(Figure 13.9)**. Some apparatus may be equipped with a front dump valve; however, these designs often do not meet the 1,000 gpm (4 000 L/min) flow requirement of NFPA® 1901. Multiple dump valves help improve efficiency and safety by eliminating the need for backing at many dump sites. Tanks must be adequately vented to ensure proper dumping operations.

In addition to the vacuum tenders mentioned earlier in the chapter, there are two primary types of large tank discharges in use on water tenders: gravity and jet-assisted dumps. With a gravity dump, gravity is used to empty water from the tank. These dumps often use 8-inch (200 mm) or larger round or square piping with a valve that extends to the exterior of the vehicle **(Figure 13.10)**. An extension may be mounted to the dump piping on the outside of the apparatus body to help direct the flow of water into portable tanks. The valve mechanism for a gravity dump valve may be designed for manual operation from the discharge location (side or rear of the apparatus), remotely from the cab of the vehicle, or from both locations. Remotely operated valves may be operated using electric, hydraulic, or pneumatic power. Installation of a remote valve on a water tender generally increases the safety of a dump operation because it reduces the chance of a firefighter being caught between the apparatus and a portable tank while attempting to dump the tender's water tank.

Jet-assisted dumps use a small diameter in-line discharge inserted into the piping of the large tank discharge. The in-line discharge is supplied by the fire pump on the water tender and creates a Venturi effect that increases the water flow through the large tank discharge. Some fire departments have chosen to install larger gravity dumps on their water tenders to limit cost and address the following operational issues concerning jet-assisted dumps:

- Apparatus must be equipped with a fire pump.
- The fire pump must be engaged before dumping. This adds time to the dumping operation.
- Although water can be discharged without engaging the pump, it will be at a lower rate than if a gravity dump valve were installed.

- High velocity of water discharge may miss the portable tank and strike people or other apparatus.
- The mechanism may freeze between dumping operations in cold weather climates.

With the exception of vacuum tenders, the onboard tank of water tenders must be properly vented to avoid a sudden pressure failure of the tank during quick-filling operations **(Figure 13.11)**. Conversely, inadequate venting during dumping operations may result in a suction effect that collapses the tank. The driver/operator must be sure that the vents are completely open during fill and dump operations. Some apparatus are equipped with remote controlled vents, which are preferable to manually operated vents that may require the driver/operator to climb on top of the tank.

NOTE: If the apparatus is parked on a grade that allows water to run out of the vents, a significant portion of the load may fail to discharge from the tank.

Setting Up a Water Shuttle

The success of a water shuttle operation relies on several decisions that must be made at the outset of the incident. These decisions include:

- Location of the dump site
- Location of the fill site

Figure 13.9 Water tenders should meet the dump requirements of NFPA® 1901.

Figure 13.10 Gravity dumps use large piping to quickly empty the water tank. *Courtesy of Bob Esposito.*

Figure 13.11 Vents help prevent damage to water tanks during fill operations.

- Route of travel for water tenders between the fill and dump sites
- Number of vehicles necessary to maintain a constant supply of water at the scene

The best time for these decisions to be made is during preincident planning for target hazards and specific geographical areas within a jurisdiction. A task force capable of supplying a predetermined volume of water should be established and identified to respond to specific incidents. By predetermining the most advantageous sites and routes, the Incident Commander or Water Supply Group Supervisor will be able to establish a reliable water supply more quickly during an incident **(Figure 13.12)**.

Selecting the Dump Site Location

The location of the dump site must be in relatively close proximity to the incident scene, but not so close where it would hamper operations or be in danger of exposure to fire or collapse. When operating at incidents located on a narrow lane, driveway, or dead end street, it may be advantageous to locate the dump site at the nearest intersection where a dump site pumper can then relay water to the attack pumper located at the fire scene **(Figure 13.13, p. 452)**.

When incidents occur on streets with two-way access (referred to as *through streets*), the area near the fire may be encumbered by apparatus and hoselines. The best location for the dump site may be at a clear intersection near the scene where water tenders can have through access to complete their water shuttle without having to turn around **(Figure 13.14, p. 452)**. Depending on the surrounding property, a large parking lot may also provide good access where a dump site may be established with portable tanks and a dump site pumper to supply the attack pumper at the fire scene **(Figure 13.15, p. 452)**. Fill and dump sites should be preplanned to allow for continual forward movement whenever possible.

Selecting the Fill Site Location

Each fire department should preplan available fill sites in its jurisdiction. Driver/operators and fire officers should have a working knowledge of the water supply capability in their response area in order to select the closest suitable site from which to conduct water shuttle operations. The most suitable site to meet the travel safety and flow requirements of a particular incident may not always be the geographically closest site. These conditions should be reviewed and tested on an individual basis.

For example, an incident requires a water shuttle to provide a flow of 750 gpm (3 000 L/min) for an extended period of time. The two closest water sources to the dump site are a rural water system hydrant with a flow of 250 gpm (1 000 L/min) that is one mile (1.5 km) away and a well maintained dry hydrant fed by a large lake that is two miles (3 km) away. The better source may be the dry hydrant. Due to the limited flow of the rural water system hydrant, tenders will not be able to fill fast enough to supply demand. However, the dry hydrant with the large lake as a water source will meet the flow requirements more quickly, thus making up the extra mile of distance to the dump site. Additionally, a lake with good access for drafting may provide opportunities for placement of an additional fill site should a greater volume of water be required. When

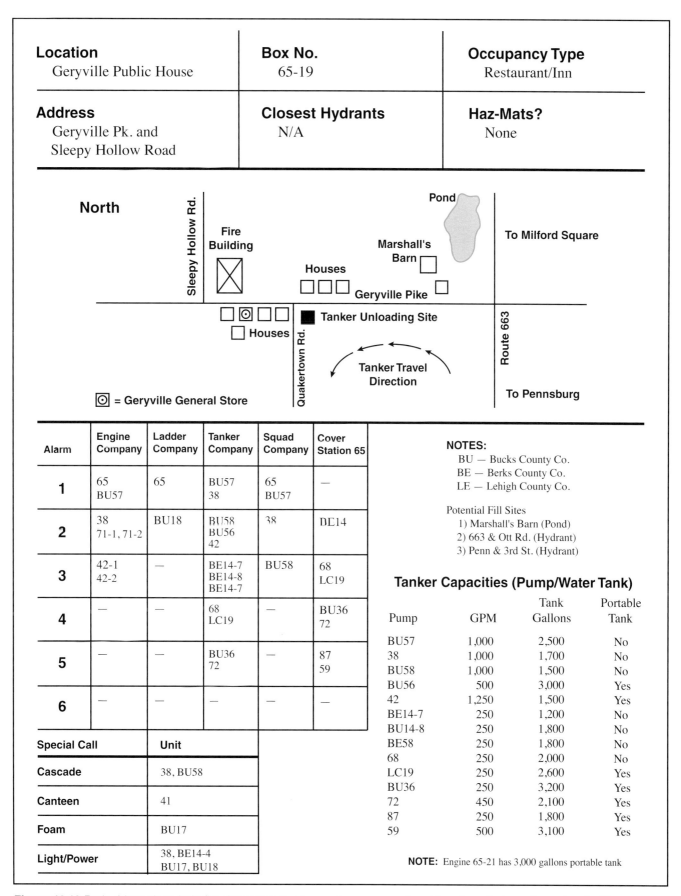

Location	Box No.	Occupancy Type
Geryville Public House	65-19	Restaurant/Inn

Address	Closest Hydrants	Haz-Mats?
Geryville Pk. and Sleepy Hollow Road	N/A	None

North

Sleepy Hollow Rd.

Fire Building

Houses

Marshall's Barn

Pond

To Milford Square

Geryville Pike

Tanker Unloading Site

Quakertown Rd.

Route 663

Houses

Tanker Travel Direction

⊙ = Geryville General Store

To Pennsburg

Alarm	Engine Company	Ladder Company	Tanker Company	Squad Company	Cover Station 65
1	65 BU57	65	BU57 38	65 BU57	—
2	38 71-1, 71-2	BU18	BU58 BU56 42	38	BE14
3	42-1 42-2	—	BE14-7 BE14-8 BE14-7	BU58	68 LC19
4	—	—	68 LC19	—	BU36 72
5	—	—	BU36 72	—	87 59
6	—	—	—	—	—

Special Call	Unit
Cascade	38, BU58
Canteen	41
Foam	BU17
Light/Power	38, BE14-4 BU17, BU18

NOTES:
BU — Bucks County Co.
BE — Berks County Co.
LE — Lehigh County Co.

Potential Fill Sites
1) Marshall's Barn (Pond)
2) 663 & Ott Rd. (Hydrant)
3) Penn & 3rd St. (Hydrant)

Tanker Capacities (Pump/Water Tank)

Pump	GPM	Tank Gallons	Portable Tank
BU57	1,000	2,500	No
38	1,000	1,700	No
BU58	1,000	1,500	No
BU56	500	3,000	Yes
42	1,250	1,500	Yes
BE14-7	250	1,200	No
BU14-8	250	1,800	No
BE58	250	1,800	No
68	250	2,000	No
LC19	250	2,600	Yes
BU36	250	3,200	Yes
72	450	2,100	Yes
87	250	1,800	Yes
59	500	3,100	Yes

NOTE: Engine 65-21 has 3,000 gallons portable tank

Figure 13.12 Preincident plans help fire departments prepare for emergencies at locations that require water shuttle operations.

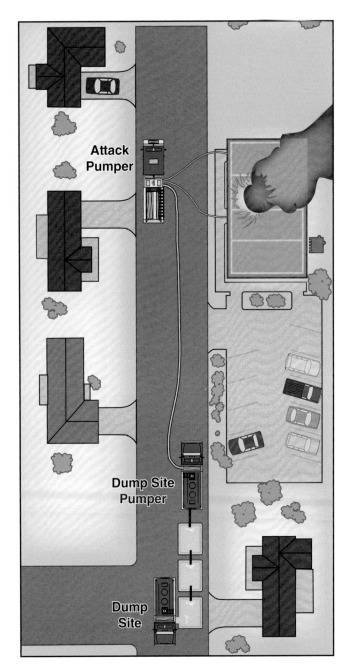

possible, a water supply source capable of supplying at least 1,000 gpm (4 000 L/min) should be chosen in order to match the NFPA® recommended rate at which tenders should be filled.

Selecting a fill or dump site that requires little or no backing of water tenders is preferable to ensure safety as well as the efficiency of a water shuttle operation. The best sites are those where a driver/operator may drive straight into the site and drive straight out when the fill or dump is complete **(Figure 13.16)**. If backing is unavoidable, a properly staffed fill site may provide a safer environment with adequate spotters for each apparatus.

Large-scale water shuttle operations may require the use of multiple fill and dump sites. This is es-

Figure 13.15 Dump sites in large open areas allow for trucks to easily maneuver into and out of the dump site.

Figure 13.13 Attack pumpers may be geographically separated from the dump site when operating on a dead-end street.

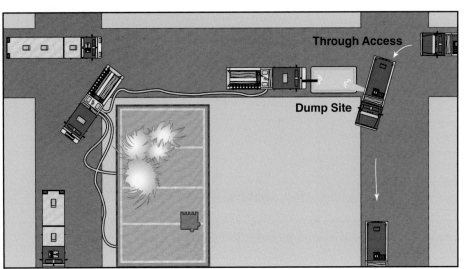

Figure 13.14 Intersections provide through access for water shuttle operations.

Figure 13.16 Fill sites where apparatus backing is not required is preferred.

pecially true when the incident is spread over a large geographical area and water supply is needed at two separate places in the operation. This scenario may be best served by establishing two completely separate water shuttle operations.

Selecting the Route of Travel

Driving the travel route may be one of the most hazardous tasks for a driver/operator during a water shuttle operation. The route of travel for water tenders should be selected based on safety and operational effectiveness.

A circular route is the optimum arrangement for a water shuttle circuit **(Figure 13.17)**. When a circular pattern is used, the full tenders leaving the fill site follow one route toward the dump site. The empty tenders leave the dump site and return to be refilled using a different route. This strategy eliminates the need for large tenders passing each other on narrow, rural roads and limited weight bridges. This arrangement is often employed by necessity during incidents on limited access highways.

When using a circular travel route, consider the direction of travel if there is a substantial grade on a portion of the route. Fully loaded tenders should travel down grade and empty tenders should make the return trip traveling uphill. Although not always possible, it is advantageous to have roadways closed to nonemergency vehicles during water shuttle operations to lessen traffic congestion and reduce the possibility of collision.

Traffic Control

At fill sites adjacent to roadways that are open to traffic, position water tenders off the roadway whenever possible. Use traffic cones, signs, or other traffic warning devices to advise motorists of the presence of fire apparatus. Contact local law enforcement for assistance with traffic control.

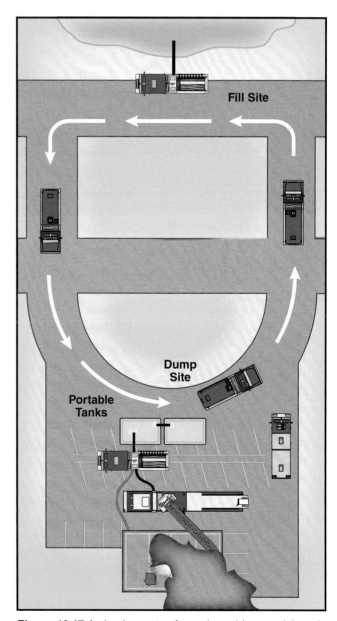

Figure 13.17 A circular route of travel provides a quick and efficient circuit for water shuttle operations.

Driver/operators must consider the following safety issues when planning a route of travel for water shuttle operations:

- **Narrow roads** — You may face difficulty passing other vehicles; narrow roads may not be wide enough for the apparatus, and the vehicle tires may leave the road surface creating the potential for a rollover.

- **Long driveways** — Narrow driveways require tight maneuvering of the apparatus. Vehicles approaching from opposite directions may require that one apparatus back out to a turnaround point. You can find additional information concerning long driveways in the dump site operations section of this manual.

- **Blind curves and intersections** — Vehicles that cross the center line on blind curves risk entering the path of an oncoming vehicle. Blind intersections pose a danger, as driver/operators cannot see oncoming cross traffic, and operators of other vehicles may not see fire apparatus approaching the intersection. When these intersections occur along a shuttle route, it is advisable to have police officers or fire police control traffic at these points.

- **Winding roads** — Maintain concentration at all times. A momentary lapse may cause a collision with another vehicle or lead to the apparatus being driven off the road.

- **Steep grades** — Uphill grades slow shuttle operations as well as creating increased wear on apparatus. Downhill grades require constant attention to vehicle speed in order to maintain control.

- **Inclement weather conditions** — Whenever possible, avoid roads covered with ice, snow, standing water, mud, or storm debris during water shuttle operations.

- **Freezing water** — Water shuttle operations may create an additional hazard, especially near fill or dump sites, where overflow or spilling of water from apparatus may freeze.

Water Shuttles in the Incident Command System

When establishing a water shuttle operation, it must be integrated into the Incident Command structure. It is recommended that the Incident Commander make designations that adhere to the **National Incident Management System (NIMS)**.

When a Water Supply Group is established, the person in charge is known as the Water Supply Group Supervisor **(Figure 13.18)**. Only this Supervisor will report directly up the chain of command to the Operations Section Chief or Incident Commander. If an incident escalates beyond the span of control for a Group Supervisor, the IC may establish a Water Supply Branch under the supervision of a Branch Director. When multiple radio frequencies are available, it may be advantageous to assign a dedicated channel to water supply operations in order to reduce traffic on the main incident channel. This will also improve communication between elements of the Water Supply Group. The Water Supply Group Supervisor may monitor two radios or switch to the main incident frequency to contact the IC or Operations Chief. The person assigned the role of Group Supervisor for the water supply operation must have consid-

National Incident Management System - Incident Command System (NIMS-ICS) — The U.S. mandated Incident Management System that defines the roles, responsibilities, and standard operating procedures used to manage emergency operations; creates a Unified Incident Response Structure for federal, state, and local governments.

Figure 13.18 The Water Supply Group Supervisor is responsible for water shuttle operations.

erable experience in pumper, water supply, and shuttle operations, as well as familiarity with local conditions and a working knowledge of the **Incident Management System**.

After the Water Supply Group Supervisor is appointed and the water supply plan formulated, the Supervisor must appoint individuals to be responsible for the fill and dump sites. Although any member competent in water supply operations may fill this role, the job often falls to the company officers or driver/operators of the apparatus stationed in these locations. The persons responsible for these sites must remain in constant contact with each other and the Group Supervisor via radio, or cell phone. Each must relay to the other when a tender has completed a portion of the relay and is headed to the opposite site.

The Water Supply Group Supervisor must monitor the fill and dump sites for potential problems. If demand begins to outpace supply, additional tenders must be summoned. The IC or Operations Chief must keep the Group Supervisor apprised of any change in flow requirements in order for the Group Supervisor to properly coordinate resources.

During large-scale incidents, it may be necessary to establish two or more water shuttle operations. In these cases, the IC may develop a Water Supply Branch. Separate fill and dump sites, as well as specifically assigned tenders, will be assigned to each travel route. Each water shuttle may be assigned a group designation with a Group Supervisor. The entire Branch Operation will be coordinated through the Water Supply Branch Director. For identification purposes, each group may be assigned a specific name, such as East Shuttle or West Shuttle, based on local policy. The Group Supervisor assigned to these groups would, in turn, appoint people to head the fill and dump site in each group. For further incident management information, consult Fire Protection Publications NIMS *Model Procedures Guide for Structural Firefighting*.

Incident Management System (IMS) — System described in NFPA® 1561, *Standard on Emergency Services Incident Management System*, that defines the roles, responsibilities, and standard operating procedures used to manage emergency operations. Such systems may also be referred to as Incident Command Systems (ICS).

Fill Site Operations

The goal of the fill site is to load tenders as safely and efficiently as possible. **Skill Sheet 13-2** provides the steps for setting up, operating, and shutting down a fill site as described in the section below. The Water Supply Group Supervisor should select the best method to accomplish these goals based on specific equipment, personnel, and conditions. The details of fill site operations are discussed in the following sections.

Positioning the Fill Site Pumper

Positioning at the fill site must allow for drafting or hydrant connection and the best possible approach and departure route for water tender traffic. Ideally, position the fill site pumper so as to allow a view of both the water source and the water tender to be filled. Apparatus with top-mounted pump panels are well suited to accomplish this goal. If at all possible, fill water tenders at a rate of 1,000 gpm (4 000 L/min).

When operating from a hydrant, the driver/operator must connect, at a minimum, a large diameter intake hose between the hydrant and the pumper intake. When operating from any hydrant, connect all available hydrant discharges to pump intakes to maximize the potential from the hydrant.

When positioning to draft at a static water supply, seek a position that requires a minimum of lift in order to maximize the flow available to supply the tender. Position the fill site pumper to a point of best advantage for the water source. Discharge lines to supply water tenders can be lengthened as necessary. In cases where the static supply is inaccessible to apparatus, high volume portable pumps may be employed to relay water to the fill site pumper. Depending on the distance from the source to the fill site pumper, multiple portable pumps may supply the fire department pumper directly, or it may supply a portable tank from which the pumper can draft. Portable pumps may increase the options available to use static water supply at many incidents.

Regardless of the source, a booster line or other small discharge should be continuously flowed in view of the driver/operator. This measure will help prevent loss of prime or overheating of the pump during drafting operations. When operating from a hydrant, the water flow will help ensure overheating does not occur when there are no tenders to be filled.

Fill Site Layout

When the fill site pumper has been positioned at the water source, lay out and make ready for use the hose and appliances necessary for the operaton. Commonly, water tenders have at least two 2½ inch (65 mm) direct tank fill connections or one LDH direct tank fill connection on the rear of the apparatus. Position the water tender so that a minimum amount of hose is required from the fill site pumper. Balance this distance with a position that allows the tender to enter and exit the fill site without having to turn around or back up. Ideally, this position should accommodate empty water tenders that may need to line up and wait their turn to be filled **(Figure 13.19)**. If this arrangement becomes too congested, make preparations to establish another water supply fill site.

When an exact fill spot has been determined, place a traffic cone or similar marker to denote the stopping point for the water tender driver/operator. Position this cone so that it is adjacent to the door of the driver/operator. This positioning system allows the fill hose to be located near the rear of the apparatus and reduces the need to move hoselines when each vehicle arrives.

Jurisdictions should attempt to standardize their water tenders so that one size hose will be used (MDH or LDH) at the fill site. When using LDH to connect to tenders with direct tank fill intakes, only one line is generally required **(Figure 13.20)**. If an inline gate valve is not available for this hose, it is pos-

Figure 13.19 Fill sites should have ample space for empty water tenders to wait in line to be refilled.

Figure 13.20 Some fill sites use LDH to fill water tenders.

sible to place an LDH manifold between the last two sections of hose to act as a valve. If neither option is available, it is best to operate LDH fill lines at the pump panel of the fill site pumper.

When using medium diameter hose (MDH), multiple hoselines will be required to flow to each mobile water supply apparatus in order to decrease fill times. Large diameter hose will generally require only one supply line to fill the tender efficiently. Flow from the fill site pumper should be controlled by using the discharge gates on the pumping apparatus.

▰▰▰▰▰▰▰▰▰▰▰▰

CAUTION

Using hose clamps on LDH may be unsafe. Flow through LDH should only be controlled at the pumper or with valve appliances.

Top Fill Methods

Equipment and policies in some jurisdictions may require that water tenders be filled through the fill or vent opening on top of the apparatus. This may be accomplished with the use of portable or stationary filling equipment. Stationary equipment naturally limits the fill site to a particular location.

One top-fill method uses an overhead pipe that may be a permanent or portable device. This device may be made of PVC, but due to the brittle nature of this product in extremely cold weather, many jurisdictions opt to use aluminum piping or another lightweight material. This fill device is operated by placing one end of the fill pipe in the static source. A pumper discharges water through a small diameter hose line into an inline water siphon inside the fill pipe. This creates an adequate flow rate through the fill pipe. These devices are used only when there is no other way of filling than through the top opening. It is more efficient to use the pumper to draft from the site and pump directly into the water tender.

Another method of overhead pipe device uses portable or permanent manifolds. A permanent manifold is located adjacent to a water source (pressurized or static) and fed by the fill site pumper When using these systems, the fill site pumper connects between the water source and the fill pipe that supplies water from overhead when a tender is positioned beneath the fill opening. When using reliable water sources, high fill rates may be achieved using this type of system. However, some time may be lost while positioning the apparatus directly under the fill spout.

CAUTION

Do not fill a water tender with a portable fill device or an open hose butt due to the reaction of the hoseline and possibility of firefighters sustaining serious injuries due to falls from the top of the tender.

Operating the Fill Site

Fill site operations may begin once the fill site pumper has been positioned and connected to the water supply, and all necessary equipment is ready. The fill site pumper should remain in pump with a waste line flowing to prevent loss of prime and/or overheating.

Figure 13.21 Each fill site firefighter should be responsible for one fill line.

Assign one firefighter to maneuver and connect each fill line that is laid out **(Figure 13.21)**. These firefighters make the fill connection(s) upon arrival of the water tender and disconnect (or break) the hose(s) when the tank is full. Personnel must staff these lines continuously during fill site operations.

Driver/operators entering a fill site should proceed cautiously into position until the driver's door is parallel to the traffic cone or other marking device that has been set as an indicator for the driver to stop. The firefighters operating the fill line(s), sometimes referred to as "make and break" personnel in reference to their duties of establishing and removing connections between the water source and the tank, should remain clear of the approach as each tender approaches and establishes a position. Only after the apparatus comes to a complete stop should the make and break personnel connect the fill hose(s) to the direct tank fill intake(s). Once the intake valve is opened, the gate valve or manifold may then be operated to allow the water supply to flow. Personnel should remain at the gate valves or manifold until the tender is full.

The tender driver/operator should remain in the apparatus cab to ensure peak efficiency in apparatus movement, allowing the vehicle to be moved as soon as the fill is complete and the hose(s) is removed. Waiting tenders must remain at a safe distance until the fill area is clear to receive a new apparatus.

If the fill site is large enough, a second set of fill lines may be established from the fill site pumper. This will allow a second tender to be positioned and connected to the lines while the first apparatus is filling. As soon as the first tender is full, the lines to the second tender may be opened.

After the onboard water tank is full, the fill site personnel should slowly close the valve(s) on the gate or manifold. Next, the direct tank fill valve on the tender should be closed and the hose(s) removed from the inlet and placed away from the path of any apparatus. The driver/operator can then be signaled to proceed. When the area is clear and it is safe to allow the next tender to move into position, a signal should be given. The hand signals (or flashlight signals used during nighttime operations) in this operation should be given by one individual in order to maintain continuity and clarity of instruction.

Personnel working at the fill site, including company officers and the fill-site officer should monitor ground conditions as the shuttle operation progresses, because some amount of water will be spilled during every operation. The effects of this spillage will vary based on temperature and terrain. In cold weather climates, ice can make site operations very dangerous. If the fill site is located on an unpaved surface, the ground may soften. Either condition is dangerous and may require relocation of the site.

Shutting Down the Fill Site

Once the need for a continuous water supply has ended, the fill site must begin to shut down. All driver/operators of responding tenders should fill their tanks before returning to quarters. This measure is a recommended practice in most jurisdictions when returning apparatus to "ready" status after an incident. An exception includes apparatus using a static water source. In order to lessen the chance of contamination, flush the apparatus as soon as practical upon return to quarters. Once all the water tenders have been refilled, the site pumper and equipment may be shut down and prepared for a return to service.

Dump Site Operations

The dump site provides a continuous supply of water to the apparatus attacking the fire. Several methods may be employed to operate the dump site and discharge water from tenders. The following sections focus on efficient methods for dump site operations during long-term, high volume water shuttle relays. **Skill Sheet 13-3** gives the steps for operating at a portable water tank dump site as part of a water shuttle operation.

Dump Site Operational Methods

The following are primary methods for operating a dump site:

- Direct pumping operations
- Nurse tender operations
- Portable water tank operations

Direct Pumping Operations

Using the direct pumping method, water tenders pump the water from their tanks directly into the pump intake of an attack pumper. This method is typically accomplished by having the attack pumper lay out a supply line that is equipped with a gated or clappered Siamese in an area accessible to tenders. The first tender supplies this line from one of the discharges on its fire pump and begins to supply the attack pumper. During this operation, a second tender may connect to the other inlet of the Siamese **(Figure 13.22)**. This line may be pumped at a slightly lower pressure than the first tender's line. When the first tender is empty, its supply line is shut down and the supply from the second tender automatically starts to feed the attack pumper without any delay. This alternating supply operation may continue until the need for water at the incident is satisfied.

NOTE: Direct pumping is generally performed only when a minimal volume of water is required.

Nurse Tender Operations

Another dump site method of delivery involves positioning a large water tender immediately adjacent to the attack pumper, serving the same role as a portable tank **(Figure 13.23)**. Jurisdictions that operate tractor-trailer tenders typically use them as **nurse tankers (tenders)**. The primary advantage of the nurse tender is the large capacity of its tank that may allow incidents to be concluded before there is a need to refill the tank. However, operating a nurse tender involves the cost of maintaining the apparatus as well as training additional driver/operators to staff the vehicle. Another consideration includes the additional time required when pumping water from a shuttle tender into the nurse tender, rather than using a large diameter discharge valve to directly dump water into a portable tank.

Portable Water Tank Operations

Using one or more portable water tanks located near the incident scene to eliminate the need for backing or turning around is an efficient way to manage dump site water supply **(Figure 13.24)**. Once a tank is positioned, a pumper,

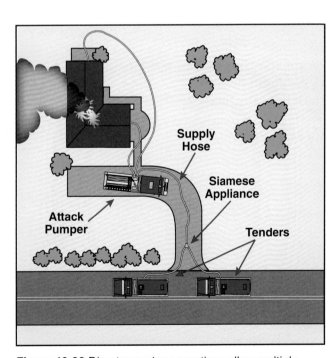

Figure 13.22 Direct pumping operations allow multiple water tenders to simultaneously resupply an attack pumper.

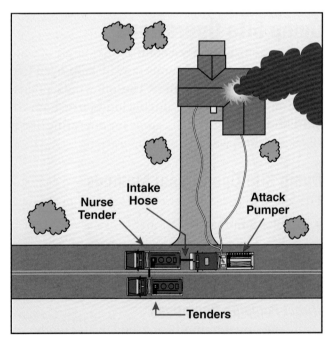

Figure 13.23 Some jurisdictions use nurse tender operations.

referred to as a *dump site pumper*, deploys a hard intake hose with a low-level strainer into the tank. Once the first tender delivers its water, the dump site pumper begins to draft. During some incidents, portable tanks are positioned for the attack pumper to draft from the tank.

When using portable tanks for dump site supply, the water tenders do not need to be equipped with a fire pump as long as they are designed with an adequately sized direct tank discharge valve (dump valve) and proper venting **(Figure 13.25)**. The portable tank method is generally considered to be the simplest and quickest method to ensure a constant water supply for fire attack operations. The primary disadvantage is the substantial amount of working space required to operate the dump site.

Some apparatus may pump its water into a portable tank or nurse tender by pumping it out a discharge and through a hoseline. The use of a discharge and hoseline is normally only used if the tender is NOT equipped with a dump valve. Generally, pumping through a discharge is less efficient than using a dump valve as the flow is limited by the capacity of the tank-to-pump line, the pump capacity, and the ability to control the hoseline at the point of delivery. In addition to taking longer to empty the tank, the amount of time for the driver/operator to engage, operate, and disengage the pump increases the overall time spent at the dump site. When pumping into portable tanks, hoselines discharging into the tank must be secured. Firefighters should not attempt to manually hold the **open butt** of a hoseline.

Open Butt — End of a charged hoseline that is flowing water without a nozzle or valve to control the flow.

Baffle — Intermediate partial bulkhead that reduces the surge effect in a partially loaded liquid tank.

The volume of water moved through the valve is dependent on the size and design of the valve, the baffling of the water tank, and the venting capability of the tank. The tank **baffles** must have opening of sufficient size to allow free movement of water at the bottom of the tank and movement of air at the top during rapid filling or

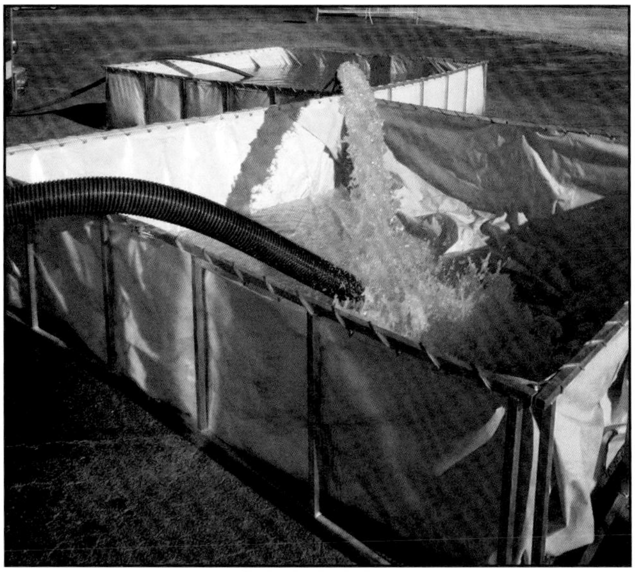

Figure 13.24 Portable water tanks allow for a ready supply of water at the dump site.

Figure 13.25 Water tenders without pumps can still be useful in water shuttle operations as long as they have a dump valve.

unloading. NFPA® 1901 requires all tenders to have the capability to dump at a minimum average flow rate of 1,000 gpm (4 000 L/min) for the first 90 percent of its tank capacity. As discussed previously, dumping from the sides or rear of the apparatus is optimal for apparatus stability and security.

Single Portable Tank Operations

A simple dump site may feature the use of one **portable tank** that is supplied directly by water shuttle tenders. This tank may then be used by the dump site pumper for drafting **(Figure 13.26)**. This operation is generally adequate for fire fighting operations that require relatively low flow rates (less than 300 gpm [1 200 L/min]). There may be considerable turbulence created by dumping into a tank. Drafting from a tank with extensive turbulence may not be successful.

The most common style of portable tank folds and is mounted and removed from the apparatus similar to a ground ladder. It is carried into position and unfolded for deployment. Some fire departments place a salvage cover between the tank and the ground to reduce wear and damage on the tank liner.

Other styles of portable tanks may require that framework be assembled at the scene and the liner attached to the inside. When assembled, this type of tank resembles a folding tank. Another portable tank variation consists of a large bladder with a floating collar around the opening. This is known as a *self-supporting* or *frameless water tank*. As water enters the tank, the collar continues to rise until it reaches capacity. A frameless tank must be set up on a level surface in order to hold its maximum capacity of water. This style of tank has a hose connection near its bottom to aid drafting operations.

Any tank, regardless of type, should be set up on a surface that is as level as possible and have a capacity at least 500 gallons (2 000 L) larger than the water tank on the apparatus that will supply it. The extra capacity will allow the tender to dump its entire load into the tank, even if the tank is set up on a slight incline or roadway with a high crown.

The dump site pumper should utilize a low-level strainer to allow for continuous drafting to a point of about 2 inches (50 mm). All strainers should be tested for flow capacity prior to use during fireground operations.

Once the portable tank has been set up in such a way as to minimize backing, the first tender may dump its load of water with the assistance of a dump site officer or spotter. The driver/operator must be guided so that the dump valve of the water tender is properly aligned with the tank. Once in position, with water flowing into the tank, the dump site pumper may prime its pump and begin to draft from the tank. As with any drafting operation, the dump site pumper should flow a small waste line back into the tank to ensure that prime is not lost when other discharges are shut down.

When finished unloading, the first tender should proceed back to the fill site to continue the shuttle. If there is space available in the portable tank, the next tender may be positioned and begin to dump its water until the portable tank is full. When the water level allows, the tender should finish unloading.

Figure 13.26 Dump site pumpers can draft water from a single portable tank.

Multiple Portable Tank Operations

Incidents that require a flow rate in excess of 300 gpm (1 200 L/min) are best served by a multiple tank operation. These operations are limited by available equipment, apparatus, and staging space. Most multi-tank operations use from two to five portable tanks. **Skill Sheet 13-4** gives steps to establish, operate, and shut down a multiple portable tank water shuttle dump site.

Each tank must be positioned so that water may be transferred from one tank to the next in series until it reaches the last tank from which the dump site pumper is drafting. The goal of a multi-tank operation is to keep the tank, from which the attack pumper is drafting, full at all times. Operating in this way empties the tank farthest away from the attack pumper first, thus allowing it to be constantly available for dumping.

There are several ways to transfer water between portable tanks. Some fire departments connect two tanks by their drain openings **(Figure 13.27)**. However, this method is generally not very efficient as most portable tanks have only one drain, limiting the operation to two tanks. In addition, this method maintains the same level of water in both tanks, which can create a delay in unloading water tenders.

A more efficient method involves the use of jet siphons to move water from one tank to another. The jet siphon is attached to a section of hard intake hose or a piece of PVC or aluminum pipe that is as large in diameter as practical. This device has an inlet for a 1½-inch (38 mm) or larger hoseline. When the jet siphon, hard intake hose, and 1½-inch (38 mm) hoseline are assembled, the end of the jet siphon is placed into the tank from which water is to be transferred **(Figure 13.28)**. When the dump site pumper charges the 1½-inch (38 mm) line, water is drawn into the hard intake hose. This water flows through the hose and into the next tank in line **(Figure 13.29, p. 464)**. When the next tank becomes full, the operator shuts down the 1½-inch (38 mm) line, stopping the flow. The driver/operator must maintain water in the apparatus water tank at all times. As with all other pump operations, should the apparatus tank be allowed to run dry, the pumper will be unable to supply the jet siphon, and the pump's prime will be lost. If only two or three tanks are to be used with a jet siphon operation, the dump site pumper should be able to supply hoselines

Figure 13.27 Portable tanks may be connected by placing hard intake hose through their drain openings.

Figure 13.28 A jet siphon is used to move water into the tank from which the dumpsite pumper is drafting.

Figure 13.29 When the siphon supply line is charged, water is transferred from one tank to the next.

for all the jet siphons. For operations that require more than three tanks and jet siphons and flows over 500 gpm (2 000 L/min), parallel jet siphons should be used to transfer water to the tank supplying the attack pumper. A second pumper may be used to draft from the tanks solely to supply the jet siphons, to relieve some of the work of the dump site pumper's driver/operator.

The dump site officer must monitor conditions around the dump site as operations progress. In cold weather climates, ice may form from any water spilled during dumping operations. It may be necessary to call for a sanding truck to maintain safe operating conditions for personnel and apparatus. Unpaved surfaces may become soft or muddy. If conditions deteriorate to a point where continued operation may be impractical, a new dump site must be determined and readied for operation and put into use with additional equipment before the original one is terminated.

Shutting Down the Dump Site

When the need for a continuous water supply at an incident has concluded, the dump site operation may be disassembled. All attack apparatus and the dump site pumper should be refilled prior to concluding operations. Then the drafting and water transfer equipment may be disassembled, cleaned, and stowed. Portable tanks should be drained of any sediment, debris, or nonpotable water before the equipment is placed back on the apparatus.

Evaluating Tender Performance

Each jurisdiction maintains certain criteria for measuring the proper specifications for water tender apparatus. Some favor the largest vehicle possible for maximum tank capacity. Other fire departments require smaller apparatus that can load, dump, and complete shuttle routes quickly.

Overall tender performance is based on a number of factors, including loading and unloading time, drive-train capabilities, and tank size. For example, a large, underpowered tender may not be able to supply water as well as a smaller, well-designed apparatus. The availability of personnel to drive and operate the apparatus as well as the vehicle's ability to traverse local roads and bridges are additional factors that determine the effectiveness of the apparatus.

It is possible to determine a gpm (L/min) rate that a tender can supply over preset distances. Fill and dump times, as well as travel time over a specific shuttle route, are tested and analyzed. The data is used in preplanning to determine how many tenders are required to provide a particular flow for a given target hazard. This method may also be used by the Incident Commander or Water Supply Officer during an incident for which no preplan is available, but a flow rate needs to be calculated at the scene. In some jurisdictions, mobile water supply apparatus are placed into a task force with an established volume of water supply capability.

There are two basic methods for calculating a flow rate for a specific tender. One method relies on actual field tests conducted under realistic water shuttle conditions. In this method, a tender is parked in position to dump its load into a portable tank. A timer is started when the dump valve is opened. The timer continues to run while the tender dumps, leaves the dump site, drives to the fill site, and returns back to the dump site. The timer is stopped when the tender is back in position at the portable tank. By dividing the amount of water the tender dumped by the time the round trip took, a flow rating can be assigned to that tender for a particular distance. **Formula 13.1** demonstrates this calculation.

Most water tenders only dump 90 percent of their load before leaving the dump site; therefore, water tenders only refill 90 percent of their tank at the fill site. This 90 percent consideration is reflected in the following formulas as 0.9TS.

Formula 13.1 (Customary and Metric) — Water Shuttle Flow Rate

$$\text{Flow} = \frac{0.9 \times TS}{\text{Trip Time}}$$

Where:

Flow = Water shuttle flow rate in gallons per minute (gpm) or liters per minute (L/min)

0.9 = A constant to represent 90 percent of water tender tank size

TS = Tank Size

Example 13.1 (Customary)

What is the water shuttle flow rate for a 3,000 gallon tender that makes the one-mile round trip between dump and fill sites in 12 minutes?

$$\text{Flow} = \frac{0.9 \times TS}{\text{Trip Time}}$$

$$\text{Flow} = \frac{0.9 \times 3000}{12} = \textbf{225 gpm}$$

Example 13.1 (Metric)

What is the water shuttle flow rate for a 12 000 liter tender that makes the 1.5 kilometer round trip between dump and fill sites in 12 minutes?

$$\text{Flow} = \frac{0.9 \times TS}{\text{Trip Time}}$$

$$\text{Flow} = \frac{0.9 \times 12\,000}{12} = \textbf{900 L/min}$$

Another method of evaluating water tender performance involves using a series of formulas originally developed by the **Insurance Services Office (ISO)**. These formulas are used to rate the water supply performance of fire departments that protect rural areas. Shuttle operations are divided into two time elements: travel time and handling time.

Insurance Services Office (ISO) — Private national insurance organization that evaluates and rates fire defense for all communities through the fire-suppression rating schedule. Also serves as an advisory organization to other property-liability insurance companies. *Also known as* Rating Bureau.

Formula 13.2 provides the means for calculating **travel time**. There is a built in factor for acceleration and deceleration times as the vehicles approach fill and dump sites. The formula assumes an average travel speed between the fill and dump site of 35 mph (55 km/h). If road conditions allow faster speeds or requires slower speeds, the formula must be adjusted accordingly.

Formula 13.2 (Customary) – Travel Time

Travel Time = 0.65 + (1.7)(Distance)

Where:

Travel Time is measured in minutes (min)

Distance is measured in miles (Round-trip)

Formula 13.2 (Metric) – Travel Time

Travel Time = 0.65 + (1.06)(Distance)

Where:

Travel Time is measured in minutes (min)

Distance is measured in kilometers (km) (Round-trip)

Example 13.2 (Customary)

What is the travel time for a tender that must complete a 5-mile water shuttle operation?

Travel Time = 0.65 + (1.7)(Distance)

Travel Time = 0.65 + (1.7)(5) = **9.15 minutes (app. 9)**

Example 13.2 (Metric)

What is the travel time for a tender that must complete an 8-kilometer water shuttle operation?

Travel Time = 0.65 + (1.06)(Distance)

Travel Time = 0.65 + (1.06)(8) = **97.151 minutes (app. 9)**

Handling time is composed of the Fill Site Time and Dump Site Time. The fill site time includes time spent positioning the apparatus and making and breaking connections, as well as the actual water fill time. In order to use the calculation, the flow rate that the fill site pumper is supplying must be established. Each jurisdiction must determine this rate based on the equipment available. Dump site time includes the time it takes to position the water tender as well as the actual dump time. Determine each tender's actual dump rate by field testing. NFPA® 1901 specifies that water tenders should be capable of dumping at a minimum of 1,000 gpm (4 000 L/min). This chapter's formulas will reflect that rate. See **Formula 13.3** for steps to calculate handling time.

Formula 13.3 (Customary and Metric) – Handling Time

Handling Time = Fill Site Time + Dump Site Time

Example 13.3 (Customary)

What is the handling time for a 4,000 gallon tender that has a fill/dump rate of 2,000 gpm? Assume that the maneuvering and make and break times total 2 minutes for each site.

Handling Time = Fill Site Time + Dump Site Time

Fill Site Time = (2 min + [4000 ÷ 2000]) = **4 min**

Dump Site Time = (2 min + [4000 ÷ 2000]) = **4 min**

Handling Time = 4 + 4 = **8 min**

Example 13.3 (Metric)

What is the handling time for an 8 000 liter tender that has a fill/dump rate of 4 000 L/min? Assume that the maneuvering and make or break times total 2 minutes for each site.

Handling Time = Fill Site Time + Dump Site Time

Fill Site Time = (2 min + [8 000 ÷ 4 000]) = **4 min**

Dump Site Time = (2 min + [8 000 ÷ 4 000]) = **4 min**

Handling Time = 4 + 4 = **8 min**

The ISO equation uses 90 percent of a tender's total tank capacity to account for water lost or undischarged and remaining in the tank after the dump valve is closed. Some fire departments have found that they actually routinely dump less than 90 percent of each load.

One of the most accurate ways to determine the amount of water left in the tank after dumping is to weigh the apparatus on a truck scale when full and again after being dumped. The difference in the two weights accounts for the amount of water actually dumped. Given the standard weight of one gallon (4 L) of water as being 8.33 pounds (4 kg), the number of gallons and percentage of the total tank capacity that was dumped can be easily determined.

Once the travel and handling times have been determined, the flow rate for a specific tender may be calculated using **Formula 13.4**.

Formula 13.4 (Customary and Metric) - Tender Flow Rate

$$\text{Flow} = \frac{0.9 \times TS}{\text{Travel Time} + \text{Handling Time}}$$

Where:

Flow = Tender flow rate in gallons per minute (gpm) or liters per minute (L/min)

0.9 = A constant to represent 90 percent of water tender tank size

TS = Tank Size

Example 13.4 (Customary)

Determine the flow rate for a 2,500 gallon tender with fill/dump rates of 1,000 gpm that must complete a shuttle run of 4 miles in each direction. Assume that the maneuvering and make and break times total 1.5 minutes at each site.

Travel Time = 0.65 + (1.7)(Distance) (Round-trip)

Travel Time = 0.65 + (1.7)(8) = **14.25 min**

Handling Time = Fill Site Time + Dump Site Time

Fill Site Time = (1.5 + [2500 ÷ 1000]) = **4 min**

Dump Site Time = (1.5 + [2500 ÷ 1000]) = **4 min**

Handling Time = 4 + 4 = **8 min**

Flow =   0.9 x TS
**   Travel Time + Handling Time**

Flow = $\underline{0.9 \times 2500}$ = $\underline{2250}$ = **101.12 gpm (app. 101)**
        14.25 + 8   22.25

Example 13.4 (Metric)

Determine the flow rate for a 10 000 liter tender with fill/dump rates of 4 000 L/min that is shuttling water 8 km in each direction. Assume that the maneuvering and make and break times at each site total 2 minutes.

Travel Time = 0.65 + (1.06)(Distance) (Round-trip)

Travel Time = 0.65 + (1.06)(16) = **17.61 min**

Handling Time = Fill Site Time + Dump Site Time

Fill Site Time = (2 + [10 000 ÷ 4 000]) = **4.5 min**

Dump Site Time = (2 + [10 000 ÷ 4 000]) = **4.5 min**

Handling Time = 4.5 + 4.5 = **9 min**

Flow =   0.9 x TS
**   Travel Time + Handling Time**

Flow = $\underline{0.9 \times 10\,000}$ = $\underline{9\,000}$ = **338.22 L/min (app. 338)**
        17.61 + 9   26.61

Local fire departments may use the previous formulas to determine how their water shuttle capabilities compare to ISO requirements. The formulas may also be used to help preplan apparatus response for incidents within the jurisdiction. Matching local capabilities with water supply requirements should be completed prior to an incident.

Some jurisdictions maintain a policy that specifies after the arrival and unloading of the first and second tenders, all subsequent mobile water supply apparatus complete their shuttle routes using nonemergency driving practices. Effective water shuttle operations are the result of safe and efficient practices and not excessive driving speeds.

Chapter Summary

Water shuttle operations are employed during incidents where the distance from a fire to the nearest suitable water supply source is too great for relay pumping. These operations often involve a water source pumper used to fill the water tenders that shuttle water to a dump site where the supply may be unloaded into a portable tank or nurse tender. The flow capability of local fire departments should be determined prior to an incident using their equipment and apparatus. This capability should be matched with local needs when preplanning incidents at specific points in a jurisdiction.

Review Questions

1. What are some of the different characteristics of water tenders used for shuttle operations? (p. 446)

2. What major decisions affect the success of a water shuttle operation? (pp. 449-450)

3. What are some considerations when positioning the fill site pumper? (p. 456)

4. What are the differences between direct pumping operations, nurse tender operations, and portable water tank operations? (pp. 459-461)

5. What are the two methods used for calculating a flow rate for a specific tender? (p. 465)

NOTE: Always follow manufacturer recommendations for mobile water supply apparatus. The following lists items that should be checked on a mobile water supply apparatus, in addition to routine tests and inspections performed. Refer to your department's SOPs for specific items on apparatus used in your department.

Step 1: Ensure that the water tank and other extinguishing levels are appropriate.

Step 2: Ensure that the pumping system is operating correctly.

Step 4: Ensure that the portable water tank and related water supply equipment are in operational condition.

Step 5: Ensure that the foam system is operating correctly.

Step 6: Report any deficiencies to the appropriate personnel.

Step 7: Document any necessary inspections and corrections.

Step 8: Properly store any tools and equipment used.

Step 3: Ensure that the rapid dump system is operating correctly.

13-2

Operate at a fill site as part of a water shuttle operation.

Positioning Fill Site Pumper at Water Supply Source

Step 1: Driver/operator: Choose the fill site pumper location/ position.

    a. Allow maximum access for tenders.

    b. Attempt to use the least amount of lift or hard intake hose if drafting.

    c. Locate the pump panel so that you can view both source and fill operations if possible.

Laying Out the Fill Site

Step 2: Water Supply Supervisor: Assign personnel tasks:

    a. One firefighter to handle each laid out tender fill line.

    b. Radio-equipped firefighter or pump operator to monitor manifold, if used.

    c. Signal firefighter.

Step 3: Driver/operator or water supply group. Determine the exact fill site location so that:

    a. The tender driver/operator can enter from one direction and exit from another.

    b. The tender driver/operator does not need to back up.

    c. There is room for tender driver/operators to line up their apparatus and wait their turn to be filled without creating a traffic hazard.

Step 4: Denote the stopping point for the tender driver/operator using a traffic cone or other similar marker on driver's side at point opposite the tender driver's side door window. This stopping point should be denoted by a marker positioned on the side of the road or at a safe spot in a parking area.

Step 5: Lay out appropriate hoselines:

    a. Two MDH hoselines (preferably 3-inch [77 mm]) at approximate rear of parked tender if tenders have two 2½-inch (65 mm) direct tank fill connections.

    b. One LDH from pumper to fill site location if tenders have LDH direct tank fill intakes.

    c. Booster or small discharge line from fill site pumper.

Step 6: Install and close gate valves, if available, in each hose-line between the last and second-to-last hose sections

Step 7: Clamp tender fill lines if gate valves are unavailable immediately behind the first coupling back from the tender.

Step 8: Standardize type of connection for all apparatus in the shuttle so that all apparatus in the shuttle have the same type of connections.

    a. (MDH tender intakes) Install sexless, cam-locks, or other adapters as necessary.

    b. (Mixed MDH and LDH tender intakes) Lay out one LDH with manifold and connect one LDH and two MDH lines to the manifold.

Operating at the Fill Site

Step 9: Pumper driver/operator or water supply group: Connect the fill site pumper to the water supply source.

a. (Hydrant water source) Connect at minimum one LDH between large pump intake and hydrant steamer connection; if strong hydrant, connect MDH lines between 2½-inch (65 mm) hydrant outlet(s) and pump auxiliary intakes in addition to the LDH.

b. (Static water source) Follow procedure outlined in Skill Sheet 10-6.

Step 10: Place pumper in pump gear and charge tender fill lines, keeping pumper in gear and fill lines charged at all times. Follow local SOPs for discharge pressure, usually between 100 and 150 psi (700 kPa and 1 050 kPa).

Step 11: Prevent loss of prime (drafting) or pump overheating (on hydrant) by continuously flowing a booster or small diameter waste line.

a. (Drafting) Flow back into the water source if possible.

b. (Hydrant) Flow into the gutter or area away from tender or foot traffic.

Step 12: Fill site personnel: Signal the first tender to pull into filling position when fill lines are charged, and set aside, and area is clear of personnel.

Step 13: Tender driver/operator: Pull into filling position slowly, obeying signaler's directions.

a. Stop with driver's side window parallel with stop marker.

b. Come to a complete stop, placing the vehicle in neutral and setting the parking brake.

c. Stay in the tender cab.

Step 14: Fill site personnel: Connect the fill hoses to the tender direct tank fill intakes and open the intake valves on the apparatus.

Step 15: Fill site personnel: Fill the tender's tank.

a. (Lines with gate valve or manifold) Slowly open the gate valves/hose clamps, or manifold on fill hose(s), remaining at the gate valve or manifold until the tender is full as indicated on the apparatus gauge or by water spilling from the tank.

b. (LDH fill lines with no gate valve or manifold) Use a hand or radio signal to coordinate opening LDH fill lines with the fill site pumper driver/operator.

Step 16: Fill site personnel: Shut off water to fill lines when the tender tank is completely full as indicated on the apparatus gauge or by water spilling from the tank.

a. (Lines with gate valve or manifold) Slowly close the gate valves/hose clamps, or manifold on fill hose(s).

13-2

Operate at a fill site as part of a water shuttle operation.

b. (LDH fill lines with no gate valve or manifold). Use a hand or radio signal to coordinate closing LDH fill lines with the fill site pumper driver/operator.

Step 17: Fill site personnel: Relieve pressure on the fill lines by proceeding to the connection at the direct tank fill inlet and operating the bleeder valve.

Step 18: Fill site personnel: Disconnect the fill lines by disconnecting hoseline(s) from the tender and pulling hose off to one side of the fill site.

Step 19: Fill site personnel: Signal driver/operator to proceed back to the dump site after checking that hoselines and personnel are clear.

Step 20: Fill site personnel: Signal the next tender to pull into the filling position after checking that first tender, hoselines, and personnel are clear.

Step 21: Water supply supervisor: Contact the dump site, advising that a tender is en route.

Shutting Down the Fill Site

Step 22: Pumper driver/operator or water supply group: Shut down the fill site after the IC determines that operation is no longer necessary. Remain in operation until all participating tenders have been refilled.

Step 23: Pumper driver/operator or water supply group: Shut down the fill site pumper and its equipment and prepare it for return to service, following appropriate procedures.

CAUTION: The apparatus should be fully emptied before allowing it to proceed to the fill site. A partially loaded tanker will cause water movement that can affect the stability of the apparatus.

Selecting Dump Site Location

Step 1: Position in the appropriate location.

   a. Close proximity to incident scene

   b. Multiple access points

   c. Consideration given to fire growth and possible exposure

   d. Allows other apparatus access to the fire scene

CAUTION: If working at night, ensure the fill site has adequate lighting, but not blinding to drivers.

Deploying Portable Tanks

Step 2: Crew and mobile water supply apparatus driver/operator: Deploy a salvage cover on the ground where the dump tank will be set-up.

Step 3: Crew and mobile water supply apparatus driver/operator: Remove the dump tank from the apparatus and follow the manufacturer's instructions for deploying the tank.

   a. Ensure a drain for the tank is in the downhill side of the tank so that the tank may be easily drained at the end of the incident.

Step 4: Crew and mobile water supply apparatus driver/operator: Connect the hard suction strainer to the hard suction hose that is connected to the dump site pumper and place the hose in the tank.

Operating at Site

Step 5: Spotter: Signal the mobile water supply apparatus into position.

CAUTION: If apparatus have to back-up, ensure that a common set of hand or radio signals are established and a spotter is always present. Immediately stop backing the apparatus if you lose sight of the ground guide spotter.

Step 6: Mobile water supply apparatus driver/operator: Come to a complete stop on command, set the parking brake and place the apparatus into neutral.

Step 7: Dump site crew: Operate the dump/discharge valve(s) to allow the tank to be dumped into the portable water tank.

Step 8: Dump site crew: Once the mobile water supply apparatus is empty, close the valve(s) and signal the driver/operator to proceed to the fill site.

Step 9: Dump site crew: Signal the next mobile water supply apparatus to pull into dumping position after checking that the first mobile water supply apparatus, hoselines, and personnel are clear.

13-4

Establish, operate, and shut down a multiple portable tank water shuttle dump site.

SKILL SHEETS

NOTE: This skill sheet is written for a jet siphon. A plain siphon, commercial tank-connecting device, permanent tank gravity drain, or drain tunnel connector may also be used.

Step 1: Set up the first portable tank in the same manner as described in Skill Sheet 13-3. Make sure that the tank drain is on the low side of the tank.

Step 2: Dump site pumper driver/operator and crew: Deploy hard intake hose and strainer into the first portable tank

Step 3: First tender on the scene: Dump water into the first tank. The dump site pumper may then begin the drafting operation.

Step 4: First tender on the scene: Set up a second portable tank next to the first one. A tip-to-tip diamond-shaped arrangement is generally the preferred method for arranging the tanks.

Step 5: First tender on the scene: Assemble the jet siphon equipment. Place the end with the siphon in the second portable tank and the discharge end of the assembly over the edge of the first portable tank.

Step 6: Next water tender: Dump a load of water into the second portable tank. Once the water level is sufficient, charge the jet siphon supply hose to begin the process of transferring water from the second tank to the first.

Step 7: Next water tender: If additional portable tanks are used, each should be set up and operated as described in steps 4 through 6. Tenders should always dump in the end-most tank that has room for water.

Step 8: Dump site pumper driver/operator or jet siphon pumper driver/operator: Monitor the level of water in each tank and adjust the siphon lines accordingly.

Foam Equipment and Systems

Chapter Contents

chapter 14

Key Terms

NFPA® Job Performance Requirements

This chapter provides information that addresses the following job performance requirements of NFPA 1002, *Standard for Fire Apparatus Driver/Operator Professional Qualifications (2014)*.

   5.1.1, 5.2.3, 10.1.1

NFPA 1002, *Standard for Fire Apparatus Driver/Operator Professional Qualifications (2017)*.

   5.1.2, 5.2.6, 10.1.1

Foam Equipment and Systems

Learning Objectives

After reading this chapter, students will be able to:

1. Summarize facts about principles of foam. (*NFPA 1002, 2014:* 5.2.3 & *NFPA 1002, 2017:* 5.2.6)

2. Distinguish among types of foam concentrates used in fire fighting. (*NFPA 1002, 2014:* 5.2.3 & *NFPA 1002, 2017:* 5.2.6)

3. Explain the operation of low energy foam proportioning systems. (*NFPA 1002, 2014:* 5.2.3 & *NFPA 1002, 2017:* 5.2.6)

4. Describe high energy foam generating systems. (*NFPA 1002, 2014:* 5.2.3 & *NFPA 1002, 2017:* 5.2.6)

5. Distinguish among portable foam application devices. (*NFPA 1002, 2014:* 5.2.3 & *NFPA 1002, 2017:* 5.2.6)

6. Identify reasons for the production of poor quality foam or the lack of foam production when using an in-line proportioner. (*NFPA 1002, 2014:* 5.1.1, 5.2.3, 10.1.1 & *NFPA 1002, 2017:* 5.1.2, 5.2.6, 10.1.1)

7. Identify foam application techniques. (*NFPA 1002, 2014:* 5.1.1, 5.2.3, 10.1.1 & *NFPA 1002, 2017:* 5.1.2, 5.2.6, 10.1.1)

8. Explain the environmental impact of foam. (*NFPA 1002, 2014:* 5.2.3 & *NFPA 1002, 2017:* 5.2.6)

9. Identify durable agents. (*NFPA 1002, 2014:* 5.2.3 & *NFPA 1002, 2017:* 5.2.6)

10. Install and operate an in-line foam eductor. (*NFPA 1002, 2014:* 5.2.3, Skill Sheet 14-1 & *NFPA 1002, 2017:* 5.2.6, Skill Sheet 14-1)

Chapter 14
Foam Equipment and Systems

Case History

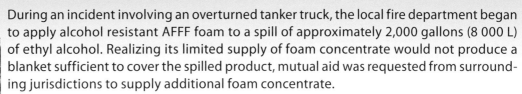

During an incident involving an overturned tanker truck, the local fire department began to apply alcohol resistant AFFF foam to a spill of approximately 2,000 gallons (8 000 L) of ethyl alcohol. Realizing its limited supply of foam concentrate would not produce a blanket sufficient to cover the spilled product, mutual aid was requested from surrounding jurisdictions to supply additional foam concentrate.

Fire departments responding on mutual aid supplied a variety of different types of foam concentrate. During operations, the foam eductor became plugged as different types of foam concentrate were substituted for the original supply. Application of foam was interrupted several times during the incident as the eductor was cleared of blockages.

Fire departments should coordinate with their mutual aid partners regarding the specifications of the foam concentrate they intend to use. Agencies that are expected to work together during an incident should be sure that their foam concentrate and other equipment are compatible, as mixing different types of foam concentrate may lead to eduction problems as well as have a detrimental effect on the quality of the foam produced.

Source: Firefighter Near Miss Reporting System

The use of foam agents in all areas of the fire service has increased dramatically in recent years. Some of the major reasons for the increase in use of foam products include:

- Magnitude and frequency of hazardous materials incidents that require foam operations for mitigation.

- Newer foam concentrates are more easily used by structural and wildland firefighters.

- Improvements in the design of foam proportioning equipment and systems have made their inclusion in apparatus more feasible.

- Use of foam may help reduce water usage; a significant factor where supply is limited.

The driver/operator should be knowledgeable in the assembly and operation of foam fire fighting equipment. Even with recent technological advances that have simplified the process, these systems require an understanding of operating principles as well as proper application procedures.

Mechanical Foam — Foam produced by a physical agitation of a mixture of foam concentrate, water, and air.

Proportioning — Mixing of water with an appropriate amount of foam concentrate in order to form a foam solution.

Aeration — Introduction of air into a foam solution to create bubbles that result in finished foam.

Eduction — Process used to mix foam concentrate with water in a nozzle or proportioner; concentrate is drawn into the water stream by the Venturi method.

Foam Concentrate — (1) Raw chemical compound solution that is mixed with water and air to produce finished foam; may be protein, synthetic, aqueous film forming, high expansion, or alcohol types. (2) Raw foam liquid as it rests in its storage container before the introduction of water and air.

Foam Proportioner — Device that injects the correct amount of foam concentrate into the water stream to make the foam solution.

Foam Solution — (1) The result of mixing the appropriate amount of foam concentrate with water; foam solution exists between the proportioner and the nozzle or aerating device that adds air to create finished foam. (2) The mixture of foam concentrate and water before the introduction of air.

Foam — An extinguishing agent formed by mixing a foam concentrate with water and aerating the solution for expansion; for use on Class A and Class B fires. Foam may be protein, fluoroprotein, film forming fluoroprotein, synthetic, aqueous film forming, high expansion, alcohol type, or alcohol-resistant type.

This chapter explores the basic concepts of foam concentrates, portable and apparatus mounted proportioning equipment, as well as foam application equipment. For additional information on foam fire fighting equipment, refer to IFSTA's **Principles of Foam Fire Fighting** manual.

Principles of Foam

Mechanical foams are the most common foams in use. These products must be **proportioned** (mixed with water) and **aerated** (mixed with air) before use. To produce fire fighting foam, foam concentrate, water, and air must be **educted** or injected in the correct ratios. If any element is removed or incorrectly applied, the result will be poor quality foam, or no foam production.

Before describing types of foams and the foam-making process, it is important to understand the following terms **(Figure 14.1)**:

- **Foam concentrate** — Raw foam liquid in its storage container before being combined with water and air.

- **Foam proportioner** — Device that injects the correct amount of foam concentrate into the water stream to make the foam solution.

- **Foam solution** — Mixture of foam concentrate and water before the introduction of air.

- **Foam** — Completed product after air is introduced into the foam solution (also known as *finished foam*).

Proper aeration should produce a blanket of uniform-sized bubbles that will maintain an effective cover over Class A or Class B fuels for the required period of time. Specifically formulated foams should be used on each class of fire.

CAUTION
Failure to match the proper foam concentrate to the type of fuel may result in an unsuccessful suppression attempt that could endanger firefighters.

Class B fuels are divided into two categories; **hydrocarbons** and **polar solvents**. Hydrocarbon fuels, such as crude oil, fuel oil, gasoline, benzene, and kerosene, are petroleum based and have a specific gravity less than one (water being considered equal to one) and will float on water. Class B foam is effective in extinguishing these fires and suppressing vapors because it floats on the surface of hydrocarbon fuels.

Polar solvent fuels, such as alcohol, acetone, ketones, and esters, are known as *miscible* liquids because they mix with water. Special alcohol-resistant (polymeric) formulations of fire fighting foam must be used when these flammable liquids are encountered.

NOTE: Many modern fuels, including gasoline, are blended with up to 15 percent solvent additives. Treat these products as polar solvents during emergency operations.

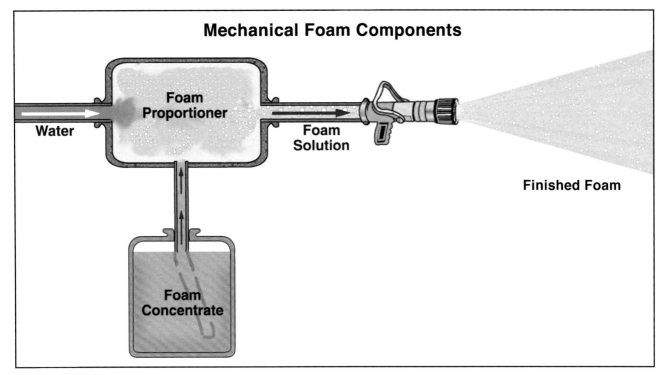

Mechanical Foam Components

Water

Foam Proportioner

Foam Solution

Finished Foam

Foam Concentrate

Figure 14.1 Foam as it progresses through the foam-making process.

Class B foams are designed solely for use on hydrocarbon fuels and are not effective on polar solvent products regardless of the concentration that is applied. However, some foams intended for use on polar solvents may be used on hydrocarbon fuel products, but only under the direction of the manufacturer. These factors illustrate the need to identify the fuel product before beginning foam application. Fire departments should conduct preincident planning to identify potential hazards so that the appropriate type of foam concentrate is available on first due pumping apparatus. More information concerning specific foam products is explained later in this chapter.

How Foam Works

Foam extinguishes and/or suppresses vapors by the following methods **(Figure 14.2, p. 482)**:

- Separating — Creates a barrier between the fuel and the fire

- Cooling — Lowers the temperature of the fuel and adjacent surfaces

- Suppressing or smothering — Prevents the release of flammable vapors, reducing the possibility of ignition or reignition

Fire fighting foam creates a film or blanket on the burning or exposed fuel. This blanket excludes oxygen making ignition difficult and stops the burning process on fuel that has been ignited. As the foam begins to break down, water is released, providing a cooling effect on the fuel suppressing the process of heat producing oxidation. The water being released may also runoff, carrying the product with it.

Hydrocarbon Fuel — A petroleum-based organic compound that contains only hydrogen and carbon.

Polar Solvents — Liquid having a molecule where the positive and negative charges are permanently separated, resulting in their ability to ionize in solution and create electrical conductivity. Water, alcohol, and sulfuric acid are examples of polar solvents.

Miscible — Materials that are capable of being mixed in all proportions.

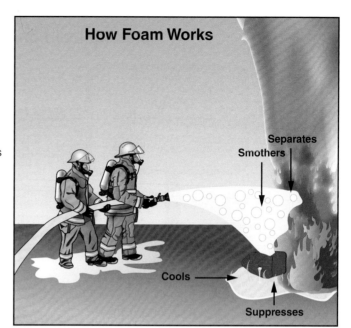

How Foam Works

Separates
Smothers
Cools
Suppresses

Figure 14.2 Foam works in a variety of ways.

Foam Proportioning

Proportioning is the act of mixing of water with foam concentrate to form a foam solution. Foam concentrates are generally intended to be mixed with fresh or salt water. In order to achieve maximum effectiveness, foam concentrates must be proportioned at the percentage specified by the manufacturer. This percentage is marked on each foam container for easy reference. Any deviation from the recommended percentage may result in poor quality foam that will not perform as expected and may create a danger to firefighters during an incident.

Most fire fighting foam concentrates are formulated to mix with 94 to 99.9 percent water. For example, when a 3 percent foam concentrate is used, the finished foam solution consists of 97 parts water mixed with 3 parts foam concentrate. The result is 100 parts foam solution **(Figure 14.3)**.

Class A foams are formulated to be proportioned within certain limits established by the manufacturer to achieve specific objectives. These percentages may range from a little as 0.1 percent to 1 percent. Firefighters may use local policy and discretion to create dry (thick) foam that may be suitable for exposure protection and fire breaks or wet, thinner foam that more easily penetrates the surface of a fuel.

The selection of a foam proportioner is governed by several factors; properly supplied water pressure and appropriate appliances, as well as the cost of the foam proportioning system all play a role in the device specified by a fire department. Proportioners are designed to work in conjunction with delivery devices (foam nozzles). Use of a foam proportioner that is incompatible with the delivery device may not produce any foam, or an inadequate foam mix makes extinguishment of the fire difficult or impossible and presents a danger to firefighters.

Foam is proportioned using one of four basic methods:

- Induction
- Injection

- Batch mixing
- Premixing

A variety of equipment types are available to proportion foam. Some equipment types are designed for apparatus or portable use, while others are intended for fixed fire protection systems. Some of the common types of proportioners are described later in this chapter.

Induction

The induction method of proportioning foam uses the pressure of a water stream to induct (draft) foam concentrate into the fire stream. This is achieved by passing the stream of water through a Venturi device called an **eductor** **(Figure 14.4)**. A **pickup tube** connected to the eductor is inserted into the foam concentrate container. The pressure differential created by the water passing through the Venturi causes a reduction in pressure in the device that allows atmospheric pressure to force foam concentrate into the water stream. In-line eductors and foam nozzle eductors are examples of foam proportioners that work by this method.

Injection

The **injection** method of proportioning foam uses an external pump to force foam concentrate into the fire stream at the proper ratio in comparison to the flow. These systems are most commonly employed in apparatus mounted or fixed fire protection systems.

Batch Mixing

A simple but potentially inaccurate method of mixing foam concentrate and water, **batch mixing** occurs when an appropriate amount of foam concentrate is poured directly into a tank of water **(Figure 14.5, p. 484)**. This method is commonly used with Class A foams. Batch mixing may not be effective during large incidents as foam lines must be shut down when the tank is emptied.

Eductor — (1) Portable proportioning device that injects a liquid, such as foam concentrate, into the water flowing through a hoseline or pipe. (2) Venturi device that uses water pressure to draw foam concentrate into a water stream for mixing; also enables a pump to draw water from an auxiliary source.

Pickup Tube — Solid or flexible tube used to transfer foam concentrate from a storage container to the in-line eductor or proportioner.

Injection — (1) Method of proportioning foam that uses an external pump or head pressure to force foam concentrate into the fire stream at the correct ratio for the flow desired. (2) Process of taking in materials through a puncture or break in the skin.

Batch Mixing — Production of foam solution by adding an appropriate amount of foam concentrate to a water tank before application; the resulting solution must be used or discarded following the incident.

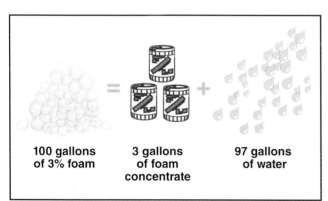

100 gallons of 3% foam = **3 gallons of foam concentrate** + **97 gallons of water**

Figure 14.3 Foam is proportioned with water based on manufacturer's recommendations.

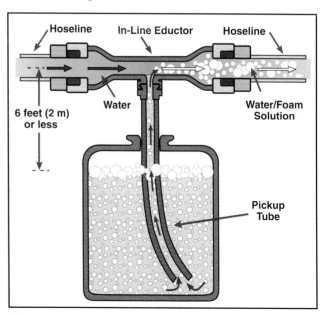

Hoseline   In-Line Eductor   Hoseline

6 feet (2 m) or less

Water

Water/Foam Solution

Pickup Tube

Figure 14.4 An eductor picks up foam concentrate and mixes it with water.

Before operations can continue, the tank must then be refilled and more concentrate added. In addition, when batch mixing Class B foam concentrates, tank water must be circulated to ensure proper mixing before discharge. The time necessary for this mixing depends on the viscosity and solubility of the foam concentrate. When a tank is refilled after batch mixing has taken place, a considerable amount of frothing of residual foam concentrate may occur. The fire pump and associated piping, as well as tanks, hose, and appliances must be thoroughly flushed after use with foams.

Batch mixing of Class A foam is accomplished using portable tanks with tender relays in some jurisdictions. This method may complicate efforts to restart drafting after a batch is mixed because the foam concentrate lowers the viscosity of the water in the portable tank.

NOTE: It may be difficult to maintain the accuracy of batch mixing, especially after the initial batch has been used.

Premixing

Premixing — Mixing premeasured portions of water and foam concentrate in a container. Typically, the premix method is used with portable extinguishers, wheeled extinguishers, skid-mounted twin-agent units, and vehicle-mounted tank systems. *See* Batch Mixing.

Premixing is a common method of proportioning in which premeasured portions of water and foam concentrate are mixed in a container. Typically, this method is used with portable and wheeled extinguishers, skid-mounted twin-agent units, and apparatus-mounted tank systems **(Figure 14.6)**.

Premixed solutions may be discharged from a pressurized tank using compressed air or an inert gas such as nitrogen or by a pump from a nonpressurized storage tank. The pump discharges the foam solution via piping or hose to the discharge devices. Premix systems are limited to one time use applications. Once used, they must be completely emptied, flushed, and refilled before they can be used again.

How Foam Is Stored

Depending on use and convenience, foam solution may be stored in a variety of containers. Four common methods of storage for most fire service applications are:

- Pails
- Totes
- Barrels
- Apparatus Tanks

Figure 14.5 Batch mixing is a simple method of proportioning foam concentrate with water.

Figure 14.6 Premixing is a foam proportioning method commonly used with portable and wheeled extinguishers.

Pails

Five-gallon (20 L) plastic pails are commonly used containers in many municipal fire departments **(Figure 14.7)**. These containers are not affected by the corrosive nature of foam concentrates and are relatively easy to store on fire apparatus. The containers must remain airtight in order to prevent a skin from forming on the surface of the concentrate. Foam concentrate may be educted directly from the plastic pail using an eductor.

Barrels

Foam concentrate is also available in 55-gallon (220 L) plastic or plastic-lined barrels. Some fire departments use these for bulk storage, but they are more common in industrial applications. Some fire departments and industrial facilities maintain apparatus designed to transport barrels to an incident scene where their contents may be transferred, or used directly from the barrels in the same manner as the 5 gallon (20 L) pails are used.

Totes

When bulk storage of foam concentrates is required, some fire departments or industrial facilities may specify 275 gallon (1 100 L) containers, called *totes*. Under conditions that may require large quantities of foam, such as aircraft rescue fire fighting (ARFF), wildland, or industrial facilities, this method of storage may be prudent. Some jurisdictional organizations operate trailers equipped with a large quantity of foam concentrate that is housed and transported by a "host" department for deployment within a specific response area during large-scale incidents **(Figure 14.8)**.

Apparatus Tanks

Fire apparatus equipped with onboard foam proportioning systems usually have foam concentrate tanks piped directly to the delivery system. This eliminates using pails or barrels to supply a foam eductor. Foam concentrate tanks may be found on many municipal fire pumpers as well as industrial foam tenders and ARFF apparatus. Foam concentrate tanks on municipal fire apparatus generally range from 20 to 200 gallons (80 to 800 L) while foam pumper or tenders may carry 8,000 gallons (32 000 L) or more of concentrate.

Figure 14.7 Many jurisdictions use 5-gallon (20 L) pails of foam.

Figure 14.8 Foam trailers may be used in jurisdictions that require large quantities of foam.

The type, location, and design of the foam concentrate tank may vary depending on the design of the apparatus. Smaller foam concentrate tanks are often located above the fire pump area. Some designs incorporate the foam concentrate tank as an integral cell within the apparatus water tank. Other apparatus may feature an additional pump and a lower connection point for refilling the concentrate tank. Larger foam concentrate tanks may be directly adjacent to the apparatus water tank. Some foam tenders and industrial foam pumpers have only a tank for foam concentrate and do not have an onboard water tank **(Figure 14.9)**. Some fire departments that have the potential to use a large quantity of foam carry drums of foam concentrate on a trailer that may be pulled behind fire apparatus, or more commonly, taken to an incident scene by a service or utility vehicle.

Regardless of the type of tank, foam storage must be airtight. Standard vented atmospheric storage tanks are not acceptable for foam concentrate. The NFPA® provides specific standards for the design of a foam storage tank. Mixing different types or brands of foam concentrate should be avoided as the result may prove ineffective for application and have reduced suppression capabilities. In addition, the foam concentrate manufacturer should be consulted for any special requirements specific to its product.

Figure 14.9 Foam tenders have an onboard tank used specifically for foam. *Courtesy of Ron Jeffers.*

Class A Foam Concentrate — Foam specially designed for use on Class A combustibles. Class A foams, hydrocarbon-based surfactants are essentially wetting agents that reduce the surface tension of water and allow it to soak into combustible materials more easily than plain water. Class A foams are becoming increasingly popular for use in wildland and structural fire fighting. *Also known as* Class A Foam.

Foam Concentrates

Although there are some foam concentrates approved for both Class A and Class B applications, the majority of foam concentrates are divided for use on either Class A (ordinary combustibles) or Class B (flammable liquids) fuels. The following sections detail concentrates for both categories of fuel.

Class A Foam

Available since the 1940s, **Class A foam** technology has only recently been widely accepted and used for increasing numbers of structure, wildland, coal, tire storage, and other fires involving deep seated fuels.

WARNING!
Use Class A foam only on Class A fuels.

Surfactant — Chemical that lowers the surface tension of a liquid; allows water to spread more rapidly over the surface of Class A fuels and penetrate organic fuels.

The formula of Class A foam includes hydrocarbon **surfactants** that reduce the surface tension of water in the foam solution. This reduced surface tension allows for better penetration and increased effectiveness. When used in conjunction with compressed air foam systems (CAFS), Class A foam provides excellent insulation qualities **(Figures 14.10)**. A compressed air foam system entrains large amounts of compressed air with small amounts of water into the foam concentrate, creating a useable foam product.

CAUTION
As with any method of fire attack, the correct flow in gallons per minute (L/min) must be applied to safely and efficiently extinguish the fire.

Class A foam may be used with fog nozzles, aerating foam nozzles, and medium and high expansion devices; and compressed air foam systems using most nozzles, including solid stream nozzles. The shelf life of properly stored foam solution can be as long as 20 years making it an economical choice to purchase in bulk quantities.

Because this product is used in such small percentages, it is generally not a significant environmental concern under ordinary conditions. However, personnel should avoid discharging foam concentrates, solutions, or finished foam diretly into a body of water. Direct skin contact should also be avoided as Class A foam concentrate has a corrosive characteristic. Driver/operators should follow manufacturer's recommendations for procedures on flushing equipment after using foam concentrate.

Proportioning

Class A foam concentrates may be mixed with percentages as little as 0.1 to 1.0 percent. As ratios are increased, the expansion and drainage characteristics of the finished product will change. Drain time increases in proportion with increases in the percentage of the solution. This characteristic is visible by the foam appearing thicker. Most foam nozzles will produce more stable foam at 1.0 percent concentration than a 0.5 percent concentration. However, using percentages greater than 0.5 percent with

Figure 14.10 Using Class A foam with a CAFS creates finished foam for Class A hazards.

a standard fog nozzle may not increase fire fighting performance. The following guidelines are commonly used for proportioning Class A foam:

- Fire attack and overhaul with standard fog nozzles — 0.2 to 0.5 percent concentrate

- Exposure protection with standard fog nozzles — 0.5 to 1.0 percent concentrate

- Any application with air aspirating foam nozzles — 0.3 to 0.7 percent concentrate

- Any application with compressed air foam systems (CAFS) — 0.2 to 0.5 percent concentrate

Rates of Application

The **application rate** refers to the minimum amount of foam solution that must be applied to a fire, per minute, per square foot (square meter) of fire. The application rate for Class A foam is the same as the minimum required flow rate for water. Flow rates for target hazards should be determined during preincident planning so that preparations can be made to satisfy these requirements.

Application of Class A Foam

The consistency of Class A foam may be tailored to meet specific applications. The following common application needs are provided:

- **Areas that require maximum penetration.** Wet foam is very fluid and will easily penetrate Class A fuels **(Figure 14.11)**.

- **Vertical surfaces.** Dry foam forms a rigid coating that adheres well. It is slow to drain, allowing the foam to cling to a vertical surface for extended periods. Dry foam, which often resembles shaving cream, has very low water content and high air content.

- **Surface of a fuel**. Foam must have the ability to cling and penetrate the surface of a fuel. Medium foam is able to penetrate a fuel while maintaining a sufficient blanket of protection.

The drain time for foam also plays a major role in the effectiveness of the product. The bubbles in the foam blanket begin to breakdown as soon as they are applied. This process allows the release of water, wetting the fuel. One measurement for the stability of foam is the rate at which this breakdown occurs. A short duration drain time provides the most rapid wetting, while a longer drain time provides an insulating layer for a longer period of time. Several elements affect the breakdown process. These include the heat of the fire or the height of a flame front in a wildfire. The ambient air temperature and prevailing wind conditions also impact the duration of the breakdown process.

Class B Foam

Class B foam is applied to suppress fires involving flammable and combustible liquids **(Figure 14.12)**. It is also used to suppress vapors from unignited spills involving these liquids. This section examines the characteristics of common types of Class B concentrates. Class B foam is proportioned into a fire stream by using apparatus mounted or portable foam proportioning equipment.

Application Rate —
Minimum amount of foam solution that must be applied to an unignited fire, spill, or spill fire to either control vapor emission or extinguish the fire; measured per minute per square foot (or square meter) of area to be covered.

Class B Foam Concentrate — Foam fire-suppression agent designed for use on ignited or un-ignited Class B flammable or combustible liquids. *Also known as* Class B Foam.

Figure 14.11 Class A foam is useful for attacking fires involving densely packed materials. *Courtesy of Bob Esposito.*

Figure 14.12 Class B foam is used to extinguish flammable and combustible liquid fires.

These foam concentrates consist of a synthetic or protein base. While synthetic foam is made from a mixture of fluorosurfactants, protein based foam is derived from animal protein. Some combination foams are also available. Types of concentrates will be detailed later in this chapter.

Class B foam concentrates should be stored in cool areas to maximize shelf life: approximately 10 years for protein based foams and 20 to 25 years for synthetic foam. Generally, different brands of foam concentrates should not be mixed together for storage in apparatus tanks as they may be chemically incompatible. However, when ready for immediate use during emergency operations, similar type concentrates such as AFFF and fluoroprotein may be mixed together immediately before application. Foam concentrates of the same type, which are manufactured to U.S. Military specifications (**Mil-Spec** concentrates), may be mixed at any time with no adverse effects.

The chemical properties of Class B foam concentrates and their impact on the environment may vary depending on the product and manufacturer. Generally protein based products are considered safer for the environment. However, consult the **safety data sheets (SDSs)** provided by the manufacturer for specific safety information.

Military Specifications (Mil-Specs) — Specifications developed by the U.S. Department of Defense (DoD) for the purchase of materials and equipment.

Safety Data Sheet (SDS) — Form provided by the manufacturer and blender of chemicals that contains information about chemical composition, physical and chemical properties, health and safety hazards, emergency response procedures, and waste disposal procedures of a specified material. *Formerly known as* Material Safety Data Sheet (MSDS).

Proportioning

Class B foams are mixed in proportions from one to six percent. The correct proportion for a specific product is found listed on the outside of each container. Some foam is formulated for use on both hydrocarbon and polar solvent fuels. These products may be used at different concentrations depending on which fuel is involved. The concentration for hydrocarbon fuels is normally one or three percent, while three or six percent is used for polar solvents, based on the manufacturer's recommendation.

Foam Expansion

Foam expansion is the increase in volume of foam solution once it has been aerated. This is an important characteristic to consider when choosing a foam concentrate for a specific application. The method used to aerate foam solution will create varying degrees of expansion based on the following:

- Type of foam concentrate used
- Accurate proportioning of the foam concentrate in the solution
- Quality of the foam concentrate
- Method of aeration

Foam Expansion — Result of adding air to a foam solution consisting of water and foam concentrate. Expansion creates the foam bubbles that result in finished foam or foam blanket.

Foam expansion is generally described as being low, medium, or high. NFPA® 11 states that low expansion foam contains an air/solution ratio of up to 20 parts finished foam for every part of foam solution, a 20:1 ratio. Medium expansion foam is commonly used at a rate of 20:1 up to 200:1 through hydraulically operated nozzle type delivery devices. When high expansion foam is used the expansion rate is from 200:1 to 1000:1.

Rates of Application

The rate at which foam is applied depends on several variables, including **(Figure 14.13)**:

- The type of concentrate used
- Whether or not the fuel is on fire
- Type of fuel involved (hydrocarbon vs. polar solvent)
- Whether the fuel is contained or uncontained

Figure 14.13 The foam application rate should be determined based on several variables. *Courtesy of Williams Fire & Hazard Control Inc./Brent Gaspard.*

The minimum foam solution application rates for ignited fuels are specified in NFPA® 11. This standard outlines the variables involved and application rate requirements for many possible scenarios. Driver/operators should consult this standard in order to assist in the preparation of plans to mitigate potential hazards in their response area.

In order to calculate the application rate available from a specific nozzle, divide the flow rate by the area of the fire. For example, a 250 gpm (1 000 L) nozzle on a 1,000 square foot (100 m²) fire equals a rate of 0.25 gpm/ft² (10 L/ [m².min]) **(Figure 14.14)**.

WARNING!
Do not enter a spill of unignited flammable liquid. An ignition source may cause the spill to ignite at any time.

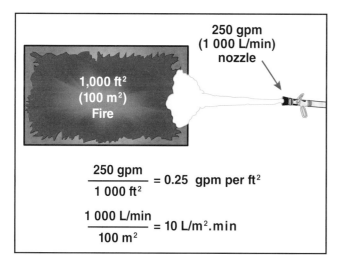

Figure 14.14 Driver/ operators should be able to determine the correct application rate.

$$\frac{250 \text{ gpm}}{1\ 000 \text{ ft}^2} = 0.25 \text{ gpm per ft}^2$$

$$\frac{1\ 000 \text{ L/min}}{100 \text{ m}^2} = 10 \text{ L/m}^2.\text{min}$$

Unignited spills do not require the same application rate due to the absence of radiant heat, open flame, and thermal drafts. NFPA® 11 does not present a specific guideline for unignited spills. However, in the event a spill does ignite, firefighters must be prepared to apply the minimum application rate for the specified amount of time based on fire conditions.

Before you start application, ensure that sufficient foam production components required to achieve the tactical objectives are available at the point of proportioning. Once you begin application, it should continue without interruption from an uphill and upwind position until extinguishment is complete. Inconsistent application time may allow the fuel and fire to consume a portion or the entire foam blanket. Polar solvents may require different application rates based on the specific type of solvent. In addition, consult the manufacturer's guidelines for the brand of foam concentration in use, as different products may have a unique rate of application independent of other variables.

Specific Foam Concentrates

Types of foam are selected by jurisdictions based on their properties and performance for likely applications and incidents **(Figure 14.15)**. Some may create a thick heat resistant blanket over burning liquids, while others are

Figure 14.15 Jurisdictions should select the appropriate type of foam for potential hazards in their jurisdiction.

thinner, spreading more rapidly. Certain foams produce a vapor sealing film or membrane on the burning liquid surface to aid in vapor suppression. Other foam products such as medium and high expansion foam may be used in large volumes to flood surfaces, or fill confined areas. In the following sections, discuss the most common types of foam concentrates. Suppressing (smothering) prevents the release of additional flammable vapors into the atmosphere where they could mix with oxygen to form a flammable mixture, thereby reducing the possibility of ignition or reignition.

Regular Protein Foams

Protein foams derived from animal protein sources such as hooves, horns, or feather meal. These sources are **hydrolyzed** in the presence of lime and converted to a protein hydrolysate that is neutralized. Stabilizers, corrosion inhibitors, and antimicrobial agents, as well as additives to inhibit freezing are also contained in the formula. Regular protein foam generally has good heat stability and **burnback resistance**. However, it is not as fluid as other low expansion foams when applied to a fuel source. In addition, regular protein foam degrades more quickly in storage than synthetic foam (an approximate ten year shelf life). Regular protein foam is becoming increasingly rare in the modern fire service. Jurisdictions that continue to maintain this product in their inventory should monitor its remaining shelf life.

Fluoroprotein Foam

Fluoroprotein foam, a combination of protein-based foam and synthetic foam, contains protein concentrate to which fluorochemical surfactants are added. The addition of these chemicals provides fluoroprotein foam with the ability to flow more readily than ordinary protein foam. This type of foam also provides longer lasting vapor suppression that may be critical during incidents involving unignited spills. Fluoroprotein foam continues to be a favored option by some municipal and industrial fire departments.

Fluoroprotein foam may be made alcohol resistant with the addition of ammonia salts suspended in organic solvents. The alcohol-resistive properties will be effective for approximately 15 minutes, offering high-water retention and resistance to heat.

Film Forming Fluoroprotein Foam (FFFP)

Film forming fluoroprotein foam (FFFP) concentrate is based on the technology of fluoroprotein foam for long lasting heat resistance and the capabilities of aqueous film forming foam (AFFF) for quick knockdown. FFFP is also available in an alcohol resistant formulation.

Aqueous Film Forming Foam (AFFF)

Aqueous film forming foam (AFFF), or commonly called *A triple F,* is currently the most commonly used synthetic foam concentrate. Its formula consists of fluorochemical and hydrocarbon surfactants combined with solvents to create a high boiling point. The fluorochemical surfactants reduce the surface tension of the water in the foam solution to a degree that a thin aqueous film is spread across a fuel product as the foam solution is applied.

Protein Foam Concentrate — Foam concentrate that consists of a protein hydrolysate plus additives to prevent the concentrate from freezing, prevent corrosion equipment and containers, prevent bacterial decomposition of the concentrate during storage, and control viscosity.

Hydrolyze — To cause or undergo a chemical process of decomposition involving the splitting of a bond and the addition of the element of water.

Burnback Resistance — Ability of a foam blanket to resist direct flame impingement such as would be evident in a partially extinguished petroleum fire.

Film Forming Fluoroprotein Foam (FFFP) — Foam concentrate that combines the qualities of fluoroprotein foam with those of aqueous film forming foam. *See* Foam Concentrate.

Aqueous Film Forming Foam (AFFF) — Synthetic foam concentrate that, when combined with water, can form a complete vapor barrier over fuel spills and fires and is a highly effective extinguishing and blanketing agent on hydrocarbon fuels. *Also known as* light water.

When AFFF or FFFP foam is applied to a fire involving a hydrocarbon fuel product, several actions will occur **(Figure 14.16)**:

- An air/vapor excluding film is released ahead of the foam blanket.

- A fast moving blanket of foam spreads across the surface of the fuel surrounding objects and providing insulation.

- As the aerated foam blanket drains its water, more film is released giving the foam an ability to recover, or "heal" areas where the foam blanket is disturbed.

▜▟▟▟▟▟▟▟▟▟▟▟▟
CAUTION
When applying foam, be aware of the potential for burnback in previously covered areas where contact with hot objects may be present. This effect may be more apparent with AFFF foam.

Alcohol-Resistant Aqueous Film Forming Foam Concentrate (AR-AFFF) — Aqueous film forming foam that is designed for use with polar solvent fuels. *See Aqueous Film Forming Foam and Foam Concentrate.*

Alcohol resistant AFFF concentrate is commonly available for use on polar solvents. This concentrate is generally used at a concentration of three or six percent, based on manufacturer's recommendations **(Figure 14.17)**. Alcohol-resistant AFFF may also be used on hydrocarbon fuels at one to six percent proportion based on the manufacturer's guidelines.

When AR-AFFF foam is applied to polar solvent fuels, a membrane is created over the fuel. This membrane separates the water in the foam blanket from the effects of the solvent. The blanket acts in much the same way as ordinary AFFF. Alcohol resistant AFFF should be applied gently to a fuel product in order to allow the membrane to form. Aspirating nozzles are generally best for preserving the membrane that forms on the surface of these products.

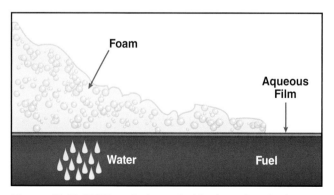

Figure 14.16 AFFF works to control hydrocarbon fuel product fires in a variety ways.

Figure 14.17 Alcohol resistant AFFF is meant for use on polar solvents, but it can also be used on hydrocarbons.

High-Expansion Foams

High-expansion foam contains a detergent base and low water content. The low water content provides less runoff and minimizes water damage. Several common applications for high-expansion foam include:

- Concealed space fire such as cellars and coal mines or subterranean spaces such as utility tunnels and sewers (**Figure 14.18**)

Figure 14.18 High-expansion foam is commonly used in subterranean spaces.

- Fixed extinguishing systems for specific industrial hazards
- Class A fire applications

Low Energy Foam Proportioning Systems

Achieving and maintaining the correct proportion of foam concentrate and water in order to produce an effective finished foam solution requires equipment that must operate within specific design specifications. An error in operation or mechanical malfunction may result in a failure to produce foam, or a foam product that is of poor quality. In general, foam proportioning devices operate by one of two basic principles:

- A Venturi effect created by the pressure of a water stream flowing through a restricted orifice inducts (drafts) foam concentrate into the water stream.
- A pressurized proportioning device injects foam concentrate into a water stream at a set ratio and at a higher pressure than the water flow.

The following section describes the various types of low energy foam proportioning systems commonly found mounted on apparatus or as portable appliances. Low energy foam systems impart pressure on the foam solution with the use of the main fire pump. This type of system introduces air into the foam solution when it either reaches the nozzle or is discharged from the nozzle.

Portable Foam Proportioners

A simple and common method of foam proportioning involves the use of a portable foam proportioner. The three common types are in-line foam eductors, foam nozzle eductors, and self educting master stream nozzles.

In-Line Foam Eductors

The **in-line foam eductor** is a basic foam proportioner that is designed to be attached directly to the pump panel discharge or connected at some point in the hose lay. In order for this device to function effectively, the driver/operator must follow the manufacturer's guidelines that specify the correct pressure

In-Line Foam Eductor — Type of foam delivery device that is located in the water supply line near the nozzle. The foam concentrate is drawn into the water line using the Venturi method.

and distance between the eductor and appropriate nozzle. See **Skill Sheet 14.1** for the steps to install an in-line foam eductor.

The in-line eductor uses the Venturi principle to draft foam concentrate into the water stream. When operating this system, several operating guidelines must be followed to achieve properly proportioned finished foam:

- The flow in gallons per minute (L/min) through the eductor must not exceed its rated capacity.

- The quality of foam may decrease or the flow may stop altogether if the gpm (L/min) capacity of the eductor is exceeded.

- The pressure at the discharge side of the eductor must not exceed 70 percent of the eductor inlet pressure. This **back pressure** is determined by adding the nozzle pressure, friction loss in the hose between the eductor and the nozzle, and the elevation pressure. Excessive back pressure may result in no foam concentrate being inducted into the water.

- The concentration of foam solution will only blend accurately if the inlet pressure at the eductor is correct (usually 150-200 psi [1 050-1 400 kPa]).

- Inlet pressure that is too low will not create the Venturi effect necessary to pick up foam concentrate or may pick up too lean a mixture for suppression.

- When inlet pressure is too high, the foam concentration may be too rich, rapidly depleting available resources.

- Eductors must be properly maintained after each use in order to ensure readiness for the next incident. Use a bucket of water to immerse the foam pick up tube, letting it induct water for at least one minute **(Figure 14.19)**.

- Metering valves must be set to draw the correct percentage needed to develop the correct quality of foam for the fuel product. An incorrect setting may result in production of a poor quality foam blanket.

- The foam concentrate inlet to the eductor should be no more than six feet (2 m) above the liquid surface of the foam concentrate **(Figure 14.20, p. 496)**. If the inlet is too high, the foam concentration will either be too lean or may not be inducted at all.

- Viscosity, or the thickness and ability of a liquid to flow freely, is affected by temperature. Foam concentrates become more viscous in cold temperatures and less viscous when heated. Frozen foam concentrate cannot be educted.

The nozzle and eductor must have the same gpm (L/min) rating in order to operate successfully. When the nozzle flows a higher rate, too much concentrate will be used, depleting resources and creating a foam blanket that is "richer" than necessary. When the nozzle flows at a lower rate, not enough concentrate will be used, resulting in poor quality foam.

Back Pressure — Pressure loss or gain created by changes in elevation between the nozzle and pump.

Figure 14.19 Driver/operators should properly clean foam equipment.

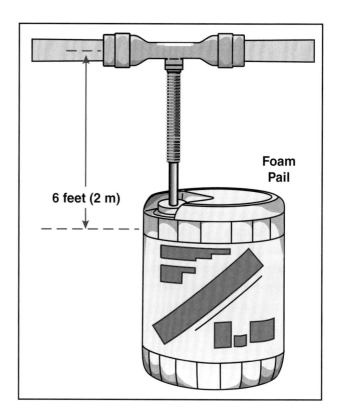

Figure 14.20 The distance between the liquid surface of the foam concentrate and the foam concentrate inlet to the eductor should be a maximum of six feet (2 m).

6 feet (2 m)

Foam Pail

Foam Nozzle Eductors

A foam nozzle eductor operates under the same principle as an in-line eductor. The eductor is built into the **self-educting nozzle** rather than attached to the hoseline. This system requires that foam concentrate be available at the point where the nozzle is operated. This often becomes a logistical problem when the line must be relocated. This problem is compounded by the number of gallons (liters) required to ensure uninterrupted supply.

Self-Educting Master Stream Foam Nozzle — Large-capacity nozzle with built-in foam eductor.

> ## CAUTION
> Use of a foam nozzle eductor may compromise firefighter safety. Firefighters cannot quickly move the hoseline and must abandon the supply of concentrate should they need to withdraw rapidly.

Self-Educting Master Stream Foam Nozzles

The **self-educting master stream foam nozzle** uses a modified Venturi design to draw concentrate into its water stream. The pickup tube is located in the center bore of the nozzle. This design produces an overproportioned solution that is diluted by the deflector plates in the nozzle as the solution is discharged. This master stream nozzle is deployed when flows in excess of 350 gpm (1 400 L/min) is required. Some master stream foam nozzles are capable of delivering 14,000 gpm (56 000 L/min). A major advantage of the self-educting nozzle is the pressure drop is much lower (10 percent or less) than most standard foam nozzle eductors. This feature allows the stream to have much greater reach capabilities.

A **jet ratio controller (JRC)** is a type of in-line eductor that may be used to supply foam concentrate to a self-educting master stream. It allows the foam concentrate supply to be located as far as 3,000 feet (900 m) away from a self-educting master stream nozzle. This distance allows firefighters charged with operating the fire pump and maintaining the foam concentrate supply to do so from a considerable distance, as well as an elevation change of up to 50 feet (15 m).

The JRC is supplied by a hoseline from the main fire pump that is supplying other hoselines. The flow of water to this device represents only about 2.5 percent of the total flow in the system. Like a standard in-line eductor water flowing through the JRC creates a venturi effect that draws foam concentrate into the pickup tube, then into the hoseline. However, a JRC proportions the concentrate at a 66.5 percent solution. This overproportioned solution is then pumped into a self-educting master stream foam nozzle where it is further proportioned with water also supplied by the fire pump, resulting in a discharge solution of three percent. In order to achieve the proper proportion the JRC and nozzle must be correctly matched.

Apparatus Mounted Foam Proportioning Systems

Foam proportioning systems are commonly mounted on structural, industrial, wildland, and ARFF apparatus, as well as fireboats. Many of the foam systems detailed in the following section are compatible for use with either Class A or Class B foam concentrates.

Installed In-Line Eductor Systems

An installed in-line eductor system operates under the same principles as portable in-line eductors **(Figure 14.21)**. The standard precautions regarding hose lengths, matching the nozzle and eductor flow capability, as well as inlet pressures apply to both apparatus mounted and portable systems. The only difference in the systems is the fixed-position mounting on the apparatus. When operating the installed system, foam concentrate may be supplied from a pickup tube into a drum or pail, or by using a tank permanently installed on the apparatus.

In some installations a bypass proportioner is installed to reduce the friction loss across the eductor **(Figure 14.22, p. 498)**. In the bypass mode, a valve directs the water through a second chamber of the eductor that contains no orifice or restrictions. This mode is used when no foam is desired, and the discharge function is to supply a plain water hoseline. When a foam line is required, a valve is directed to divert water through the eductor/orifice chamber. A metering valve is present at this point to accommodate various foam concentrates. Installed in-line eductors are most commonly used to proportion Class B foam. Installed in-line foam eductors are generally not effective for proportioning the very low concentrations used in Class A foam operations.

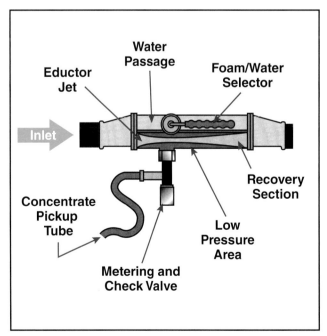

Figure 14.21 Some pumping apparatus are equipped with an installed in-line eductor.

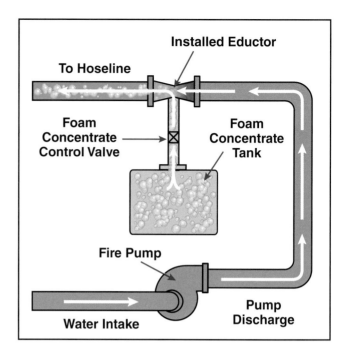

Figure 14.22 The pump will discharge plain water when the proportioner is in bypass mode.

Around-the-Pump Proportioners

Around-the-pump proportioners are one of the most common types of installed proportioners used in modern fire apparatus. This system consists of a small return (bypass) water line connected from the discharge side of the pump back to the intake side of the pump **(Figure 14.23)**. An in-line eductor is installed in this line with a valve controlling the flow of water passing through it. In the open position the valve allows

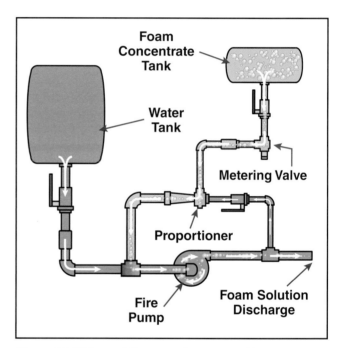

Figure 14.23 Around-the-pump foam proportioners are commonly used on pumping apparatus.

approximately 10 to 40 gpm (40 to 160 L/min) to flow through the piping. This flow passes through the eductor, creating a Venturi effect that draws foam from the onboard concentrate tank. The foam solution that is created is pumped through the bypass piping to the intake side of the fire pump where it is pumped to a discharge and into a hoseline. Around-the-pump proportioners should generally be used at the specific flow for which they are rated.

Older model around-the-pump proportioners may only be operated when the apparatus is operating from the onboard water tank, because an inlet water pressure of greater than 10 psi (70 kPa) will not allow foam concentrate to enter the pump intake. Newer models capable of handling higher intake pressure may be used where that capacity is needed. Another disadvantage to the around-the-pump proportioner is the inability to pump both foam and plain water from the pump at the same time.

NOTE: In order to prevent excess foam concentrate from being drawn into the eductor, the driver/operator must close the bypass valve whenever the line is not flowing.

Bypass-Type Balanced Pressure Proportioners

The **bypass-type balanced pressure proportioner**, used on large mobile apparatus installations, such as ARFF vehicles, is one of the most accurate methods of foam proportioning. This system features the ability to monitor the demand for foam concentrate and adjust the amount of concentrate supplied. In addition the bypass type balanced proportioner has the ability to allow foam discharge from some outlets, and plain water from others simultaneously.

Apparatus with a bypass-type balanced pressure proportioner feature a foam concentrate line supplied by a separate foam concentrate pump connected to each discharge outlet **(Figure 14.24)**. The concentrate, drawn from an onboard tank, is supplied at the same pressure as the water supplied by the main fire pump. The pressure of the concentrate and water are monitored by a hydraulic pressure control valve that ensures a proper balance.

The orifice of the foam concentrate line is adjustable at the point where it connects to the discharge line. The orifice is set to reflect the percent desired for a particular application. Because the water and foam concentrate are supplied at the same pressure and the sizes of the discharges are proportional, the foam is proportioned correctly.

Bypass-Type Balanced Pressure Proportioner — Foam concentrate proportioner that operates in tandem with a fire water pump to ensure a proper foam concentrate-to-water mixture.

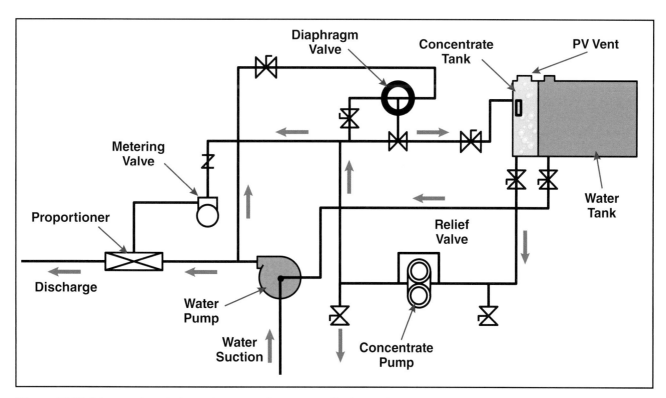

Figure 14.24 A bypass-type balanced pressure foam proportioning system.

Some limitations in this system include the need for a foam pump with a PTO or other means of power supply. In addition, the bypass of concentrate may cause some heating, turbulence, or aeration (bubbling) in the onboard storage tank.

Variable-Flow Variable-Rate Direct Injection Systems

Variable-flow variable-rate direct injection proportioners generally operate off power supplied by the apparatus electrical system, although some larger units may use a combination of electric and hydraulic power. The foam concentrate ratio is controlled by the speed of a positive displacement foam concentrate pump that injects foam concentrate into the water flow. No flow restricting devices are equipped in the proportioning system because the water flow governs the foam concentrate injection, enabling full flow through the fire pump.

Variable flow variable rate direct injection systems proportion foam concentrate at rates from 0.1 to 3 percent. Control units feature a display that monitors the current water or foam solution flow rate, the total amount of water or solution flowed, as well as the amount of foam concentrate used in real time.

These systems may be employed with all Class A and many Class B foam concentrates. However, this type of system is not useable with alcohol resistant foam concentrates due to the viscous (thick) nature of the product. The concentrate is supplied from atmospheric pressure foam tanks on the apparatus.

Variable flow variable rate direct injection systems offer the ability to proportion any flow rate or pressure within the design limits of the equipment. This system is also able to adjust to changes in water flow as nozzles are opened or shut, and the nozzles may be operated either above or below the pump without adversely affecting foam proportioning. In addition, this method is compatible with high energy foam systems detailed later in this chapter.

A drawback to this system design is that the foam injection point must be within the piping before any distribution to manifolds, or multiple pump discharges. This means that if foam solution is flowing through one pump discharge, only foam may be flowed to the other discharges plumbed to that manifold.

Variable-Flow Demand-Type Balanced Pressure Proportioners

A **variable-flow demand-type balanced pressure proportioning system**, also known as a *pumped/demand system,* consists of a variable speed mechanism driven electrically or hydraulically, that operates a foam concentrate pump. The foam concentrate pump supplies a Venturi-type proportioning device attached to a water line. During operation, the foam concentrate pump is monitored so that its flow is appropriate for the flow of water, producing an effective foam solution.

An advantage to this system lies in the fact that the flow of concentrate matches the pressure demand. There is no recirculation of product back to the foam concentrate tank. The system is maintained in a ready to pump condition that requires no flushing after use. In addition, water and/or foam solution may be discharged simultaneously from any number of outlets, up to the rated capacity of the pump.

Variable-Flow Variable-Rate Direct-Injection System — Apparatus-mounted foam system that injects the correct amount of foam into the pump piping, thereby supplying all discharges with foam. The system automatically monitors the operation of the hoselines and maintains a consistent quality of foam solution.

Variable-Flow Demand-Type Balanced-Pressure Proportioner — Foam proportioning system that is used in both fixed and mobile applications; a variable speed mechanism drives the foam pump and automatically monitors the flow of foam to produce an effective foam solution.

Variable-flow demand-type balanced proportioners have ratio controllers installed in the discharges, reducing the discharge area, resulting in pressure drops more severe than those of standard fire department pumpers.

Batch Mixing

Batch mixing or the dump in method is the simplest method of proportioning foam. The approximate amount of concentrate required for a given amount of water is poured into the tank by the driver/operator using the top fill opening in the tank at the time when the foam is needed.

The size of the water tank and the desired proportioning percentage indicate the quantity of concentrate that must be poured in to the tank. For example, when using 3 percent foam concentrate to produce 100 gallons of foam solution, 3 gallons of concentrate must be added to 97 gallons of water. In metrics, when using 3 percent foam concentrate to produce 100 liters of foam solution, 3 liters of concentrate must be added to 97 liters of water. Refer to **Table 14.1** for the amounts of concentrate required at various percentages for different size water tanks.

Generally batch mixing is only used with Class A foam concentrates and regular AFFF concentrates (not alcohol resistant). Class A foam solutions do not retain their foaming properties when mixed in water for more than 24 hours, making pre-mixing virtually impossible. Regular AFFF concentrate mixes readily with water and will stay suspended in the solution for an extended period of time. When batch mixing this product, the driver/operator should slowly circulate the water in the tank to avoid frothing and continue to do so for a short period of time to ensure mixing is complete.

In addition, when refilling the water tank, the foam residue leftover on the interior surface may cause frothing. This foam solution acts as a cleansing agent that removes lubricants from pump seals. To avoid this, driver/operators should thoroughly flush out the tank and pump to remove all foam. Afterward, the driver/operator should check the seals for proper lubrication. Failure to do so may result in difficulty priming, pump cavitation, as well as inaccurate measurements of some gauges.

Table 14. 1
Amount of Concentrate Needed for Various Sizes of Water Tanks

	Foam Concentrate Proportioning	Water Tank Size in Gallons (Liters)				
	%	500 (2 000)	750 (3 000)	1,000 (4 000)	1,500 (6 000)	2,000 (8 000)
Concentrate to be added in gallons (Liters)	1%	5 (20)	7.5 (30)	10 (40)	15 (60)	20 (80)
	3%	15 (60)	22.5 (90)	30 (120)	45 (180)	60 (240)
	6%	30 (120)	45 (180)	60 (240)	90 (360)	120 (480)

Another significant disadvantage of batch mixing is that the entire tank is converted to foam solution. This process does not allow for continuous foam discharge from the apparatus, as the stream must be shut down while the tank is refilled. It is difficult to maintain the correct ratio of foam concentrate and water when refilling unless the water tank is completely empty. Because of these shortcomings batch mixing is used only if no other proportioning method is available.

Figure 14.25 A CAFS stream can be discharged further than an ordinary foam stream.

High Energy Foam Generating Systems/CAFS

High energy systems differ from other methods in that they introduce compressed air into the foam solution prior to discharge into a hoseline. The turbulence created by the foam solution and air flowing through the piping and/or hoseline creates finished foam. In addition to forming the foam, the compressed air allows the stream to be discharged to greater distances than an ordinary foam or water fire stream **(Figure 14.25)**.

In the mid-1980s, the U.S. Bureau of Land Management conducted research that resulted in the development of the type of high energy Class A foam system that is now in common use on both wildland and structural fire apparatus across the United States. The compressed air foam system (CAFS) features a rotary air compressor and a standard centrifugal fire pump. A direct injection foam proportioning system is attached to the discharge side of the pump. Once the foam concentrate is mixed with water to form a foam solution, compressed air is added to the mix before being discharged from the apparatus to the hoseline.

Compressed air foam offers several tactical advantages, including:

- The reach of the fire stream is considerably longer than those of low energy systems.

- A CAFS system produces small uniform air bubbles that are very durable.

- Foam produced by a CAFS adheres to a fuel surface and resists heat longer than low energy foam.

- Hoselines containing high energy foam solution weigh less than those containing plain water, or low energy foam solution.

- CAFS may provide a safer fire attack that allows effective reach from a greater distance.

However, CAFS does have a number of limiting factors, including:

- A CAFS increases the purchase price and maintenance costs of new apparatus.

- Hose reaction may be erratic if the foam solution is not supplied to the hoseline in sufficient quantities.

- In the event of a hose burst, the compressed air will intensify the reaction of the hoseline.

- Additional training is required for personnel who will operate and conduct fire attack operations using CAFS equipment.

Most apparatus equipped with a CAFS also flow plain water. Generally the CAFS system is designed to flow foam only through preselected discharges, while other discharges are provided to flow plain water.

CAFS apparatus use a standard centrifugal pump with an automatic discharge side proportioning system. Due to the low eduction rates, a variable flow rate sensing proportioner is required to supply the fire stream at the rate of 0.1 to 1.0 percent.

Generally, 2 cubic feet per minute (0.06 m³/min) of airflow per gallon per minute (4 L/min) of foam solution produces a dry foam of up to 100 gpm (400 L/min) of foam solution. This creates a substantial amount of foam at a 10:1 expansion ratio. Most structural and wildland suppression operations conducted with CAFS use an airflow rate of 0.5 to 1.0 ft³/min (0.01 to 0.03 m³/min) of foam solution. This rate allows adequate drainage of solution from the blanket to wet the fuel and prevent re-ignition as well as controlling any smoldering from beneath the foam blanket.

CAUTION
To protect the attack team when using Class A foam, nozzle flow rates should be the same as those for plain water.

Portable Foam Application Devices

Once the foam concentrate and water have mixed to form a foam solution, the solution must be mixed with air (aerated) and delivered to the surface of the fuel. When using low energy foam systems the aeration and discharge functions are completed by the aerating foam nozzle. Low expansion foams may be delivered by handlines or master stream appliances. Standard fire fighting nozzles may be employed for application of some types of low expansion foam. However, it may be best to use nozzles specifically designed to deliver the foam product in use in order to achieve the most efficient application.

NOTE: Foam nozzle eductors and some self-educting master stream foam nozzles may also be considered portable foam nozzles. Those devices were described earlier in this chapter.

Handline Nozzles

Firefighters often use **handline nozzles** during foam fire fighting operations. The most common handline nozzles used for foam application are smooth bore nozzles, fog nozzles, and air-aspirating foam nozzles. The following section discusses these types in further detail.

Handline Nozzle — Any nozzle that can be safely handled by one to three firefighters and flows less than 350 gpm (1 400 L/min).

Figure 14.26 A smooth bore nozzle provides a stream with excellent reach. *Courtesty of Shad Cooper/Wyoming State Fire Marshal's Office.*

Figure 14.27 Fog nozzles are effective in agitating water droplets and achieving a foaming action.

Smooth Bore Nozzles

The use of smooth bore nozzles is limited to the application of Class A foam from a CAFS **(Figure 14.26)**. Smooth bore nozzles provide an effective stream with excellent reach capabilities using this system. This is an exception to the standard rule that dictates the discharge orifice be no greater than half the diameter of the hose.

Fog Nozzles

Firefighters may operate fixed flow, selective flow, or automatic fog nozzles when applying a low expansion, short duration foam blanket. These nozzles break the foam solution into droplets while using the agitation of water droplets moving through air to achieving the foaming action **(Figure 14.27)**. Expansion ratios for most fog nozzles are in the 2:1 up to 4:1 range. Their most efficient usage is during application of regular AFFF and Class A foam. However, they may also be used with alcohol resistant AFFF on hydrocarbon fires. Fog nozzles are not an acceptable choice for delivery of fluoroprotein foams as insufficient aspiration is created. Likewise, they should not be employed for incidents involving polar solvents. Many nozzle manufacturers have designed foam aeration attachments that may be added to the end of a fog nozzle to increase aspiration of the foam solution.

Air-Aspirating Foam Nozzle

Air-aspirating foam nozzles induct air into the foam solution by a Venturi action. These nozzles can be used with Class A foam in wildland fire fighting applications, and are the only nozzles that should be used with protein and fluoroprotein concentrates. They provide maximum expansion of the agent, but since most of the stream's energy is used to introduce air, it is not able to reach as far as a standard fog nozzle **(Figure 14. 28)**.

Master Stream Foam Nozzles

Large-scale flammable and combustible liquid fires often require the delivery of an amount of foam that is beyond the capability of the handlines. Like handline nozzles, fixed flow or automatic fog master stream appliances may be used to deliver foam. They perform in a similar manner to the handline nozzles discussed in the preceding section. Industrial foam pumpers and ARFF apparatus are often equipped with aerating foam master stream nozzles.

Figure 14.28 Air-aspirating nozzles induct air into the foam solution allowing for maximum expansion of the foam.

Medium- and High-Expansion Foam Generating Devices

There are two basic types of medium- and high-expansion foam generators: water aspirating and **mechanical blower**. They both produce foam containing high air content. The air content of medium expansion foam ranges from 20:1 to 200:1. For high expansion foam, the ratio ranges from 200:1 to 1000:1.

Water aspirating devices for medium- and high-expansion foam are similar to other foam producing nozzles, except that they are considerably larger and longer. The back portion of the nozzle is open for airflow **(Figure 14.29)**. Foam solution is pumped through the nozzle as a fine spray, mixing with air to form a moderate expansion. The end of the nozzle features a screen, or series of screens, that break up the foam and mix it with additional air. These nozzles typically generate a lower air volume foam product than mechanical blowers.

Mechanical blowers look very similar to an ordinary smoke ejector. They operate on the same principle as the water aspirating nozzle, except that air is forced through the foam solution by the fan instead of being pulled by water movement. The mechanical blower produces foam containing a very high air content that is well suited for incidents requiring total flooding. Its use is limited to high-expansion applications.

Figure 14.29 Nozzles that allow more airflow are used for high-expansion foam.

Assembling a Foam Fire Stream

Placing a foam line into operation using an in-line proportioner is a basic method of achieving foam delivery. Driver/operators must be proficient in the steps required to complete this operation.

The following information provides the causes for the production of poor quality foam or the lack of foam production:

- Incorrect match between eductor and nozzle flow, resulting in no pickup of foam concentrate.
- Air leaks at fittings may cause a loss of suction.
- Clogged proportioning equipment.
- Partially closed nozzle will result in a flow rate that will not allow the creation of a Venturi effect capable of picking up foam concentrate.
- Too long of an attack line on the discharge side of the eductor.
- Kinked hose.
- Nozzle placed too far above the eductor, resulting in excessive elevation pressure.
- Different manufacturers foam concentrates should not be mixed together (except for mil-spec concentrates) as they may be chemically incompatible.
- Different classes of foam should not be mixed as they may produce an ineffective foam product or prevent any foam delivery.

The driver/operator must be aware of the specific manufacturer's recommendations for the foam concentrate and foam proportioning equipment in use. This information combined with department policy should provide working guidelines for operational use.

Foam Application Techniques

Under certain circumstances driver/operators may be required to operate a handline or master stream during an incident at which foam lines are used. In order to maintain maximum effectiveness and scene safety, correct techniques must be used for application. The techniques for applying foam to a fire or spill include:

- Direct-application method
- Roll-on method
- Bank-down method
- Rain-down method

NOTE: Many storage or industrial facilities feature fixed discharge methods of foam application. Refer to IFSTA's **Principles of Foam Fire Fighting** manual for information concerning these systems.

Direct Application

The direct application method of fire attack with Class A foam consists of applying finished foam directly onto the burning material. This technique follows the same procedure as direct attack using plain water, yet is usually more effective due to Class A foam's enhanced extinguishing capabilities.

Roll-On Method

Roll-On Application Method — Method of foam application in which the foam stream is directed at the ground at the front edge of the unignited or ignited liquid fuel spill; foam then spreads across the surface of the liquid. *Also known* as Bounce.

A method for Class B foam application, the **roll-on method** involves directing a foam fire stream on the ground near the front edge of a burning liquid spill. The foam will then roll across the surface of the fuel. Application of the foam should continue until it spreads across the entire surface of the fuel and the fire is completely extinguished, or the vapors are suppressed. Firefighters may need to re-position the stream to different areas to ensure the entire surface of the spill is adequately covered. This method is effective for use only on a pool of liquid fuel on the open ground **(Figure 14.30)**.

Bank-Down Method

Another method employed with Class B foam when a vertical surface is near or within a pool of ignitable liquid is the bank-down method. Using this type of application foam is directed onto the vertical surface and allowed to run down and spread across the pooled fuel product **(Figure 14.31)**.

Rain-Down Method

Rain-Down Application Method — Foam application method that directs the stream into the air above the unignited or ignited spill or fire, allowing the foam to float gently down onto the surface of the fuel. *See* Bank-Down Application Method and Roll-On Application Method.

When the first two methods are impractical due to the elevation of the fuel above grade, the **rain-down method** of application may be employed. This is the most common method of application for aboveground storage tank fires. It involves the direction of a Class B foam fire stream into the air above the fire, allowing the foam to gently rain down on the surface of the fuel **(Figure 14.32, p. 508)**. The firefighters operating the attack line must position within reach and sweep the stream back and forth across the surface of the fuel until it is completely covered and the fire is extinguished.

Figure 14.30 The roll-on method is used by pointing the foam fire stream at the base of a pool of burning liquid and rolling the foam over the surface of the fuel.

Figure 14.31 The bank-down method is used when a vertical surface is nearby a pool of burning liquid.

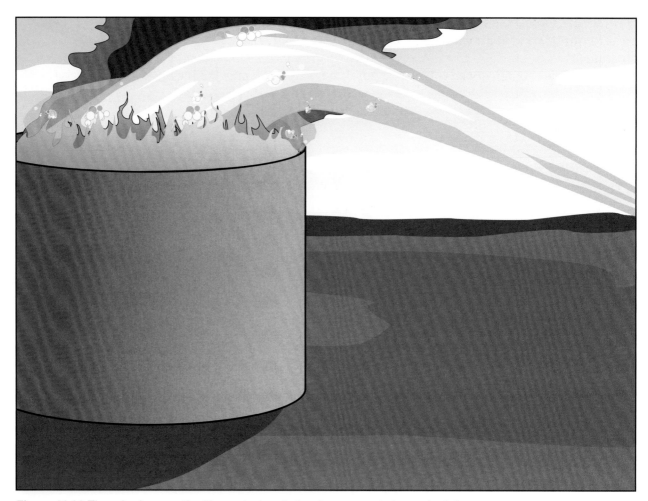

Figure 14.32 The rain-down method is used primarily for aboveground storage tank fires.

Biodegradable — Capable of being broken down into innocuous products by the actions of living things, such as microorganisms.

Decomposition — Chemical change in which a substance breaks down into two or more simpler substances. Result of oxygen acting on a material that results in a change in the material's composition; oxidation occurs slowly, sometimes resulting in the rusting of metals.

Environmental Impact

The primary concern regarding the environmental impact of foam is the effect of finished foam after application to a fire or spill. The severity of impact may vary based on the concentrate and type of Class A or B solution. **Biodegradability** of these products is determined by the rate at which natural bacteria can degrade the foam. The process of **decomposition** results in the consumption of oxygen. When foam solution makes its way to a natural water source this reduction of oxygen may result in the destruction of vegetation and aquatic life. Studies by the U.S. Forest Service have shown that release of Class A foam into bodies of water can be lethal to fish. No foam concentrates, solutions, or finished foam should be discharged into any body of water. Foam manufacturers safety data sheets (SDSs) as well as NFPA® 1150 *Standard on Foam Chemicals for Fire in Class A Fuels* will provide additional information regarding this topic.

Durable Agents

Other additives are currently available for use as extinguishing agents as well as pre-treatment of structures threatened by fire spread. Generally known as durable or **gelling agents**, fire blocking gels, or aqueous fire fighting gels, these products retain their fire retarding properties longer then Class A foam.

Although used in the same manner as Class A foam, these durable agents are structurally and chemically quite different. Chemically these products are water absorbent polymers as opposed to hydrocarbon based surfactants like Class A foam. When mixed with water, durable agents form small bubbles filled with water, unlike Class A foam in which bubbles are filled with air. These products are nontoxic and biodegradable and pose no adverse environmental impact. However once applied, surfaces coated with these products become very slippery for walking or driving. Durable agents are also considerably more expensive than Class A foam.

These products are usually siphoned from a container with an eductor, but may be batch mixed in a tank if necessary. Durable agents are applied for extinguishment, fire line construction, or structure protection through any standard handline nozzle or master stream device. They may also be **air dropped** via tanker or helicopter.

When used as an extinguishing agent, the standard application ratio is 1:100 (one percent solution in water). When used on a fire line, durable agents are often applied at 1½ to 2 percent. For structure protection, the application ratio is 2 to 3 percent. With this application, durable agents will adhere to vertical structural surfaces for up to 24 hours. In addition, the products may be rehydrated by using a fine water mist, thus extending protection for up to several days.

Gelling Agents — Superabsorbent liquid polymers capable of absorbing hundreds of times their own weight in water. These gels can be used as fire suppressants and fire retardants. Gels function by entrapping water in their structure rather than air, as is the case with fire fighting foams. *Also known as* Durable Agents.

Air Drop — Process of dropping water, short-term fire retardant, or long-term fire retardant from an air tanker or helicopter onto a wildland fire.

Chapter Summary

Foam technology is used to some degree by most fire departments. It is incumbent on the driver/operator to be proficient with the systems and understand the technology behind the products and delivery methods used in their jurisdiction. Establishing, maintaining, and troubleshooting foam fire fighting operations as well as restoring the system to a proper state of readiness after use are generally within the responsibilities of the driver/operator.

Review Questions

1. What are the various ways that foam works? (p.481)

2. What are the uses of Class A foam and Class B foam? (pp. 486-488)

3. What types of portable foam proportioners are used in the fire service? (p. 494)

4. What types of apparatus-mounted foam proportioners are used in the fire service? (pp. 497-500)

5. What are the advantages and limitations of compressed air foam systems? (pp. 502-503)

6. What are the major types of portable foam application devices? (pp. 503-505)

7. What are some causes of the production of poor quality foam or the lack of foam production? (p. 505)

8. What are the differences between the direct application, roll-on, bank-down, and rain-down methods of applying foam? (p. 506)

9. What can occur when foam solution makes its way to a natural water source? (p. 508)

10. What are some characteristics of durable agents? (p. 509)

Step 1: Select the proper foam and percentage of application for the fuel type.

Step 2: Check the nozzle and eductor, and ensure they are hydraulically compatible.

Step 3: Check and set the eductor for the percentage of concentration needed.

Step 4: Attach the eductor to the discharge outlet or in the hose line.

Step 5: Connect the nozzle to the discharge end of the hose. Check with the manufacturer's instructions to ensure the length of hose does not exceed recommendations.

Step 6: Place the eductor pick-up tube into the foam concentrate. Ensure that the tube is not more than 6 feet (2 m) below the eductor.

Step 7: Increase the water pressure in accordance with manufacturer's instructions and local SOPs.

Step 8: Ensure the nozzle operator has sufficient foam in accordance with manufacturer's instructions and local SOPs. If the foam line is not operating properly, refer to the troubleshooting guide.

Step 9: Once the foam evolutions are complete, make sure all appliances are thoroughly flushed with clean water.

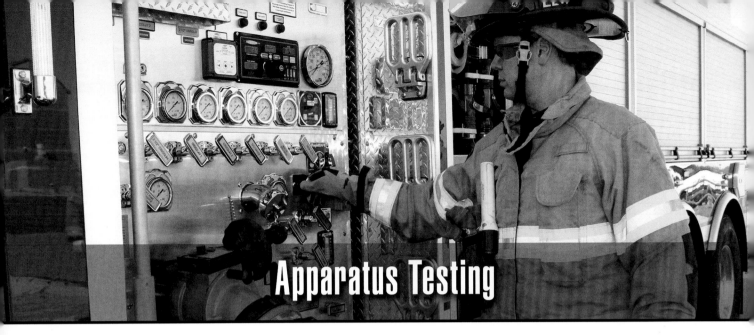

Apparatus Testing

Chapter Contents

Key Terms

NFPA® Job Performance Requirements

This chapter provides information that addresses the following job performance requirements of NFPA® 1002, *Standard for Fire Apparatus Driver/Operator Professional Qualifications (2014)*.

4.2.2, 5.1.1

NFPA 1002, *Standard for Fire Apparatus Driver/Operator Professional Qualifications (2017)*.

4.2.2, 5.1.2

Apparatus Testing

Learning Objectives

After reading this chapter, students will be able to:

1. Distinguish among preperformance tests for pumping apparatus. (*NFPA 1002, 2014:* 4.2.2, 5.1.1 & *NFPA 1002, 2017:* 4.2.2, 5.1.2)

2. Summarize facts about performance testing of fire pumps. (*NFPA 1002, 2014:* 4.2.2, 5.1.1 & *NFPA 1002, 2017:* 4.2.2, 5.1.2)

3. Describe methods for testing a foam proportioning system. (*NFPA 1002, 2014:* 4.2.2, 5.1.1 & *NFPA 1002, 2017:* 4.2.2, 5.1.2)

4. Perform an engine speed test. (*NFPA 1002, 2014:* 4.2.2, 5.1.1, Skill Sheet 15-1 & *NFPA 1002, 2017:* 4.2.2, 5.1.2, Skill Sheet 15-1)

5. Perform a vacuum test. (*NFPA 1002, 2014:* 4.2.2, 5.1.1, Skill Sheet 15-2 & *NFPA 1002, 2017:* 4.2.2, 5.1.2, Skill Sheet 15-2)

6. Prepare the pumper and complete a performance test of a fire pump including the priming system, pumping overload, and pressure control tests. (*NFPA 1002, 2014:* 4.2.2, 5.1.1, Skill Sheet 15-3 & *NFPA 1002, 2017:* 4.2.2, 5.1.2, Skill Sheet 15-3)

7. Perform discharge gauge and flowmeter operational tests. (*NFPA 1002, 2014:* 4.2.2, 5.1.1, Skill Sheet 15-4 & *NFPA 1002, 2017:* 4.2.2, 5.1.2, Skill Sheet 15-4)

8. Perform a tank-to-pump flow test. (*NFPA 1002, 2014:* 4.2.2, 5.1.1, Skill Sheet 15-5 & *NFPA 1002, 2017:* 4.2.2, 5.1.2, Skill Sheet 15-5)

Chapter 15
Apparatus Testing

Case History

As part of a routine check, a pumper was placed in gear to check pumping operations and operate its fixed master stream appliance. The driver/operator set the pump at idle and opened the supply to the master stream. Once charged, the appliance began to react violently, slamming back and forth until the water supply to the appliance was closed. An inspection of the master stream appliance found a missing part that allowed the device to lose control when water pressure was supplied.

All personnel working around apparatus pumping operations must wear full PPE and maintain an awareness of their surroundings as failure of a hoseline, nozzle, or other pressurized appliance is always possible and may happen catastrophically with little or no warning.

Source: *http://www.firefighterclosecalls.com/news/fullstory/newsid/181732/layout/no*

New fire apparatus is tested upon completion and periodically for its entire service life. The two basic categories of testing are grouped as preservice and performance tests. Usually the driver/operator is not involved in preservice testing; however, basic knowledge of the criteria and standards for these tests will aid in understanding performance tests, in which the driver/operator often is involved.

Preservice testing includes manufacturer's tests, pump certification tests, and acceptance tests. Performance tests are conducted on an annual basis and after major repairs during the service life of an apparatus. Generally, the driver/operator is expected to assist in the testing process. The following sections describe both types of tests including the procedures for each, as well as equipment requirements, troubleshooting, and safety precautions.

Preservice Tests

Pumping apparatus must undergo extensive testing before being placed in service to ensure the purchaser that the pump and the powertrain will perform as specified under normal use. These tests may be grouped into the categories of manufacturers' tests, certification tests, and acceptance tests. The purchaser should require these tests when writing specifications for the apparatus bid.

NFPA® 1901, *Standard for Automotive Fire Apparatus*, NFPA® 1906, *Standard for Wildland Fire Apparatus*, and NFPA® 414, *Standard for Aircraft Rescue and Firefighting Vehicles* are commonly used as a basis for most apparatus bid specifications. Generally, specifications will require the apparatus to meet the pertinent chapters of the aforementioned standards. Failure to comply usually results in rejection of the apparatus by the purchaser.

Fire department personnel are not normally involved in manufacturer or certification tests. These tests are performed by personnel from the manufacturer or Underwriters Laboratories. However, fire department personnel, especially driver/operators, may be involved in acceptance testing. These tests are commonly performed after delivery to the purchaser but before final acceptance by the purchaser. The following sections explain the major components of most preperformance tests.

Figure 15.1 Driver/operators should conduct the road test at a safe location.

Road Tests — Preservice apparatus maneuverability tests designed to determine the road-worthiness of a new vehicle.

Performance Requirements — Written list of expected capabilities for new apparatus. The list is produced by the purchaser and presented to the manufacturer as a guide for what is expected.

Manufacturers' Tests

If the requirements of NFPA® 1901 are included in the apparatus bid specifications, the manufacturer is required to perform two specific tests in addition to the pump certification tests described in this chapter: the road test and the hydrostatic test.

Road Test

NFPA® 1901 contains numerous minimum standards to which apparatus should comply after construction is complete. The **road test** is to be conducted with the vehicle loaded to the same weight as it will be when placed in service. The testing area must be in a location that will not violate any traffic laws or motor vehicle codes **(Figure 15.1)**. The road surface must be flat, paved, dry, and in good condition. The apparatus being tested must meet the following minimum standards:

● The apparatus must accelerate to 35 mph (55 km/h) from a standing start within 25 seconds. This test is conducted in two runs in opposite directions over the same course.

● The apparatus must achieve a maximum top speed of 50 mph (80 km/h). This requirement may be waived for vehicles not designed for use on public roadways.

● The apparatus must come to a full stop from 20 mph (30 km/h) within 35 feet (10.5 m).

● The parking brake installed on the vehicle must conform to the specifications listed by its manufacturer.

In addition to these minimum standards, other tests specified by a particular jurisdiction may be added to the specifications to ensure the apparatus will perform as required under local conditions. This may include special requirements for acceleration, deceleration, or braking on roads with specific degrees of slope. If special requirements are sought from the apparatus manufacturer, the purchaser should write them into the bid specifications as **performance requirements** as opposed to engineering or equipment specifications.

Hydrostatic Test

A **hydrostatic test** is performed to ensure that the pump and associated piping are capable of withstanding high pressure pumping demands. The pump body as well as the entire intake and discharge piping system, with the exception of the tank fill and tank-to-pump lines on the tank side of the valves, are subjected to a minimum hydrostatic test pressure of 500 psi (3 500 kPa) for a minimum of 10 minutes.

Pump Certification Tests

Pump certification tests are performed by an independent testing organization such as Underwriters Laboratories, and are designed to ensure that the fire pump will operate as designed on the completed apparatus. These tests are performed at the manufacturing plant before final acceptance of the vehicle. The results of the tests are stamped on a plate affixed to the pump panel of the apparatus. Certification testing requirements should be part of the apparatus bid specifications. Commonly, fire departments reference the requirements of NFPA® 1901 *Standard for Automotive Fire Apparatus*. The NFPA® 1901 standard requires the following certification tests be conducted for apparatus equipped with a fire pump of 750 gpm (3 000 L/min) up to 3,000 gpm (12 000 L/min):

- Engine speed check
- Pumping test
- Pumping engine overload test
- Pressure control system test
- Priming system test
- Vacuum test
- Water tank-to-pump test
- Engine speed interlock test
- Gauge and flowmeter test
- Manufacturer's predelivery test

For apparatus equipped with an onboard water tank, a tank-to-pump **flow test** must also be performed. For complete information regarding required testing for various fire pumps the reader should consult NFPA® 1901.

Acceptance Testing

Acceptance testing is conducted to demonstrate to the purchaser that the apparatus conforms to all bid specifications at the time of delivery. Testing is conducted at the jurisdiction to which the apparatus has been sold with representatives from the purchasing agency and the manufacturer available to review the procedures. Acceptance testing should feature a pump test in addition to the pump certification test that was previously performed at the factory. This process should be adequate to prove the validity of the pump certification.

If the apparatus fails to perform to the requirements outlined in the bid specifications, it should be rejected by the purchaser. Provisions may be made to give the manufacturer an opportunity to correct any deficiencies or supply another apparatus that will fit the specifications. Or, depending on the contract, the purchaser may consider the order void and choose another vendor to fill the stated requirements.

In jurisdictions that are higher than 2,000 feet (600 m) above sea level, a pumping engine overload test should be performed as part of acceptance testing. This will ensure that the engine develops the necessary power to operate in the conditions of higher altitudes.

Performance Testing of Fire Pumps (Pumper Performance Tests)

The requirements for fire department service testing are contained in NFPA® 1911, *Standard for the Inspection, Maintenance, Testing and Retirement of In-Service Automotive Fire Apparatus*. Based on this standard, a pumper must be performance tested at least once each year, or whenever it has undergone major pump or powertrain repair. This testing ensures that the pump will perform as designed, and any defects will be noticed and repaired before the apparatus is placed in service. See **Appendix F** for a sample annual pumper service test record.

The following sections feature information on minimum performance testing as required in NFPA® 1911. These tests include:

- Engine speed check
- Pump shift indicator
- Pump engine control interlock
- Priming system test
- Vacuum test
- Pumping test for fire pumps
- Overload test
- Pressure control test for fire pumps
- Intake relief valve system test
- Gauge test flowmeter test
- Tank-to-pump flow rate

Site Considerations for Pumper Performance Tests

Although the NFPA® 1911 standard allows performance testing to be conducted using a hydrant or static water supply, many jurisdictions prefer a static water source because it will provide easier evaluation for pump performance **(Figure 15.2)**. The water level of the static source must be at least 4 feet (1.2 m) deep, with the strainer submerged at least 2 feet (600 mm) below the surface. The distance of the centerline of the pumper intake above the surface of the water is based on its capacity. For pumps rated at 1,500 gpm (6 000 L/min) or less, 10 feet (3 m) is the maximum distance, while 2,000 gpm (8 000 L/min) pumps use a 6 foot (2 m) maximum lift.

The air temperature when the testing is conducted should be between 0° F (-18° C) and 110° F (43° C). The water temperature should be between 35° F (2° C) and 90° F (32° C). The barometric pressure should be at least 29 inches

Figure 15.2 A static water source may provide better conditions for pumper performance tests.

of Mercury (Hg) (100 kPa) when corrected to sea level. This adjustment is necessary because a 1-inch (3.5 kPa) drop in barometric pressure reduces the static lift of a pumper by approximately 1 foot (300 mm).

NFPA® 1911 lists the minimum intake hose arrangements necessary to perform tests on pumps of various capacities. These figures are accurate for testing that is performed at altitudes of up to 2,000 feet (600 m) above sea level. When testing at higher altitude locations, the intake hose diameter or the number of hoses may need to be increased in order for the pump to reach its rated capacity.

When conducting the pump test a sufficient number of discharge hoses must be stretched and operated. The minimum diameter hoseline for this purpose is 2½-inch (65 mm) hose, although larger diameter hoselines may be employed if so desired. This hose should be tested to ensure it is capable of withstanding the pressures expected during the pump test procedure. **Tables 15.1 a** and **b, p. 520,** show the minimum hose and nozzle arrangements required to discharge sufficient water for various capacity fire pumps.

To monitor the continued serviceability of the hose throughout the test, a mark may be scribed where the hose and couplings meet. During the testing process, check the couplings periodically to be sure that they are not pulling apart. If the scribe mark is found to have moved away more than 3/8 of an inch (9 mm) from the coupling, stop the test and replace the hose **(Figure 15.3, p. 520)**.

Correcting Net Pump Discharge Pressure for Testing

Net pump discharge pressure is the difference between the intake pressure and the discharge pressure. Performance tests are conducted at 150 psi (1 050 kPa), 165 psi (1 150 kPa), 200 psi (1 400 kPa), and 250 psi (1 750 kPa) net pump discharge pressure. When operating at draft, the net pump discharge pressure is more than the pressure displayed on the discharge gauge. When tests are conducted, the friction loss in the intake hose and the height of the

Table 15.1a Hose and Nozzle Layouts for Pump Tests (Customary)	
Pump Capacity in gpm	**Hose and Nozzle Layout (all hose 2½-inch in diameter)**
250-350	One 50-foot line with a 1⅛-inch or 1¼-inch nozzle
400-500	One 50-foot line with a 1⅜-inch or 1½-inch nozzle
600-750	Two 100-foot lines with a 1½-inch or 1¾-inch nozzle
1,000	Two or three 100-foot lines with a 2-inch nozzle
1,250	Two 100-foot lines with a 1¾-inch nozzle and one 50-foot line with a 1½-inch nozzle
1,500	Three 100-foot lines with a 2-inch nozzle and one 50-foot line with a 1½-inch nozzle
1,750	Two sets of twin 100-foot lines, each set supplying a 2-inch nozzle
2,000	Two sets of twin 100-foot lines, each set supplying a 2-inch nozzle
2,250	Two sets of three 100-foot lines, each set supplying a 2¼-inch nozzle
2,500	Two sets of three 100-foot lines, each set supplying a 2¼-inch nozzle

Table 15.1b Hose and Nozzle Layouts for Pump Tests (Metric)	
Pump Capacity in L/min	**Hose and Nozzle Layout (all hose 65 mm in diameter)**
1 000 to 1 400	One 15 m line with a 29 mm or 32 mm nozzle
1 600 to 2 000	One 15 m line with a 35 mm or 38 mm nozzle
2 400 to 3 000	Two 30 m lines with a 38 mm or 45 mm nozzle
4 000	Two or three 30 m lines with a 50 mm nozzle
5 000	Two 30 m lines with a 45 mm nozzle and one 15 m with a 38 mm nozzle
6 000	Three 30 m lines with a 50 mm nozzle and one 15 m with a 38 mm nozzle
7 000	Two sets of twin 30 m lines, each set supplying a 50 mm nozzle
8 000	Two sets of twin 30 m lines, each set supplying a 50 mm nozzle
9 000	Two sets of three 30 m lines, each set supplying a 57 mm nozzle
10 000	Two sets of three 30 m lines, each set supplying a 57 mm nozzle

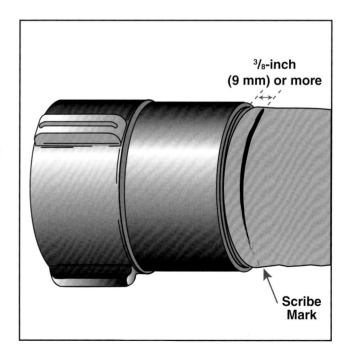

Figure 15.3 Scribe marks around couplings are used to determine if a hose should be taken out of service.

lift must be considered. NFPA® 1911 provides information on friction loss allowances for various sizes of intake hose that may be used during pump testing.

The friction loss allowances are then used to determine the correct pump discharge pressure for each test. When correcting net pump discharge pressure for apparatus testing, use the pressure correction formula from Chapter 11.

Example 15.1 (Customary)

Assume that a 1,000 gpm pumper is being tested. The lift is 9 feet through 20 feet of 5-inch intake hose. What is the pressure correction for this text?

$$PC = \underline{\textbf{Lift + Total Intake Hose Friction Loss}}$$
$$\textbf{2.3}$$

Lift = 9

Total Intake Hose Friction Loss = 8.4 from NFPA® 1911

$$PC = \underline{9 + 8.4} = \textbf{7.57 psi (app. 7.5)}$$
$$2.3$$

Example 15.1 (Metric)

Assume that a 4 000 L/min pumper is being tested. The lift is 2.7 m through 6 m of 125 mm intake hose. Find the necessary pressure correction for this test.

$$PC = \underline{\textbf{Lift + Total Intake Hose Friction Loss}}$$
$$\textbf{0.1}$$

Lift = 2.7

Total Intake Hose Friction Loss = 2.6 from NFPA® 1911

$$PC = \underline{2.7 + 2.6} = \textbf{53 kPa (app. 50)}$$
$$0.1$$

The pressure correction is subtracted from the desired net pump discharge pressure to determine the likely actual discharge pressure of the pump.

Equipment Required for Performance Tests

NFPA® 1911 specifies that all gauges used for service testing must be calibrated within 60 days of the testing. The following equipment is required for performance tests on fire department pumpers:

- A gauge to determine intake pressure. The gauge should be calibrated to a range of 30 in Hg to zero (-100 to 0 kPa) for a vacuum gauge, or 30 in Hg (-100 kPa) vacuum to 150 psi (1 050 kPa) for a compound gauge **(Figure 15.4, p. 522)**.

- A gauge with a range of 0 to at least 400 psi (2 800 kPa) (with + or - 5 % accuracy) to determine pump discharge.

Figure 15.4 External pressure gauges are used during performance tests.

Figure 15.5 A pitot tube and gauge may be used to measure pressure of a fire stream.

- A pitot tube with knife edge and air chamber rated from 0 to at least 160 psi (1 100 kPa) is required if a flowmeter is not used **(Figure 15.5)**.

- Smooth bore nozzles of the appropriate size to provide the volumes pumped for the required tests. (If a flowmeter is used, fog nozzles may be substituted, providing they are rated for the required flows).

- A means to secure the nozzles (rope, chain, or test stand).

- A hand tachometer (if applicable).

- Appropriate means to record the test results (written form or computer program).

The following additional equipment may serve to make the testing process easier and more efficient:

- Two 6-foot (2 m) lengths of ¼-inch (6 mm) diameter, 300 psi (2 100 kPa) hose with screw fittings and gauges. These gauges are connected to fittings at the pump panel.

- Clamp to hold the pitot tube to the test nozzle.

- Test stand to hold the gauges.

- Stopwatch.

Flowmeters

A flowmeter, which indicates flow in gallons (or liters) per minute, within plus or minus three percent of accuracy, offers increased efficiency over a pitot gauge when determining flow from nozzles during a pump test. Using a flowmeter during pump testing may be conducted without shutting down the pump, changing nozzles, or converting the pressure reading of the pitot gauge to gallons per minute (L/min). When using a flowmeter during pump testing the driver/operator must ensure that it has been properly calibrated to the manufacturer's specifications.

Safety During Service Testing

To perform fire pump service testing safely, personnel should:

- Wear protective head gear, eyewear, gloves, and hearing protection if noise levels have the potential to reach or exceed 90 decibels (dB)

- Open and close valves and nozzles slowly to prevent water hammer.
- Operate the engine throttle slowly to prevent sudden pressure changes that may damage equipment or injure personnel.
- Secure test nozzles and observe hose from a safe distance.
- Ensure that no people or obstructions are in the path of a hose stream.
- Be sure that personnel are protected from any open **manholes** if using a test pit.
- Chock apparatus wheels.
- Monitor air quality for the presence of carbon monoxide.

Manhole — (1) Hole through which a person may go to gain access to an underground or enclosed structure. (2) Opening usually equipped with a removable, lockable cover, that is large enough to admit a person into a tank trailer or dry bulk trailer. *Also known as* Manway.

Engine Speed Check

An engine speed check should be conducted under no-load conditions after ensuring all fluid levels are within manufacturer's recommendations. **Skill Sheet 15-1** provides the steps to determine if the engine is running at the same governed speed at which it was rated when the apparatus was new. If it is not running at the correct speed (plus or minus 50 rpm), the apparatus should be evaluated by a qualified mechanic before any further tests are performed. Engine speed may be determined by the engine **tachometer** and/or a properly calibrated handheld tachometer.

Tachometer — Instrument that indicates the rotational speed of a shaft in revolutions per minute (rpm); usually used to indicate engine speed.

Vacuum Test

A vacuum test evaluates the priming device, pump, and intake hose for air leaks. Many fire departments perform this test first, as it will be difficult to proceed if the pump will not hold the necessary vacuum. See **Skill Sheet 15-2** for the steps to perform a vacuum test.

If the pump fails to reach 22 inches of mercury (-75 kPa), remove the apparatus from service until repairs can be made. Check the internal condition of the suction hose and refer to Chapter 2.

Upon completion of the above tests, the pumper may be prepared for the remainder of the tests:

- Open a discharge valve to allow pressure in the pump to equalize.
- Remove the cap from the end of the intake hose and attach a strainer.
- Prepare the intake hose for drafting. The strainer should be a minimum of 24 inches (600 mm) below the surface of the water, with at least 24 inches (600 mm) of water around the sides and bottom of the strainer.
- Connect the discharge pressure test gauge to the pressure side of the test fitting on the pump panel.
- Refer to **Tables 15.2 a** and **b, p. 524**, and connect the proper number of hoselines and nozzles in order to flow the rated capacity of the fire pump.
- Attach the pitot gauge by clamping it into position at the nozzle.

CAUTION

Before beginning the test, secure all nozzles to prevent injury to personnel. Never attempt to hold a nozzle during the test procedure.

Table 15.2a
Flow in GPM from Various-Sized Solid Stream Nozzles (Customary)

Nozzle Diameter in Inches

Nozzle Pressure in psi	1	1⅛	1¼	1⅜	1½	1⅝	1¾	1⅞	2	2¼
50	209	265	326	396	472	554	643	740	841	1065
55	219	277	342	415	495	581	674	765	881	1118
60	229	290	357	434	517	607	704	810	920	1168
65	239	301	372	451	537	631	732	843	958	1215
70	246	313	386	469	558	655	761	875	994	1260
75	256	324	399	485	578	678	787	905	1030	1305
80	264	335	413	500	596	700	813	935	1063	1347

Table 15.2b
Flow in L/min from Various-Sized Solid Stream Nozzles (Metric)

Nozzle Diameter in mm

Nozzle Pressure in kPa	25	29	32	35	38	42	45	48	50	57
350	791	1 003	1 234	1 499	1 786	2 097	2 434	2 801	3 183	4 031
385	829	1 048	1 294	1 571	1 873	2 200	2 551	2 896	3 334	4 232
420	867	1 098	1 351	1 643	1 957	2 297	2 665	3 066	3 483	4 421
455	905	1 139	1 408	1 707	2 033	2 389	2 771	3 191	3 626	4 600
490	931	1 185	1 461	1 775	2 112	2 480	2 880	3 312	3 763	4 770
525	969	1 226	1 510	1 835	2 188	2 567	2 980	3 425	3 899	4 940
560	1 000	1 000	1 563	1 893	2 256	2 650	3 077	3 539	4 024	5 099

Priming System Test

When the driver/operator has the apparatus prepared for the pumping test, operate the priming system until the pump achieves prime and is discharging water. According to NFPA® 1911, fire pumps of 1,250 gpm (5 000 L/min) capacity must achieve prime in 30 seconds or less, and those rated at 1,500 gpm (6 000 L/min) must be primed within 45 seconds. Additional specifications offer increased time based on the size of intake piping.

Pumping Test

The pumping test evaluates the overall operation of the engine and fire pump. In order to achieve the correct engine and nozzle pressures for the pump capacity, the testing of a series of adjustments will be required. Any pressure changes should be made slowly to avoid damage to the pump and other equipment, as well as to ensure the safety of personnel conducting the test. Time must also be allowed for pressure changes to register on the test gauges. Follow the steps in **Skill Sheet 15-3** to prepare the pump for service testing.

Consider the following when conducting the pumping test:

- A fixed pitot with a remote gauge capable of being read at the pump panel is recommended for this procedure. If a handheld pitot gauge is used instead, it should be held with the blade opening at the center of the stream with the tip approximately one-half the nozzle diameter from the end of the nozzle. A pitot gauge held too close to the nozzle will register a reading higher than the actual pressure.

- The driver/operator must ensure the apparatus engine temperature and oil pressure remain within normal operating ranges for the duration of the test.

- Any unusual vibration or performance defect that is encountered while conducting the test should be documented and reported.

Pressure Control Test

Pressure control devices installed on the fire pump must be tested to ensure they operate as designed, maintaining a safe level of pressure on the pump when valves are closed at a range of discharge pressures. The pressure control test is performed in a three-part sequence and may be completed while the pump is still set up from the pumping test for a more efficient operation. Refer to **Skill Sheet 15-3** for the steps to perform the pumping, overload, and pressure control tests.

Discharge Pressure Gauge and Flowmeter Operational Tests

The discharge pressure gauges and flowmeter (if so equipped) must be tested to ensure that the driver/operator has accurate information on which to base decisions on pump operation. Gauges that are not properly calibrated may cause the driver/operator to unintentionally supply dangerously low or high pressures to firefighters operating attack lines. See **Skill Sheet 15-4** to perform discharge gauge and flowmeter operational tests.

When discharges are equipped with a flowmeter, a different procedure must be used. A hoseline equipped with a solid stream nozzle is connected to each discharge that is to be tested (this can be done one at a time). Refer to Table 15.2 a and b to determine the appropriate hose and nozzle arrangements for this procedure. The minimum flow rates that must be achieved for each discharge pipe size are listed in NFPA® 1911. The actual flow rate that is achieved will be determined using a pitot gauge reading measured at the discharge of the solid stream nozzle. The difference in readings between the flowmeter and pitot gauge must not be more than ten percent. Any reading beyond those margins requires repair or replacement of the flowmeter.

Tank-to-Pump Flow Test

A tank-to-pump flow test must be conducted on any apparatus with an onboard water tank. This test verifies that the piping between the onboard tank and pump is sufficient to supply the minimum amount of water specified by NFPA® 1901 and the design of the manufacturer. Pumpers with an onboard tank capacity of 500 gallons (2 000 L) or less must be capable of flowing 250 gpm (1 000 L/min) from their onboard tank. Pumpers with a capacity of greater than 500 gallons (2 000 L) must be capable of flowing at least 500 gpm (2 000 L/min). Some jurisdictions may specify higher flows based on local requirements. If an apparatus with specifications greater than the NFPA® minimum is being tested, it is recommended that the specified capacity be achieved during testing. Use the following procedures in **Skill Sheet 15-5** to check the operation of the tank-to-pump line.

Internal Intake Pressure Relief Valve Test

The operation of the internal intake pressure relief valve as well as intake relief valves on any other appliances used on the apparatus should be tested. The steps required to test this valve are as follows:

- A discharge hoseline from a second pumper is connected to the intake of the apparatus being tested.

- The discharge pressure from the supply pumper should be increased until the internal intake relief valve on the test pumper opens.

- The pressure at which the internal intake relief valve actuated is recorded.

- The recorded pressure should be compared to past test results as well as operating procedures used by the jurisdiction where the pumper is in service. If necessary the valve may be adjusted to the desired setting.

Reviewing Test Results

During the testing process the pumper must not show signs of overheating, power loss, or other mechanical issues. Upon completion of testing, all fluid levels should again be checked and any losses noted. The results of any tests conducted should be recorded per the policy of the jurisdiction where the pumper is in service. Any apparatus that achieves results less than 90 percent of its originally rated capabilities has two options for continued use: It may be placed out of service and restored to its original capabilities and tested again, or the apparatus may be given a lower rating based on the results of the most recent testing.

Troubleshooting During Service Testing

When a pump fails to meet the requirements of the service test, one or more of the following issues should be investigated as a possible cause of the problem before the test results are concluded:

- Transmission in wrong gear
- Lockup clutch with automatic transmission apparatus not functioning
- Clutch slipping
- Engine overheating
- Muffler clogged
- Tachometer inaccurate
- Engine governor malfunctioning
- Insufficient intake hose
- Intake strainer submerged incorrectly or intake screen clogged
- Lift higher than 10 feet (3 m)

- Intake hose clogged or lining collapsed
- Excessive air leaks on intake side of pump as a result of bad pump seals
- Pump impellers clogged
- Clearance rings that are excessively worn
- Pump or intake hose not fully primed
- Malfunctioning relief valve or pressure governor
- Transfer valve in wrong position
- Malfunction of gauges
- Pitot gauge malfunctioning or clogged
- Nozzle too large or too small

Foam Proportioning Equipment Testing

Foam proportioning equipment installed on an apparatus must also be tested for proper operation before being placed in service, and periodically thereafter. This equipment is generally checked by one of two methods:

- Testing the foam to water concentration that the system and associated equipment are able to produce
- Testing the rate at which foam concentrate is consumed in proportion to a known flow of water through the system

The accuracy of an apparatus foam system must be tested prior to delivery per NFPA® 1901. However, the standard does not require the system to be tested on a yearly basis. IFSTA recommends that driver/operators have the ability to perform the four basic testing methods specified in NFPA 1901® so that the operability of the foam system may be verified periodically during the service life of the apparatus. The methods for testing a foam proportioning system for calibration accuracy are:

- Foam concentrate displacement method
- Foam concentrate pump discharge volume method
- Foam solution refractivity testing
- Foam solution conductivity testing

Foam Concentrate Displacement Method

This method checks the volume of foam concentrate that is drawn through the system to determine the accuracy of the proportioning equipment. The foam system is operated at a predetermined flow using water instead of foam concentrate. The water is drawn from a calibrated tank instead of the foam concentrate tank or five gallon (20 L) pails. The volume of water drawn from the tank over a measured period of time is correlated to the actual percentage of foam concentrate that the system would have drawn.

NOTE: Because water has a different viscosity than foam concentrate, it will be drawn into the proportioning system at a slightly different rate. The manufacturer of the proportioning system or the foam concentrate should be able to supply a correction factor that can be applied to ensure testing accuracy when water replaces foam.

Foam Concentrate Pump Discharge Volume Method

Certain direct injection type proportioning systems may use this method to check the volume of foam concentrate that is proportioned into a fire stream. Water may also be used as a substitute for foam concentrate during testing with this procedure. To begin the test, the foam system is operated at a predetermined flow while the discharge from the foam concentrate pump is collected in a calibrated tank for a specified period of time. The volume in the calibrated tank may then be correlated to the actual percentage of foam concentrate that the system should proportion at the test flow rate.

Foam Solution Refractivity Testing

A foam solution refractivity test ensures the quality of a foam solution after it has been created by a foam proportioning system. This test is accurate for protein and fluoroprotein based foam solutions.

Refractometer — Device used to measure the amount of foam concentrate in the solution; operates on the principle of measuring the velocity of light that travels through the foam solution.

The amount of foam concentrate present in the solution is measured using a **refractometer**. This device measures the velocity of light that travels through a medium. The refractometer compares samples of solution drawn from a system being tested to a base reading. Any deviation in the content of foam concentrate in the solution will result in a different bending of light beams through the refractometer. The scale readings on the refractometer do not directly represent the actual foam proportioning percentage, so results must be plotted on a graph in order to be interpreted.

In order to develop a base calibration curve for refractivity test analysis, the proportion rate of the foam concentrate must be determined (usually 1, 3, or 6%). Foam concentrate and water are taken from the foam system being tested to make the base curve solutions. One solution contains the exact concentration required, a second solution contains 0.3 percent less concentrate than recommended, and the third solution contains 0.3 percent more concentrate than recommended.

The example outlined in the following paragraphs illustrates the preparation of samples for testing a 3 percent foam concentrate. The solutions for this test may be mixed as follows:

- Carefully add foam concentrate to each of three labeled plastic 100 ml or larger graduated bottles. Place 2.7 ml of concentrate into one bottle, 3 ml into the second, and 3.3 ml into the third bottle.

- Fill each bottle with water to the 100 ml mark.

- Add a plastic stirring bar to each bottle and cap tightly.

- Thoroughly shake each bottle to mix the water with the foam concentrate.

When conducting tests on a proportioner with multiple settings (1, 3, and 6%), three samples must be taken, and a chart prepared for each concentration.

A refractive index of the sample is prepared by placing a few drops on the refractor prism, closing the cover plate, then waiting approximately 10 to 20 seconds until the refractor adjusts to temperature fluctuations. Each reading may then be plotted on a graph. One axis contains the refractometer reading, while the other notes the proportioning percentage. Using these points, a baseline curve is established.

Samples of actual foam solution produced by the system to be tested are obtained and tested on the refractometer and plotted on the graph. The results of the testing must fall within the NFPA® standards for acceptable limits discussed previously.

Foam Solution Conductivity Testing

Conductivity testing is used to ensure the quality of synthetic based foam produced by various foam proportioning systems and equipment. Due to the very light color of synthetic based foam, refractivity testing is not an accurate measure of the foam's quality. However, conductivity testing verifies the ability of the foam product to conduct electricity.

Domestic and static water sources used for firefighting have the ability to conduct electrical current. When foam concentrate is proportioned with water, the resulting level of conductivity will measure at some point between the conductivity of plain water and plain foam concentrate. The difference in the level of conductivity can be used to measure the amount of foam concentrate in a given solution.

These are three methods of performing foam solution conductivity testing:

- Direct reading conductivity testing
- Conductivity comparison testing
- Conductivity calibration curve testing

Direct Reading Conductivity Testing

This method may be employed when a direct reading conductivity meter is available. The actual percentage of foam concentrate in a solution may be indicated on certain meters. Other meters may require that the individual conducting the testing develop a calibration curve. The procedure for developing a calibration curve for conductivity testing is the same as for refractivity testing.

Before performing a test, the meter must be reset to zero using plain water, using one of the following methods:

1. Collect a sample of the water used for the test in a container and immerse the sensor head to zero the meter.

2. Mount the sensor to the pump discharge line and zero in the meter while flowing plain water.

After the meter is properly zeroed, a sample of foam solution from the proportioning system is obtained in a container or directly from the pump discharge following the same process as discussed using plain water. If the meter used for testing does not display the percentage of foam concentrate in the solution, the reading must be plotted on the calibration curve to achieve the rest results.

Conductivity Comparison Testing

This method is used during testing with a meter that displays units of microsiemens per centimeter (ms/cm). Readings for plain water and foam solution produced by the proportioning system are obtained. The percentage of foam concentrate in the solution is then determined using **Formula 15.1.**

Formula 15.1 – Conductivity Test for Foam Concentrate in Solution

$$\text{Percent of Concentrate in Solution} = \frac{(\text{Conductivity of Solution}) - (\text{Conductivity of Water})}{500}$$

The divisor of 500 is used only if the meter in use is incremented in units of ms/cm. A different divisor will be required for other types of meters. Specific information is provided by the manufacturer of the meter.

Conductivity Calibration Curve Testing

Conductivity calibration testing is performed using a handheld temperature compensated conductivity meter. This test procedure is similar to that described for refractivity testing. A calibration curve is developed using the same process as refractivity testing. However, the readings are obtained using a conductivity meter. More detailed information concerning foam system testing, including testing compressed air foam systems (CAFS) may be found in the IFSTA **Principles of Foam Fire Fighting** Manual.

Chapter Summary

Pumping apparatus are inspected at various times to ensure they perform as designed. Immediately after construction, pre-performance tests are conducted prior to acceptance by the organization that ordered the apparatus. Upon delivery, pumpers are once again testing before being placed in service. Driver/operators are often involved in delivery as well as annual testing performed to ensure the continued serviceability of apparatus.

In order to properly assist in the testing process, driver/operators must be familiar with the fundamental goals and procedures for each test, as well as the equipment, safety precautions, and troubleshooting steps that may be required to successfully complete necessary tests. Successful completion of comprehensive apparatus testing will help ensure safe and reliable daily operation.

Review Questions

1. What is the difference between manufacturers' tests, certification tests, and acceptance tests? (pp. 516-517)

2. What tests are included when conducting performance testing? (p. 518)

3. What are some site considerations when performing pumper performance tests? (pp. 518-519)

4. What equipment is required for performance tests on fire department pumpers? (pp. 521-522)

5. What methods are used for testing a foam proportioning system for calibration accuracy? (p. 527)

Step 1: Mount the apparatus cab, using appropriate steps and handrails.

Step 2: Turn on the vehicle battery(ies), hitting Battery 1, Battery 2, or both on battery switch or moving simple switch to ON position. Follow apparatus manufacturer's directions and departmental SOPs.

CAUTION: Never operate the battery switch while the engine is running.

NOTE: Depending on the location of this switch, you may choose to operate this switch prior to entering the cab or immediately upon sitting in the driver's seat.

Step 3: Check that the parking brake is set.

Step 4: Place the transmission in neutral if it is not already in neutral.

Step 5: Turn on the ignition switches located on the dashboard.

Step 6: Operate the starter control using the key, appropriate toggle switch(es), or push button depending on the apparatus.

Operate the starter control at intervals of no more than 30 seconds, with a rest of 60 seconds between each try if the vehicle does not start sooner.

Step 7: Idle the engine.

Step 8: Dismount the apparatus, using appropriate steps and handrails.

Step 10: Read and record the tachometer reading, comparing it with the governed speed for which it was rated when the apparatus was new.

NOTE: If it is not running at the correct speed, no further testing should be started until the situation is corrected by a trained mechanic.

Step 11: Mount the apparatus cab, using the appropriate steps and handrails.

Step 12: Shut off the engine.

Step 13: Turn the battery switch to the OFF position.

Step 9: Attach the tachometer to the engine or to the service connection on the pump panel. Follow directions provided by the tachometer and apparatus manufacturers.

Step 1: Make sure that the pump is completely drained of all water.

Step 2: Inspect gaskets on hard intake hose and caps for any noticeable damage such as cracks, flexibility, physical damage and cleanliness.

Step 3: Look for foreign matter in the intake hose. Clean the hose if necessary.

Step 4: Connect 20 feet (6 m) of the correct intake hose to the pump intake connection (check original test records for correct diameter of hose).

Step 5: Cap the free end of the intake hose.

Step 6: Make sure that all intake valves are open and the intake connections are tightly capped. As well, all discharge valves should be closed and their caps should be removed.

Step 7: Connect an accurate vacuum gauge (or mercury manometer) to the threaded test-gauge connection on the intake side of the pump.

CAUTION: If the gauge is not connected to the intake side, it will be irreparably damaged.

Step 8: Check oil level of priming pump reservoir (if so equipped) and replenish if necessary.

Step 9: Make pump packing glands accessible to check for leakage (raise floorboards or open compartment doors).

Step 10: Run the priming device until the test gauge shows 22 inches of mercury (-75 kPa) developed.

Step 11: Compare readings of the apparatus intake gauge and test gauge. Record any difference.

Step 12: Shut off the engine. Listen for air leaks. No more than 10 inches (35 kPa) of vacuum should be lost in 5 minutes. Excessive leaks will affect the results of subsequent tests and should be located and corrected before performing the rest of the test.

15-3

Prepare the pumper and complete a performance test of a fire pump including the priming system, pumping overload, and pressure control tests.

NOTE: Preparing the pumper for service testing is done after the vacuum test has been performed (Skill Sheet 15-2).

Preparing the Pumper for Service Testing

Step 1: Open a discharge valve to allow the pressure in the pump to equalize.

Step 2: Replace the cap at the end of the intake hose with the intake strainer.

Step 3: Use standard departmental procedures to tie off intake hose in preparation for drafting, then lower the hose into the water.

a. The strainer should be at least 24 inches (600 mm) below the surface.

b. The sides and bottom of the strainer should also have at least 24 inches (600 mm) of water surrounding them.

Step 4: Connect the discharge pressure test gauge to the pressure side of the pump at the test fitting on the operator's panel.

Step 5: Connect an adequate number of hoselines to carry the capacity of the pump to the test nozzle.

a. The test nozzle must be the correct size to handle the capacity of the pump.

b. Refer to tables 15.2a and 15.2 b.

Step 6: Make sure that the nozzle is secured so that it cannot come loose and injure personnel. NEVER hold the test nozzle by hand during a test.

Step 7: Connect the pitot gauge and test stand gauges.

NOTE: It is recommended that a commercial calibrated tip set and fixed pitot combination be used or the pitot gauge shall be clamped in position at the nozzle.

Performing the Priming Test

Step 8: Perform a priming system test if the pump is tested from draft. Do this test in connection with priming the pump for the pumping test.

a. With the apparatus set up for the pumping test, the primer shall be operated in accordance with the manufacturer's instructions until the pump has been primed and is discharging water.

b. The interval from the time the primer is started until the time the pump is discharging water shall be timed and documented.

c. For information about the allowed time, refer to NFPA® 1911.

Performing the Pumping, Overload, and Pressure Control Tests

Step 9: Gradually speed up the pump until the net pump discharge pressure is 150 psi (1 050 kPa), adjusted for intake hose friction loss and altitude. If the pump is a two-stage pump, the transfer valve must be in the PARALLEL (VOLUME) position.

Step 10: Adjust the flow at the nozzle to achieve the capacity noted on the certification plate, using either a pitot gauge or a flowmeter.

    a. If the flow is too great, close a valve further. Reduce engine speed to correct discharge pressure.

    b. If the flow is too low, open a valve further. Increase engine speed to correct discharge pressure.

NOTE: All these adjustments must be made without the engine speed exceeding 80 percent of its peak. A remote gauge from the fixed pitot to the gauge test stand is recommended so it is possible to see the vacuum, main pump discharge pressure, and the pitot flow pressure all at the same time.

Step 11: Make and record the following readings at the beginning of the test and at 5-minute intervals thereafter until the 20 minutes of the test are over.

    a. Time of day

    b. RPM using portable rpm counter (optional)

    c. Test tachometer or tachometer from information center

    d. Panel tachometer

    e. Engine coolant temperature

    f. Oil pressure

    g. Voltage

    h. Automatic transmission fluid temperature (optional)

    i. Test intake gauge

    j. Panel intake pressure gauge

    k. Test discharge gauge

    l. Panel discharge pressure

    m. Nozzle pressure (or flow)

Step 12: Perform an overload test consisting of pumping rated capacity at 165 psi (1 150 kPa) net pump pressure for at least 5 minutes if the pump has a rated capacity of 750 gpm (3 000 L/min) or greater.

Step 13: Perform the capacity pressure control tests.

    a. The pressure control device shall be tested at rated capacity at 150 psi (1 050 kPa) net pump pressure.

    b. The pressure control device shall be set in accordance with the manufacturer's instructions to maintain the discharge at 150 psi (1 050 kPa) net pump pressure.

    c. All discharge valves shall be closed no faster than in 3 seconds and no slower than in 10 seconds.

Step 14: The pressure control device shall be tested at 90 psi (630 kPa) net pump pressure.

    a. The original conditions of pumping rated capacity at 150 psi (1 050 kPa) net pump pressure shall be reestablished.

    b. The discharge pressure shall be reduced to 90 psi (630 kPa) net pump pressure by throttling the engine fuel supply with no change to the discharge valve setting, hose, or nozzles.

    c. The pressure control device shall be set in accordance with the manufacturer's instructions to maintain the discharge at 90 psi (630 kPa) net pump pressure.

    d. All discharge valves shall be closed no faster than in 3 seconds and no slower than in 10 seconds.

Step 15: Increase the net pump discharge pressure to 200 psi (1 400 kPa).

    a. At this point, the pump should be delivering at least 70 percent of its rated volume capacity.

    b. The pump should be allowed to run at this setting for 10 minutes.

NOTE: Two-stage pump transfer valves may be in either the PARALLEL (VOLUME) or SERIES (PRESSURE) position for this portion of the test. It is usually best to see the pump certification information to see which position the transfer valve was in during certification testing and use that position at this time.

Step 16: Increase the net pump discharge pressure to 250 psi (1 750 kPa). At this point, the pump should be delivering at least 50 percent of its rated volume capacity.

NOTE: Two-stage pump transfer valves must be in the SERIES (PRESSURE) position for this portion of the test. The pump should be allowed to run at this setting for 10 minutes.

Step 17: The pressure control device shall be tested at 50 percent of rated capacity at 250 psi (1 750 kPa) net pump pressure.

    a. The pressure control device shall be set in accordance with the manufacturer's instructions to maintain the discharge at 250 psi (1 750 kPa) net pump pressure.

    b. All discharge valves shall be closed no faster than in 3 seconds and no slower than in 10 seconds

Step 18: Record any defects in engine or pump performance on the appropriate departmental form.

Step 19: Correct minor defects immediately, if possible.

Testing the Discharge Gauges

Step 1: Cap each discharge on the apparatus by disconnecting the preconnected hoselines and screwing caps or closed nozzles onto the discharges.

Step 2: Open each discharge valve slightly.

Step 3: Increase the throttle speed until:
- a. The test pressure discharge gauge reads 150 psi (1 050 kPa).
- b. Master pressure gauge reads 150 psi (1 050 kPa).
- c. Each line discharge pressure gauge reads 150 psi (1 050 kPa).

Step 4: Increase the throttle speed until:
- a. The test pressure discharge gauge reads 200 psi (1 400 kPa).
- b. Master pressure gauge reads 200 psi (1 400 kPa).
- c. Each line discharge pressure gauge reads 200 psi (1 400 kPa).

Step 5: Increase the throttle speed until:
- a. The test pressure discharge gauge reads 250 psi (1 750 kPa).
- b. Master pressure gauge reads 250 psi (1 750 kPa).
- c. Each line discharge pressure gauge reads 250 psi (1 750 kPa).

Step 6: If the master pressure gauge or any discharge pressure gauge is off more than 10 psi (70 kPa) from the test gauge, you should recalibrate, repair, or replace the faulty gauge.

Testing the Flowmeter

Step 7: Connect a hoseline equipped with a solid stream nozzle to each discharge to be tested.

NOTE: Refer to Tables 15.1 a and 15.1 b to determine appropriate hose and nozzle arrangements.

Step 8: Engage the pump and flow water out the discharge being tested.

Step 9: Measure the water flowing out of the solid stream nozzle using a pitot tube and gauge.

Step 10: Compare the pitot tube gauge reading with the discharge's flowmeter.

Step 11: Document all readings. If readings are off by more than 10 percent, the flowmeter must be repaired or replaced.

Step 1: Make sure that the water tank is filled until it is overflowing.

Step 2: Close the tank fill line, bypass cooling line, and all pump intakes.

Step 3: Attach sufficient hoselines and nozzles to flow the desired discharge rate.

Step 4: With the pump in gear, open the discharge(s) to which the hose(s) is (are) attached, and begin flowing water.

Step 5: Increase the engine throttle until flow rate is obtained per manufacturer's recommendations.

Step 6: Close the discharge valve, without changing the throttle setting, and refill the tank. The bypass valve may be temporarily opened during this operation to prevent pump overheating.

Step 7: Reopen the discharge valve, and check the flow through the nozzle using a pitot tube or flowmeter. Adjust the engine throttle if the pressure needs to be brought back to the amount determined in Step 5.

Step 9: Compare the flow rate being measured to the NFPA® minimum or the manufacturer's designed rate.

NOTE: If the flow rate is less than this, a problem exists in the tank-to-pump line. Remember that the minimum flow rate should be continuously discharged until at least 80 percent of the capacity of the tank has been emptied.

Step 8: Using a stopwatch, time the maximum constant discharge flow until the discharge pressure gauge starts decreasing.

Fire Service Knowledge and Skills for Driver/Operators

Chapter Contents

chapter Addendum

Key Terms

Fire Service Knowledge and Skills for Driver/Operators

NFPA® Job Performance Requirements

This chapter provides information that addresses the following job performance requirements of NFPA® 1002, *Standard for Fire Apparatus Driver/Operator Professional Qualifications*, 2017 Edition.

5.1.1	**5.2.2**
5.2.1	**5.2.3**

Learning Objectives

After reading this chapter, students will be able to:

1. Explain the mission of the fire service. [5.1.1]

2. Describe how fire departments are organized. [5.1.1]

3. Describe fire department SOPs, rules, and regulations that affect a driver/operator. [5.1.1]

4. Explain ways that fire departments may interact with other organizations and agencies. [5.1.1]

5. Explain the roles and duties of a driver/operator. [5.1.1]

6. Describe fire and life safety initiatives aimed at reducing firefighter illnesses, injuries and fatalities. [5.1.1]

7. Describe the aspects of NFPA® 1500 related to firefighter safety and health. [5.1.1]

8. Describe fire department programs intended to reduce firefighter illnesses, injuries, and fatalities. [5.1.1]

9. Describe the various types and uses of personal protective equipment worn by firefighters. [5.2.1]

10. Describe the inspection, cleaning, and maintenance of PPE. [5.1.1]

11. Summarize general guidelines for operating safely at structural fire scenes. [5.2.1, 5.2.2]

12. Summarize safe practices for riding in fire service vehicles and apparatus. [5.2.1]

13. Summarize general guidelines for operating safely at highway/roadway incidents. [5.2.2]

14. Describe methods of supplying water for fire fighting operations. [5.2.3]

15. Skill Sheet A-1: Don structural personal protective equipment. [5.2.1, 5.2.2]

16. Skill Sheet A-2: Doff personal protective equipment. [5.2.1, 5.2.2]

17. Skill Sheet A-3: Mount and dismount an apparatus for incident response. [5.2.2]

18. Skill Sheet A-4: Demonstrate scene management at a roadway incident using traffic and scene safety control devices. [5.2.1, 5.2.2]

19. Skill Sheet A-5: Make soft-sleeve and hard-suction hydrant connections. [5.2.3]

20. Skill Sheet A-6: Connect and place a hard-suction hose for drafting from a static water source. [5.2.3]

21. Skill Sheet A-7: Deploy a portable water tank. [5.2.3]

22. Skill Sheet A-8: Make a hydrant connection from a forward lay. [5.2.3]

23. Skill Sheet A-9: Make a reverse hose lay. [5.2.3]

Chapter Addendum
Firefighter Knowledge and Skills for Driver/Operators

Publisher's Note: This Chapter Addendum is included to meet new job performance requirements in NFPA® 1002, 2017 Edition. The new requirements are intended to train driver/operators in some specific firefighter knowledge and skills. As a result, this chapter and the accompanying skills are written from a firefighter's perspective. The page numbering in this chapter is different than the pagination in the rest of the book. We have made this change to alleviate confusion in companion products — curriculum and exam prep — that reference page numbers. Regular page numbering will resume following this chapter beginning with Appendix A. That appendix, the glossary, and the index have all been updated to reflect the addition of this addendum to this printing of the book.

Case History

On February 20, 2009, a 45-year-old male Oklahoma volunteer firefighter responded to an 800-acre wildland fire. After fighting the fire for approximately 10 hours, he collapsed while assisting with "mop-up" duties. His colleagues administered immediate medical assistance, but he was unresponsive and not breathing. Soon afterwards his pulse stopped, and cardiopulmonary resuscitation (CPR) was ineffective. A shock from an automated external defibrillator (AED) restored his pulse, but he died en route to the hospital.

After performing an autopsy, the medical examiner determined that death had been caused by severe underlying heart disease. National Institute for Occupational Safety and Health (NIOSH) investigators concluded that the physical stress of performing fire extinguishing activities, when coupled with the underlying heart disease, had probably triggered a fatal heart attack.

The NIOSH line-of-duty death (LODD) report recommended that fire departments take the following actions (NIOSH, 2009):

- Provide preplacement and annual medical evaluations, consistent with National Fire Protection Association® (NFPA®) 1582, *Standard on Comprehensive Occupational Medical Program for Fire Departments*.

- Incorporate exercise stress tests, following standard medical guidelines, into fire department medical evaluation programs.

- Phase in a comprehensive wellness and fitness program for firefighters, consistent with NFPA® 1583, *Standard on Health-Related Fitness Programs for Fire Department Members*.

- Perform annual physical fitness evaluations consistent with NFPA® 1500, *Standard on Fire Department Occupational Safety and Health Program*.

- Require firefighters to receive medical clearance to wear self-contained breathing apparatus (SCBA) as part of the fire department's medical evaluation program.

This chapter addresses:

- Fire service mission and organization
- Fire department regulations
- Departmental interaction with other agencies
- Roles and skills of the driver/operator
- Reduction of firefighter injuries and fatalities
- Firefighter safety, health, and wellness
- Operational safety and scene management

Embracing Cultural Change

The fire service has a rich cultural history full of traditions, techniques, and best practices that you will learn about during your career. Being included in that fire service history should be a point of pride for any firefighter.

As with any culture, over time the fire service culture has continuously changed due to new information, technology, and shared knowledge and experience. Sometimes that change was slow and met with a great deal of resistance from fire service personnel. However, without changes to cultural norms, fireground strategies and tactics, firefighter skills, and traditional ways of thinking, the fire service would be less diverse, less efficient, and less safety conscious than it is today. Part of fire service culture should be embracing and acknowledging the need to change the culture for the better. As you begin your training to become a new member of the fire service, recognize that you can be part of those positive changes that will improve the fire service in the future.

Fire Service Mission and Organization

To perform as a firefighter and driver/operator, you must understand the fire service mission and how the fire and emergency services are organized. The following sections will address the fire service:

- Mission
- Organization
- Specializations

Fire Service Mission

The authority having jurisdiction (AHJ) usually mandates the fire service mission. The AHJ determines what services are needed to protect its citizens and establishes the fire service to meet that need. Different communities require different types of services; therefore, the mission of each fire department will vary among different cities, states/provinces, and regions.

The fire service's mission is to save lives and to protect property and the environment from fires and other hazardous situations. Many modern fire departments take an **all-hazard concept** approach and provide such services as **(Figure A.1)**:

All-Hazard Concept — A coordinated approach to a wide variety of incidents; all responders use a similar, coordinated approach with a common set of authorities, protections, and resources.

Figure A.1 Modern fire and emergency services organizations provide a wide variety of services. *Structural fire suppression photo courtesy of Bob Esposito.*

- Community risk reduction (fire prevention and public education)
- Fire suppression
- Fire cause determination
- Emergency medical services (EMS)
- Technical rescue services
- Hazardous materials mitigation
- Airport and/or seaport protection
- Emergency management services

Your local department's mission will depend on the legal mandate that established it and your community's needs. Your role will be to fulfill the stated goals and objectives of your department's mission statement, which are part of the department's rules and regulations. These goals and objectives should be posted in every department facility and made available to all department personnel and to the community you protect.

Fire Service Organization

The AHJ is responsible for establishing the manner in which its fire service is organized to include the following:

- Type of department
- Number of facilities and their locations
- Types and number of apparatus

- Number of personnel
- Organizational hierarchy
- Functions and responsibilities for specific jobs and ranks
- Minimum training and certification level requirements to attain those ranks

Fire departments are organized to meet their mission(s). To understand the organizational layout of your department, you need to know the following:

- Organizational structure and principles
- Types of fire departments
- Fire companies
- Staffing

Organizational Structure and Principles

An organization's structure and principles establish the foundation for how the organization will function and operate to achieve its mission(s). The most common fire department organizational structure is scalar, defined as having an uninterrupted series of steps. Decisions and information are directed from the top (fire chief) of the organizational structure down through intermediate levels to the base of the structure **(Figure A.2)**. The levels in between are composed of personnel assigned by rank and duty. Feedback and information, in turn, are transmitted up from the bottom through the structure to the top positions. When a person is promoted, his or her level of authority and responsibility will increase.

To function effectively as a member of your organization, you must operate according to the following organizational principles:

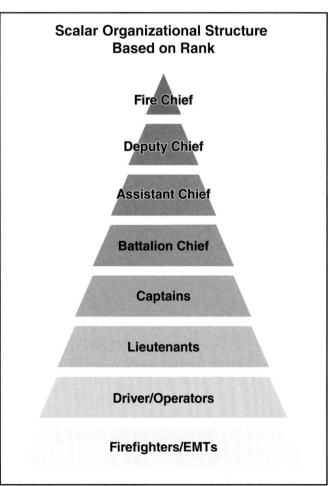

Scalar Organizational Structure Based on Rank

Fire Chief

Deputy Chief

Assistant Chief

Battalion Chief

Captains

Lieutenants

Driver/Operators

Firefighters/EMTs

Figure A.2 An example of a scalar organizational structure showing where fire department personnel fit within the organization.

- **Chain of command** — The chain of command is the formal line of authority, responsibility, and communication within an organization. The chain of command can be shown on an organizational chart with the fire chief at the top and the firefighters at the bottom. Adhering to the chain of command helps ensure unity of command within an organization **(Figure A.3)**.

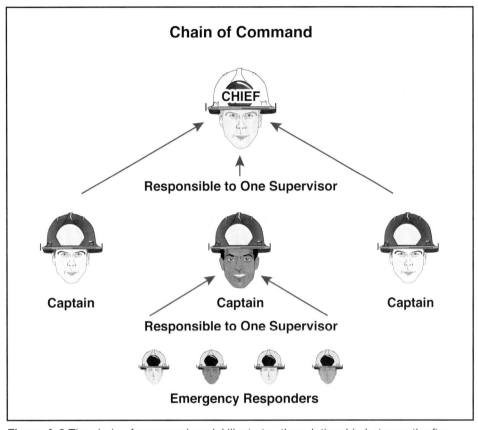

Figure A.3 The chain of command model illustrates the relationship between the fire chief and other personnel at other levels within the department.

- **Unity of command** — Each employee reports directly to just one supervisor. Moving up the chain of command, all personnel ultimately report to the fire chief.

- **Span of control** —The maximum number of subordinates or functions that any one supervisor can control. This number is typically three to seven, with five considered optimum **(Figure A.4)**.

- **Discipline** — Discipline refers to an organization's responsibility to provide leadership, and an individual's responsibility to follow orders. Discipline is administered through rules, regulations, and policies that define acceptable performance and expected outcomes. It can only be properly enforced if rules are clearly written and communicated throughout the organization.

- **Division of labor** — Division of labor is the process of dividing large jobs into smaller jobs to make them more manageable, to equalize workloads,

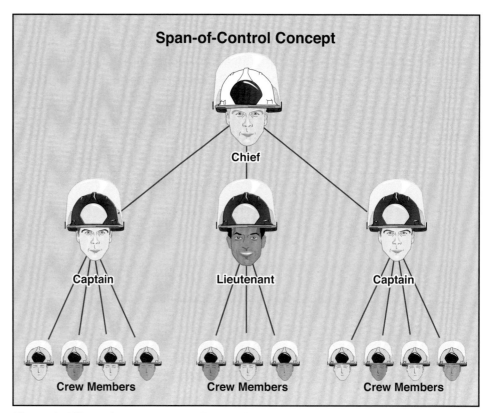

Figure A.4 Illustrating the concept of span of control used to effectively supervise personnel or functions.

and to increase efficiency. Division of labor is necessary in the fire service for the following reasons:

— To assign responsibility

— To assign specific and clear-cut tasks

— To prevent duplication of effort

Types of Fire Departments

Fire and emergency services organizations can be public or private. Most fire and emergency services organizations in North America are public. They are funded by the community (a municipality, county, district, or other area as defined by the AHJ) through taxes (state/provincial and federal), fees, grants, fundraisers, donations, and contracts.

Private organizations raise money through contracts, billing for services, and revenue provided by their parent organization. They may provide services to a single company, facility, or municipality.

Firefighters may work for a variety of different types of departments. These are typically categorized as career, volunteer, or combination departments.

Career departments. Most large cities and some counties maintain the department's facilities and equipment. They employ full-time, career firefighters and other personnel to provide necessary services. Departments that serve military installations and private industrial sites are typically career organizations.

Full-time career departments are continually staffed, meaning there is always someone on duty. Emergency responders must live in the fire station while on duty, while administrative staff typically works conventional hours.

Volunteer departments. A volunteer department may be overseen by the local government, or it may be independent and governed by an elected board of directors. Many of these departments are not continuously staffed with firefighters. Instead, volunteer firefighters respond to emergencies when necessary **(Figure A.5)**.

Some volunteer departments are publicly funded. The town or county provides the facility for the fire station, purchases equipment, and pays for its maintenance. Some volunteer departments rely on other funding sources. They raise money through subscription fees, fund-raising events, and billing customers for emergency response costs such as vehicle response and replacement materials costs.

Figure A.5 Volunteer firefighters preparing to respond to an emergency from their station.

Combination departments. Combination departments are staffed by a mixture of career and volunteer firefighters. In Canada, a combination fire department is called a *composite department*. Federal combination departments may contain both government and civilian personnel.

Fire Companies

The basic unit of fire fighting operations is a **company**, which consists of an apparatus, firefighters, and is led by a company officer. Actual staffing levels are determined by the AHJ. Multiple companies within a response area are grouped into a **battalion** or **response district**, whose day-to-day functions are overseen by the operations division.

There are different types of companies, each organized based on local needs. In large departments, most companies are specialized, such as structural fire fighting, rescue, or EMS companies. In smaller departments, a single company typically performs all of these functions.

The general types of companies and their primary duties include:

- **Engine company** — Performs fire suppression duties at structure, vehicle, wildland, and other types of fires. Additional duties may include search and rescue, extrication, ventilation, and emergency medical care. Assigned to a pumping apparatus.

- **Truck (Ladder) company** — Performs forcible entry, search and rescue, ventilation, salvage, overhaul, and utilities control. Provides access to upper levels of a structure. May also provide elevated water streams, extrication, and emergency medical care.

- **Rescue company** — Searches for and removes victims from areas of danger or entrapment, may be specially trained to perform technical rescues and may serve as the rapid intervention crew/team (RIC/RIT).

Company — Basic fire fighting organizational unit consisting of firefighters and apparatus; headed by a company officer.

Battalion — Fire department organizational subdivision consisting of several fire service companies in a designated geographic area. A battalion is usually the first organizational level above individual companies or stations.

Response District — Geographical area to which a particular apparatus is assigned to be first due on a fire or other emergency incident.

- **Brush company** — Extinguishes ground cover or grass fires and protects structures in areas close to fields and woodlands.
- **Hazardous materials company** — Mitigates hazardous materials incidents.
- **Emergency medical/ambulance company** — Provides emergency medical care to patients and may transport them to a medical facility.
- **Aircraft rescue and fire fighting (ARFF) company** — Performs rescue and fire suppression activities involving aircraft incidents.

Staffing

The different staffing classifications are based on whether or not firefighters are paid and how often they work. Career firefighters are full-time, paid employees of their jurisdiction. They work a required schedule and receive pay and benefits for their work.

Volunteer firefighters may or may not work a set schedule, but they are required to attend regular training sessions and station workdays. They may be full-time but are not considered jurisdictional employees. They may be part-time paid, paid-on-call, fully volunteer, or a combination of these. Part-time and paid-on-call firefighters usually do not live in the fire station. Volunteer firefighters are summoned to the station or emergency scene by telephone, pager, or community signal. They are usually paid an hourly wage or a set fee per response. These forms of compensation may also be used to pay part-time personnel in full-time career organizations.

In some volunteer and most career departments, personnel are divided into two groups: Line and Staff. **Line personnel** deliver emergency services to the public. **Staff personnel** provide administrative and logistical support for line personnel, in areas such as finance, maintenance, and training. In some departments, staff officers deliver services to both internal and external customers such as providing cardiopulmonary resuscitation (CPR) training to firefighters and the public. Both line and staff functions are critical to the successful operation of any organization.

Fire Department Regulations

Written regulations clarify expectations, delegate authority, and assign responsibility based on the organization's structure and mission. Departmental regulations consist of policies and procedures. The department and its employees are also governed by municipal ordinances, state/provincial and federal laws, and the codes and standards adopted by the AHJ.

Departments that have labor/management agreements with a union or bargaining agent will have written contracts that directly affect members. A copy of the contract is usually provided to all members and maintained in every workplace.

It is your responsibility to learn and adhere to your department's regulations. You must be able to locate these documents and find the parts that apply to your duties, authority, and responsibility. To provide access to regulations, organizations do the following:

- Distribute them in written or electronic format.
- Communicate them verbally to all members.
- Post them in a conspicuous place in all facilities.

If you have a question about departmental regulations, it is important to know where to find them. If you do not know, ask your supervisor who may be able to answer your question directly. If not, he or she can probably tell you where to find the documents so that you can look up the answer for yourself. Regulations are always filed in the administrative office, and each station, facility, or division office typically keeps a copy. New policies or amendments should also be posted on bulletin boards. Once you have located the documents, you will have to know where to look for the information you seek.

Policies

A **policy** is a guide to decision-making within an organization. Policies are determined by top management, and then distributed to lower ranks to be implemented. Policies set boundaries and establish standards of conduct that an organization expects from its members. They address issues such as working hours, emergency response guidelines, and chain of command.

Policies may be created in response to government mandates, such as certification training or changes to operational needs. Most policies involve written criteria, but some remain unwritten and are known as *organizational norms* or *past practices.* They typically result from an organization's traditional approach to routine tasks and are implied rather than formally stated.

Unwritten policies are common when no clear policy exists, or policies are out of date. If either situation occurs, it is important for organizations to create clear written policies. If they do not create written policies, there may be dangerous consequences that result in legal liability.

Procedures

Procedures are detailed written plans that list specific steps for approaching a recurring problem or situation. Examples include the steps required to ventilate a roof or handle hazardous materials spills. Most organizations provide personnel with **standard operating procedures (SOPs)** that enable all members to perform specific tasks to the required standard.

Some departments issue standard operating guidelines (SOGs). These are similar to SOPs but may allow firefighters some leeway in particular situations, whereas SOPs are hard and fast rules.

Departmental Interaction with Other Agencies

The fire department is one of many organizations that provides services to the public during emergencies. To work efficiently with members of these organizations, driver/operators need to know the types of services they provide.

Policy — Organizational principle that is developed and adopted as a basis for decision-making.

Procedure — Outline of the steps that must be performed in order to properly follow an organizational policy. Procedures help an organization to ensure that it consistently approaches a task in the correct way, in order to accomplish a specific objective.

Standard Operating Procedure (SOP) — Formal methods or rules to guide the performance of routine functions or emergency operations. Procedures are typically written in a handbook, so that all firefighters can consult and become familiar with them.

Fire departments frequently interact with the following agencies and organizations **(Figure A.6)**:

- **Emergency medical services and local hospitals** — EMS organizations may provide complete medical services, or they may supplement the services provided by the fire department. Local hospitals may provide direct assistance to units at an emergency incident, either by radio communication or by dispatching a medical professional to the scene.

- **Emergency/Disaster management** — These agencies manage emergency and disaster response by coordinating multi-agency activities. The agency may be local, state/provincial, or federal.

- **Law enforcement** — Law enforcement agencies may assist with incident scene security, traffic and crowd control, firefighter protection, fire investigation, and explosives disposal.

- **Utility companies and public works** — Utility personnel assist at incidents by shutting off natural gas lines, electricity, or public water mains. Public works departments typically oversee the construction and maintenance of public roads, buildings, and sewers. Either of these entities may manage the hydrants and hydrant testing in the jurisdiction.

- **Media** — The media can alert the public of traffic incidents, evacuations, and fire department activities. They can also inform the public about fire and life safety topics and initiatives.

Roles and Skills of Driver/ Operators

As part of working with a team of emergency responders, driver/operators will assist other team members in meeting the incident priorities of life safety, incident stabilization, and property conservation. As a driver/operator, you transport other responders to the scene and supply the water firefighters need to protect themselves and possible victims at a scene.

Specific emergency and nonemergency duties of a driver/operator as required in NFPA® 1002 include:

- Inspect, test, and perform some basic maintenance service on department fire apparatus and apparatus aerial devices.

- Drive fire apparatus, transporting all firefighters safely on response in accordance with local traffic laws and safe driving techniques.

- Maneuver apparatus including:
  - Backing the apparatus
  - Negotiating obstacles
  - Positioning at the scene
  - Negotiating areas with restricted clearance

- Operate all the fixed systems on the apparatus including the pump and any equipped aerial devices.

- Supply water for effective hose streams, master streams, and foam streams.

- Supply water to supplement standpipe and automatic sprinkler systems.

Figure A.6 Hospital personnel, emergency management personnel, and the news media are three examples of personnel that firefighters may have to interact with.

Reduction of Firefighter Illnesses, Injuries, and Fatalities

Reduction of firefighter illnesses, injuries, and fatalities is an ongoing challenge within the fire service. Although most people would assume that firefighters die as a direct result of fire fighting, the highest risk factor to firefighters is sudden cardiac arrest as a result of overexertion, poor health habits, or occupational stress. Firefighters and driver/operators are often injured or killed in motor vehicle incidents while responding to and returning from emergencies.

The following organizations publish annual statistics, information, in-

Table A.1
NIMS-ICS Courses

Responder	Level Courses
Entry Level Responders And Disaster Workers	FEMA IS-700: NIMS, An Introduction ICS-100: Introduction to ICS *(or equivalent)*
First Line Supervisors	FEMA IS-700: NIMS, An Introduction ICS-100: Introduction to ICS *(or equivalent)* ICS-200: Basic ICS *(or equivalent)*
Middle Management	FEMA IS-700: NIMS, An Introduction FEMA IS-800: National Response Plan (NRP), An Introduction ICS-100: Introduction to ICS *(or equivalent)* ICS-200: Basic ICS *(or equivalent)* ICS-300: Intermediate ICS *(or equivalent)*
Command and General Staff	FEMA IS-700: NIMS, An Introduction FEMA IS-800: National Response Plan (NRP), A Introduction ICS-100: Introduction to ICS *(or equivalent)* ICS-200: Basic ICS *(or equivalent)* ICS-300: Intermediate ICS *(or equivalent)* ICS-400: Advanced ICS *(or equivalent)*

vestigations, and recommendations about firefighter fatalities and injuries:

- National Fire Protection Association® (NFPA®)
- United States Fire Administration (USFA)
- National Institute for Occupational Safety and Health (NIOSH)
- Occupational Safety and Health Administration (OSHA)
- National Near-Miss Reporting System
- National Institute of Standards and Technology (NIST)

NOTE: Reporting in Canada is performed at the provincial or territorial level. Canada has no national reporting system.

The 16 Firefighter Life Safety Initiatives

The nonprofit National Fallen Firefighters Foundation (NFFF) was created in 1992 by Congress. Its mission is "to honor and remember America's fallen fire heroes, to provide resources to assist their survivors in rebuilding their lives, and work within the Fire Service Community to reduce firefighter deaths and injuries." Annually, the Foundation honors those firefighters who died in the line of duty during the previous year. They also honor the families of those firefighters.

In 2004, the Foundation developed 16 Firefighter Life Safety Initiatives to provide the fire service with a blueprint for making changes. Currently, the Foundation is working to establish training on the Fire and Life Safety Initiatives throughout the fire service in the United States. For more information about the NFFF and its activities, visit their website.

The 16 Firefighter Life Safety Initiatives, also known as *Everyone Goes Home*®, are:

1. Define and advocate the need for a cultural change relating to safety; incorporating leadership, management, supervision, accountability and personal responsibility.

2. Enhance personal and organizational accountability for health and safety.

3. Focus greater attention on the integration of risk management with incident management at all levels, including strategic, tactical, and planning responsibilities.

4. All firefighters must be empowered to stop unsafe practices.

5. Develop and implement national standards for training, qualifications, and certification (including regular recertification) that are equally applicable to all firefighters based on the duties they are expected to perform.

6. Develop and implement national medical and physical fitness standards that are equally applicable to all firefighters, based on the duties they are expected to perform.

7. Create a national research agenda and data collection system that relates to the initiatives.

8. Utilize available technology wherever it can produce higher levels of health and safety.

9. Thoroughly investigate all firefighter fatalities, injuries, and near misses.

10. Grant programs should support the implementation of safe practices and/or mandate safe practices as an eligibility requirement.

11. National standards for emergency response policies and procedures should be developed and championed.

12. National protocols for response to violent incidents should be developed and championed.

13. Firefighters and their families must have access to counseling and psychological support.

14. Public education must receive more resources and be championed as a critical fire and life safety program.

15. Advocacy must be strengthened for the enforcement of codes and the installation of home fire sprinklers.

16. Safety must be a primary consideration in the design of apparatus and equipment.

Safety Stand-Down

The International Association of Fire Chiefs (IAFC) initiated a Fire Fighter Safety Stand-Down in 2005. The purpose of the annual day-long stand-down (usually held on each work shift in the third week in June) is to focus on firefighter safety. All nonemergency work ceases and safety training sessions are held. Topics typically include safety-related procedures, policies, and skills.

Firefighter Safety, Health, and Wellness

Fire fighting is one of the most hazardous professions. Traditionally, firefighters have accepted injuries, illnesses, and fatalities as part of their job. This attitude has been compounded by the stereotypical image of the firefighter as heroic and fearless in the face of danger. However, the fire service **culture** has progressed to a more safety-conscious image. Firefighters now understand that these injuries, illnesses, and fatalities are preventable and can be avoided. Departments should have a health and safety plan, which is intended to create a safe working environment.

Culture — The shared assumptions, beliefs, and values of a group or organization.

Numerous occupational safety standards and regulations address the inherent danger of fire fighting. The most prominent of these come from the NFPA® and the U.S. Occupational Safety and Health Administration (OSHA). NFPA® 1500, *Standard on Fire Department Occupational Safety and Health Program* specifies the minimum requirements for a fire department safety and health program. It may be applied to any fire department or similar organization, public or private.

Because it is a minimum standard, any department or jurisdiction is free to exceed the standard's specified requirements. Many governing bodies in both the U.S. and Canada have chosen to adopt one or more of the NFPA® standards into their laws and ordinances.

Among the topics covered in NFPA® 1500 are the following:

- Safety and health-related policies and procedures
- Training and education
- Fire apparatus, equipment, and driver/operators
- Protective clothing and equipment
- Emergency operations
- Facility safety
- Medical and physical requirements
- Firefighter wellness programs
- Member assistance programs
- Infection and exposure control programs

Safety and Health-Related Policies and Procedures

Safety and health are important aspects of fire service culture. Driver/operators, just like firefighters, must take a proactive approach to safety, health, and fitness. The departmental safety and health program must address all anticipated hazards to which members might be exposed, such as:

- Hazardous materials releases
- Communicable diseases
- Energized electrical equipment
- Driving/riding in apparatus during emergency responses
- Nonemergency issues, such as substance abuse (both on and off duty)
- Other hazards associated with fire fighting

Training and Education

NFPA® 1500 also outlines requirements of a fire department training program in order to prevent occupational illnesses, injuries, and fatalities. Requirements include initial training for new recruits, methods for becoming proficient in firefighter duties, and a process for evaluating firefighter skills and knowledge. Personnel may not be assigned to fire fighting duties until they have completed the required skills evaluation and training. This training must meet the requirements of the NFPA® 1000 series of professional qualification (ProQual) standards. All such training must be thoroughly documented.

Annual proficiency training and evaluations are required to ensure that members maintain their knowledge and skills. Training is also required whenever policies, procedures, or guidelines are updated.

While it is important to train in conditions that are close to actual emergencies, it is unacceptable for training to result in injuries or fatalities. Follow the orders of your superiors and training officers, adhere to safety policies and procedures, and stay aware of your own physical limitations.

Maintaining personnel safety during **training evolutions** includes:

- **Using appropriate protective clothing and equipment (PPE)** — All personnel participating in training should be fully clothed in the appropriate protective gear **(Figure A.7)**. PPE must be used for raising ladders, deploying hose, operating extrication tools, or performing any other activity that simulates actual emergency scene conditions.

- **Maintaining situational awareness** — Maintain your situational awareness at all times during live fire training. Apply your knowledge of fire dynamics, listen to your instructors, and remain with your team or partner. Remain calm and take slow, regular breaths. Breathing rapidly uses up your air supply faster, reducing the time you have to work in a hazardous atmosphere. Be aware of your physical condition. Tell your supervisor if you feel that you are getting stressed or overheated. Take advantage of the rehabilitation breaks that are provided and stay hydrated by drinking fluids.

Training Evolution — Operation of fire and emergency services training covering one or several aspects of fire fighting.

Figure A.7 Firefighters wearing full personal protective equipment (PPE) and self-contained breathing apparatus (SCBA) during a live-fire training exercise.

- **Being healthy and in good physical condition** — Training safety is also influenced by your physical condition. Physical discomfort or illness can make you less alert and more prone to injury. If you experience any severe physical discomfort or illness, you should consult a physician for evaluation before participating in training.

- **Adhering to all safety regulations** — Remain focused on the training exercise at all times. Rowdy play or other unprofessional conduct is not allowed. It is distracting and can lead to accidents and injuries. How you train determines how you will perform in the field.

- **Maintaining PPE and training equipment** — Equipment used for training evolutions can wear out faster than equipment used less frequently on emergency calls. Inspect and clean the tools, equipment, and PPE that are assigned to you for training. Clean your PPE thoroughly when it becomes contaminated with smoke or soot **(Figure A.8)**. Disinfect your SCBA facepiece, CPR manikins, and medical equipment after each training session. Items needing to be repaired or replaced must be reported to your supervisor. The way you maintain training equipment will be the way you maintain your equipment on duty.

Figure A.8 Contaminated protective clothing and equipment should be cleaned in an area of the station dedicated to decontamination.

Fire Apparatus, Equipment, and Driver/Operators

NFPA® 1500 establishes safety requirements for all uses of fire department apparatus. Design requirements include restraint devices (seat belts) for all apparatus occupants. Maintenance and inventory records for all equipment must be maintained by the department.

The standard also establishes minimum requirements for driver/operators. It requires that they wear a seat belt, obey all traffic signals and regulations, and be thoroughly trained before operating the apparatus in an emergency.

Protective Clothing and Equipment (PPE)

NFPA® 1500 requires all personnel operating in an **immediately dangerous to life and health (IDLH)** atmosphere or hazardous area to be fully equipped with personal protective clothing and equipment (PPE), including self-contained breathing apparatus (SCBA). Fire departments should provide all members

Immediately Dangerous to Life and Health (IDLH) — Description of any atmosphere that poses an immediate hazard to life or produces immediate irreversible, debilitating effects on health.

with at least one full set of protective clothing (preferably two) and appropriate protective equipment.

Protective equipment can refer to:

- Respiratory protection such as SCBA and supplied-air respirators (SARs)
- Body armor for personnel responding to potentially violent incidents
- Protection against blood and airborne pathogens
- Hearing protection

Protective clothing must comply with the appropriate NFPA® design standard. The edition of the standard it complies with is the edition that was current when the clothing was manufactured.

Importance of Clean PPE

PPE can absorb the carcinogens in smoke and therefore should be cleaned after every exposure to smoke. Whenever possible, firefighters should have two sets of PPE so that a clean ensemble is available while a contaminated one is being cleaned. If you only have one ensemble, wash the gear as soon as possible after each use.

Emergency Operations

NFPA® 1500 requires that emergency operations be managed through an Incident Management System (IMS), also known as an Incident Command System (ICS). The system must include a **risk management plan** and a personnel accountability system.

The standard limits emergency operations to those that can be safely conducted by personnel on scene. Emergency operations must include rapid intervention crews for firefighter rescue, **rehabilitation** (rehab) facilities, and **postincident analysis**.

Facility Safety

All fire service facilities need to reflect the fire service's focus on safety. NFPA® 1500 sets minimum design requirements for fire department facilities such as fire stations, training centers, administration buildings, and maintenance shops **(Figure A.9)**. Among these requirements is that these facilities are designed and constructed in compliance with NFPA® 101, *Life Safety Code®*. Facilities must have a space and means for cleaning, disinfecting, and storing infection control devices. The standard also requires inspection, maintenance, and prompt repairs and prohibits all tobacco use in the facilities.

Risk — Likelihood of suffering harm from a hazard; exposure to a hazard. The potential for failure or loss.

Risk-Management Plan — Written plan that identifies and analyzes the exposure to hazards, selects appropriate risk management techniques to handle exposures, implements those techniques, and monitors the results.

Rehabilitation — Allowing firefighters or rescuers to rest, rehydrate, and recover during an incident; also refers to a station at an incident where personnel can rest, rehydrate, and recover.

Postincident Analysis — Overview and critique of an incident by members of all responding agencies, including dispatchers. Typically takes place within two weeks of the incident. In the training environment it may be used to evaluate student and instructor performance during a training evolution.

Figure A.9 Examples of common fire and emergency services facilities: a fire station, an administration building, an apparatus maintenance facility, and a training center with multiple buildings and training props.

Medical and Physical Requirements

All driver/operators must comply with the medical and physical requirements of the AHJ. Some of the medical and physical requirements of NFPA® 1500 include:

- Medical evaluations to ensure that candidates can perform firefighter duties.

- Development of physical performance standards for hiring emergency responders.

- Availability of a designated physician to advise personnel about health and wellness issues.

- Establishment of job-related physical fitness standards.

- Establishment of a fitness program that allows members to maintain the required level of fitness.

- Annual medical exams to verify continued fitness.

- Documentation of all on-the-job injuries and exposures.

- Operation of an infection control program.

- Medical records for all personnel must be kept in a confidential health database.

- Prohibition of participating in fire department operations when under the influence of alcohol or drugs.

Firefighter Wellness Programs

NFPA® 1500 requires fire service organizations to establish wellness programs and initiatives. These programs are intended to guide firefighters toward a healthy lifestyle and maintain their fitness-for-duty. Wellness programs overall are meant to help reduce firefighter illnesses, injuries, and fatalities by ensuring that firefighters are healthy.

Adopt safe behaviors and a healthy lifestyle. Exercise and a healthy diet help firefighters better withstand stress. In career departments, firefighters are typically required to participate in a physical fitness program. In volunteer departments, firefighters must establish their own regimen to remain fit for duty.

Good nutrition is also important to prevent you from becoming overweight. Being overweight can lead to cardiovascular disease, diabetes, and musculo-skeletal injuries. These conditions affect your overall health and may make you unfit for duty.

To maintain your personal health, follow these general guidelines (**Figure A.10**):

- Stay informed about job-related health issues.
- Wear incident-appropriate PPE.
- Clean all PPE at least twice annually and after every exposure to smoke.
- Follow recommendations for vaccination against hcpatitis B.
- Use precautions to avoid exposure to airborne and bloodborne pathogens.
- Use proper lifting techniques to avoid muscle strains and other related injuries.
- Use lifting tools or get help with lifting heavy objects.
- Clean, disinfect, and properly store tools and equipment used in patient care.
- Maintain a regular exercise program.
- Maintain a diet low in cholesterol, fat, and sodium.
- Reduce heart attack and stroke risk by maintaining blood pressure and cholesterol levels within acceptable limits.
- Reduce cancer risk by eliminating the use of all tobacco products.
- Have regular physicals and medical checkups.

A wellness program should also offer counseling and education for firefighters struggling with health-related problems, such as:

- Nutrition
- Hypertension
- Weight control
- Physical conditioning

Figure A.10 Each firefighter is responsible for remaining healthy and physically fit.

For more information on firefighter fitness and health considerations, refer to NFPA® 1500 and the IFSTA manuals, **Occupational Safety, Health, and Wellness** and the **Essentials of Fire Fighting**. The sections that follow outline some of the health risks associated with fire fighting that should be addressed in wellness programs.

Additional Health and Wellness Resources

The following are additional resources related to firefighter health and wellness:

- USFA Emerging Health and Safety Issues in the Volunteer Fire Service
- USFA Health and Wellness Guide for the Volunteer Fire and Emergency Services
- NVFC Heart-Healthy Firefighter Resource Guide
- IAFF Fit to Survive

Injuries

Physically fit firefighters are more productive and less likely to suffer injuries. Firefighter injuries range from minor strains and sprains, to those requiring hospitalization and lost duty time **(Figure A.11)**. Injuries may occur during training, during all types of operations, and while responding to or returning from incidents.

Firefighter injuries can be prevented by:

- Providing effective training
- Maintaining company discipline and accountability
- Following established safety-related SOPs
- Using personal protective clothing and equipment
- Maintaining high levels of physical fitness
- Following risk management guidelines
- Using rehabilitation facilities at emergency incidents

Acute — Sharp or severe; having a rapid onset and short duration.

Chronic — Long-term and reoccurring.

Illnesses

Acute and **chronic** illnesses are another source of lost duty time. Acute illnesses, such as colds and viruses, last only a few days and result in little lost duty time. Chronic illnesses, such as cancer or diabetes, are long-lasting and can even be fatal. Chronic illnesses could be behavioral or they could

Figure A.11 EMS personnel preparing to provide help to a firefighter who collapsed at an incident and needed to be rescued.

be as a result of exposures to chemicals or products of combustion in your work environment. For example, research is beginning to prove that the products of combustion encountered during fire fighting may result in a greater instance of cancer among firefighters later in life.

Cardiovascular diseases. Cardiovascular disease is the leading cause of firefighter fatalities. Among the work-related causes are:

- Exposure to smoke and chemicals
- Heat stress from fires and high temperatures
- Psychological stress
- Long, irregular work hours

These causes can be mitigated by departmental policies, procedures, and equipment as part of the wellness program. Your responsibility is to adhere to these policies and procedures, wear required PPE, and reduce exposure to **hazards**.

Non-job-related causes of cardiovascular disease include obesity, tobacco use, and lack of physical fitness. These can be controlled by eating a healthy diet and ceasing tobacco use. Physical exercise also helps lower stress and reduces the risk of cardiac arrest and strokes.

Respiratory diseases. Common respiratory diseases include asthma, lung cancer, and **chronic obstructive pulmonary disease (COPD)**. Respiratory diseases are typically caused by cigarette smoking, but firefighters are also exposed to smoke, gases, and chemicals (such as carbon monoxide and phosgene). Wearing proper respiratory protective equipment can help you avoid these deadly hazards.

Hazard — Condition, substance, or device that can directly cause injury or loss; the source of a risk.

Chronic Obstructive Pulmonary Disease (COPD) — Term for several diseases that result in obstructive problems in the airways.

Chemicals Found in Smoke that Contribute to COPD

The following chemicals found in smoke contribute to COPD:

- Carbon monoxide
- Sulfur dioxide
- Hydrogen chloride
- Phosgene
- Nitrogen oxides
- Aldehydes
- Particulates

Always follow departmental regulations for wearing respiratory protective equipment. Always wear protective equipment in situations that are IDLH. Choose the appropriate level of protection during medical emergencies or when working around paints, thinners, cleaners, dust, or particulates.

Smoking or being exposed regularly to secondhand smoke will deteriorate your respiratory efficiency and could lead to respiratory disease over time. A healthy lifestyle, including not smoking, helps ensure that you have the lung capacity to perform your duties.

Carcinogen — Cancer-producing substance.

Cancer. Fire research continues to demonstrate that numerous **carcinogens** are present in almost all types of fires. Today's firefighters encounter fires with toxic gases, vapors, and particulate matter in smoke that contaminate protective gear and increase the risk of dermal contamination and the severity of inhalation injury. Because of larger amounts of manufactured products are found in modern residential, commercial, automobile, and manufacturing fires, the amount and variety of contaminants at fires is much greater than in traditional construction. These manufactured products also tend to burn at higher temperatures. As temperatures increase so does the skin's ability to absorb chemicals deposited on it. Increased rates of absorption combined with increased amounts of toxic chemicals mean firefighters are more likely to be contaminated.

In fact, absorption rates increase 400 percent for every 5 degree rise in temperature ("Taking ..." 2013). Areas with high absorption rates include the groin (highest), jaw, forehead, and back. Absorption rates also increase on the arms, hands, and ankles to a lesser extent. As a result, firefighters are at greater risk of contracting four types of cancer ("Taking ..." 2013): testicular cancer, prostate cancer, non-Hodgkin's lymphoma, and multiple myeloma, a cancer of the bone marrow **(Figure A.12)**. Exposure to carcinogens that are present in all fires and in the exhaust fumes of apparatus are the main causes of these cancers.

The wellness program should outline ways to mitigate the risk of cancer. An ongoing cooperative study between the University of Illinois Fire Service Institute (IFSI), the UL Firefighter Safety Research Institute (FSRI) and the National Institute for Occupational Safety and Health (NIOSH) is researching the cardiovascular and chemical exposure risks in modern fire fighting. The interim report (Horn, et al, 2016) identified several immediate recommendations for preventing or limiting chemical exposures at fires.

- Always wear SCBA when working in or around fire damaged structures.

- Remain upwind of fires and smoke plumes. Wear SCBA if in the smoke plume or around diesel exhaust.

- Doff contaminated gear before entering the rehab area.

- Do not wear or store contaminated turnouts inside the apparatus cab, in personal vehicle compartments, or in station or home living areas.

- Decontaminate and/or launder turnouts, fire hood, and other equipment that readily contacts the skin after each fire response.

- Wash hands and neck skin immediately after the fire and shower as soon as possible.

Obesity

Wellness programs, in part, are intended to help combat obesity by encouraging a healthy diet and mandating regular exercise to pass fit-for-duty evaluations. Obesity puts additional strain on the body and makes it harder to perform fire fighting duties. Being overweight or obese puts a person at a higher risk of:

- Type 2 diabetes
- Coronary heart disease
- Stroke

- Hypertension
- Some forms of cancer (breast, colorectal, endometrial, and kidney)

Infection and Exposure Control Programs

NFPA® 1500 also requires infection and exposure control programs to be in place. Exposures to infectious diseases, chemicals, the products of combustion, or engine exhaust (among other occupational and environmental exposures) can have short-term (acute) and long-term (chronic) health consequences for firefighters. The intention of exposure control programs is to limit exposures, to document any exposures that do occur, and to provide access to the correct treatment options for firefighters who are exposed to illnesses or chemicals.

Exposures to chemicals and the products of combustion are linked to increased occurrences of illnesses and diseases. Firefighters should take every precaution to reduce exposures, maintain heightened health, and utilize all safety equipment available for the task at hand.

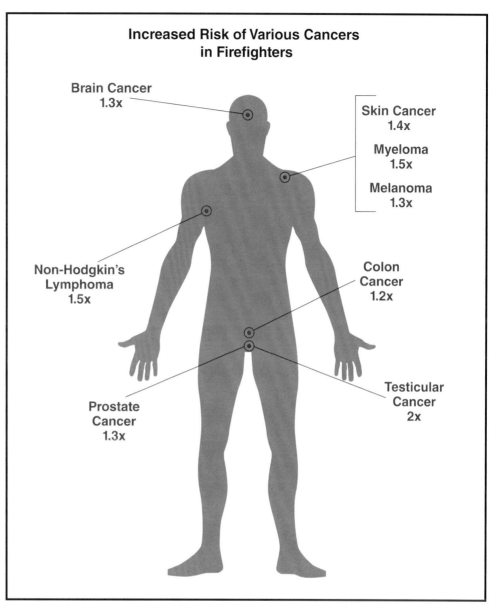

Increased Risk of Various Cancers in Firefighters

Brain Cancer 1.3x

Skin Cancer 1.4x

Myeloma 1.5x

Melanoma 1.3x

Non-Hodgkin's Lymphoma 1.5x

Colon Cancer 1.2x

Prostate Cancer 1.3x

Testicular Cancer 2x

Figure A.12 Common cancer risks for fire service personnel. The same studies show an increased risk for Leukemia and breast cancer, but studies are ongoing to determine the rate of risk more conclusively.

Treating medical patients can expose you to AIDS, hepatitis, tuberculosis, MRSA, C-diff and many other communicable diseases. To protect yourself, limit unnecessary physical contact, maintain the recommended separation distance, always wear appropriate protective clothing and equipment, and use **body substance isolation (BSI)** methods to treat all patients **(Figure A.13)**. Departments may also provide vaccinations against some diseases, such as hepatitis.

Member Assistance Programs

A member assistance program (MAP) provides services to both firefighters and their families. Chapter 11 of NFPA® 1500 includes MAP as part of the overall Behavioral Health and Wellness Programs required. A MAP offers eas-

Body Substance Isolation (BSI) — Comprehensive method of infection control in which every patient is assumed to be infected; personal protective equipment is worn to prevent exposure to bodily fluids and bloodborne and airborne pathogens.

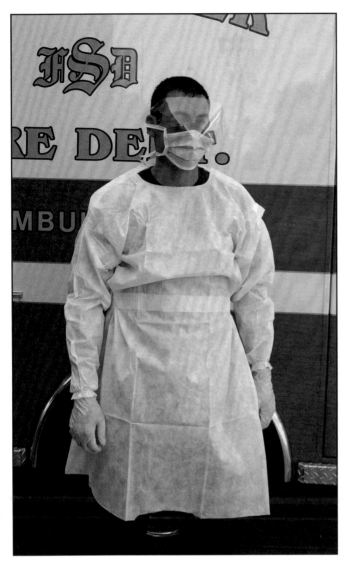

Figure A.13 A firefighter/emergency medical technician wearing body substance isolation (BSI) garments to limit exposure to communicable diseases.

ily accessible, confidential assistance with personal problems that can affect job performance. It provides education, counseling, and referrals to professional services for concerns such as:

- Substance abuse
- Tobacco use
- Personal problems
- Stress
- Depression
- Anxiety
- Marital problems
- Financial problems

Firefighters should know what services their MAP provides. Personal issues such as depression and anxiety, marital problems, or financial problems should not go unattended. Utilizing MAP services can help firefighters maintain a healthy lifestyle and remain fit-for-duty. The sections that follow highlight some of the common features of MAP services.

Substance Abuse

Drugs and alcohol impair your ability to function and slow your reaction time. Most departments prohibit firefighters from responding to an emergency if they have consumed alcohol beforehand, or if they are taking prescription drugs that cause impairment. Some departments also prohibit candidates from using alcohol.

You are responsible for controlling your use of drugs and alcohol when you are on-call or prior to reporting for duty. You must not respond to a call or report to the station if you are under the influence of drugs and/or alcohol or are taking medication that causes impairment.

CAUTION

Consuming drugs and alcohol can slow reaction times and impair judgment. These substances and fire fighting do NOT mix.

Tobacco Use/Dependence

Tobacco use can cause cancer, heart disease, and COPD, and make other chronic diseases last longer. Many departments prohibit tobacco use (smoking/chewing/dipping) within all facilities. They may further require that probationary firefighters not use tobacco and offer tobacco cessation programs for members who do use it. If you do not use tobacco, do not start. If you do, take advantage of one of the many programs available for help in stopping its use.

Occupational Stress

Occupational stress is a contributing factor to stress-induced hypertension, one type of cardiovascular disease. The damage occupational stress does to your body accumulates over time and can take years to develop **(Table A.2)**. Controlling stress can be difficult. Staying in good physical condition, having a positive mental attitude, and relaxing whenever possible can mitigate the effects of stress. A personal stress management program can help. A sample program is provided in the following information box. If your personal stress management program is not working, the organization's MAP should be able to assist you with stress management.

Table A.2
Warning Signs and Symptoms of Stress

Cognitive Symptoms
- Memory problems
- Inability to concentrate
- Poor judgment
- Dwelling on the negative
- Anxious thoughts
- Constant worrying

Physical Symptoms
- Diarrhea or constipation
- Nausea, dizziness
- Loss of sex drive
- Frequent colds
- Pain in the chest, shoulders, neck, or low back
- Stomach/abdominal pain
- Muscle tension, spasms, or nervous tics
- Unexplained rashes or skin irritations
- Sweaty palms
- Sweating when not physically active
- 'Butterflies' in stomach
- Indigestion
- Inability to sleep or excessive sleep
- Shortness of breath
- Holding breath
- Loss of energy

Emotional Symptoms
- Moodiness
- Irritability or short temper
- Agitation, inability to relax
- Feeling overwhelmed
- Feeling lonely and isolated
- Depression or general unhappiness

Behavioral Symptoms
- Eating more when you are not hungry
- Sleeping too much or too little
- Isolating yourself from others
- Procrastinating or neglecting responsibilities
- Using alcohol, cigarettes, or drugs to relax
- Nervous habits (nail biting, pacing)
- Feeling frustrated at having to wait for something
- Feeling restless
- Being easily confused
- Negative self-talk
- Feeling you can't cope
- Difficulty making decisions
- Having emotional outbursts
- Generally feeling upset
- Lack of sense of humor

Personal Stress Management Program

General concepts:

- Be positive and do not dwell on the negative aspects of a situation.
- Be good to yourself and your body.
- Plan enjoyable activities.
- Take regular breaks from stressful activities.

Physical activity:

- Start a physical activity/fitness program. Twenty minutes of aerobic activity three times per week is recommended.
- Exercise with a partner or group.

Nutrition:

- Select healthy foods
- Eat normal-sized portions on a regular schedule.
- Refer to the U.S. Department of Agriculture's MyPlate guide or the Canada Food Guide.

Social support:

- Make an effort to socialize. Being with friends can help you to feel less stressed.
- Be good to yourself and others.

Relaxation:

- Use relaxation techniques, such as yoga, meditation, or listening to music.
- Listen to your body when it tells you to slow down or take a break.
- Get enough sleep. Good sleep habits are one of the best ways to manage stress.
- Take time for personal interests and hobbies.

Atypically Stressful Events

The level of stress firefighters deal with on a regular basis is greater than that of most of the civilian population. Even firefighters can experience events that are more stressful, or atypical, than they routinely encounter. Individuals may be able to cope with some amount of stress on their own but may need professional help in dealing with an atypically stressful event.

Recognizing Posttraumatic Stress Disorder (PTSD)

Personnel should be trained to recognize the signs of PTSD. Potential indicators of PTSD include but are not limited to:

- Substance abuse
- Disconnection with the world around them
- Trouble sleeping
- Irritability
- Lack of concentration
- Hypersensitivity to stimuli
- Disproportionate reactions to everyday events
- Tunnel vision

Historically, the Critical Incident Stress Management (CISM) method of dealing with **atypically stressful events** would be to conduct a Critical Incident Stress Debriefing (CISD) shortly after the event. This debriefing would involve having a counselor come speak with the personnel involved in the event and encourage them as a group to speak about their experiences.

Recent research referenced in NFPA® standards has revealed that CISD is not as effective as once thought and may have actually made situations worse. It is now recommended that officers and supervisors monitor their personnel following an atypically stressful event for signs of **posttraumatic stress disorder (PTSD)**. This would be a sign that an individual(s) is/are experiencing difficulty in resolving the event. The officer or supervisor should then confidentially recommend that the individual(s) receive assistance from licensed/certified specialists. Some personnel may see signs of stress within their coworkers and may report such concerns to the individual or their supervisor. In some instances, an individual may self-report a need for assistance.

Personal Protective Equipment (PPE)

Firefighters should wear **personal protective equipment (PPE)** that is appropriate for the type of incident and activity being performed. Properly wear all PPE with all closures fastened. Procedures for donning PPE are included in **Skill Sheet A-1**. Your helmet's faceshield, if so equipped, can provide a secondary layer of eye protection.

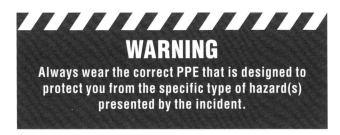

WARNING

Always wear the correct PPE that is designed to protect you from the specific type of hazard(s) presented by the incident.

Atypically Stressful Event — Term used in National Fire Protection Association® (NFPA®) standards to describe incidents that have a likelihood of causing critical incident stress.

Posttraumatic Stress Disorder (PTSD) — Disorder caused when persons have been exposed to a traumatic event in which they have experienced, witnessed, or been confronted with an event or events that involve actual death, threatened death, serious injury, or the threat of physical injury to self or others.

Personal Protective Equipment (PPE) — General term for the equipment worn by fire and emergency services responders; includes helmets, coats, trousers, boots, eye protection, hearing protection, protective gloves, protective hoods, self-contained breathing apparatus (SCBA), personal alert safety system (PASS) devices, and chemical protective clothing. When working with hazardous materials, bands or tape are added around the legs, arms, and waist.

Personal Alert Safety System (PASS) — Electronic lack-of-motion sensor that sounds a loud alarm when a firefighter becomes motionless; can also be manually activated.

Helmet — Headgear worn by firefighters that provides protection from falling objects, side blows, elevated temperatures, and heated water.

Protective Gloves — Protective clothing designed to protect the hands.

Protective Hood — Hood designed to protect the firefighter's ears, neck, and face from heat and debris; typically made of Nomex®, Kevlar®, or PBI®, and available in long or short styles.

Hearing Protection — Device that limits noise-induced hearing loss when firefighters are exposed to extremely loud environments, such as apparatus engine noise, audible warning devices, and the use of power tools and equipment.

Structural Fire Fighting — Activities required for rescue, fire suppression, and property conservation in structures, vehicles, vessels, and similar types of properties.

Structural Fire Fighting Protective Clothing — General term for the equipment worn by fire and emergency services responders; includes helmets, coats, pants, boots, eye protection, gloves, protective hoods, self-contained breathing apparatus (SCBA), and personal alert safety system (PASS) devices.

PPE is designed to protect you from hazards and minimize the risk of injury or fatality. PPE usually consists of the following:

- Respiratory protection equipment
- **Personal alert safety system (PASS)**
- **Helmets**, coats, trousers, boots, **protective gloves**, and **protective hoods**
- Eye protection
- **Hearing protection**

Some emergency situations require full PPE ensembles, including respiratory protection, while others require only protective clothing. Types of PPE include:

- Station and work uniforms
- **Structural fire fighting protective clothing**
- Wildland fire fighting protective clothing
- Roadway operations protective clothing
- Emergency medical protective clothing
- Special protective clothing such as chemical protective clothing

Driver/operators are typically assigned to operate pumpers or aerial devices at incident scenes. They are not usually operating in the hot zone or IDLH atmospheres. For that reason, this section focuses on protective clothing rather than respiratory protection such as SCBA. If your jurisdiction also requires driver/operators to wear SCBA and to be prepared for fireground operations beyond pump and aerial operation, the AHJ should provide additional training. In addition, you can study on your own from IFSTA's **Essentials of Fire Fighting.**

Station and Work Uniforms

Station and work uniforms perform two basic functions. First, they identify the wearer as a member of the organization. Second, they provide a layer of protection against direct flame contact **(Figure A.14)**. Firefighters should not wear clothing made of non-fire-resistant synthetic materials while on duty or under PPE because these materials can melt when heated and stick to skin, causing serious burns. Types of non-fire-resistant synthetic materials include:

- Nylon
- Polyester
- Iron-on patches
- Transfer decals

NOTE: Refer to department policies concerning what can and cannot be worn while on duty or under PPE.

Figure A.14 Examples of various fire service uniforms from a formal dress uniform on the left to station workout attire on the right.

![caution symbol]

⚠ CAUTION

Do not wear clothing made of non-fire-resistant synthetic materials under PPE.

All station and work uniforms should meet NFPA® 1975, *Standard on Emergency Services Work Clothing Elements.* This standard provides the minimum requirements for work wear that is functional, will not contribute to firefighter injury, and will not reduce the effectiveness of outer PPE. Garments addressed in this standard include trousers, shirts, jackets, and coveralls, but not underwear. Underwear made of 100 percent cotton is recommended.

NFPA® 1975 compliant garments have a permanently attached label stating their compliance certification. While this clothing is designed for fire resistance, it is not designed for fire fighting operations. You must always wear structural fire fighting protective clothing over these garments during structural fire fighting activities. Depending on their design and local protocols, you may wear wildland protective clothing over station and work uniforms or directly over undergarments. Some station and work uniforms are dual certified as both work uniforms and wildland protective clothing. Dual certified uniforms will always carry the appropriate certification labels.

Safety shoes or boots are part of the station and work uniform. They are required footwear when working around the station. Safety shoes or boots usually have steel toes, puncture-resistant soles, or special inserts. Do not wear station footwear during emergency operations because they might contaminate living quarters with potentially hazardous substances when you return to the station.

Any emergency response can soil or contaminate uniforms. Therefore, you should not take uniforms home or wash them in personal washing machines or at public laundromats. Contaminated uniforms must be laundered at the fire station or by a contractor.

Figure A.15 A firefighter wearing standard structural fire fighting personal protective clothing on the left and an airport firefighter wearing proximity fire fighting clothing on the right. *Photo courtesy of Brian Canady/DFW Airport Fire Rescue.*

Structural Fire Fighting PPE

All PPE designed for structural and **proximity fire fighting** must meet the requirements of NFPA® 1971, *Standard on Protective Ensembles for Structural Fire Fighting and Proximity Fire Fighting* (**Figure A.15**). This standard addresses the requirements for:

- Helmets
- Coats
- Trousers
- Boots
- Eye protection
- Protective gloves
- Protective hoods

Proximity Fire Fighting — Activities required for rescue, fire suppression, and property conservation at fires that produce high radiant, conductive, or convective heat; includes aircraft, hazardous materials transport, and storage tank fires.

Figure A.16 NFPA 1971 compliance label in a structural fire fighting garment. *Courtesy of Jason Arias, Arlington (TX) Fire Department.*

NFPA® 1971 requires that all components must include a permanent label that shows compliance with the standard **(Figure A.16)**. Labels must include the following information:

- Manufacturer's name, identification, or designation
- Manufacturer's address
- Country of manufacture
- Manufacturer's lot or serial number
- Month and year of manufacture
- Model name, number, or design
- Size or size range
- Principal materials of construction
- Footwear size and width (where applicable)
- Cleaning precautions

PPE components must be compatible with each other to provide the level of protection intended by the NFPA® standard. Each component is designed to protect you from specific hazards and may not protect you from other hazard types. For instance, structural PPE offers no protection against many types of hazardous materials.

Firefighters should never alter their protective clothing. Changing, adding, or removing components may endanger your life, void the manufacturer's warranty, and/or affect your workers' compensation benefits. Alterations include:

- Removing the moisture barrier or liner of coats and trousers
- Sewing hooks, loops, or clasps to the outer shell
- Adding combustible decals to the helmet.

WARNING
Unauthorized alteration of your PPE may expose you to fire scene hazards and endanger your life.

CAUTION
Unauthorized alteration of your PPE may affect the worker's compensation benefits provided to you by your jurisdiction.

Structural fire fighting PPE is designed to cover all portions of your skin when you are reaching, bending, or moving. It is also designed to prevent heat transfer from the fire to your body. During heat exposure the clothing absorbs the heat, which prevents transfer to the skin, but there are limits to how much heat the structural protective clothing can absorb. When the gear reaches its limits, the clothing will become hot enough to cause contact burns when trapped heat permeates the firefighter's underclothing or the firefighter's bare skin touches the material. The usual temperature limit is somewhere above 400° F (200° degrees C). The time until the protective clothing reaches a dangerous absorption limit varies based upon the heat transfer rate. The lower the heat transfer rate, the longer the protective clothing will protect you and stay within tolerable limits.

Since protective clothing absorbs and stores heat, it can take longer than expected to cool. Simply leaving a hot environment for a short period of time may not be long enough to cool the clothing to safe levels for reentry into a fire environment. You may experience contact burns or heat stress even after leaving a heated environment if you do not follow rehab protocols that allow enough time for the clothing to cool.

Protective clothing also prevents heat from being transferred *away* from your body. Usually your body sweats to cool itself, but the protective clothing traps body heat and moisture inside the clothing barriers. This may significantly increase the following conditions **(Figure A.17)**:

- Breathing and heart rate
- Skin temperature
- Core temperature
- Physiological stress

Personal Protective Clothing Can Trap Heat and Humidity

Figure A.17 Protective clothing can trap body heat and moisture inside the clothing adding to the stress of fire fighting operations.

If environmental conditions allow, open your protective clothing to permit air flow around your body during authorized breaks or trips to rehabilitation facilities. This will lessen heat stress and reduce your heart rate.

Helmets

One of the primary concerns for firefighters is head protection. Helmets are manufactured in a wide variety of designs and styles **(Figure A.18)**. They are designed to provide multiple benefits during structural fire fighting operations, including:

- Preventing heated or scalding water and embers from reaching the ears and neck

- Protecting the head from impact injuries caused by objects or falls

- Providing protection from heat and cold

Helmets can also help identify personnel. Shell color indicates the firefighter's rank; markings indicate the unit; and removable identification labels indicate accountability. All of these uses are based on a department's standard operating procedures (SOPs) **(Figure A.19)**.

To ensure proper protection, you must wear your helmet correctly. Place the helmet on your head; secure the chin strap under your chin and tighten

Figure A.18 Examples of three types of fire helmets.

Figure A.19 A firefighter's helmet may show the individual's and fire department's names on the front, the firefighter's rank or unit on the sides, the firefighter's nickname on the back, and may hold accountability tags under the rear edge of the helmet.

it; and fold the ear flaps down to cover your ears and neck. You must fold the ear flaps down even if you are wearing a protective hood. Some helmets have a ratchet at the back of the headband to allow fit adjustment.

Eye Protection

Eye injuries are some of the most common injuries at emergency incidents, but they are not always reported because they are not always debilitating. Although eye injuries can be serious, they are fairly easy to prevent. Eye protection comes in many forms including **(Figure A.20)**:

- SCBA facepieces
- Helmet-mounted faceshields
- Goggles
- Safety glasses

Helmets must come equipped with faceshields or goggles. Keep in mind, however, that faceshields alone do not provide adequate protection from flying particles or splashes and should be used in combination with a primary

Figure A.20 Examples of common types of eye protection that firefighters wear.

SCBA Facepiece

Helmet Faceshield

Safety Goggles

Safety Glasses

form of eye protection. NFPA® 1500 requires that goggles or other appropriate primary eye protection be worn when participating in operations where protection from flying particles or chemical splashes is necessary. During fire fighting operations, your primary eye protection is your SCBA facepiece.

In other situations, you will need eye protection when respiratory protection is not required. Some of these situations include:

● Emergency medical responses where exposure to body fluids is possible

● Vehicle extrication operations

● Industrial occupancy inspections

● Station maintenance

These situations call for safety glasses or goggles, which protect against most eye hazards. Several styles are available, including some that fit over prescription glasses. Prescription safety glasses are another option, although these must have frames and lenses that meet ANSI or CSA standards for safety glasses. In fire department facilities and maintenance areas, you should be aware of warning signs posted near power equipment requiring the use of eye protection. Always follow your department's safety policies and procedures regarding appropriate eye protection.

CAUTION
Metal frames on prescription glasses can transfer heat to the skin even when they are covered by safety glasses.

Protective Hoods

Protective hoods are fire-resistant fabric coverings that protect your ears, neck, and face from exposure to heat, embers, and debris. They cover areas that may not be protected by the SCBA, such as:

- Facepiece
- Helmet
- Ear flaps
- Coat collar

The protective hood's face opening has an elastic edge that fits tightly to the SCBA facepiece, forming a seal. Hoods are available with long or short skirts and are designed to fit inside the protective coat, forming a continuous layer of protection **(Figure A.21)**.

Pull the hood on before the protective coat to help keep the hood's skirt under the coat. To ensure a secure seal between the hood and the SCBA facepiece, secure the facepiece first before pulling up the hood. This way you will not compromise the facepiece-to-face seal.

Figure A.21 A firefighter wearing a protective hood. *Courtesy of Shad Cooper/Sublette County Unified Fire.*

Protective Coats

NFPA® 1971 requires that all structural fire fighting **protective coats** be made of three components **(Figure A.22)**:

- Outer shell
- Moisture barrier
- Thermal barrier

Protective Coat — Coat worn during fire fighting, rescue, and extrication operations.

These barriers absorb heat and trap insulating air that prevents heat transfer from the fire to your body. Removing the liner and wearing only the shell compromises the design of the coat, increasing the likelihood of injuries or death. Protective barriers also provide limited protection from:

- Direct flame contact
- Hot water
- Steam
- Cold temperatures
- Other environmental hazards

Figure A.22 The three component layers of a protective coat include the a) outer shell, b) moisture barrier, and c) thermal barrier.

Protective coats have many design features that provide protection and convenience. Design features required by NFPA® 1971 include **(Figure A.23)**:

Retroreflective Trim — Surfaces such as those used on road signs, emergency vehicle markings, protective clothing, or safety vests which are designed to reflect light along multiple planes at once, giving the surface the appearance of illumination.

- **Retroreflective trim** — Strips of reflective trim on the torso and sleeves that make the coat more visible at night or in low light conditions.

- **Wristlets** — Fabric interface between a sleeve's end and a firefighter's palm that protects the wrist from water, embers, and other debris. Keeps coat sleeves from riding up when reaching.

- **Collar** — Protects the neck from water, embers, and other debris. The collar must be turned up under the helmet ear flap.

- **Closure system** — Snaps, clips, zippers, or Velcro® fasteners that secure the coat's front.

- **Drag Rescue Device (DRD)** — Harness and hand loop at the back of the neck that enables a rescuer to grab and drag a downed firefighter.

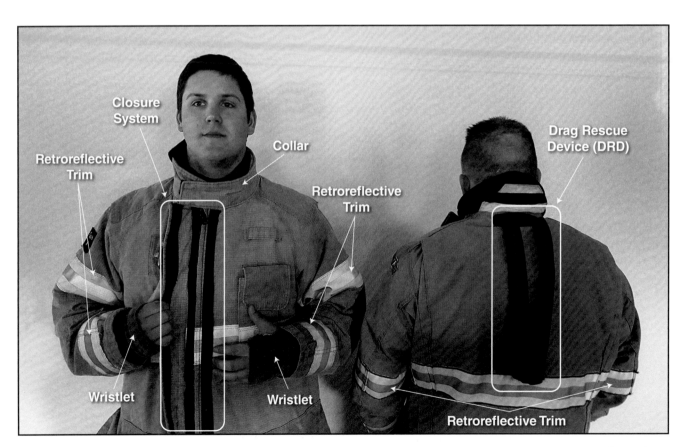

Figure A.23 Common design features of modern fire coats. *Courtesy of Assistant Chief Brandon LeMay and the South Bay Fire Department, Olympia (WA).*

Coats typically contain reinforcement in high compression areas, such as the shoulders, and areas prone to wear, such as the elbows. Optional design features such as cargo, radio, or SCBA facepiece pockets are also common, which must be attached by the manufacturer to meet the NFPA® standard.

Protective Trousers

Protective trousers are constructed from the same fabric, moisture barrier, and thermal layering used in protective coats **(Figure A.24)**. Much like the coats, high compression areas and areas prone to wear contain reinforcement, and cargo or patch pockets may be attached for carrying gloves and small tools. Heavy-duty suspenders hold up the trousers. Closure systems are the same as those found on the protective coat. NFPA® 1971 also requires retroreflective trim on protective trousers.

Protective Gloves

Protective gloves protect hands and wrists from heat, steam, or cold penetration, and resist cuts, punctures, and liquid absorption. Gloves must allow enough dexterity and tactile feel for you to perform your job effectively. For instance, gloves must permit you to grasp tools and nozzles or manipulate small objects such as control knobs on portable radios **(Figure A.25)**. Properly worn, the gloves cover the wristlet of the protective coat to form a complete seal. Gloves worn for structural fire fighting must be NFPA®-compliant for this type of activity.

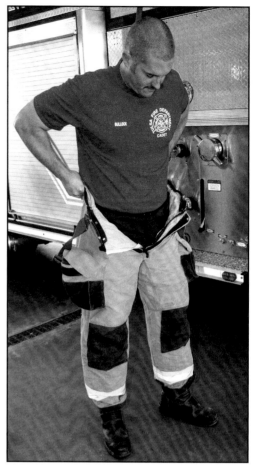

Figure A.24 A firefighter donning protective trousers.

Protective Trousers — Trousers worn to protect the lower torso and legs during emergency operations.

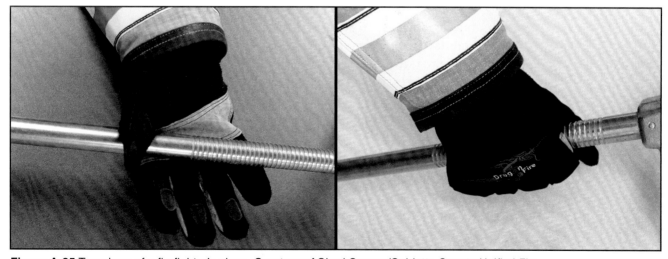

Figure A.25 Two views of a firefighter's glove. *Courtesy of Shad Cooper/Sublette County Unified Fire.*

Protective Footwear

Fire fighting boots are available in a variety of styles and materials and should meet the requirements of NFPA® 1971 **(Figure A.26)**. They protect the foot, ankle, and lower leg from:

- Puncture wounds to the sole caused by nails, broken glass, and other sharp objects

- Crushing wounds to the toes and instep

- Scalding water or contaminated liquids

- Burns from embers and debris

Fire fighting boots have a steel inner sole and a steel or reinforced toe cap and must be high enough to protect the lower leg. The outer shell may be made of rubber, leather, or other water-resistant material. Thermal, physical, and moisture barriers are required inside the shell **(Figure A.27)**. Boot tops fit inside the trouser legs, providing a complete barrier even when you kneel.

Hearing Protection

Firefighters are exposed to a variety of loud noises in the fire station, during training, en route to incidents, and at the emergency scene. Hearing protection devices guard against temporary and permanent hearing loss **(Figure A.28, p.43)**.

NFPA® 1500 requires hearing protection devices. To comply with this standard, departments must protect firefighters from the effects of harmful noise. Eliminating or reducing noise is the best solution, but sometimes this is not possible. In these cases, departments must provide hearing protection devices and establish a hearing conservation plan.

Rubber

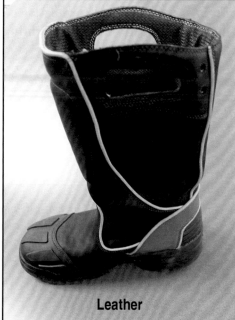

Leather

Figure A.26 Two common types of fire fighting boots. *Courtesy of Shad Cooper/ Sublette County Unified Fire.*

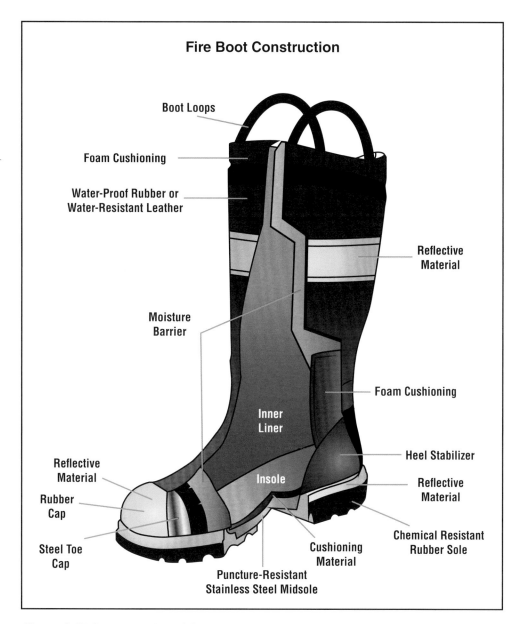

Fire Boot Construction

Boot Loops

Foam Cushioning

Water-Proof Rubber or
Water-Resistant Leather

Reflective
Material

Moisture
Barrier

Foam Cushioning

Inner
Liner

Heel Stabilizer

Reflective
Material

Insole

Reflective
Material

Rubber
Cap

Steel Toe
Cap

Puncture-Resistant
Stainless Steel Midsole

Cushioning
Material

Chemical Resistant
Rubber Sole

Figure A.27 A cutaway view of the components that make up a fire boot.

Firefighters should use hearing protection when riding on an apparatus where the noise exceeds legal noise exposure levels (90 decibels in the U.S., 85 decibels in Canada). Intercom/ear protection systems are most effective for this purpose. They also allow the crew to communicate with each other or monitor radio communications.

Hearing Protection

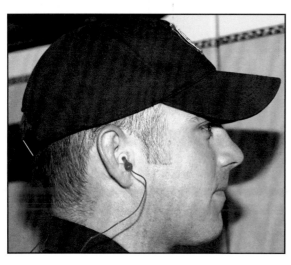

Figure A.28 There are a variety of styles of hearing protection. Regardless of the protection available, wearing hearing protection should be advocated when appropriate. *(Photo upper left) Courtesy of Alan Braun*

You must also wear hearing protection when operating:

- Power tools
- Generators
- Apparatus pumps
- PASS device tests

In some situations, hearing protection is impractical and may even be dangerous. For example, during structural fire fighting, it prevents you from:

- Communicating with other firefighters
- Hearing radio transmissions
- Hearing changes in fire behavior
- Hearing calls from a trapped victim

Roadway Operations Clothing

Emergency operations along roadways are extremely dangerous for firefighters and emergency responders. No amount of PPE can prevent injuries when a person is struck by a rapidly moving vehicle. The best protection is to be visible to motorists and to work behind a barrier formed by your apparatus.

U.S. Department of Transportation (DOT) regulations require all personnel at roadway incidents to wear high-visibility vests. These vests should be at a minimum rated ANSI 107, Class 2 or 3 (ANSI 207 rated vests are also options). These vests must have reflective trim and five-point breakaway fasteners at the shoulders, side, and waist to meet NFPA® safety standards in the U.S. and the CSA Z1006 series of regulations in Canada. Reflective trim on structural PPE does not provide enough visibility to meet these standards. You should wear vests over your PPE if possible, but not while performing fire fighting or hazardous materials activities at the scene. Don the vest only after you have completed these activities or if you have been assigned duties other than fire fighting or hazardous materials control (**Figure A.29**).

Safety Considerations for PPE

PPE is designed to create a protective barrier between you and your work environment. However, this barrier can also isolate you, preventing you from being aware of important environmental changes and making you overconfident of your own safety (**Figure A.30**).

Keep in mind these important safety considerations that relate to your personal protective equipment:

- Always consider the design and purpose of your protective clothing, and be especially aware of each garment's limitations.

- Moisture in the shell and liner material can transfer heat rapidly, resulting in serious steam burns. Always ensure that the garment is dry before wearing it into a fire.

- PPE insulates you from the heat of a fire. This will protect your life, but it will also delay your awareness of temperature increases.

- Never wear protective clothing that does not fit because it will provide reduced protection. Tight clothing will not close

Figure A.29 Firefighters should wear reflective safety vests when working on or near roadways.

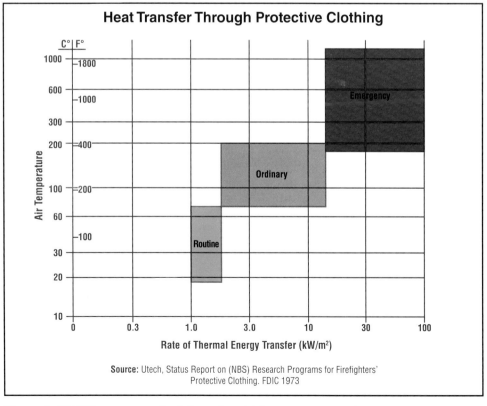

Heat Transfer Through Protective Clothing

Source: Utech, Status Report on (NBS) Research Programs for Firefighters' Protective Clothing. FDIC 1973

Figure A.30 PPE can protect firefighters from high temperature environments.

properly, leaving gaps in the protective materials. Loose clothing can hinder mobility and dexterity by bunching up at shoulders, elbows, and knees. Loose articles can also:

— Snag on debris

— Create a tripping hazard

— Absorb contaminants

— Reduce thermal protection

- Make sure that the overlap between coat and trousers is a minimum of 2 inches (50 mm) at the waist when you bend over at a 90° angle.

- Donning standard protective clothing will significantly impair your balance and gait (manner of walk).

- Thermal burns may occur at compression points where the garment layers are pressed together, such as under the SCBA shoulder harness, along sleeves in contact with hoselines, and on knees when kneeling on hot debris and embers.

- The thermal environment will heat the exterior of the PPE resulting in thermal saturation that can cause contact burns. If you feel contact burns developing, withdraw from the area immediately.

- Prolonged exposure to hot environments will cause your body to sweat in order to cool itself. The protective clothing liner will retain the moisture produced by sweating, which may cause heat stress or burns. When you feel the symptoms of heat exhaustion, including weakness, dizziness, rapid pulse, or headache, move to a cool, safe area. Remove your PPE, and follow established rehabilitation procedures.

- PPE is designed to protect you, but it is not designed to protect against fire conditions such as backdraft, flashover, or other rapid fire development.

- PPE absorbs heat which delays heat transfer to the wearer. This heat can build until the PPE is hotter than the ambient temperature.

- Heating of PPE's Velcro® fasteners can fuse the Velcro® components together. In such cases, the PPE will need to be cut open to remove it from the firefighter **(Figure A.31)**.

- Eventually, the buildup of heat will penetrate through all layers of the PPE and can cause burns and raise the firefighter's temperature.

- RIT and rescue personnel must exercise caution and wear their fire fighting gloves when trying to remove firefighters from super-heated PPE. The heat of the PPE can burn rescuers' hands.

Figure A.31 PPE may need to be cut away from a downed firefighter if the PPE's Velcro fasteners fuse together.

Preparation of PPE for Reuse

Your PPE is your primary barrier protecting you from injury and illness. However, it can also cause injury or illness if it is not properly maintained. Hydrocarbon contamination will reduce the fire resistance of your PPE. Chemicals, oils, and petroleum products in or on the outer shell can ignite when exposed to fire. Some contaminants can reduce the effectiveness of retroreflective trim, and soot can obscure its visibility. Hydrocarbons, body fluids, and toxins that contaminate PPE can be inhaled, ingested, or absorbed, causing serious and sometimes fatal illness. **Skill Sheet A-2** provides procedures for doffing PPE.

You are responsible for the inspection, cleaning, and condition of the PPE assigned to you. You can find procedures for the care of your PPE in your department's SOPs, the manufacturer's instructions, and NFPA® 1851, *Standard on Selection, Care, and Maintenance of Protective Ensembles for Structural Fire Fighting and Proximity Fire Fighting*.

Inspecting PPE for Damage or Contamination

You should frequently inspect your PPE. Inspection periods should occur **(Figure A.32)**:

- At the start of your work shift
- After every use
- After washing, repair, or decontamination
- On a periodic basis, such as weekly or monthly

Conditions that you should look for during a routine inspection include:

- Soiling
- Contamination
- Missing or damaged hardware and closure systems
- Physical damage including rips, tears, fraying hems and cuffs, and damaged stitching on seams

Figure A.32 A firefighter inspecting his PPE at the start of his work shift.

- Wear due to friction under arms, in the crotch, and at knee and elbow joints
- Thermal damage, including charring, melting, discoloration, and burn holes
- Shrinkage
- Damaged or missing retroreflective trim or reinforcing trim
- Loss of reflectivity of shell on proximity equipment
- Cracks, melting, abrasions, or dents in helmet shell
- Missing or damaged faceshield or hardware
- Missing or damaged earflaps or neck shroud
- Loss of watertight integrity in footwear
- Damage to or faulty installation of drag rescue device (DRD)
- Date of manufacture to determine time in service

NOTE: A member of your department who is trained in advanced inspection requirements, such as the department's Health and Safety Officer (HSO), should perform an annual inspection.

CAUTION
Only personnel trained or certified to repair PPE should be allowed to conduct repairs.

Cleaning PPE
The amount and type of contamination and whether or not the equipment must be removed from service determines the type of cleaning.

NFPA® 1851 defines four types of cleaning for PPE:

- Routine
- Advanced
- Specialized
- Contract

Many fire departments provide spare sets of PPE to replace units removed from service for cleaning, decontamination, or repairs. NFPA® standards recommend that each firefighter be issued two sets of structural fire fighting PPE. Having two sets of gear ensures that one set of gear can be laundered immediately following an incident while the spare set can be donned in case there is an incident before the first set is cleaned. Wearing uncontaminated PPE is a preventative measure against the risk of cancer later in life.

Routine cleaning. Routine cleaning does not require that the clothing be removed from service. At an incident scene, the process for routine cleaning includes:

- Brushing off loose debris with a broom or soft bristle brush
- Using a gentle spray of water to rinse off debris and soil

To remove heavy soil, you should perform cleaning manually in a utility sink in the designated cleaning area at the fire station **(Figure A.33)**. Whether you are at the scene or in the station, always follow the manufacturer's recommendations and wear appropriate gloves and eye protection.

Advanced cleaning. Personnel trained in the care and cleaning of protective clothing should perform advanced cleaning. Those personnel should use a washing machine dedicated to cleaning protective clothing that is designed to handle heavy loads **(Figure A.34)**.

Figure A.33 A firefighter cleaning his helmet. *Courtesy of Assistant Chief Brandon LeMay and the South Bay Fire Department, Olympia (WA).*

Figure A.34 PPE should only be cleaned in washing machines designated for that use. *Courtesy of Assistant Chief Brandon LeMay and the South Bay Fire Department, Olympia (WA).*

WARNING
Do not wash contaminated protective clothing in washing machines used for other garments or items, such as your home washing machine or a public laundry. This may expose you, your family, or others to dangerous contaminants.

Specialized cleaning. When clothing is contaminated with hazardous materials or body fluids that cannot be removed by routine or advanced cleaning, trained department member or an outside contractor may perform the cleaning.

Contract cleaning. Contract cleaning typically removes accumulated grime or contaminants. Contractors who perform specialized cleaning may include the manufacturer, the manufacturer's representative, or a certified vendor. Some contractors provide replacement PPE while clothing is being cleaned.

WARNING
Do not take contaminated protective clothing into the living or sleeping quarters of the fire station or your residence.

WARNING
PPE should not be stored where it can come in contact with vehicle exhausts.

CAUTION
PPE that is carried in personal vehicles should be placed in closable garment bags to protect it from sunlight degradation.

Repairing PPE

The manufacturer, an approved repair facility, or a trained department member must remove damaged protective clothing *immediately*. Clothing damaged beyond repair must be removed from service and destroyed. Some damaged clothing may be marked "for training use only" and used in training that does not involve fire.

Operational Safety and Scene Management

While responding to an emergency and operating at an emergency scene, follow safe practices and procedures. The following sections describe:

- Response safety
- Structural fire scene safety
- Highway/roadway incident scene safety

Situational Awareness: Safe Operations

Driver/operators are expected to receive and follow instructions from a supervisor, crew leader, company officer, or incident commander (IC) on the fireground. Even though your primary role is to safely and efficiently perform tasks assigned to you, it is also imperative for you to maintain situational awareness throughout the entire operation. Situational awareness means recognizing and remaining mindful of identified hazards as well as remaining observant about changing conditions on the fireground and evaluating the changes you see against the safety of what you are doing. A large part of situational awareness is communicating what you see to your immediate supervisor, crew leader, company officer, or IC. New information about conditions may lead them to change their orders and strategies during an incident.

Response Safety

Response to an emergency begins the moment you are notified of the emergency. If you are in the fire station, then you must safely reach your apparatus, don the appropriate PPE, mount the apparatus, and fasten your seat belt before your apparatus can respond.

Mounting and Dismounting Apparatus

Mount the apparatus using the available handholds and steps built for that purpose, maintaining three points of contact while mounting or dismounting. Face the apparatus, grip the handholds firmly with both hands then step up into or onto the apparatus. When dismounting, back out of the cab using the handholds and steps. Do not exit an apparatus face first as this presents a serious trip or fall hazard **(Figure A.35)**.

Figure A.35 Firefighters should maintain three points of contact while mounting and dismounting apparatus.

Exiting your vehicle can be particularly hazardous, so always use extreme caution. Whenever possible, both drivers and passengers should mount and dismount on the side of the vehicle that is not exposed to oncoming traffic. If you must dismount on the exposed side, watch for oncoming vehicles before opening your door, and wait for a break in traffic before exiting. **Skill Sheet A-3** describes the procedure for mounting and dismounting apparatus.

Response Hazards for Passengers

There are numerous hazards to firefighters riding in an apparatus. These may include but are not limited to:

- Excessive noise levels that may damage hearing
- Loose equipment that might strike the firefighters
- Danger of falls inside the apparatus if not seated and belted in
- Danger of injury during vehicle accidents

CAUTION
Never stand on or in a moving apparatus.

Safe Practices When Riding Apparatus

Follow your organization's SOPs as well as the requirements listed in NFPA® 1500 for riding in an apparatus. For example, NFPA® 1500 prohibits the wearing of fire fighting helmets inside the cab of fire apparatus stating that "Helmets shall not be worn by persons riding in an enclosed cab." Additional guidelines for safely riding in or on an apparatus include **(Figure A.36)**:

- Always be seated and securely belted in before the apparatus moves.

- Always wear hearing protection or radio headsets.

- Secure all loose tools and equipment.

- Close cab doors securely.

- On unenclosed apparatus, close safety gates or bars securely.

Figure A.36 To be safe while riding inside an apparatus, firefighters should wear seat belts and some type of hearing protection.

Structural Fire Scene Safety

Although responding to any emergency involves risk, you can minimize your exposure to risk by following these operational guidelines:

- Follow your supervisor's orders.

- Follow departmental SOPs.

- Wear appropriate PPE.

- Work as a team.

- Maintain communications with team members and Command.

- Do a risk/benefit analysis for every action.

- Employ safe and effective tactics.

- Never operate alone or without supervision.

- Perform an initial assessment and maintain situational awareness.

Situational awareness is critical at the scene of any incident. Your safety depends on being able to understand what is going on around you and recognize potential threats. All firefighters must train themselves to develop this vital skill.

NOTE: Many of the topics discussed in this section are also vital elements to incident types other than structural emergency scenes, such as a vehicle crash or a wildland fire.

Scene Security

Emergency responders typically secure an incident scene by establishing control zones. The scene is cordoned off by tying rope, fireline, or caution tape to a stationary object. It is not recommended to tie the rope, line, or tape to a vehicle because vehicles often have to be moved as the incident progresses.

Control zones are called by a variety of names depending upon operations within those zones. The most common terms are hot zone, warm zone, and cold zone **(Figure A.37)**.

The hot zone is where trained personnel work to resolve the problem at the scene. Only personnel who are directly involved in mitigating the incident are allowed to enter this zone, which limits crowds and confusion at the most critical area of the scene. Personnel in the hot zone must wear full PPE appropriate for the hazards present.

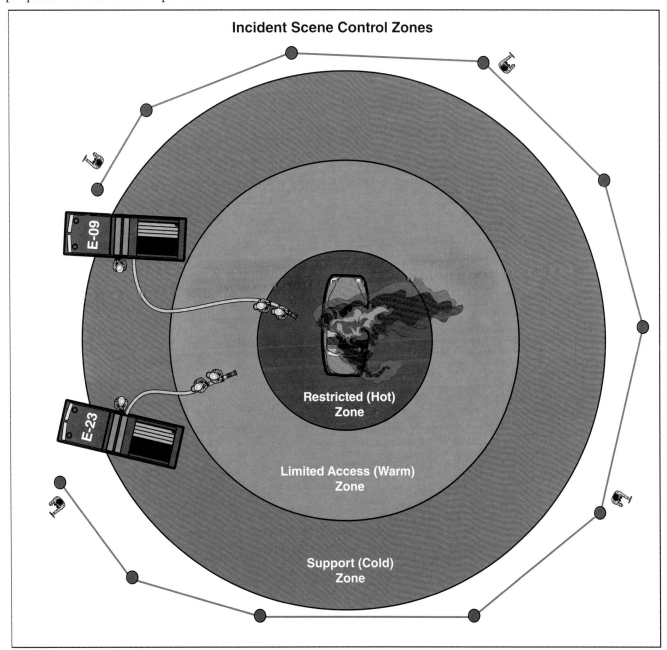

Incident Scene Control Zones

Restricted (Hot)
Zone

Limited Access (Warm)
Zone

Support (Cold)
Zone

Figure A.37 Illustrating the concept of incident scene control zones at a vehicle fire.

The warm zone is immediately outside the hot zone. Personnel in the warm zone directly support personnel working in the hot zone. Driver/operators may work in the warm zone depending upon apparatus placement at the scene. These personnel are also in full protective clothing and equipment and are ready to enter the hot zone if needed.

The cold zone immediately surrounds the hot and warm zones and may include the Incident Command Post (ICP), locations of rapid intervention crews (RICs), the location of the public information officer (PIO), rehabilitation area, and staging areas for personnel and portable equipment. The outer boundary of this area is the control line for the general public (crowd-control line).

Environmental Conditions

The environmental conditions at a structural fire scene can affect your performance. Temperature extremes, heavy rains, winds, and lightning will influence your operations and the duration of your ability to perform your assigned tasks. You must maintain situational awareness of the environmental conditions and the effects they are causing.

Highway/Roadway Incident Scene Safety

At motor vehicle fires and accidents, both firefighters and victims are in danger of being struck by traffic. To ensure your safety, you must be visible, work within a protected area, and exercise situational awareness.

Apparatus lights and scene lighting also contribute to visibility, but they can make the situation more hazardous if they are improperly used. For example, during the early stages of an incident, emergency vehicle warning lights help ensure the safety of responders, victims, and drivers approaching the scene. But these lights do not provide effective traffic control and are often confusing to civilian motorists, especially at night. Some departmental SOPs limit their use and require responders to:

- Turn off all forward facing lights, including headlights.
- Minimize flashing lights on the vehicle's sides and rear.
- Turn off lights that face approaching traffic, to avoid blinding or distracting drivers.
- Turn off all headlights, unless they are being used to illuminate the work area or warn motorists that the vehicle is in an unexpected location.

General guidelines for maintaining situational awareness at a roadway incident are:

- Look before you move.
- Keep an eye on moving traffic.
- Walk facing oncoming traffic.
- Follow departmental SOPs.

Always use extreme caution when exiting your vehicle. If possible, drivers and passengers should mount and dismount on the side of the vehicle opposite oncoming traffic **(Figure A.38)**. If you must dismount on the exposed side, check for oncoming vehicles before opening your door, and wait for a break in traffic before exiting.

Figure A.38 Whenever possible, firefighters should exit their apparatus so that they avoid oncoming traffic.

Scene management during incidents on streets and highways can be critical to preventing firefighter injuries or fatalities. Procedures for scene management at roadway incidents are illustrated in **Skill Sheet A-4**.

Highway/Roadway Incident Hazards

Emergency responders can encounter a number of hazards at highway/roadway incidents related to the vehicle(s) involved and the surrounding area. Common highway/roadway incident hazards include but are not limited to:

- Debris
- Fuel spills
- Hydraulic and battery fluid spills
- Downed high-voltage power lines

Debris. Vehicle crashes can spread debris over a large area around the incident scene. This debris can pose tripping and fall hazards. The edges of some pieces may be sharp and pose a danger to responders who may be cut by these edges. Personnel should exercise caution around debris to avoid trips, falls, or cuts.

Fuel spills. Damaged fuel tanks or lines can lead to fuel spills at a vehicle accident scene. These spills can present a significant fire danger to rescuers and victims alike. Firefighters tasked with standing by with a charged handline should wear full PPE and SCBA.

Hydraulic and battery fluid spills. Spills of hydraulic and battery fluids can also present a hazard to rescuers and patients. These substances can cause toxic reactions, skin irritation, and burns. Firefighters should avoid coming in contact with these materials and cover these spills with approved absorption materials. First aid may be required if someone comes in contact with these materials.

Downed high-voltage power lines. A vehicle striking a power pole can sever a high-voltage line that falls onto the vehicle. The first priority is to contact the electric company to shut off the power. With the power off, the incident becomes a vehicle extrication incident.

WARNING

Do not approach downed power lines until the electric company has shut off the power.

Electrical wires on the ground can be dangerous without even being touched. Downed lines can energize wire fences or other metal objects with which they come in contact. Energized electrical wires in contact with the ground cause current to flow outward in all directions from the point of contact. As the current flows away from the point of contact, the voltage drops progressively. This energized area is called the **ground gradient**. Depending on voltage and other variables, such as ground moisture, it can extend for several yards (meters) from the point of contact. To avoid this hazard, estimate the distance between two nearby power poles, and stay that distance away from the downed line until you are sure the power has been shut off.

Traffic Incident Management

Traffic control zones should be established for any incident on or near a highway/roadway. Personnel should coordinate a traffic management system with local law enforcement to ensure responder and civilian safety. The *Manual on Uniform Traffic Control Devices (MUTCD)* describes the minimum requirements for establishing traffic control zones.

A traffic control zone may have hot, warm, and cold zones within it, depending on the type of hazard present. Traffic control zones should be coordinated with local law enforcement to ensure an appropriate safe working zone while maintaining as much traffic flow as reasonably possible.

Traffic Control Measures and Devices

Use emergency vehicles to form a protective barrier between oncoming traffic and working personnel. The company officer and driver/operator are responsible for positioning the emergency vehicle to form that protective barrier. Signs and traffic cones are also used to detour traffic around the emergency scene as it approaches. Deploy them to close off at least one lane of traffic next to the scene **(Figure A.39)**. Traffic control assistance should also be requested from local law enforcement.

Supplying Water

Water is easily stored and can be transferred over large distances in well-designed distribution systems. Familiarize yourself with the types of water supply distribution systems in your community. This section provides the knowledge and skills needed to connect to water supplies: fire hydrants and mobile water supplies.

Ground Gradient — Electrical field that radiates outward from where the current enters the ground; its intensity dissipates rapidly as distance increases from the point of entry.

Traffic Control Zone — Operational zone established on or near a roadway for the rerouting of traffic and protection of civilians and responders; may include a hot, warm, and cold zone depending on the incident.

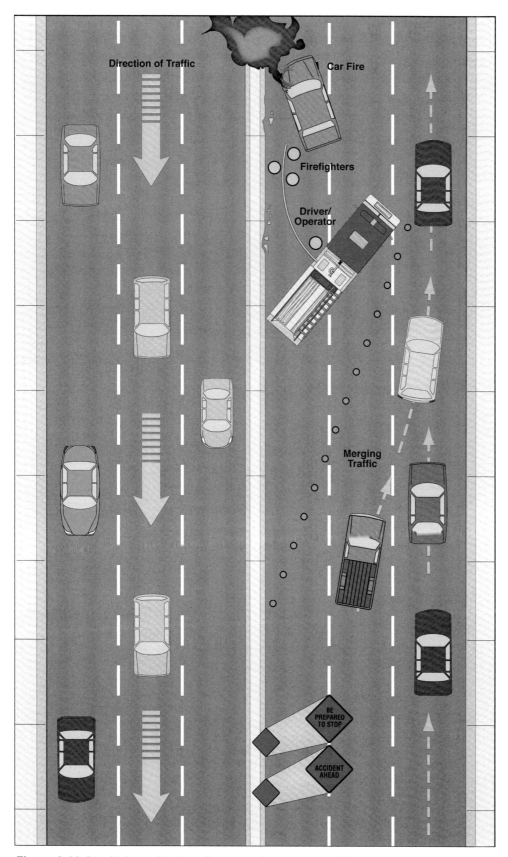

Figure A.39 At vehicle accidents, a fire apparatus can be positioned to serve as a protective barrier between the victims and emergency responders and oncoming traffic.

Fire Hydrants

Although the initial source of water that firefighters may use is the water tank on their pumper, the most dependable sources are fire hydrants near the incident. Fire hydrants can provide a consistent volume of water under constant pressure **(Figure A.40)**. However, hydrants and water supply systems can fail. When hydrants fail to provide sufficient volume or pressure, it is necessary to select an alternative water supply.

Figure A.40 An apparatus connected to a hydrant with a large diameter hose. *Courtesy of Ron Jeffers.*

Failures or reduction in water supply (volume) or pressure from hydrants can result from:

- Damaged hydrant valves and connections
- Broken water mains
- Greater demand than the system can provide
- Hydrants located on dead-end water mains
- Closed isolation valves
- Restricted mains
- Pipes or hydrants that are frozen

Because hydrants are a basic tool used in fire fighting, you must know hydrant types, markings, use, inspections, and maintenance. Firefighters, inspectors, water department personnel, or private contractors may perform hydrant testing.

In general, fire hydrant bonnets, barrels, and foot pieces are made of cast iron. The internal working parts are usually made of bronze; valve facings may be made of rubber, leather, or composite materials. The primary types of fire hydrants used in North America are **dry-barrel** and **wet-barrel**. While they serve the same purpose, their designs and operating principles differ considerably.

Regardless of the location, design, or type, hydrant discharge outlets are considered standard if they contain the following two components:

- At least one large (4 or 4½-inch [100 mm or 115 mm]) outlet often referred to as the **pumper outlet nozzle** or **steamer connection**
- Two hose outlet nozzles for 2½-inch (65 mm) couplings

Dry-Barrel Hydrant — Fire hydrant that has its operating valve at the water main rather than in the barrel of the hydrant. When operating properly, there is no water in the barrel of the hydrant when it is not in use. These hydrants are used in areas where freezing may occur.

Wet-Barrel Hydrant — Fire hydrant that has water all the way up to the discharge outlets; may have separate valves for each discharge or one valve for all the discharges. This type of hydrant is only used in areas where there is no danger of freezing weather conditions.

Pumper Outlet Nozzle — Fire hydrant outlet that is 4 inches (102 mm) in diameter or larger.

Steamer Connection — Large-diameter outlet, usually 4½ inches (115 mm), at a hydrant or at the base of an elevated water storage container.

Hydrant specifications require a 5-inch (125 mm) valve opening for standard three-way hydrants and a 6-inch (150 mm) connection to the water main. The male threads on all hydrant discharge outlets must conform to the female hose couplings that the local fire department uses. NFPA® 1963, *Standard for Fire Hose Connections*, sets regulations for the number of threads per inch and the outside diameter of the male thread.

Dry-Barrel Hydrants

Designed for use in climates with freezing temperatures, the main control valve of the dry-barrel hydrant is located at the base or foot of the hydrant below the frost line, and it has an isolation valve on the distribution line **(Figure A.41)**. The stem nut used to open and close the control valve is on top of the hydrant. Water is only allowed into the hydrant when the stem nut is operated. Any water remaining in a closed dry-barrel hydrant drains through a small drain valve that opens at the bottom of the hydrant when the main valve approaches a closed position. Turning the stem in a counterclockwise direction opens the valve. Turning the stem in a clockwise direction closes the valve.

Wet-Barrel Hydrants

Wet-barrel hydrants have water in the hydrant at all times **(Figure A.42)**. These hydrants are usually installed in climates without prolonged periods of subfreezing weather. Horizontal compression valves are usually located at each outlet, but there may be another control valve in the top of the hydrant to control the water flow to all outlets.

Out-of-Service Hydrants

When a hydrant is taken out-of-service, the water department or fire department should take the following actions:

• Place "out-of-service" tags or devices on the hydrant.

• Notify fire station personnel within the response district the hydrant serves that it is out-of-service and approximately when it will return to service.

• Notify hydrant repair personnel.

If water is seen bubbling up out of the ground at the base of a dry-barrel hydrant when the hydrant is fully open, a broken component in the hydrant barrel is allowing water to get past the drain opening. This hydrant should be reported to the water authority that will mark it out-of-service until it is repaired.

Other reasons for a hydrant to be out-of-service may include:

• Damage to the hydrant, water system piping, or pump that support that location.

• Repairs or upgrades being performed on the water system.

• Obstructions placed within the hydrant.

• A frozen hydrant during extreme cold temperatures.

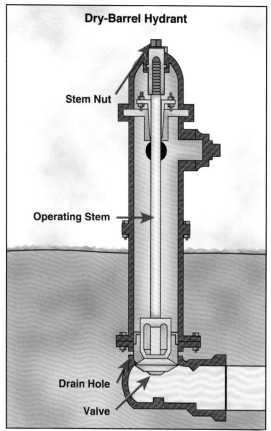

Figure A.41 A cutaway illustration of a dry-barrel hydrant.

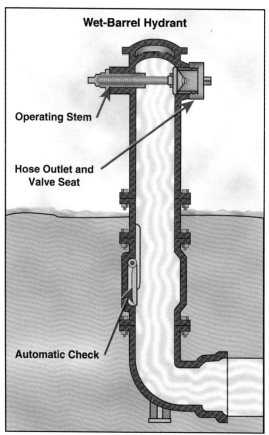

Figure A.42 A cutaway illustration of a wet-barrel hydrant.

Fire Hydrant Connection Tools

Firefighters use a variety of tools when making fire hydrant connections, including **(Figure A.43)**:

- Spanner wrenches
- **Hydrant wrenches**
- Rubber mallets
- Gate valves
- Hydrant valves

Hydrant Wrench — Specially designed tool used to open or close a hydrant and to remove hydrant caps.

Figure A.43 Common tools that firefighters use to make hydrant connections. *Courtesy of Oklahoma City (OK) Fire Department/Lt. Ray Lujan.*

Hydrant wrenches are primarily used to remove discharge caps from fire hydrant outlets and to open fire hydrant valves. The hydrant wrench has a pentagonal opening in its head that fits most standard fire hydrant operating nuts. The lever handle may be threaded into the operating head to make it adjustable, or the head and handle may be the ratchet type. The head may be equipped with a spanner to help make or break coupling connections.

A rubber mallet can be used to tighten or loosen hose couplings. Striking the lugs with a rubber mallet makes it easier for firefighters to achieve an airtight connection.

Gate valves control the flow from a hydrant. Turning a screw-type handle lowers the baffle of the gate valve into the path of the water.

A variety of hydrant valves are available for use in supply-line operations. Use these valves when a forward lay is made from a low-pressure hydrant to the fire scene. A hydrant valve has four main functions:

- Allow additional hoselines to be laid to the hydrant.

- Connect a supply pumper to the hydrant.

- Boost the pressure in the original supply line without interrupting the flow of water in the line.

- Allow the original supply line to be connected to the hydrant and charged before the arrival of another pumper at the hydrant.

Hose Clamps

A hose clamp can be used to stop the flow of water in a hoseline to:

- Prevent charging the hose bed during a forward lay from a hydrant

- Allow replacement of a burst section of hose without stopping the water supply

- Allow extension of a charged hoseline without stopping the water supply

There are four types of hose clamps: screw-down, press-down, hydraulic press, and wildland hose clamps **(Figure A.44)**. Wildland clamps are designed for the small hose diameters used in wildland fire fighting. Applied incorrectly, a hose clamp can injure firefighters and/or damage the hose. Some general rules for hose clamps include:

- Apply the hose clamp at least 20 feet (6 m) behind the apparatus.

- Apply the hose clamp approximately 5 feet (1.5 m) from the coupling on the supply side.

- Center the hose evenly in the jaws to avoid pinching the hose.

- Close and open the hose clamp slowly to avoid water hammer.

- Stand to one side when applying or releasing any type of hose clamp (the operating handle or frame can snap open suddenly).

CAUTION
Never stand over the handle of a hose clamp when applying or releasing it. The handle or frame may pop open and swing violently upward.

Fire Hydrant Connections

According to NFPA® standards, fire hydrants should be operated and inspected at least once a year to verify reliable function and address needed repairs. You must know how to operate fire hydrants in order to:

- Provide water through hoses for fire suppression operations.

- Flow water from hydrant discharge openings to flush sediment.

Figure A.44 Examples of the four types of hose clamps.

- Perform periodic inspections.
- Ensure proper operation of valves and caps.
- Assist in flow tests.

Considerations for wet and dry-barrel hydrants. All hydrants must be opened and closed slowly to prevent damage to fire hose, hydrants, and other equipment, or injury to firefighters **(Figure A.45)**. Opening a hydrant too fast may cause the connected fire hose to flail uncontrollably as water pressure straightens the hose. Closing a hydrant too fast may cause a surge in pressure (water hammer) within the water supply system, which can damage the system piping or appliances attached to the system, such as water heaters in adjacent residences. **Skill Sheet A-5** provides the steps for connecting soft-sleeve suction and hard-suction hoses.

Considerations specific to dry-barrel hydrants. To prevent freezing, the dry-barrel hydrant main valve is located underground below the frost line. Normally, the hydrant barrel from the top of the stem down to the main valve is empty. This prevents water in the barrel from freezing during extended periods of subfreezing temperatures.

When the stem nut is turned counterclockwise, the main valve moves down and allows water to flow into the hydrant. As the main valve moves down, a drain valve plate attached to the stem closes a drain hole located near the bottom of the hydrant, but allows water to flow past it into the hydrant barrel.

Figure A.45 A firefighter opening a hydrant slowly.

Slowly turning the stem nut clockwise shuts down the hydrant. The main valve rises and shuts off the flow of water into the hydrant barrel. At the same time, the drain valve plate rises, opening the drain hole. The remaining water in the hydrant barrel empties through the drain hole.

Additional precautions should be taken when operating dry-barrel hydrants in areas where subfreezing weather is common. If a dry-barrel hydrant is not opened fully, the drain may be left partially open. The resulting flow through the drain hole can erode the soil around the base of the hydrant. Over time, this erosion can destroy the hydrant's support and cause it to leak badly. This can put the hydrant out of service and necessitate it being reinstalled. Therefore, dry-barrel hydrants should be either completely open or completely closed.

When a dry-barrel hydrant is shut down, verify that the water in the hydrant barrel is draining out. To test the water level, take the following steps:

1. Turn the stem nut clockwise until resistance is felt to close the main valve, then turn it a quarter-turn counterclockwise.

2. Cap all discharges except one.

3. Place the palm of one hand over the open discharge.

If the hydrant is draining, a slight vacuum should be felt pulling the palm toward the discharge. If this vacuum is not felt, repeat the entire process and try again. If the hydrant still is not draining, the drain hole is probably plugged. Notify the water authority and have them inspect the hydrant. If this occurs in winter, the hydrant must be pumped until empty to prevent the water from freezing in the barrel before the hydrant is repaired or replaced.

Soft Intake Connections

Not all hydrants have large steamer outlets capable of accepting direct connections from soft intake hose. Operations on hydrants equipped with two 2½-inch (65 mm) outlets require the use of two 2½- or 3-inch (65 mm or 77 mm) hoselines **(Figure A.46)**. These smaller intake hoses can be connected to a siamese at the pump. It is more efficient to connect a 4½-inch (115 mm) or larger intake hose to a hydrant with only 2½-inch (65 mm) outlets. That connection is made by connecting a 4½-inch (115 mm) hose, or whatever size intake hose coupling is used, to a 2½-inch (65 mm) reducer coupling.

Hard Intake Connections for Dry-Barrel Hydrants

Connecting a pumper to a fire hydrant using hard intake hose requires coordination and teamwork because more people are needed to connect hard intake hose than are needed to connect soft intake hose. Making hydrant connections with some types of hard intake hose is also considerably more difficult than making connections with a soft intake hose. The first aspect

Figure A.46 This hydrant lacks a steamer connection so two supply lines are connected to the hydrant's 2½-inch outlets.

that is important is the positioning of the pumper in relation to the hydrant. No definite rule can be given to determine this distance because not all hydrants are the same distance from the curb or road edge, and the hydrant outlet may not directly face the street or road.

Figure A.47 Position apparatus slightly ahead of a hydrant to make it easier to connect hard-intake hose.

While most apparatus have pump intakes on both sides, others may have one at the front or rear. It is considered good policy to stop the apparatus with the intake of choice just in front of the hydrant outlet **(Figure A.47)**. Depending on local protocols, the hard intake hose may be connected to either the apparatus or the hydrant first when making hydrant connections.

NOTE: If the hard intake is marked FOR VACUUM USE ONLY, do not use it for hydrant connections and pressurized systems. This type of hard intake is only for drafting operations from a static source.

Mobile Water Supply Operations

Many rural areas lack public water distribution systems or they have systems with inadequate volume and pressure for fire fighting operations. In those areas, mobile water supply operations must be performed. Information on mobile water supply operations can be found in Chapter 10, Operating Fire Pumps; Chapter 11, Static Water Supply Sources; and Chapter 13, Water Shuttle Operations. For driver/operators who have not completed firefighter training, NFPA® 1002 recommends two basic skills for those individuals to learn in addition to the information in those three chapters as follows:

• **Skill Sheet A-6** describes the process of connecting and placing a hard-suction hose for drafting from a static water source.

• **Skill Sheet A-7** for the steps in deploying a portable water tank.

Forward Lay

Chapter 10, Operating Fire Pumps, describes a forward lay from a driver/operator's point-of-view. This section describes a forward lay from a firefighter's perspective. NFPA® 1002 requires a driver/operator to be able to understand and perform either role (driver or firefighter) to create a forward lay.

In a forward hose lay, hose is deployed from the water source to the incident. The first coupling to come off the hose bed for a forward lay should be female unless two-way couplings (Storz) are used, in which case either coupling will work. Deploying hose for a forward lay consists of stopping the apparatus at the hydrant and allowing a firefighter to safely leave the apparatus and secure the hose. The firefighter making the hydrant connection must know the proper procedures for securing and connecting to the hydrant and correct operation of the hydrant valve if one is used. When signaled, the apparatus then proceeds to the fire deploying either a single hoseline or parallel hoselines **(Figure A.48)**.

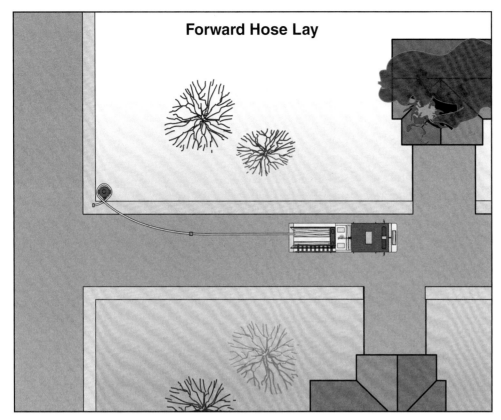

Forward Hose Lay

Figure A.48 Illustrating the concept of a forward hose lay.

The primary advantage of a forward lay is that a pumper can remain at the incident scene so its hose, equipment, and tools are readily available if needed. The pump operator can see the fire suppression operation and better react to changes at the fire scene than if the pumper were at the hydrant.

Making the Hydrant Connection

Local SOPs and resources dictate the method used for connecting the fire hose to the hydrant in a forward hose lay operation. At its simplest, the firefighter takes a hydrant wrench, the finish section of hose, and preferably a radio with him or her when connecting to the hydrant. Departments that use the four-way hydrant valve may have it preconnected to the hose or in a bag stored near the finish section.

To ensure that water arrives quickly at the pump intake, some form of communication between the driver/operator and the firefighter at the hydrant is essential. The radio typically provides this link. If radios are not assigned to all personnel, some means of visual or audible signal must be practiced. Horns and sirens can be a problem when other apparatus respond to a scene. At a minimum, the driver/operator and firefighter making the connection should establish a time for opening the hydrant when the connecting firefighter can be sure that water will arrive before the apparatus tank is empty.

The first task when starting a forward lay is for the hydrant catcher to remove enough hose to reach the hydrant and wrap around it. The finish section of hose is usually long enough to accomplish this task. If not, place the finish section, along with the hydrant wrench, on the ground near the tailboard and pull a second section from the hose bed.

Next take the end of the finish section and wrap it around the hydrant base. The hydrant catcher can place a foot on the hoseline and against the hydrant to further anchor the hose. Then, the firefighter signals the driver/operator it is safe to proceed to the fire **(Figure A.49)**. The procedures for making a hydrant connection from a forward lay are given in **Skill Sheet A-8**.

Using Four-Way Hydrant Valves

If a long length of 2½- or 3-inch (65 mm or 77 mm) hose is laid, or if

Figure A.49 After anchoring the hose to the hydrant, the firefighter signals the driver/operator.

the hydrant has inadequate flow pressure, it may be necessary for a second pumper to position at the hydrant to increase the line pressure. The first pumper in this scenario must have used a **four-way hydrant valve** if the transition from hydrant pressure to pump pressure is to be made without interrupting the flow of water in the supply hose. Another disadvantage is that one member of the crew is temporarily unavailable for a fire fighting assignment because that person must stay at the hydrant long enough to make the hose connection and open the hydrant.

A four-way hydrant valve allows a forward-laid supply line to be immediately charged and allows a later-arriving pumper to connect to the hydrant. The second pumper can supply additional supply lines and/or increase the pressure to the original line **(Figure A.50)**. When the four-way hydrant valve is preconnected to the end of the supply line, the firefighter making the connection can secure the valve and the hose to the hydrant in one action.

Reverse Lay

Chapter 10, Operating Fire Pumps, describes a reverse lay from a driver/operator's pont-of-view. This section describes a reverse lay from a firefighter's perspective. NFPA® 1002 requires a driver/operator to be able to understand and perform either role (driver or firefighter) to create a reverse lay.

When a pumper must go to the fire location before laying a supply line, a reverse hose lay should be deployed from the incident scene to the water source **(Figure A.51)**. This deployment is also the quickest way to lay hose if the apparatus that lays the hose must stay at the water source, such as when drafting or boosting hydrant pressure to the supply line. Hose beds set up for

Four-Way Hydrant Valve — Device that permits a pumper to boost the pressure in a supply line connected to a hydrant without interrupting the water flow.

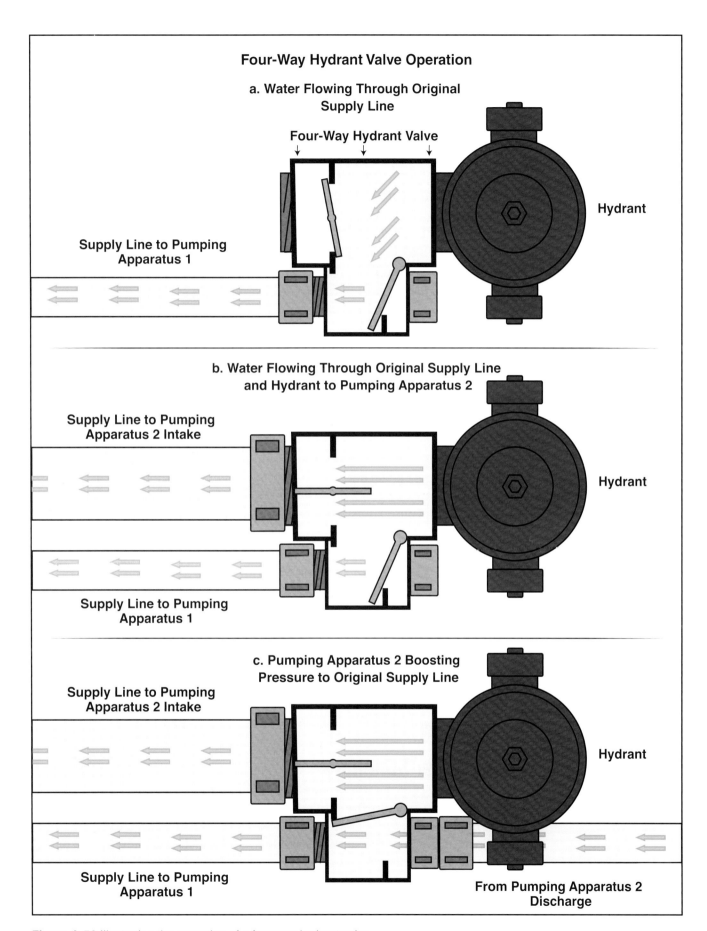

Figure A.50 Illustrating the operation of a four-way hydrant valve.

reverse lays should be loaded so that the first coupling to come off the hose bed is male.

Laying hose from the incident scene to the water source has become a standard method for establishing a relay pumping operation when using 2½- or 3-inch (65 mm or 77 mm) hose as a supply line. With long lays of this size hose, it is necessary to place a pumper at the hydrant to increase the pressure in the supply hose. The reverse lay most directly supplements hydrant pressure and establishes drafting operations.

Deploying a reverse hose lay can delay the initial fire attack because tools and equipment, including attack hose, must be removed from the apparatus and placed at the fire scene before it proceeds to the water source. The reverse lay also causes the pump operator to stay with the pumper at the water source, preventing the operator from performing other essential fireground activities.

A common operation involving two pumpers — an attack pumper and a water-supply pumper — calls for the first-arriving pumper to start an initial attack on the fire using water from its tank, while the second-arriving pumper lays supply line from the attack pumper back to the water source. The second pumper only needs to connect its just-laid hose to their discharge outlet, connect an intake hose, and begin pumping.

When reverse-laying a supply hose, connecting a four-way hydrant valve is optional. One can be used if the pumper may have to disconnect from the supply hose later and leave the hose connected to the hydrant. Disconnecting may be desirable when water demand diminishes to the point that the second pumper can be made available for response to other incidents. As with a forward lay, using the four-way valve in a reverse lay provides the means to switch from pump pressure to hydrant pressure without interrupting the flow.

The reverse lay is also used when the first pumper arrives at a fire and must work alone for an extended period of time. In this case, the hose laid in reverse becomes an attack line. It is often connected to a reducing wye so that two smaller hoses can be used to make a two-directional attack on a fire **(Figure A.52)**. The reverse-lay procedures outlined in **Skill Sheet A-9** describe how the second pumper lays a line from an attack pumper to a hydrant. They can be modified to accommodate most types of apparatus, hose, and equipment.

Frequently, firefighters will assist pumper driver/operators in making hydrant connections following a reverse lay. Either soft or hard intake hose designed for hydrant operations may be used to connect to hydrants. Hard intake hose must be used when drafting from a static water supply source.

Chapter Summary

As members of the fire service, driver/operators should be familiar with the safety culture in the fire service and standards that inform fire service safety. They should also understand the fire service's mission and the organizational structure of their fire service organization. They should know how to operate safely at a scene and how to use all provided PPE correctly. As the personnel on the scene responsible for providing water for fire attack, driver/operators should also be able to make water supply hose connections to hydrants and static water sources.

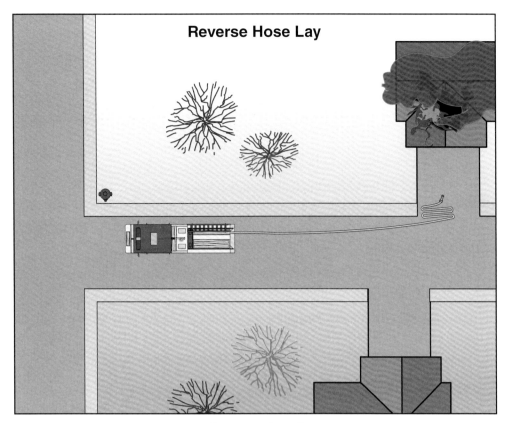

Figure A.51 Illustrating the concept of a reverse hose lay.

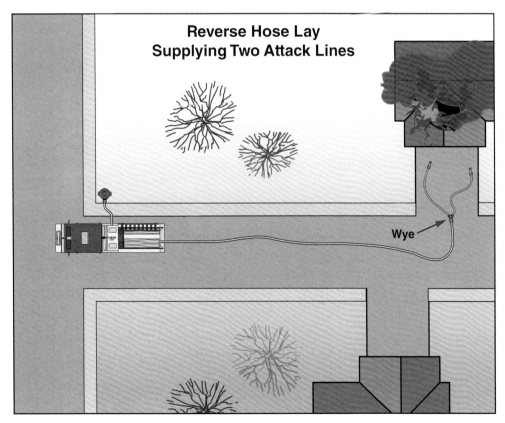

Figure A.52 Illustrating the concept of a reverse hose lay supplying two attack lines.

Review Questions

1. What is the overall mission of the fire service?

2. How are fire departments organized?

3. What types of written regulations affect firefighters?

4. How do fire departments interact with other organizations and agencies?

5. What are the duties of a driver/operator?

6. What initiatives have been created to help reduce firefighter line-of-duty illnesses, injuries, and fatalities?

7. What are some requirements of NFPA® 1500 that relate to firefighter safety and health?

8. How do fire department programs help combat illnesses, injuries, and fatalities?

9. What are the most common line-of-duty illnesses and injuries that affect firefighters?

10. How do physical fitness and healthy lifestyle practices affect firefighter performance and safety?

11. How do fire department member assistance programs benefit firefighters?

12. What are the components of structural fire fighting personal protective equipment?

13. What can occur if PPE is not properly inspected, cleaned, and maintained?

14. What safety guidelines should be followed when riding in fire department apparatus?

15. What should firefighters do to ensure safety at a structural fire scene?

16. What safety guidelines should be followed at highway/roadway incidents?

17. What tools are used to make hydrant connections?

18. What are two types of hydrant connections?

19. What is the difference between a forward lay and a reverse lay?

Chapter Addendum End Notes

Horn, Gavin; Kerber, Steve; Fent, Kenneth W; Hernhall, Bo; Smith, Denise L. "Cardiovascular & Chemical Exposure Risks in Modern Firefighting: Interim Report." 2016 Illinois Fire Service Institute (IFSI): University of Illinois at Urbana-Champaign.

National Institute for Occupational Safety and Health (NIOSH). "Fire Fighter Suffers a Fatal Heart Attack During Wildland Fire Operations – Oklahoma." 2009. LODD Report F2009-09.

"Taking Action Against Cancer in the Fire Service." 2013. Firefighter Cancer Support Network, www.firefightercancersupport.org

NOTE: Always maintain control of equipment and clothing to avoid personal injury or damage. Also ensure that skin or facepiece straps are not exposed.

Step 1:   Don pants, suspenders, and boots.

Step 2:   Don hood.

Step 3:   Don coat with closure secure and collar up.

Step 4: Don helmet with eye protection on and chin strap in place and fastened.

Step 5: Don structural gloves.

A-2
Doff personal protective equipment, including SCBA, and prepare for reuse.

SKILL SHEETS

Step 1: Remove PPE.

SKILL SHEETS

A-2

Doff personal protective equipment, including SCBA, and prepare for reuse.

Step 2: Inspect PPE for damage.

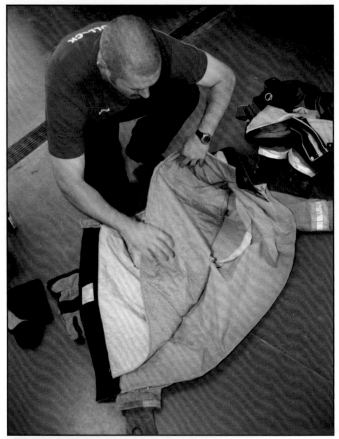

Step 3: Clean and dry equipment as needed.

Step 4: Remove damaged equipment from service and report damage to company officer.

Step 5: Place PPE in a ready state.

Step 1: Don appropriate personal protective equipment (PPE).

Step 2: Mount apparatus using handrails and steps per local procedures.

NOTE: Be sure to use three points of contact at all times (e.g., one hand and two feet, or two hands and one foot).

Step 3: Sit in a seat within the cab and fasten safety belt. Follow all local safety regulations.

Step 4: Remain seated with safety belt fastened while vehicle is in motion.

Step 5: When vehicle comes to a complete stop, unfasten safety belt and prepare to dismount.

CAUTION: Before fully opening the apparatus door, look for oncoming traffic. Always use situational awareness. If possible, dismount on the side opposite of traffic.

Step 6: Dismount apparatus using handrails and steps per local procedures.

NOTE: Be sure to use three points of contact at all times.

NOTE: Follow local procedures for roadway incidents.

Step 1: Set up traffic cones and scene control devices appropriate to the assignment.

Step 2: Set up established work areas.

Step 3: Perform all other tasks as directed to complete the assignment.

A-4

SKILL SHEETS

Demonstrate scene management at a roadway incident using traffic and scene safety control devices.

Step 4: Remove traffic cones and scene control devices after completion of the assignment.

Soft-Sleeve Connection

Step 1: Remove the hydrant cap. Use a spanner wrench if the cap is too tight.

Step 2: Inspect the hydrant for exterior damage and check for debris or damage inside the outlet.

Step 3: Place the hydrant wrench on the valve stem opening nut.

Step 4: Flush the hydrant to ensure that it is free of debris.

Step 5: Connect the intake hose to the pump intake. Hand-tighten the connection.

Step 6: Make the hydrant connection to the steamer outlet (use with adapter as needed). Hand-tighten the connection.

Hard-Suction Connection

Step 1: Remove the hydrant cap. Use a spanner wrench if the cap is too tight.

Step 2: Inspect the hydrant for exterior damage and check for debris or damage in the outlet.

Step 3: Connect the intake hose to the hydrant or apparatus (depending on local SOPs). Hand-tighten the connection.

Step 4: Connect the opposite end to the hydrant or apparatus. Hand-tighten the connection.

Step 5: Tighten any leaking connections using a rubber mallet or spanner wrench.

Step 7: Open the hydrant slowly until the hose is full.

Step 8: Tighten any leaking connections using a rubber mallet or spanner wrench.

A-6
Connect and place a hard-suction hose for drafting from a static water source.

SKILL SHEETS

Step 1: Check the hard-suction couplings.

a. Remove any dirt or debris.

b. Replace worn gaskets.

Step 2: Connect the sections of hard-suction hose.

a. Align sections.

b. Hand-tighten the connection.

c. Use rubber mallet to make an airtight connection, if necessary.

d. Keep the hose off of the ground.

Step 3: Connect the strainer to one end of the hard-suction hose.

a. Hand tighten the connection.

b. Use a rubber mallet to make an airtight connection, if necessary.

c. Fasten the rope to the strainer.

SKILL SHEETS

A-6

Connect and place a hard-suction hose for drafting from a static water source.

Step 4: Put the strainer into the water. If using a barrel strainer, use the rope to maneuver the hose and keep the strainer off the bottom.

Step 5: Prepare the pump intake for coupling by removing the cap and keystone intake valve, if applicable.

Step 6: Connect the hard-suction hose to the pump intake.

a. Align the sections.

b. Hand tighten the connection.

Step 7: Tie the strainer rope (if used) to the pumper or stationary object.

Step 8: Dismantle drafting equipment and return to proper storage per local SOPs.

Step 1: Carry equipment to designated location for the water tank setup.

Step 2: Check the area for debris.

Step 3: Open the tarps and spread them flat on the ground.

Step 4: Set up two portable tanks.

Step 5: Connect the intake and discharge hoses to the jet siphon.

Step 6: Position the jet siphon properly to draw and discharge water.

Step 7: Dismantle the portable tanks.

Step 8: Shake and fold the tarps.

Step 9: Return equipment to the proper storage locations on the apparatus.

Step 1: Firefighter #1: Pull enough supply hose from the apparatus to reach and wrap around the hydrant.

Step 2: Firefighter #1: Secure a loop of hose around the hydrant. Wrap the hose around the hydrant in a manner that restrains it when the pumper moves away from the hydrant.

Step 3: Firefighter #1: Signal the driver/operator to proceed and deploy the hose to the incident.

Step 4: Firefighter #1: Connect the supply hose to the hydrant.

a. Remove the cap from the hydrant.

b. Place the hydrant wrench on the valve stem operating nut.

c. Flush the hydrant.

d. Connect the hose to the appropriate outlet.

Step 5: Firefighter #2: Complete the hose lay to the scene.

Step 6: Firefighter #2: Connect the hose to the fire pump intake valve.

Step 7: Firefighter #1: Slowly and fully open the hydrant.

Step 8: Firefighter #1: Proceed along the hose to the pumper, removing kinks and checking for leaks.

Step 1: Firefighter #1: Pull sufficient hose from the supply pumper to reach the intake valve on the attack pumper.

Step 2: Firefighter #1: Anchor the hose while the supply pumper proceeds to the water source.

Step 3: Firefighter #1: Make an intake connection at the attack pumper as directed by the driver/operator.

Step 4: Firefighter #2: Pull the remaining length of the last section of hose from the hose bed.

Step 5: Firefighter #2: Disconnect the couplings and return the unused coupling to the hose bed.

Step 6: Firefighter #2: Connect the supply hose to a discharge valve.

Step 7: Firefighter #2: Make an intake hose connection on the supply pumper.

Step 8: Firefighter #2: Proceed along the hose to the fire scene, removing kinks and checking for leaks.

Appendix

Courtesy of Ron Jeffers

Appendix A
NFPA® Job Performance Requirements (JPRs) with Chapter and Page References: NFPA 1002, 2014 Edition

NFPA® 1002 JPR Numbers	Chapter References	Page References
4.2.1	2	29-30, 36-39, 40-41, 42-44, 44-45, 46-48
4.2.2	2, 15	29-30, 36-39, 40-41, 44-45, 48, 515-518, 518-527, 527-530
4.3.1	3	83-84, 84-89, 90-93, 93-96, 96-99, 100-104, 102-103, 105-112, 118-119
4.3.2	3	100-104, 113-116, 118-119
4.3.3	3	100-104, 113-116, 118-119
4.3.4	3	100-104, 113-116, 118-119
4.3.5	3	100-104, 118-119
4.3.6	3	83-84, 84-89, 90-93, 96-99, 100-104, 102-103, 105-112, 113-116, 118-119
4.3.7	2	40-41
5.1.1	2, 10, 14, 15	29-30, 48, 336-339, 339-351, 506, 366, 515-518, 518-527, 527-530
5.2.1	4, 5, 6, 7, 8, 9, 10, 11	136-140, 141,178-181, 188-189, 193-199, 199-202, 200-202, 202-204, 210, 218-219, 222-272, 281-282, 287, 288-289, 295-296, 298-307, 307-312, 312-318, 318-321, 322-324, 324-329, 329, 352, 403-407, 410-414, 414-418
5.2.2	4, 5, 7, 8, 9, 10, 12	141-146, 144, 178-181, 188-189, 211-214, 218-219, 283-284, 287, 288-289
10.2.2	10	336-339, 339-351
10.2.3	11	410-414, 443-449

NFPA® Job Performance Requirements (JPRs) with Chapter and Page References: NFPA 1002, 2017 Edition

NFPA® 1002 JPR Numbers	Chapter References	Page References
4.2.1	2	29-30, 36-39, 40-41, 42-44, 44-45, 46-48
4.2.2	2, 15	29-30, 36-39, 40-41, 44-45, 48, 515-518, 518-527, 527-530
4.3.1	3	83-84, 84-89, 90-93, 93-96, 96-99, 100-104, 102-103, 105-112, 118-119
4.3.2	3	100-104, 113-116, 118-119
4.3.3	3	100-104, 113-116, 118-119
4.3.4	3	100-104, 113-116, 118-119
4.3.5	3	100-104, 118-119
4.3.6	3	83-84, 84-89, 90-93, 96-99, 100-104, 102-103, 105-112, 113-116, 118-119
4.3.7	2	40-41
5.1.1	Addendum	A-4 thru A-30, A-46 thru A-49
5.1.2	2, 10, 14, 15	29-30, 48, 336-339, 339-351, 506, 366, 515-518, 518-527, 527-530
5.2.1	Addendum	A-30 thru A-45, A-49 thru A-54, A-70 thru A-73, A-76, A-77
5.2.2	Addendum	A-49, A-50, A-53 thru A-55, A-70 thru A-77
5.2.3	10, 11, 13, Addendum	352-362, 396, 397, 410-419, 455-459, 474, 475, A-55 thru A-68, A-78 thru A-86
5.2.4	4, 5, 6, 7, 8, 9, 10, 11	136-140, 141,178-181, 188-189, 193-199 199-202, 200-202, 202-204, 210, 218-219, 222-272, 281-282, 287, 288-289, 295-296, 298-307, 307-312, 312-318, 318-321, 322-324, 324-329, 329, 352, 403-407, 410-414, 414-418
5.2.5	4, 5, 7, 8, 9, 10, 12	141-146, 144, 178-181, 188-189, 211-214, 218-219, 283-284, 287, 288-289, 296-298, 307-312, 312-318, 318-321, 322-324, 324-329, 329, 352-362, 425-427, 427-432, 432-434, 435, 435-436
5.2.6	14	480-486, 486-494, 502-503, 503-505, 506, 508-509
5.2.7	4, 7, 10	137, 141, 362-366, 214-218
7.2.1	3	100-104, 113-116, 118-119
7.2.2	3, 14	117-118, 506
10.1.1	2, 13, 14	35-41, 48, 464-468, 506

NFPA® 1002 JPR Numbers	Chapter References	Page References
10.2.1	11, 13	410-414, 450-455, 455-459
10.2.2	10	336-339, 339-351
10.2.3	11	410-414, 443-449

Appendix B

Sample Fire Department Vehicle Inspection Form

Sample Fire Department Vehicle Inspection Form			
Vehicle:	**Mileage:**		**Date:**

Exterior Inspection		Interior Inspection	
Item	**Sat/Unsat**	**Item**	**Sat/Unsat**
General Body Condition/Damage		Seat/Seat Belts	
Tires/Wheels/Suspension		Windshield/Mirrors	
Undercarriage		Heater/Defroster	
Doors/Windows		Dashboard Gauges (Fuel, Oil, etc.)	
Compartments		Horns/Sirens	
Lights (Head, Indicator, Reverse)		Maps, Pre-Fire Plans, etc.	
Emergency Lights		Communication Equipment	
Other		Other	

Engine Compartment		Fire Pump	
Item	**Sat/Unsat**	**Item**	**Sat/Unsat**
Engine Oil		Agent Level (Water, Foam, etc.)	
Transmission Fluid		Engage/Disengage	
Power Steering Fluid		Priming Device	
Radiator Coolant		Tank-to-Pump	
Belts/Hoses/Fan Blades		Throttle	
Air Intake/Filter		Discharge Valves	
Batteries		Relief Valves	
Other		Other	

Equipment		Other	
Item	**Sat/Unsat**	**Item**	**Sat/Unsat**
Supply Hose		Pneumatic/Air	
Preconnected Hose		Hydraulic	
Ladder(s)		Electrical	
Hand Tools		Brakes (Parking, Road)	
Power Tools		Auxiliary	
Emergency Medical Supplies		Breathing Air	
Fire Extinguisher		Generator	
Other		Other	

Discrepancies:

Driver/Operator Signature:

Captain Signature:

Appendix C
Appliance Test Method

The following procedures may be used to determine the actual friction loss that occurs within portable monitors and turrets.

Portable Monitors

Items required:

- Two 50-foot (15 m) lengths of 2½-inch (65 mm) or larger hose

- One solid stream nozzle capable of flows in range of appliance to be tested

- One pitot gauge

Based on the formulas presented in the text, the basic equation to be used is the following:

PDP = NP + FL + AL + Elev. Press.

Where:

$$\begin{aligned} \text{PDP} &= \text{Pump discharge pressure} \\ \text{NP} &= \text{Nozzle pressure} \\ \text{FL} &= \text{Friction loss} \\ \text{AL} &= \text{Appliance loss} \\ \text{Elev. Press.} &= \text{Elevation pressure loss} \end{aligned}$$

To determine a single variable in the previous equation, it is best to eliminate as many of the other variables as possible. This can be accomplished by making all those variables that might change the same for each test. This allows you to isolate the particular variable that you are trying to determine, which in this case is the appliance loss (AL). Therefore, to determine appliance loss, remove each variable by the following:

- Eliminate friction loss (FL) by using equal flows and equal hose lengths for each test.

- Eliminate elevation pressure loss by conducting the test on level ground.

- Eliminate nozzle pressure (NP) by taking pitot readings at the nozzle and varying the pump discharge pressure to maintain a constant nozzle pressure (and thus a constant flow).

This reduces the basic equation so that now a change in the system (adding the appliance) will have a direct effect on pump discharge pressure.

Two lengths of 2½-inch (65 mm) or larger hose are laid out. A safely secured nozzle is added directly to the end of the hose using appropriate adapters as necessary. The size of the nozzle depends on the amount of flow being tested **(Table B.1)**.

Table B.1 (Customary) Determining Nozzle Size and Discharge Pressure		
Desired Test Flow	**Required Nozzle Size**	**Required Discharge Pressure**
340 gpm	1⅛ inch	80 poi
500 gpm	1⅜ inch	80 psi
750 gpm	1¾ inch	70 psi

Table B.1 (Metric) Determining Nozzle Size and Discharge Pressure		
Desired Test Flow	**Required Nozzle Size**	**Required Discharge Pressure**
1 350 L/min	32 mm	410 kPa
2 000 L/min	35 mm	620 kPa
3 000 L/min	45 mm	520 kPa

Once the equipment is laid out and connected, the flow is started and pump discharge pressure is increased to the point where nozzle pressure is at the desired pressure (target flow). Note the required pump discharge pressure to achieve this flow. This is pressure PDP_a.

Shut down the flow, and add the portable monitor appliance between the nozzle and the last coupling(s). Once connected, again begin the flow and increase the pump discharge pressure to the point where nozzle pressure (and hence flow) is the same as in the previous step. Note the required pump discharge pressure. This is pressure PDP_b. It should be higher than the first test. To determine the amount of friction loss caused by the monitor, use the following equation:

PDP_b – PDP_a = AL

This tells how much friction loss can be expected from that appliance around the flow for which it was tested.

Example B.1

Determine the appliance friction loss in a portable monitor being supplied by 3-inch (77 mm) hose flowing 500 gpm (2 000 L/min).

Solution

For a 500 gpm flow (2 000 L/min), add a 1⅜-inch (35 mm) tip to the hoseline. When the pitot pressure reaches 80 psi (560 kPa), the resulting pump discharge pressure is 102 psi (714 kPa). This is PDP_a.

Now add the portable monitor to be tested. Increase pump discharge pressure until pressure on the nozzle is 80 psi (560 kPa). The new pump discharge pressure is 128 psi (896 kPa). This is PDP_b. Pressure loss for the monitor is as follows:

$$PDP_b – PDP_a = AL$$
$$128 – 102 = 26 \text{ psi}$$
$$896 – 714 = 182 \text{ kPa}$$

Because it is not necessary to determine the exact friction loss in the hose, any layout or number of hoses can be used to deliver the needed flow. The important point is that the number and sizes of hoses used are the same for both tests.

Turrets

To calculate losses through turrets (or portable monitor in the truck-mounted mode), as well as losses between the turret and the pump, an additional item is necessary. A side wall pressure reading piezometer is added between the exit nozzle and the turret. Increase the pressure until desired flow is attained (as determined by a pitot pressure on the nozzle). The pressure loss between the pump and the exit of the turret is shown by the difference between the sidewall piezometer on the exit and the compound pressure gauge in the pump panel. Note that this pressure difference only applies to that particular flow. For other flows, other values must be determined.

Appendix D
IFSTA Friction Loss Calculations (Customary)

The following tables that include imperial gallons may be used to identify the friction loss for the given flows in imperial gallons per minute. The coefficients used to determine friction loss using U.S. gallons per minute *may not* be used when calculating friction loss using imperial gallons per minute.

Table D.1 ¾-Inch Rubber Hose C-Factor: 1,100					
Flow in gpm					
(U.S. Gallons)	**20**	**30**	**40**	**50**	**60**
(Imperial Gallons)	**17**	**25**	**33**	**42**	**50**
Lay Length Feet	**Friction Loss in psi**				
50	22	50	88	138	198
100	44	99	176		
150	66	149			
200	88	198			
250	110				
300	132				
350	154				
400	176				

Table D.2 1-Inch Rubber Hose C-Factor: 150					
Flow in gpm					
(U.S. Gallons)	**20**	**30**	**40**	**50**	**60**
(Imperial Gallons)	**17**	**25**	**33**	**42**	**50**
Lay Length Feet	**Friction Loss in psi**				
50	3	7	12	19	27
100	6	14	24	38	54
150	9	20	36	56	81
200	12	27	48	75	108
250	15	34	60	94	135
300	18	41	72	113	162
350	21	47	84	131	189
400	24	54	96	150	

Table D.3 1½-Inch Hose C-Factor: 24					
Flow in gpm					
(U.S. Gallons)	**40**	**60**	**80**	**95**	**125**	**150**
(Imperial Gallons)	**33**	**50**	**67**	**79**	**104**	**125**
Lay Length Feet	**Friction Loss in psi**					
50	2	4	8	11	19	27
100	4	9	15	22	38	54
150	6	13	23	32	56	81
200	8	17	31	43	75	108
250	10	22	38	54	94	135
300	12	26	46	65	113	162
350	13	30	54	76	131	189
400	15	35	61	87	150	216
450	17	39	69	97	169	
500	19	43	77	108	188	

Table D.4
1¾-Inch Rubber Hose
C-Factor: 15.5

Flow in gpm					
(U.S. Gallons)	95	125	150	175	200
(Imperial Gallons)	79	104	125	146	167

Lay Length Feet	Friction Loss in psi				
50	7	12	17	24	31
100	14	24	35	47	62
150	21	36	52	71	93
200	28	48	70	95	124
250	35	61	87	119	155
300	42	73	105	142	186
350	49	85	122	166	
400	56	97	140	190	
450	63	109	157		
500	70	121	174		

Table D.5
2-Inch Rubber Hose
C-Factor: 8

Flow in gpm					
(U.S. Gallons)	100	125	150	175	200
(Imperial Gallons)	83	104	125	146	167

Lay Length Feet	Friction Loss in psi				
50	4	6	9	12	16
100	8	13	18	25	32
150	12	19	27	37	48
200	16	25	36	49	64
250	20	31	45	61	80
300	24	38	54	74	96
350	28	44	63	86	112
400	32	50	72	98	128
450	36	56	81	110	144
500	40	63	90	123	160

Table D.6
2½-Inch Hose
C-Factor: 2

				Flow in gpm			
(U.S. Gallons)	175	200	225	250	275	300	350
(Imperial Gallons)	146	167	187	208	229	250	292

Lay Length Feet	Friction Loss in psi						
50	3	4	5	6	8	9	12
100	6	8	10	13	15	18	25
150	9	12	15	19	23	27	37
200	12	16	20	25	30	36	49
250	15	20	25	31	38	45	61
300	18	24	30	38	45	54	74
350	21	28	35	44	53	63	86
400	25	32	41	50	61	72	98
450	28	36	46	56	68	81	110
500	31	40	51	63	76	90	123
550	34	44	56	69	83	99	135
600	37	48	61	75	91	108	147
650	40	52	66	81	98	117	159
700	43	56	71	88	106	126	172
750	46	60	76	94	113	135	184
800	49	64	81	100	121	144	196
850	52	68	86	106	129	153	208
900	55	72	91	113	136	162	221
950	58	76	96	119	144	171	233
1,000	61	80	101	125	151	180	245
1,050	64	84	106	131	159	189	
1,100	67	88	111	138	166	198	
1,150	70	92	116	144	174	207	
1,200	74	96	122	150	182	216	
1,250	77	100	127	156	189	225	
1,300	80	104	132	163	197	234	
1,350	83	108	137	169	204	243	
1,400	86	112	142	175	212		
1,450	89	116	147	181	219		
1,500	92	120	152	188	227		
1,550	95	124	157	194	234		
1,600	98	128	162	200	242		
1,650	101	132	167	206	250		
1,700	104	136	172	213			
1,750	107	140	177	219			
1,800	110	144	182	225			
1,850	113	148	187	231			
1,900	116	152	192	238			
1,950	119	156	197	244			
2,000	123	160	203	250			

			Table D.7			
			3-Inch Hose			
			C-Factor: 0.8			

	Flow in gpm					
(U.S. Gallons)	**250**	**325**	**500**	**750**	**1,000**	**1,250**
(Imperial Gallons)	**208**	**271**	**417**	**625**	**833**	**1,041**
Lay Length Feet	Friction Loss in psi					
50	3	4	10	23	40	63
100	5	8	20	45	80	125
150	8	13	30	68	120	188
200	10	17	40	90	160	250
250	13	21	50	113	200	
300	15	25	60	135	240	
350	18	30	70	158		
400	20	34	80	180		
450	23	38	90	203		
500	25	42	100	225		
550	28	46	110	248		
600	30	51	120			
650	33	55	130			
700	35	59	140			
750	38	63	150			
800	40	68	160			
850	43	72	170			
900	45	76	180			
950	48	80	190			
1,000	50	85	200			
1,050	53	89	210			
1,100	55	93	220			
1,150	58	97	230			
1,200	60	101	240			
1,250	63	106	250			
1,300	65	110				
1,350	68	114				
1,400	70	118				
1,450	73	123				
1,500	75	127				
1,550	78	131				
1,600	80	135				
1,650	83	139				
1,700	85	144				
1,750	88	148				
1,800	90	152				
1,850	93	156				
1,900	95	161				
1,950	98	165				
2,000	100	169				

Table D.8					
3-Inch Hose with 3-Inch Couplings					
C-Factor: 0.677					

	Flow in gpm				
(U.S. Gallons) (Imperial Gallons)	250	350	500	750	1,000
Lay Length Feet	Friction Loss in psi				
50	2	4	8	19	34
100	4	8	17	38	68
150	6	12	25	57	102
200	8	17	34	76	135
250	11	21	42	95	169
300	13	25	51	114	
350	15	29	59	133	
400	17	33	68	152	
450	19	37	76	171	
500	21	41	85		
550	23	46	93		
600	25	50	102		
650	28	54	110		
700	30	58	118		
750	32	62	127		
800	34	66	135		
850	36	70	144		
900	38	75	152		
950	40	79	161		
1,000	42	83	160		
1,050	44	87	178		
1,100	47	91	186		
1,150	49	95			
1,200	51	100			
1,250	53	104			
1,300	55	108			
1,350	57	112			
1,400	59	116			
1,450	61	120			
1,500	63	124			
1,550	66	129			
1,600	68	133			
1,650	70	137			
1,700	72	141			
1,750	74				
1,800	76				
1,850	78				
1,900	80				
1,950	83				
2,000	85				

	Flow in gpm					
(U.S. Gallons)	500	750	1,000	1,250	1,500	1,750
(Imperial Gallons)	417	625	833	1,041	1,250	1,458
Lay Length Feet	Friction Loss in psi					
50	3	6	10	16	23	31
100	5	11	20	31	45	61
150	8	17	30	47	68	92
200	10	23	40	63	90	123
250	13	28	50	78	113	153
300	15	34	60	94	135	184
350	18	39	70	109	158	
400	20	45	80	125	180	
450	23	51	90	141		
500	25	56	100	156		
550	28	62	110	172		
600	30	68	120			
650	33	73	130			
700	35	79	140			
750	38	84	150			
800	40	90	160			
850	43	96	170			
900	45	101	180			
950	48	107				
1,000	50	113				
1,050	53	118				
1,100	55	124				
1,150	58	129				
1,200	60	135				
1,250	63	141				
1,300	65	146				
1,350	68	152				
1,400	70	158				
1,450	73	163				
1,500	75	169				
1,550	78	174				
1,600	80	180				
1,650	83					
1,700	85					
1,750	88					
1,800	90					
1,850	93					
1,900	95					
1,950	98					
2,000	100					

	Flow in gpm					
(U.S. Gallons)	**500**	**750**	**1,000**	**1,250**	**1,500**	**1,750**
(Imperial Gallons)	**417**	**625**	**833**	**1,041**	**1,250**	**1,458**
Lay Length Feet	Friction Loss in psi					
50	1	3	5	8	11	15
100	3	6	10	16	23	31
150	4	8	15	23	34	46
200	5	11	20	31	45	61
250	6	14	25	39	56	77
300	8	17	30	47	68	92
350	9	20	35	55	79	107
400	10	23	40	63	90	123
450	11	25	45	70	101	138
500	13	28	50	78	113	153
550	14	31	55	86	124	168
600	15	34	60	94	135	184
650	16	37	65	102	146	
700	18	39	70	109	158	
750	19	42	75	117	169	
800	20	45	80	125	180	
850	21	48	85	133		
900	23	51	90	141		
950	24	53	95	148		
1,000	25	56	100	156		
1,050	26	59	105	164		
1,100	28	62	110	172		
1,150	29	65	115	180		
1,200	30	68	120			
1,250	31	70	125			
1,300	33	73	130			
1,350	34	76	135			
1,400	35	79	140			
1,450	36	82	145			
1,500	38	84	150			
1,550	39	87	155			
1,600	40	90	160			
1,650	41	93	165			
1,700	43	96	170			
1,750	44	98	175			
1,800	45	101	180			
1,850	46	104	185			
1,900	48	107				
1,950	49	110				
2,000	50	113				

Table D.11
5-Inch Hose
C-Factor: 0.08

	Flow in gpm					
(U.S. Gallons)	750	1,000	1,250	1,500	1,750	2,000
(Imperial Gallons)	625	833	1,041	1,250	1,458	1,666
Lay Length Feet	Friction Loss in psi					
50	2	4	6	9	12	16
100	5	8	13	18	25	32
150	7	12	19	27	37	48
200	9	16	25	36	49	64
250	11	20	31	45	61	80
300	14	24	38	54	74	96
350	16	28	44	63	86	112
400	18	32	50	72	98	128
450	20	36	56	81	110	144
500	23	40	63	90	123	160
550	25	44	69	99	135	176
600	27	48	75	108	147	192
650	29	52	81	117	159	208
700	32	56	88	126	172	224
750	34	60	94	135	184	240
800	36	64	100	144	196	
850	38	68	106	153	208	
900	41	72	113	162	221	
950	43	76	119	171	233	
1,000	45	80	125	180	245	
1,050	47	84	131	189		
1,100	50	88	138	198		
1,150	52	92	144	207		
1,200	54	96	150	216		
1,250	56	100	156	225		
1,300	59	104	163	234		
1,350	61	108	169	243		
1,400	63	112	175	252		
1,450	65	116	181	261		
1,500	68	120	188			
1,550	70	124	194			
1,600	72	128	200			
1,650	74	132	206			
1,700	77	136	213			
1,750	79	140	219			
1,800	81	144	225			
1,850	83	148	231			
1,900	86	152	238			
1,950	88	156	244			
2,000	90	160	250			

Table D.12
Two 2½-Inch Hoses
C-Factor: 0.5

	Flow in gpm					
(U.S. Gallons)	**500**	**750**	**1,000**	**1,250**	**1,500**	**1,750**
(Imperial Gallons)	**417**	**625**	**833**	**1,041**	**1,250**	**1,458**
Lay Length Feet	Friction Loss in psi					
50	6	14	25	39	56	77
100	13	28	50	78	113	153
150	19	42	75	117	169	230
200	25	56	100	156	225	
250	31	70	125	195		
300	38	84	150	234		
350	44	98	175			
400	50	113	200			
450	56	127	225			
500	63	141	250			
550	69	155				
600	75	169				
650	81	183				
700	88	197				
750	94	211				
800	100	225				
850	106	239				
900	113					
950	119					
1,000	125					
1,050	131					
1,100	138					
1,150	144					
1,200	150					
1,250	156					
1,300	163					
1,350	169					
1,400	175					
1,450	181					
1,500	188					
1,550	194					
1,600	200					
1,650	206					
1,700	213					
1,750	219					
1,800	225					
1,850	231					
1,900	238					
1,950	244					
2,000	250					

Table D.13
Three 2½-Inch Hoses
C-Factor: 0.22

(U.S. Gallons) (Imperial Gallons)	Flow in gpm					
	250	500	750	1,000	1,250	1,500
Lay Length Feet	Friction Loss in psi					
50	1	3	6	11	17	25
100	1	6	12	22	34	50
150	2	8	19	33	52	74
200	3	11	25	44	69	99
250	3	14	31	55	86	124
300	4	17	37	66	103	149
350	5	19	43	77	120	173
400	6	22	50	88	138	198
450	6	25	56	99	155	
500	7	28	62	110	172	
550	8	30	68	121	189	
600	8	33	74	132		
650	9	36	80	143		
700	10	39	87	154		
750	10	41	93	165		
800	11	44	99	176		
850	12	47	105	187		
900	12	50	111	198		
950	13	52	118			
1,000	14	55	124			
1,050	14	58	130			
1,100	15	61	136			
1,150	16	63	142			
1,200	17	66	149			
1,250	17	69	155			
1,300	18	72	161			
1,350	19	74	167			
1,400	19	77	173			
1,450	20	80	179			
1,500	21	83	186			
1,550	21	85	192			
1,600	22	88	198			
1,650	23	91				
1,700	23	94				
1,750	24	96				
1,800	25	99				
1,850	25	102				
1,900	26	105				
1,950	27	107				
2,000	28	110				

Table D.14						
One 3-Inch and One 2½-Inch Hose						
C-Factor: 0.3						

	Flow in gpm					
(U.S. Gallons)	**500**	**750**	**1,000**	**1,250**	**1,500**	**1,750**
(Imperial Gallons)	**417**	**625**	**833**	**1,041**	**1,250**	**1,458**
Lay Length Feet	Friction Loss in psi					
50	4	8	15	23	34	46
100	8	17	30	47	68	92
150	11	25	45	70	101	138
200	15	34	60	94	135	184
250	19	42	75	117	169	
300	23	51	90	141	203	
350	26	59	105	164		
400	30	68	120	188		
450	34	76	135			
500	38	84	150			
550	41	93	165			
600	45	101	180			
650	49	110	195			
700	53	118				
750	56	127				
800	60	135				
850	64	143				
900	68	152				
950	71	160				
1,000	75	169				
1,050	79	177				
1,100	83	186				
1,150	86	194				
1,200	90	203				
1,250	94					
1,300	98					
1,350	101					
1,400	105					
1,450	109					
1,500	113					
1,550	116					
1,600	120					
1,650	124					
1,700	128					
1,750	131					
1,800	135					
1,850	139					
1,900	143					
1,950	146					
2,000	150					

Table D.15
Two 2½-Inch and One 3-Inch Hose
C-Factor: 0.16

			Flow in gpm			
(U.S. Gallons) (Imperial Gallons)	500	750	1,000	1,250	1,500	1,750
Lay Length Feet			Friction Loss in psi			
50	2	5	8	13	18	25
100	4	9	16	25	36	49
150	6	14	24	38	54	74
200	8	18	32	50	72	98
250	10	23	40	63	90	123
300	12	27	48	75	108	147
350	14	32	56	88	126	172
400	16	36	64	100	144	196
450	18	41	72	113	162	
500	20	45	80	125	180	
550	22	50	88	138	198	
600	24	54	96	150		
650	26	59	104	163		
700	28	63	112	175		
750	30	68	120	188		
800	32	72	128	200		
850	34	77	136			
900	36	81	144			
950	38	86	152			
1,000	40	90	160			
1,050	42	95	168			
1,100	44	99	176			
1,150	46	104	184			
1,200	48	108	192			
1,250	50	113	200			
1,300	52	117				
1,350	54	122				
1,400	56	126				
1,450	58	131				
1,500	60	135				
1,550	62	140				
1,600	64	144				
1,650	66	149				
1,700	68	153				
1,750	70	158				
1,800	72	162				
1,850	74	167				
1,900	76	171				
1,950	78	176				
2,000	80	180				

Table D.16
Two 3-Inch Hoses
C-Factor: 0.2

	Flow in gpm					
(U.S. Gallons)	**500**	**750**	**1,000**	**1,250**	**1,500**	**1,750**
(Imperial Gallons)	**417**	**625**	**833**	**1,041**	**1,250**	**1,458**
Lay Length Feet	Friction Loss in psi					
50	3	6	10	16	23	31
100	5	11	20	31	45	61
150	8	17	30	47	68	92
200	10	23	40	63	90	123
250	13	28	50	78	113	153
300	15	34	60	94	135	184
350	18	39	70	109	158	
400	20	45	80	125	180	
450	23	51	90	141		
500	25	56	100	156		
550	28	62	110	172		
600	30	68	120	188		
650	33	73	130	203		
700	35	79	140			
750	38	84	150			
800	40	90	160			
850	43	96	170			
900	45	101	180			
950	48	107	190			
1,000	50	113	200			
1,050	53	118				
1,100	55	124				
1,150	58	129				
1,200	60	135				
1,250	63	141				
1,300	65	146				
1,350	68	152				
1,400	70	158				
1,450	73	163				
1,500	75	169				
1,550	78	174				
1,600	80	180				
1,650	83	186				
1,700	85	191				
1,750	88	197				
1,800	90	203				
1,850	93					
1,900	95					
1,950	98					
2,000	100					

Table D.17
Two 3-Inch and One 2½-Inch Hose
C-Factor: 0.12

(U.S. Gallons) (Imperial Gallons)	Flow in gpm					
	500	750	1,000	1,250	1,500	1,750
Lay Length Feet	Friction Loss in psi					
50	2	3	6	9	14	18
100	3	7	12	19	27	37
150	5	10	18	28	41	55
200	6	14	24	38	54	74
250	8	17	30	47	68	92
300	9	20	36	56	81	110
350	11	24	42	66	95	129
400	12	27	48	75	108	147
450	14	30	54	84	122	
500	15	34	60	94	135	
550	17	37	66	103	149	
600	18	41	72	113		
650	20	44	78	122		
700	21	47	84	131		
750	23	51	90	141		
800	24	54	96	150		
850	26	57	102			
900	27	61	108			
950	29	64	114			
1,000	30	68	120			
1,050	32	71	126			
1,100	33	74	132			
1,150	35	78	138			
1,200	36	81	144			
1,250	38	84	150			
1,300	39	88				
1,350	41	91				
1,400	42	95				
1,450	44	98				
1,500	45	101				
1,550	47	105				
1,600	48	108				
1,650	50	111				
1,700	51	115				
1,750	53	118				
1,800	54	122				
1,850	56	125				
1,900	57	128				
1,950	59	132				
2,000	60	135				

Appendix E
IFSTA Friction Loss Calculations (Metric)

Table E.1
20 mm Rubber Hose
C-Factor: 1 741

Lay Length Meters	Flow in L/min				
	80	120	160	200	240
	Friction Loss in kPa				
15	167	376	669	1 045	1 504
30	334	752	1 337		
45	501	1 128			
60	669	1 504			
75	836				
90	1 003				
105	1 170				
120	1 337				

Table E.2
25 mm Rubber Hose
C-Factor: 238

Lay Length Meters	Flow in L/min				
	80	120	160	200	240
	Friction Loss in kPa				
15	23	51	91	143	206
30	46	103	183	286	411
45	69	154	274	428	617
60	91	206	366	571	823
75	114	257	457	714	1 028
90	137	308	548	857	1 234
105	160	360	640	1 000	1 439
120	183	411	731	1 142	1 645

Table E.3
38 mm Hose
C-Factor: 38

Lay Length Meters	Flow in L/min				
	240	320	400	500	600
	Friction Loss in kPa				
15	33	58	91	143	205
30	66	117	182	285	410
45	98	175	274	428	616
60	131	233	365	570	821
75	164	292	456	713	1 026
90	197	350	547	855	1 231
105	230	409	638	998	
120	263	467	730	1 140	
135	295	525	821		
150	328	584	912		

Table E.4
45 mm Hose
C-Factor: 21.6

Lay Length Meters	Flow in L/min				
	380	500	600	700	800
	Friction Loss in kPa				
15	53	92	133	181	236
30	107	185	266	362	472
45	160	277	399	542	708
60	213	369	531	723	945
75	266	461	664	904	1 181
90	320	554	797	1 085	1 417
105	373	646	930	1 266	1 653
120	426	738	1 063	1 446	
135	480	830	1 196	1 627	
150	533	923	1 328		

Table E.5
50 mm Hose
C-Factor: 12.7

Lay Length Meters	Flow in L/min				
	400	500	600	700	800
	Friction Loss in kPa				
15	30	48	69	93	122
30	61	95	137	187	244
45	91	143	206	280	366
60	122	191	274	373	488
75	152	238	343	467	610
90	183	286	411	560	732
105	213	333	480	653	853
120	244	381	549	747	975
135	274	429	617	840	1 097
150	305	476	686	933	1 219

Table E.6
65 mm Hose
C-Factor: 3.17

Lay Length Meters	700	800	900	1 000	1 100	1 200	1 400
	\multicolumn{7}{c}{Flow in L/min}						

Lay Length Meters	700	800	900	1 000	1 100	1 200	1 400
	\multicolumn{7}{c}{Friction Loss in kPa}						
15	23	30	39	48	58	68	93
30	47	61	77	95	115	137	186
45	70	91	116	143	173	205	280
60	93	122	154	190	230	274	373
75	116	152	193	238	288	342	466
90	140	183	231	285	345	411	559
105	163	213	270	333	403	479	652
120	186	243	308	380	460	548	746
135	210	274	347	428	518	616	839
150	233	304	385	476	575	685	932
165	256	335	424	523	633	753	1 025
180	280	365	462	571	690	822	1 118
195	303	396	501	618	748	890	1 212
210	326	426	539	666	805	959	1 305
225	349	456	578	713	863	1 027	1 398
240	373	487	616	761	921	1 096	1 491
255	396	517	655	808	978	1 164	1 584
270	419	548	693	856	1 036	1 232	1 678
285	443	578	732	903	1 093	1 301	
300	466	609	770	951	1 151	1 369	
315	489	639	809	999	1 208	1 438	
330	513	670	847	1 046	1 266	1 506	
345	536	700	886	1 094	1 323	1 575	
360	559	730	924	1 141	1 381	1 643	
375	582	761	963	1 189	1 438	1 712	
390	606	791	1 001	1 236	1 496		
405	629	822	1 040	1 284	1 553		
420	652	852	1 078	1 331	1 611		
435	676	883	1 117	1 379	1 669		
450	699	913	1 155	1 427			
465	722	943	1 194	1 474			
480	746	974	1 232	1 522			
495	769	1 004	1 271	1 569			
510	792	1 035	1 310	1 617			
525	815	1 065	1 348	1 664			
540	839	1 096	1 387	1 712			
555	862	1 126	1 425				
570	885	1 156	1 464				
585	909	1 187	1 502				
	932	1 217	1 541				

			Flow in L/min			
	1 000	1 200	1 400	2 000	3 000	4 000
Lay Length Meters	Friction Loss in kPa					
15	19	27	37	76	171	305
30	38	55	75	152	343	610
45	57	82	112	229	514	914
60	76	110	149	305	686	1 219
75	95	137	187	381	857	1 524
90	114	165	224	457	1 029	
105	133	192	261	533	1 200	
120	152	219	299	610	1 372	
135	171	247	336	686	1 543	
150	191	274	373	762	1 715	
165	210	302	411	838		
180	229	329	448	914		
195	248	357	485	991		
210	267	384	523	1 067		
225	286	411	560	1 143		
240	305	439	597	1 219		
255	324	466	635	1 295		
270	343	494	672	1 372		
285	362	521	709	1 448		
300	381	549	747	1 524		
315	400	576	784	1 600		
330	419	604	821	1 676		
345	438	631	859			
360	457	658	896			
375	476	686	933			
390	495	713	971			
405	514	741	1 008			
420	533	768	1 045			
435	552	796	1 083			
450	572	823	1 120			
465	591	850	1 157			
480	610	878	1 195			
495	629	905	1 232			
510	648	933	1 269			
525	667	960	1 307			
540	686	988	1 344			
555	705	1 015	1 382			
570	724	1 042	1 419			
585	743	1 070	1 456			
	762	1 097	1 494			

Table E.7
77 mm Hose with 65 mm Couplings
C-Factor: 1.27

Table E.8
77 mm Hose with 77 mm Couplings
C-Factor: 1.06

Lay Length Meters	Flow in L/min					
	1 000	1 200	1 400	2 000	3 000	4 000
	Friction Loss in kPa					
15	16	23	31	64	143	254
30	32	46	62	127	286	509
45	48	69	93	191	429	763
60	64	92	125	254	572	1 018
75	80	114	156	318	716	1 272
90	95	137	187	382	859	1 526
105	111	160	218	445	1 002	
120	127	183	249	509	1 145	
135	143	206	280	572	1 288	
150	159	229	312	636	1 431	
165	175	252	343	700	1 574	
180	191	275	374	763	1 717	
195	207	298	405	827		
210	223	321	436	890		
225	239	343	467	954		
240	254	366	499	1 018		
255	270	389	530	1 081		
270	286	412	561	1 145		
285	302	435	592	1 208		
300	318	458	623	1 272		
315	334	481	654	1 336		
330	350	504	686	1 399		
345	366	527	717	1 463		
360	382	550	748	1 526		
375	398	572	779	1 590		
390	413	595	810	1 654		
405	429	618	841	1 717		
420	445	641	873			
435	461	664	904			
450	477	687	935			
465	493	710	966			
480	509	733	997			
495	525	756	1 028			
510	541	778	1 060			
525	557	801	1 091			
540	572	824	1 122			
555	588	847	1 153			
570	604	870	1 184			
585	620	893	1 215			
	636	916	1 247			

	Table E.9					
	100 mm Hose					
	C-Factor: 0.305					

	Flow in L/min					
	2 000	3 000	4 000	5 000	6 000	7 000
Lay Length Meters	**Friction Loss in kPa**					
15	18	41	73	114	165	224
30	37	82	146	229	329	448
45	55	124	220	343	494	673
60	73	165	293	458	659	897
75	92	206	366	572	824	1 121
90	110	247	439	686	988	
105	128	288	512	801	1 153	
120	146	329	586	915		
135	165	371	659	1 029		
150	183	412	732	1 144		
165	201	453	805	1 258		
180	220	494	878			
195	238	535	952			
210	256	576	1 025			
225	275	618	1 098			
240	293	659	1 171			
255	311	700	1 244			
270	329	741				
285	348	782				
300	366	824				
315	384	865				
330	403	906				
345	421	947				
360	439	988				
375	458	1 029				
390	476	1 071				
405	494	1 112				
420	512	1 153				
435	531	1 194				
450	549	1 235				
465	567	1 276				
480	586					
495	604					
510	622					
525	641					
540	659					
555	677					
570	695					
585	714					
	732					

Lay Length Meters	Flow in L/min					
	2 000	3 000	4 000	5 000	6 000	7 000
	Friction Loss in kPa					
15	10	23	40	63	90	123
30	20	45	80	125	180	245
45	30	68	120	188	271	368
60	40	90	160	251	361	491
75	50	113	200	313	451	614
90	60	135	240	376	541	736
105	70	158	281	438	631	859
120	80	180	321	501	721	982
135	90	203	361	564	812	1 105
150	100	225	401	626	902	1 227
165	110	248	441	689	992	
180	120	271	481	752	1 082	
195	130	293	521	814	1 172	
210	140	316	561	877	1 263	
225	150	338	601	939		
240	160	361	641	1 002		
255	170	383	681	1 065		
270	180	406	721	1 127		
285	190	428	762	1 190		
300	200	451	802	1 253		
315	210	473	842			
330	220	496	882			
345	230	519	922			
360	240	541	962			
375	251	564	1 002			
390	261	586	1 042			
405	271	609	1 082			
420	281	631	1 122			
435	291	654	1 162			
450	301	676	1 202			
465	311	699	1 242			
480	321	721				
495	331	744				
510	341	767				
525	351	789				
540	361	812				
555	371	834				
570	381	857				
585	391	879				
	401	902				

Table D.11
125 mm Hose
C-Factor: 0.138

Lay Length Meters	Flow in L/min					
	3 000	4 000	5 000	6 000	7 000	8 000
	Friction Loss in kPa					
15	19	33	52	75	101	132
30	37	66	104	149	203	265
45	56	99	155	224	304	397
60	75	132	207	298	406	530
75	93	166	259	373	507	662
90	112	199	311	447	609	795
105	130	232	362	522	710	927
120	149	265	414	596	811	1 060
135	168	298	466	671	913	1 192
150	186	331	518	745	1 014	
165	205	364	569	820	1 116	
180	224	397	621	894	1 217	
195	242	431	673	969		
210	261	464	725	1 043		
225	279	497	776	1 118		
240	298	530	828	1 192		
255	317	563	880	1 267		
270	335	596	932			
285	354	629	983			
300	373	662	1 035			
315	391	696	1 087			
330	410	729	1 139			
345	428	762	1 190			
360	447	795	1 242			
375	466	828				
390	484	861				
405	503	894				
420	522	927				
435	540	960				
450	559	994				
465	578	1 027				
480	596	1 060				
495	615	1 093				
510	633	1 126				
525	652	1 159				
540	671	1 192				
555	689	1 225				
570	708	1 259				
585	727					
	745					

Table E.12
Two 65 mm Hoses
C-Factor: 0.789

	Flow in L/min					
	1 000	2 000	3 000	4 000	5 000	6 000
Lay Length Meters	Friction Loss in kPa					
15	12	47	107	189	296	426
30	24	95	213	379	592	852
45	36	142	320	568	888	1 278
60	47	189	426	757	1 184	1 704
75	59	237	533	947	1 479	
90	71	284	639	1 136	1 775	
105	83	331	746	1 326		
120	95	379	852	1 515		
135	107	426	959	1 704		
150	118	473	1 065			
165	130	521	1 172			
180	142	568	1 278			
195	154	615	1 385			
210	166	663	1 491			
225	178	710	1 598			
240	189	757	1 704			
255	201	805				
270	213	852				
285	225	899				
300	237	947				
315	249	994				
330	260	1 041				
345	272	1 089				
360	284	1 136				
375	296	1 184				
390	308	1 231				
405	320	1 278				
420	331	1 326				
435	343	1 373				
450	355	1 420				
465	367	1 468				
480	379	1 515				
495	391	1 562				
510	402	1 610				
525	414	1 657				
540	426	1 704				
555	438	1 752				
570	450					
585	462					
	473					

Table E.13
Three 65 mm Hoses
C-Factor: 0.347

	Flow in L/min					
	1 000	2 000	3 000	4 000	5 000	6 000
Lay Length Meters	Friction Loss in kPa					
15	5	21	47	83	130	187
30	10	42	94	167	260	375
45	16	62	141	250	390	562
60	21	83	187	333	520	750
75	26	104	234	416	651	937
90	31	125	281	500	781	1 124
105	36	146	328	583	911	1 312
120	42	167	375	666	1 04.	1 499
135	47	187	422	750	1 171	1 686
150	52	208	468	833	1 301	
165	57	229	515	916	1 431	
180	62	250	562	999	1 561	
195	68	271	609	1 083	1 692	
210	73	291	656	1 166		
225	78	312	703	1 249		
240	83	333	750	1 332		
255	88	354	796	1 416		
270	94	375	843	1 499		
285	99	396	890	1 582		
300	104	416	937	1 666		
315	109	437	984	1 749		
330	115	458	1 031			
345	120	479	1 077			
360	125	500	1 124			
375	130	520	1 171			
390	135	541	1 218			
405	141	562	1 265			
420	146	583	1 312			
435	151	604	1 359			
450	156	625	1 405			
465	161	645	1 452			
480	167	666	1 499			
495	172	687	1 546			
510	177	708	1 593			
525	182	729	1 640			
540	187	750	1 686			
555	193	770				
570	198	791				
585	203	812				
	208	833				

Table E.14 One 77 mm and One 65 mm Hose C-Factor: 0.473

	Flow in L/min					
	2 000	3 000	4 000	5 000	6 000	7 000
Lay Length Meters	Friction Loss in kPa					
15	28	54	102	192	364	688
30	57	107	203	384	727	
45	85	161	305	577	1 091	
60	114	215	406	769	1 455	
75	142	268	508	961		
90	170	322	610	1 153		
105	199	376	711	1 345		
120	227	430	813	1 538		
135	255	483	914			
150	284	537	1 016			
165	312	591	1 117			
180	341	644	1 219			
195	369	698	1 321			
210	397	752	1 422			
225	426	805	1 524			
240	454	859	1 625			
255	482	913				
270	511	967				
285	539	1 020				
300	568	1 074				
315	596	1 128				
330	624	1 181				
345	653	1 235				
360	681	1 289				
375	710	1 342				
390	738	1 396				
405	766	1 450				
420	795	1 503				
435	823	1 557				
450	851	1 611				
465	880	1 665				
480	908	1 718				
495	937					
510	965					
525	993					
540	1 022					
555	1 050					
570	1 078					
585	1 107					
	1 135					

Table E.15
Two 65 mm and One 77 mm Hose
C-Factor: 0.253

Lay Length Meters	Flow in L/min					
	2 000	3 000	4 000	5 000	6 000	7 000
	Friction Loss in kPa					
15	15	34	61	95	137	186
30	30	68	121	190	273	372
45	46	102	182	285	410	558
60	61	137	243	380	546	744
75	76	171	304	474	683	930
90	91	205	364	569	820	1 116
105	106	239	425	664	956	1 302
120	121	273	486	759	1 093	1 488
135	137	307	546	854	1 230	1 674
150	152	342	607	949	1 366	
165	167	376	668	1 044	1 503	
180	182	410	729	1 139	1 639	
195	197	444	789	1 233		
210	213	478	850	1 328		
225	228	512	911	1 423		
240	243	546	972	1 518		
255	258	581	1 032	1 613		
270	273	615	1 093	1 708		
285	288	649	1 154			
300	304	683	1 214			
315	319	717	1 275			
330	334	751	1 336			
345	349	786	1 397			
360	364	820	1 457			
375	380	854	1 518			
390	395	888	1 579			
405	410	922	1 639			
420	425	956	1 700			
435	440	990				
450	455	1 025				
465	471	1 059				
480	486	1 093				
495	501	1 127				
510	516	1 161				
525	531	1 195				
540	546	1 230				
555	562	1 264				
570	577	1 298				
585	592	1 332				
	607	1 366				

Table E.16
Two 77 mm Hoses
C-Factor: 0.316

Flow in L/min

Lay Length Meters	2 000	3 000	4 000	5 000	6 000	7 000
	Friction Loss in kPa					
15	19	43	76	119	171	232
30	38	85	152	237	341	465
45	57	128	228	356	512	697
60	76	171	303	474	683	929
75	95	213	379	593	853	1 161
90	114	256	455	711	1 024	
105	133	299	531	830	1 194	
120	152	341	607	948		
135	171	384	683	1 067		
150	190	427	758	1 185		
165	209	469	834			
180	228	512	910			
195	246	555	986			
210	265	597	1 062			
225	284	640	1 138			
240	303	683	1 213			
255	322	725				
270	341	768				
285	360	811				
300	379	853				
315	398	896				
330	417	939				
345	436	981				
360	455	1 024				
375	474	1 067				
390	493	1 109				
405	512	1 152				
420	531	1 194				
435	550	1 237				
450	569					
465	588					
480	607					
495	626					
510	645					
525	664					
540	683					
555	702					
570	720					
585	739					
	758					

Table E.17
Two 77 mm and One 65 mm Hose
C-Factor: 0.189

Lay Length Meters	Flow in L/min					
	2 000	3 000	4 000	5 000	6 000	7 000
	Friction Loss in kPa					
15	11	26	45	71	102	139
30	23	51	91	142	204	278
45	34	77	136	213	306	417
60	45	102	181	284	408	556
75	57	128	227	354	510	695
90	68	153	272	425	612	833
105	79	179	318	496	714	972
120	91	204	363	567	816	1 111
135	102	230	408	638	919	1 250
150	113	255	454	709	1 021	1 389
165	125	281	499	780	1 123	1 528
180	136	306	544	851	1 225	1 667
195	147	332	590	921	1 327	
210	159	357	635	992	1 429	
225	170	383	680	1 063	1 531	
240	181	408	726	1 134	1 633	
255	193	434	771	1 205	1 735	
270	204	459	816	1 276		
285	215	485	862	1 347		
300	227	510	907	1 418		
315	238	536	953	1 488		
330	249	561	998	1 559		
345	261	587	1 043	1 630		
360	272	612	1 089	1 701		
375	284	638	1 134			
390	295	663	1 179			
405	306	689	1 225			
420	318	714	1 270			
435	329	740	1 315			
450	340	765	1 361			
465	352	791	1 406			
480	363	816	1 452			
495	374	842	1 497			
510	386	868	1 542			
525	397	893	1 588			
540	408	919	1 633			
555	420	944	1 678			
570	431	970	1 724			
585	442	995				
	454	1 021				

Appendix F
Sample Fire Department Annual Pumper Service Test Record

FIRE DEPARTMENT ANNUAL PUMPER SERVICE TEST RECORD

City of _____

Unit #: _____ Date: _____ Time: _____ Pump Serial Number _____

Type of Primer _____ Engine oil level start _____ Engine oil level finish _____

Ambient air temperature _____ Ambient water temperature _____

Barometric pressure _____ (Go to http://www.weather.gov)

INTAKE SIDE LAYOUT

Length of suction hose: _____ Diameter of suction hose _____

Lift distance from centerline of intake: _____ Priming time in seconds _____
(Priming time shall not exceed 30 secs for pumps to 1250 GPM capacity and 45 secs for larger pumps)

Suction strainer submerged at least 2 ft? _____ _____ Electrical devices on? _____

Discharge hose couplings marked? _____

_____

VACUUM TEST

1. Open all intake valves. Cap or plug inlets. _____

2. Remove all discharge caps. Close all discharges. _____

3. Operate primer and attain at least 22" Hg. Record start time after at least 22" Hg point is reached and primer if "OFF". _____

4. Vacuum should not drop more than 10" Hg in 5 minutes. Record finish time _____

5. Primer shall not be used to reestablish vacuum after test has started.

6. Engine is to be operated at or below governed speed.

Pass _____ Fail _____

100% CAPACITY TEST DATA (Record test data at 5 minute intervals)(20 minute test)

Number of hose lines: _____ Length of hose lines: _____ Diameter of hose: _____

Nozzle tip size: _____ Average intake pressure: _____ Average discharge pressure: _____

Pressure Control Test @ 100 % Capacity

Test #1 1. Set flow to capacity @ 150 PSI.

2. Set relief valve @150 PSI

3. Close discharge valves no faster than 3 secs and no slower than 10 secs.

4. Pressure rise shall not exceed 30 PSI.

Pressure rise _____ Pass _____ Fail _____

Test #2 1. Set flow to capacity @150 PSI.

2. Reduce pressure by throttle manipulation only to 90 PSI.

3. Set relief valve @ 90 PSI

4. Close discharge valves no faster than 3 secs and no slower than 10 secs.

5. Pressure rise shall not exceed 30 PSI,

Pressure rise _____ Pass _____ Fail _____

Time	Discharge Pressure	Intake Pressure	Nozzle Pressure	GPM Flow	Engine RPM	Per Cent of Peak speed	Engine Temp	Oil Pressure
Start								
5 Min								
10 Min								
15 Min								
20 Min								

165% CAPACITY (OVERLOAD) TEST   (5 minute test)

Hose layout remains the same as the 100% capacity test

Time	Discharge Pressure	Intake Pressure	Nozzle Pressure	GPM Flow	Engine RPM	Per cent of Peak speed	Engine Temp	Oil Pressure
Start								
5 Min								

70% CAPACITY TEST DATA (Record test data at 5 minute intervals)(10 minute test)

Number of hose lines: _____   Length of hose lines: _____   Diameter of hose: _____

Nozzle tip size: _____   Average intake pressure: _____   Average discharge pressure: _____

Time	Discharge Pressure	Intake Pressure	Nozzle Pressure	GPM Flow	Engine RPM	Per cent of Peak speed	Engine Temp	Oil Pressure
Start								
5 Min								
10 Min								

50% CAPACITY TEST DATA (Record test data at 5 minute intervals)(10 minute test)

Number of hose lines: _____   Length of hose lines:_____   Diameter of hose: _____

Nozzle tip size: _____   Average intake pressure: _____   Average discharge pressure: _____

Time	Discharge Pressure	Intake Pressure	Nozzle Pressure	GPM Flow	Engine RPM	Per cent of Peak speed	Engine Temp	Oil Pressure
Start								
5 Min								
10 Min								

Pressure Control Test at 50% Capacity

1. Set flow to capacity @ 250 PSI.
2. Set relief valve @ 250 PSI.
3. Close all discharge valves no faster than 3 secs and no slower than 10 secs.
4. Pressure rise shall not exceed 30 PSI.

Pressure Rise _____ Pass _____ Fail _____

TANK TO PUMP FLOW RATE TEST

1. Fill booster tank until it overflows.
2. Close all pump intakes.
3. Close tank fill and bypass cooling line.
4. Connect hose(s) for anticipated flow rate.
5. Open tank to pump and appropriate discharge lines.
6. Adjust throttle to maximum constant pressure and measure flow. Record data.
7. Close all valves and refill booster tank
8. Conduct second test, going immediately to discharge pressure found in (6) above.
9. Measure flow and record data.

Capacity of booster tank _____ Measured flow rate _____

Number of hose lines: _____ Length of hose lines: _____

Diameter of hose: _____ Nozzle tip size: _____ Pitot reading _____

Tested by_____

Assisted by _____

_____

Test location _____

Glossary

Glossary

A

Acceleration Skids — Sliding and loss of control caused by applying a vehicles gas pedal too quickly.

Acceptance Testing — Preservice tests on fire apparatus or equipment, performed at the factory or after delivery, to assure the purchaser that the apparatus or equipment meets bid specifications.

Acute — Sharp or severe; having a rapid onset and short duration.

Aeration — Introduction of air into a foam solution to create bubbles that result in finished foam.

Aerial Apparatus — Fire fighting vehicle equipped with a hydraulically operated ladder, elevating platform, or other similar device for the purpose of placing personnel and/or water streams in elevated positions.

Aerial Device — General term used to describe the hydraulically operated ladder or elevating platform attached to a specially designed fire apparatus.

Aerial Ladder — Power-operated ladder, usually employing hydraulics, that is mounted on a special truck chassis.

Aerial Ladder Truss — Assembly of bracing bars or rods in triangular shapes that form a rigid framework for the aerial device.

Air-Actuated Braking Systems — Braking system that uses compressed air to hold off a spring brake (parking brake) and applies air pressure to a service brake for vehicle stopping.

Air Brake Test — Series of tests used to ensure the serviceability of an air braking system. Tests include air loss, air compressor buildup, air warning, and emergency parking brake activation.

Air Drop — Process of dropping water, short-term fire retardant, or long-term fire retardant from an air tanker or helicopter onto a wildland fire.

Alcohol-Resistant Aqueous Film Forming Foam Concentrate (AR-AFFF) — Aqueous film forming foam that is designed for use with polar solvent fuels. *See* Aqueous Film Forming Foam and Foam Concentrate.

All-Hazard Concept — A coordinated approach to a wide variety of incidents; all responders use a similar, coordinated approach with a common set of authorities, protections, and resources.

Altitude — Geographic position of a location or object in relation to sea level. The location may be either above, below, or at sea level.

Ammeter — Gauge that indicates both the amount of electrical current being drawn from and provided to the vehicle's battery.

Anchor Point — Point from which a fire line is begun; usually a natural or man-made barrier that prevents fire spread and the possibility of the crew being "flanked" while constructing the fire line. Examples include lakes, ponds, streams, roads, earlier burns, rockslides, and cliffs.

Anti-Lock Braking Systems — An electronic system that monitors wheel spin. When braking and a wheel are sensed to begin locking up, the brake on that wheel is temporarily released to prevent skidding.

Apparatus Typing — Categorization and description of apparatus commonly exchanged in disasters via mutual aid by capacity and/or capability.

Application Rate — Minimum amount of foam solution that must be applied to an unignited fire, spill, or spill fire to either control vapor emission or extinguish the fire; measured per minute per square foot (or square meter) of area to be covered.

Aqueous Film Forming Foam (AFFF) — Synthetic foam concentrate that, when combined with water, can form a complete vapor barrier over fuel spills and fires and is a highly effective extinguishing and blanketing agent on hydrocarbon fuels. *Also known as* light water.

Around-the-Pump Proportioner — Apparatus-mounted foam proportioner in which a small quantity of water is diverted from the apparatus pump through an inline proportioner; there it picks up the foam concentrate and carries it to the intake side of the pump. It is the most common apparatus-mounted foam proportioner in service.

Articulating Aerial Platform — Aerial device that consists of two or more booms that are attached with hinges and operate in a folding manner. A passenger-carrying platform is attached to the working end of the device.

Atypically Stressful Event — Term used in National Fire Protection Association® (NFPA®) standards to describe incidents that have a likelihood of causing critical incident stress.

Auger — Tool for boring (drilling) holes in floors and other solid barriers including ice.

B

Back Flushing — Cleaning a fire pump or piping by flowing water through it in the opposite direction of normal flow.

Back Pressure — Pressure loss or gain created by changes in elevation between the nozzle and pump.

Baffle — Intermediate partial bulkhead that reduces the surge effect in a partially loaded liquid tank.

Base — Location at which the primary Incident Management Logistics functions are coordinated and administered; the Incident Command Post may be co-located with the base. There is only one base per incident.

Battalion — Fire department organizational subdivision consisting of several fire service companies in a designated geographic area. A battalion is usually the first organizational level above individual companies or stations.

Batch Mixing — Production of foam solution by adding an appropriate amount of foam concentrate to a water tank before application; the resulting solution must be used or discarded following the incident.

Bed Ladder Pipe — Nontelescoping section of pipe, usually 3 or 3½ inches (77 or 90 mm) in diameter, attached to the underside of the bed section of the aerial ladder for the purpose of deploying an elevated master stream.

Biodegradable — Capable of being broken down into innocuous products by the actions of living things, such as microorganisms.

Bleed — Process of releasing a liquid or gas under pressure, such as releasing air from the regulator or cylinder of a self-contained breathing apparatus; or allowing air to escape from a hoseline before or during operations.

Blitz Attack — Attack a fire aggressively from the exterior with a large diameter (2½-inch [65 mm] or larger) fire stream.

Body Substance Isolation (BSI) — Comprehensive method of infection control in which every patient is assumed to be infected; personal protective equipment is worn to prevent exposure to bodily fluids and bloodborne and airborne pathogens.

Box Stabilizer — Two-piece aerial apparatus stabilization device consisting of an extension arm that extends directly out from the vehicle and a lifting jack that extends from the end of the extension arm to the ground. *Also known as* H-Jack or H-stabilizers.

Brake Fade — Loss of braking function that occurs due to excessive use of the brakes.

Braking Distance — Distance the vehicle travels from the time the brakes are applied until it comes to a complete stop.

Burnback Resistance — Ability of a foam blanket to resist direct flame impingement such as in a partially extinguished petroleum fire.

C

Carcinogen — Cancer-producing substance.

Cavitation — Condition in which vacuum pockets form, due to localized regions of low pressure at the vanes in the impeller of a centrifugal pump causing vibrations, loss of efficiency, and possibly damage to the impeller.

Centrifugal Pump — Pump with one or more impellers that rotate and utilize centrifugal force to move the water. Most modern fire pumps are of this type.

Chain of Command — Order of rank and authority in the fire and emergency services.

Chassis Lubrication — Applying grease and other lubricants to specific parts of a chassis to reduce wear, noise, and binding.

Check Valves — Automatic valve that permits liquid flow in only one direction. For example, the inline valve that prevents water from flowing into a foam concentrate container when the nozzle is turned off or there is a kink in the hoseline.

Chronic — Long-term and reoccurring.

Chronic Obstructive Pulmonary Disease (COPD) — Term for several diseases that result in obstructive problems in the airways.

Circle or Walk-Around Method — Inspection method in which the driver or inspector starts at one point of the apparatus and continues in either a clockwise or counterclockwise direction inspecting the entire apparatus.

Cistern — Water storage receptacle that is usually underground and may be supplied by a well or rainwater runoff.

Clapper Valves — Hinged valve that permits the flow of water in one direction only.

Class A Foam Concentrate — Foam specially designed for use on Class A combustibles. Class A foams, hydrocarbon-based surfactants are essentially wetting agents that reduce the surface tension of water and allow it to soak into combustible materials more easily than plain water. Class A foams are becoming increasingly popular for use in wildland and structural fire fighting. *Also known as* Class A Foam.

Class B Foam Concentrate — Foam fire suppression agent designed for use on ignited or unignited Class B flammable or combustible liquids. *Also known as* Class B Foam.

Cold Zone — Safe area outside of the warm zone where equipment and personnel are not expected to become contaminated and special protective clothing is not required; the Incident Command Post and other support functions are typically located in this zone.

Collapse Zone — Area beneath a wall in which the wall is likely to land if it loses structural integrity.

Commercial Drivers' License (CDL) — A driver's license that is issued to individuals who demonstrate competence inspecting and driving vehicles with a Gross Vehicle Rating of 26,001 pounds or more.

Company — Basic fire fighting organizational unit consisting of firefighters and apparatus; headed by a company officer.

Compressed Air Foam Systems (CAFS) — Generic term used to describe a high-energy foam-generation system consisting of a water pump, a foam proportioning system, and an air compressor (or other air source) that injects air into the foam solution before it enters a hoseline.

Culture — The shared assumptions, beliefs, and values of a group or organization.

D

Deadheading — Operating a hydraulic pump without allowing flow through the system, which generates tremendous heat and pressure and can damage components.

Decomposition — Chemical change in which a substance breaks down into two or more simpler substances. Result of oxygen acting on a material that result in a change in the material's composition; oxidation occurs slowly, sometimes resulting in the rusting of metals.

Defensive Attack — Exterior fire attack that is limited to controlling the spread of a fire, with an emphasis on exposure protection. *Also known as* Defensive Fire Attack.

Dependable Lift — Height a column of water may be lifted in sufficient quantity to provide a reliable fire flow. Lift may be raised through a hard suction hose to a pump, taking into consideration the atmospheric pressure and friction loss within the hard suction hose; dependable lift is usually considered to be 14.7 feet (4.48 m).

Diesel Particulate Filter (DPF) — Device designed to remove diesel particulate matter or soot from the exhaust gas of a diesel engine.

Distribution Systems — Part of an overall water supply system that receives the water from the pumping station and delivers it throughout the area to be served.

Drafting — Process of acquiring water from a static source and transferring it into a pump that is above the source's level; atmospheric pressure on the water surface forces the water into the pump where a partial vacuum was created.

Dry-Barrel Hydrant — Fire hydrant that has its operating valve at the water main rather than in the barrel of the hydrant. When operating properly, there is no water in the barrel of the hydrant when it is not in use. These hydrants are used in areas where freezing may occur.

Dry Hydrant — Permanently installed pipe that has pumper suction connections installed at static water sources to speed drafting operations.

Dual Pumping — Operation where a strong hydrant is used to supply two pumpers by connecting the pumpers intake-to-intake. The second pumper receives the excess water not being pumped by the first pumper, which is directly connected to the water supply source.

Due Regard — Driver/operators drive with "due regard" for the safety of others using the highways. State vehicle codes provide and give special privileges to the operators or emergency vehicles; however, this does not relieve the operator from the duty and responsibility to drive with "due regard" for the safety of others.

Dump Line — Secured hoseline that is used to handle excess water during a relay operation.

Dump Site — Location approved for water shuttle apparatus to discharge their water for other apparatus to draw during incident operations.

Dynamic Load — Loads that involve motion. They include the forces arising from wind, moving vehicles, earthquakes, vibration, or falling objects, as well as the addition of a moving load force to an aerial device or structure. *Also known as* Shock Loading.

E

Eduction — Process used to mix foam concentrate with water in a nozzle or proportioner; concentrate is drawn into the water stream by the Venturi method.

Eductor — (1) Portable proportioning device that injects a liquid, such as foam concentrate, into the water flowing through a hoseline or pipe. (2) Venturi device that uses water pressure to draw foam concentrate into a water stream for mixing; also enables a pump to draw water from an auxiliary source.

Elevating Platform — Work platform attached to the end of an articulating or telescoping aerial device.

Elevation — Height of a point above sea level or some other reference point.

Elevation Pressure — Gain or loss of pressure in a hoseline due to a change in elevation. *Also known as* Elevation Loss.

Engine Compression Brake — Any device that uses the engine and transmission to impede the forward motion of the motor vehicle by compression of the engine.

F

Fill Site — Location at which tankers/tenders will be loaded during a water shuttle operation.

Film Forming Fluoroprotein Foam (FFFP) — Foam concentrate that combines the qualities of fluoroprotein foam with those of aqueous film forming foam.

Fireboat — Vessel or watercraft designed and constructed for the purpose of fighting fires; provides a specified level of pumping capacity and personnel for the extinguishment of fires in the marine environment. *Also known as* Marine Unit.

Fire Department Connection (FDC) — Point at which the fire department can connect into a sprinkler or standpipe system to boost the water pressure and flow in the system. This connection consists of a clappered siamese with two or more 2½-inch (64 mm) intakes or one large-diameter (4-inch [102 mm] or larger) intake.

Fire Fighting Boots — Protective footwear meeting the design requirements of NFPA®, OSHA, and CAN/CSA Z195-02 (R2008).

Fire Flow Testing — Procedure used to determine the rate of water flow available for fire fighting at various points within the distribution system.

Flowmeter — Mechanical device installed in a discharge line that senses the amount of water flowing and provides a readout in units of gallons per minute or (liters per minute).

Fly Section — Extendable section of ground extension or aerial ladder. *Also known as* Fly.

Foam — Extinguishing agent formed by mixing a foam concentrate with water and aerating the solution for expansion; for use on Class A and Class B fires. Foam may be protein, fluoroprotein, film forming fluoroprotein, synthetic, aqueous film forming, high expansion, alcohol type, or alcohol-resistant type.

Foam Concentrate — (1) Raw chemical compound solution that is mixed with water and air to produce finished foam; may be protein, synthetic, aqueous film forming, high expansion, or alcohol types. (2) Raw foam liquid as it rests in its storage container before the introduction of water and air.

Foam Expansion — Result of adding air to a foam solution consisting of water and foam concentrate. Expansion creates the foam bubbles that result in finished foam or foam blanket.

Foam Proportioner — Device that injects the correct amount of foam concentrate into the water stream to make the foam solution.

Foam Solution — (1) The result of mixing the appropriate amount of foam concentrate with water; foam solution exists between the proportioner and the nozzle or aerating device that adds air to create finished foam. (2) The mixture of foam concentrate and water before the introduction of air.

Fog Stream — Water stream of finely divided particles used for fire control.

Force — Simple measure of weight, usually expressed in pounds or kilograms.

Four-Way Hydrant Valve — Device that permits a pumper to boost the pressure in a supply line connected to a hydrant without interrupting the water flow.

Free Play — Amount of travel the clutch has before it begins to disengage the engine from the transmission.

Friction Loss — Loss of pressure created by the turbulence of water moving against the interior walls of the hose or pipe.

Front-Mount Pump — Fire pump mounted in front of the radiator of a vehicle and powered off the crankshaft.

Fulcrum-Type Stabilizer — Stabilizing device that extends at an angle down and away from the chassis of an aerial fire apparatus. *Also known as* A-Frame, Scissor, or X-Style Stabilizer.

Functional Check — An inspection where a certain system or component of an apparatus is operated to ensure that it is functioning properly.

G

Gelling Agents — Superabsorbent liquid polymers capable of absorbing hundreds of times their own weight in water. These gels can be used as fire suppressants and fire retardants. Gels function by entrapping water in their structure rather than air, as is the case with fire fighting foams. *Also known as* Durable Agents.

Gravity Circle — Theoretical safety zone that surrounds the center of gravity on an aerial apparatus.

Grid System — Water supply system that utilizes lateral feeders for improved distribution.

Gross Axle Weight Rating — Maximum amount of weight that an axle system can safely carry.

Gross Negligence — Willful and wanton disregard.

Ground Fault Circuit Interrupter (GFCI) — Device designed to protect against electrical shock; when grounding occurs, the device opens a circuit to shut off the flow of electricity. *Also known as* Ground Fault Indicator (GFI) Receptacle.

Ground Gradient — Electrical field that radiates outward from where the current enters the ground; its intensity dissipates rapidly as distance increases from the point of entry.

H

Hazard — Condition, substance, or device that can directly cause injury or loss; the source of a risk.

Hazard-Control Zones — System of barriers surrounding designated areas at emergency scenes, intended to limit the number of persons exposed to a hazard and to facilitate its mitigation. A major incident has three zones: Restricted (Hot) Zone, Limited Access (Warm) Zone, and Support (Cold) Zone.

Head — Alternate term for pressure, especially pressure due to elevation. For every 1-foot increase in elevation, 0.434 psi is gained (for every 1-meter increase in elevation, 9.8 kPa is gained). *Also known as* Head Pressure.

Hearing Protection — Device that limits noise-induced hearing loss when firefighters are exposed to extremely loud environments, such as apparatus engine noise, audible warning devices, and the use of power tools and equipment.

Hoisting Cylinder — Hydraulic cylinders used to lift the aerial device from its bed to a working position. *Also known as* Elevation Cylinder or Lift Cylinder.

Hot Zone — Potentially hazardous area immediately surrounding the incident site; requires appropriate protective clothing and equipment and other safety precautions for entry. Typically limited to technician-level personnel.

Huck Bolt — Mechanically applied rivet used in the construction of some aerial devices; huck bolts can only be removed by drilling.

Hydrant Wrench — Specially designed tool used to open or close a hydrant and to remove hydrant caps.

Hydraulic Braking Systems — Braking system that uses a fluid in a closed system to pressurize wheel cylinders when activated.

Hydrocarbon Fuel — Petroleum-based organic compound that contains only hydrogen and carbon.

Hydrolyze — To cause or undergo a chemical process of decomposition involving the splitting of a bond and the addition of the element of water.

Hydrostatic Test — Testing method that uses water under pressure to check the integrity of pressure vessels.

I

Ice Shrugging — Slowly extending and retracting the aerial device to remove accumulated ice.

Immediately Dangerous to Life and Health (IDLH) — Description of any atmosphere that poses an immediate hazard to life or produces immediate irreversible, debilitating effects on health.

Impeller — Vaned, circulating member of the centrifugal pump that transmits motion to the water.

Impeller Eye — Intake orifice at the center of a centrifugal pump impeller.

Incident Commander (IC) — Person in charge of the Incident Command System and responsible for the management of all incident operations during an emergency.

Incident Management System (IMS) — System described in NFPA® 1561, *Standard on Emergency Services Incident Management System*, that defines the roles, responsibilities, and standard operating procedures used

to manage emergency operations. Such systems may also be referred to as the Incident Command Systems (ICS).

Initial Attack Fire Apparatus — Fire apparatus whose primary purpose is to initiate a fire attack on structural and wildland fires and support associated fire department actions. *Also known as* Midi-Pumper or Mini-Pumper.

Injection — Method of proportioning foam that uses an external pump or head pressure to force foam concentrate into the fire stream at the correct ratio for the flow desired.

In-Line Eductor — Eductor that is placed along the length of a hoseline.

In-Line Proportioner — Type of foam delivery device that is located in the water supply line near the nozzle. The foam concentrate is drawn into the water line using the Venturi method.

Insurance Services Office (ISO) — Private national insurance organization that evaluates and rates fire defense for all communities through the fire-suppression rating schedule. Also serves as an advisory organization to other property-liability insurance companies. *Also known as* Rating Bureau.

Intake Hose — Hose used to connect a fire department pumper or a portable pump to a nearby water source; may be soft sleeve or hard suction hose.

Interlock — Safety device that prevents a component from functioning when another component is functioning.

Inverter — Step-up transformer that converts a vehicle's 12- or 24-volt DC current into 110- or 220-volt AC current.

J

Jackknifing — Condition of truck tractor/semitrailer combination when their relative positions to each other form an angle of 90 degrees or less about the trailer kingpin, such as turning the tractor portion of a tractor-tiller aerial apparatus at an angle from the trailer to increase stability when the aerial device is being used.

Jet Ratio Controller (JRC) — Type of foam eductor that is used to supply self-educting master stream nozzles; may be located at distances up to 3,000 feet (900 m) from the nozzle.

K

Kickplate — Four-inch (100 mm) metal plate that runs around the bottom edge of an elevating platform to prevent a firefighter's foot from slipping off the edge of the platform. *Also known as* Footplate.

Knuckle — Joint between two sections of boom in an articulating aerial device.

L

Large Diameter Hose (LDH) — Relay-supply hose of 3½ to 6 inches (90 to 150 mm) in diameter; used to move large volumes of water quickly with a minimum number of pumpers and personnel.

Level I Staging — Used on all multiple-company emergency responses. The first-arriving vehicles of each type proceed directly to the scene, and the others stand by a block or two from the scene and await orders. Units usually stage at the last intersection on their route of travel before reaching the reported incident location.

Level II Staging — Used on large-scale incidents where a larger number of fire and emergency services companies are responding; these companies are sent to a specified remote location to await assignment.

Lift — Theoretical, scientific height that a column of water may be lifted by atmospheric pressure in a true vacuum. At sea level, this height is 33.8 feet (10 m). The height will decrease as elevation increases.

Line Personnel — Personnel who provide emergency services to external customers (the public).

Load Chart — Graphical or tabular description of the load that can be distributed on an aerial device based on factors such as extension, elevation, stabilizer setup, wind, waterflow, and ice-load.

Load Management System — Electrical monitoring system that will shed electrical load in a predetermined order if the chassis voltage begins to drop below a predetermined level.

Load Monitor — Device that "watches" an electrical system for added loads that may threaten to overload the system.

Load Sequencer — Device in an electrical system that turns on lights at specified intervals so that the start-up load for all the devices does not occur at the same time.

Load Shedding — When an overload condition occurs, the load monitor shuts down less important electrical equipment to prevent the overload.

Locked Wheel Skid — Skid usually caused by braking too hard at a high rate of speed and locking the wheels. The vehicle will skid no matter which way the steering wheel is turned.

M

Maintenance — Keeping equipment or apparatus in a state of usefulness or readiness.

Manhole — (1) Hole through which a person may go to gain access to an underground or enclosed structure. (2) Opening usually equipped with a removable, lockable cover, that is large enough to admit a person into a tank trailer or dry bulk trailer. *Also known as* Manway.

Manual Shift Transmission — Component of the power train that receives torque from the engine and converts it to rotation to the wheels. A clutch is used to disengage the transmission from the engine to allow the apparatus to start, stop, or change gears to maximize engine performance.

Maximum Lift — Maximum height to which any amount of water may be raised through a hard suction hose to a pump; determined by the ability of the pump to create a vacuum.

Mechanical Blower — High-expansion foam generator that uses a fan to inject the air into the foam solution as it passes through the unit.

Mechanical Foam — Foam produced by a physical agitation of a mixture of foam concentrate, water, and air.

Midi-Pumper — Apparatus sized between a mini-pumper and a full-sized fire department pumper, usually with a gross vehicle weight of 12,000 pounds (6 000 kg) or greater. The midi-pumper has a fire pump with a rated capacity generally not greater than 1,000 gpm (4 000 L/min).

Military Specifications (Mil-Specs) — Specifications developed by the U.S. Department of Defense (DoD) for the purchase of materials and equipment.

Mini-Pumper — Small fire apparatus mounted on a pickup-truck-sized chassis, usually with a pump having a rated capacity less than 500 gpm (2 000 L/min). Its primary advantage is speed and mobility, which enables it to respond to fires more rapidly than larger apparatus.

Miscible — Materials that are capable of being mixed in all proportions.

Mitigate — To cause to become less harsh or hostile; to make less severe, intense or painful; to alleviate.

Mop-Up — (1) Overhaul of a fire or hazardous material scene. (2) In wildland fire fighting, the act of making a fire safe after it is controlled by extinguishing or removing burning material along or near the control line, felling dead trees (snags), and trenching logs to prevent rolling.

N

National Incident Management System - Incident Command System (NIMS-ICS) — U.S. mandated Incident Management System that defines the roles, responsibilities, and standard operating procedures used to manage emergency operations; creates a Unified Incident Response Structure for federal, state, and local governments.

Negligence — Breach of duty in which a person or organization fails to perform at the standard required by law or that would be expected by a reasonable person under similar circumstances.

Net Pump Discharge Pressure (NPDP) — Actual amount of pressure being produced by the pump; difference between the intake pressure and the discharge pressure. *Also known as* Engine Pressure or Net Pressure.

Nondestructive Testing — Method of testing metal objects that does not subject them to stress-related damage.

Nonpotable Water — Water that has not been examined, properly treated, or approved by appropriate authorities as being safe for consumption.

Nozzle Reaction — Counterforce directed against a person holding a nozzle or a device holding a nozzle by the velocity of water being discharged.

Nurse Tanker — Very large water tanker (generally 4,000 gallons [16 000 L] or larger) that is stationed at the fire scene and serves as a portable reservoir rather than as a shuttle tanker. *Also known as* Nurse Tender.

O

Open Butt — End of a charged hoseline that is flowing water without a nozzle or valve to control the flow.

Operational Readiness Inspection — Inspecting an apparatus and equipment on the apparatus to ensure that all equipment is in place, clean, and ready for service.

Outside Screw and Yoke (OS&Y) Valve — Outside stem and yoke valve; a type of control valve for a sprinkler system in which the position of the center screw indicates whether the valve is open or closed.

Overload — Operation of equipment or a conductor in excess of its rated ampacity; continuous overload may result in overheating that damages the equipment.

Overthrottling — Process of injecting or supplying the diesel engine with more fuel than can be burned.

P

Parapet Wall — Vertical extension of an exterior wall, and sometimes an interior fire wall, above the roofline of a building.

Performance Requirements — Written list of expected capabilities for new apparatus. The list is produced by the purchaser and presented to the manufacturer as a guide for what is expected.

Personal Alert Safety System (PASS) — Electronic lack-of-motion sensor that sounds a loud alarm when a firefighter becomes motionless; can also be manually activated.

Personal Protective Equipment (PPE) — General term for the equipment worn by fire and emergency services responders; includes helmets, coats, trousers, boots, eye protection, hearing protection, protective gloves, protective hoods, self-contained breathing apparatus (SCBA), personal alert safety system (PASS) devices, and chemical protective clothing. When working with hazardous materials, bands or tape are added around the legs, arms, and waist.

Pickup Tube — Solid or flexible tube used to transfer foam concentrate from a storage container to the in-line eductor or proportioner.

Pin — Mechanical means to secure the master stream monitor to the ladder; anchoring mechanisms may include pins, levers, or clamps.

Piston pumps — Positive-displacement pump using one or more reciprocating pistons to force water from the pump chambers.

Polar Solvents — Liquid having a molecule in which the positive and negative charges are permanently separated, resulting in their ability to ionize in solution and create electrical conductivity. Water, alcohol, and sulfuric acid are examples of polar solvents.

Policy — Organizational principle that is developed and adopted as a basis for decision-making.

Portable Tank — Collapsible storage tank used during a relay or shuttle operation to hold water from water tanks or hydrants; this water can then be used to supply attack apparatus. *Also known as* Catch Basin, Fold-a-Tank, Porta-Tank, or Portable Basin.

Positive Displacement Pumps — Self-priming pump that utilizes a piston or interlocking rotors to move a given amount of fluid through the pump chamber with each stroke of the piston or rotation of the rotors. Used for hydraulic pumps on aerial devices' hydraulic systems and for priming pumps on centrifugal fire pumps.

Post Indicator Valve (PIV) — Type of valve used to control underground water mains that provides a visual means for indicating "open" or "shut" positions, found on the supply main of installed fire protection systems. The operating stem of the valve extends aboveground through a "post," and a visual means is provided at the top of the post for indicating "open" or "shut."

Post-Maintenance/Repair Inspection — Specific inspection to an area of a chassis or apparatus to ensure that the unit is operating properly in accordance with the manufacturer's initial design.

Postincident Analysis — Overview and critique of an incident by members of all responding agencies, including dispatchers. Typically takes place within two weeks of the incident. In the training environment it may be used to evaluate student and instructor performance during a training evolution.

Posttraumatic Stress Disorder (PTSD) — Disorder caused when persons have been exposed to a traumatic event in which they have experienced, witnessed, or been confronted with an event or events that involve actual death, threatened death, serious injury, or the threat of physical injury to self or others.

Power Take-Off (PTO) System — Mechanism that allows a vehicle engine to power equipment such as a pump, winch, or portable tool; it is typically attached to the transmission.

Preincident Planning — Act of preparing to manage an incident at a particular location or a particular type of incident before an incident occurs.

Premixing — Mixing premeasured portions of water and foam concentrate in a container. Typically, the premix method is used with portable extinguishers, wheeled extinguishers, skid-mounted twin-agent units, and vehicle-mounted tank systems.

Pressure — Force per unit area exerted by a liquid or gas measured in pounds per square inch (psi) or kilopascals (kPa).

Pressure Differential — Effect of altering the atmospheric pressure within a confined space by mechanical means. When air is exhausted from within the space, a low-pressure environment is created and replacement air will be drawn in; when air is blown into the space, a high-pressure environment is created and air within will move to the outside.

Pressure Governor — Pressure control device that controls engine speed, eliminating hazardous conditions that result from excessive pressures.

Pretrip Road Worthiness Inspection — Visual inspection of an apparatus to ensure the major components of the chassis are present and in proper working condition.

Priming Device — Any device, usually a positive-displacement pump, used to exhaust the air from inside a centrifugal pump and the attached hard suction; this creates a partial vacuum, allowing atmospheric pressure to force water from a static source through the suction hose into the centrifugal pump.

Procedure — Outline of the steps that must be performed in order to properly follow an organizational policy. Procedures help an organization to ensure that it consistently approaches a task in the correct way, in order to accomplish a specific objective.

Proportioning — Mixing of water with an appropriate amount of foam concentrate in order to form a foam solution.

Protective Coat — Coat worn during fire fighting, rescue, and extrication operations.

Protective Gloves — Protective clothing designed to protect the hands.

Protective Hood — Hood designed to protect the firefighter's ears, neck, and face from heat and debris; typically made of Nomex®, Kevlar®, or PBI®, and available in long or short styles.

Protective Trousers — Trousers worn to protect the lower torso and legs during emergency operations.

Protein Foam Concentrate — Foam concentrate that consists of a protein hydrolysate plus additives to prevent the concentrate from freezing, prevents corrosion of equipment and containers, prevents bacterial decomposition of the concentrate during storage, and controls viscosity.

Proximity Fire Fighting — Activities required for rescue, fire suppression, and property conservation at fires that produce high radiant, conductive, or convective heat; includes aircraft, hazardous materials transport, and storage tank fires.

Pump and Roll — Ability of an apparatus to pump water while the vehicle is in motion.

Pump Charts — Charts carried on a fire apparatus to aid the pump operator in determining the proper pump discharge pressure when supplying hoselines.

Pump Discharge Pressure (PDP) — Actual pressure of the water as it leaves the pump and enters the hoseline; total amount of pressure being discharged by a pump. In mathematical terms, it is the pump intake pressure plus the net pump discharge pressure. Measured in pounds per square inch.

Pumper Outlet Nozzle — Fire hydrant outlet that is 4 inches (102 mm) in diameter or larger.

Pumper/Tender — Mobile water supply apparatus equipped with a fire pump. In some jurisdictions, this term is used to differentiate a fire pump equipped mobile water supply apparatus whose main purpose is to attack the fire.

Q

Quint — Apparatus that serves as an engine and as a ladder truck; equipped with a fire pump, water tank, ground ladders, hose bed, and aerial device.

R

Reaction Distance — Distance a vehicle travels while a driver transfers a foot from the accelerator to the brake pedal after perceiving the need for stopping.

Reckless Disregard — Act of proceeding to do something with a conscious awareness of danger, while ignoring any potential consequences of so doing. Reckless disregard, while not necessarily suggesting an intent to cause harm, is a harsher condition than ordinary negligence.

Refractometer — Device used to measure the amount of foam concentrate in the solution; operates on the principle of measuring the velocity of light that travels through the foam solution.

Rehabilitation — Allowing firefighters or rescuers to rest, rehydrate, and recover during an incident; also refers to a station at an incident where personnel can rest, rehydrate, and recover.

Relay — To shuttle water between a source and an emergency scene using mobile water supply apparatus.

Relay Operation — Using two or more pumpers to move water over a long distance by operating them in series; water discharged from one pumper flows through hoses to the inlet of the next pumper, and so on.

Repair — To restore or put together something that has become inoperable or out of place.

Rescue Pumper — Specially designed apparatus that combines the functions of both a rescue vehicle and a fire department pumper.

Residual Pressure — Pressure at the test hydrant while water is flowing; represents the pressure remaining in the water supply system while the test water is flowing and is that part of the total pressure that is not used to overcome friction or gravity while forcing water through fire hose, pipe, fittings, and adapters.

Response District — Geographical area to which a particular apparatus is assigned to be first due on a fire or other emergency incident.

Retroreflective Trim — Surfaces such as those used on road signs, emergency vehicle markings, protective clothing, or safety vests which are designed to reflect light along multiple planes at once, giving the surface the appearance of illumination.

Risk — Likelihood of suffering harm from a hazard; exposure to a hazard. The potential for failure or loss.

Risk-Management Plan — Written plan that identifies and analyzes the exposure to hazards, selects appropriate risk management techniques to handle exposures, implements those techniques, and monitors the results.

Road Tests — Preservice apparatus maneuverability tests designed to determine the road-worthiness of a new vehicle.

Roll-On Application Method — Method of foam application in which the foam stream is directed at the ground at the front edge of the unignited or ignited liquid fuel spill; foam then spreads across the surface of the liquid. *Also known as* Bounce.

Rotary Vane Pumps — Type of positive displacement pump commonly used in hydraulic systems. A rotor with attached vanes is mounted off-center inside the pump housing; pressure is imparted on the water as the space between the rotor and the pump housing wall decreases.

S

Safety Data Sheet (SDS) — Form provided by the manufacturer and blender of chemicals that contains information about chemical composition, physical and chemical properties, health and safety hazards, emergency response procedures, and waste disposal procedures of a specified material. *Formerly known as* Material Safety Data Sheet (MSDS).

Selector Valve — Three-way valve on a fire department aerial apparatus that directs oil to either stabilizer control valves or the aerial device control valves. *Also known as* Diverter Valve.

Self-Educting Master Stream Foam Nozzle — Large-capacity nozzle with built-in foam eductor.

Self-Educting Nozzle — Handline nozzle that has the foam eductor built into it. *Also known as* Self-Educting Foam Nozzle.

Shock Loading — Loads that involve motion; includes the forces arising from wind, moving vehicles, earthquakes, vibration, falling objects, or the addition of a moving load force to an aerial device or structure. *Also known as* Dynamic Load.

Short-Jacking — Setting the stabilizers on one side of an apparatus shorter than the stabilizers on the other side; usually done when access for full stabilization is restricted.

Siamese Appliance — Hose appliance that has two or more female inlets and a single male outlet. It is equipped with hinged gates (clapper valves) that prevent water from being discharged through an open inlet.

Situational Awareness — Perception of one's surrounding environment and the ability to anticipate future events.

Size-Up — Ongoing evaluation of influential factors at the scene of an incident.

Skid — Uncontrolled slide across a surface in a wheeled vehicle.

Slack Adjusters — Devices used in an air brake system that connect between the activation pads and the brake pads that compensate for brake pad wear.

Solid Fire Stream — Hose stream that stays together as a solid mass, as opposed to a fog or spray stream; a solid stream is produced by a smooth bore nozzle and should not be confused with a straight stream.

Span of Control — Maximum number of subordinates that one individual can effectively supervise; ranges from three to seven individuals or functions, with five generally established as optimum.

Spotting — (1) Positioning the apparatus in a location that provides the utmost efficiency for operating on the fireground. (2) Positioning a ladder to reach an object or person.

Stabilizer — Device that transfers the center of gravity of an apparatus and prevents it from tipping as the aerial device, hydraulic lifting boom, gin pole, or A-frame is extended away from the centerline of the chassis. *Also known as* Outrigger or Stabilizing Jack.

Stabilizer Pad — Unattached flat metal plate that is larger in area than the stabilizer foot; placed on the ground beneath the intended resting point of the stabilizer foot, in order to provide better weight distribution. *Also known as* Jack Pad or Jack Plate.

Stabilizer Shoe — Flat metal plate attached to the bottom of the aerial apparatus stabilizer to provide firm footing on the stabilizing surface. *Also known as* Stabilizer Boot or Stabilizer Foot.

Staff Personnel — Personnel who provide administrative and logistical support to line units (internal customers).

Staging — Standardized process or procedure by which available resources responding to a fire or other emergency incident are held in reserve at a location away from the incident while awaiting assignment.

Staging Area Manager — Company officer of the first-arriving company at the staging who takes command of the area and is responsible for communicating available resources and resource needs to the operations section chief.

Standard Operating Procedure (SOP) — Formal methods or rules to guide the performance of routine functions or emergency operations. Procedures are typically written in a handbook, so that all firefighters can consult and become familiar with them.

Static Water Supply — Supply of water at rest that does not provide a pressure head for fire suppression but may be employed as a suction source for fire pumps; for example, water in a reservoir, pond, or cistern.

Steamer Connection — Large-diameter outlet, usually 4½ inches (115 mm), at a hydrant or at the base of an elevated water storage container.

Steering Wheel Play — In a steering system, the amount of travel between turning the wheel and when the steering system moves.

Stokes Basket — Wire or plastic basket-type litter suitable for transporting patients from locations where a standard litter would not be easily secured, such as a pile of rubble, a structural collapse, or the upper floor of a building; may be used with a harness for lifting.

Structural Fire Fighting — Activities required for rescue, fire suppression, and property conservation in structures, vehicles, vessels, and similar types of properties.

Structural Firefighters' Protective Clothing — General term for the equipment worn by fire and emergency services responders; includes helmets, coats, pants, boots, eye protection, gloves, protective hoods, self-contained breathing apparatus (SCBA), and personal alert safety system (PASS) devices.

Surfactant — Chemical that lowers the surface tension of a liquid; allows water to spread more rapidly over the surface of Class A fuels and penetrate organic fuels.

T

Tachometer — Instrument that indicates the rotational speed of a shaft in revolutions per minute (rpm); usually indicates engine speed.

Tandem Pumping — Short relay operation in which the pumper taking water from the supply source pumps into the intake of the second pumper; the second pumper then boosts the pressure of the water even higher. This method is used when pressures higher than the capability of a single pump are required.

Telescoping Aerial Platform — Elevating platform equipped with piping systems and nozzles for elevated master stream operations. Telescoping aerial devices are not meant to be climbed and are equipped with a small ladder that is to be used only for escape from the platform in emergency situations.

Tender — Term used within the Incident Command System for a mobile piece of apparatus that has the primary function of supporting another operation; examples include a water tender that supplies water to pumpers, or a fuel tender that supplies fuel to other vehicles.

Theoretical Lift — Theoretical, scientific height that a column of water may be lifted by atmospheric pressure in a true vacuum; at sea level, this height is 33.8 feet (10 m). The height will decrease as elevation increases.

Throw-Out Bearing — Component used to push on the internal clutch fingers connected to the clutch pedal and when activated, disengages the clutch from the engine.

Tillered Trailer — Trailer equipped with steerable rear wheels.

Tiller Operator — Driver/operator of the trailer section of a tractor-tiller aerial ladder apparatus. *Also known as* Tillerman.

Tilt Cab — Truck that uses a cab that lowers over the power train.

Torsional Stress — Twisting action or an applied force resulting in a rotational twist.

Torque — (1) Force that tends to create a rotational or twisting motion. (2) Measurement of engine shaft output. (3) Force that produces or tends to produce a twisting or rotational action.

Total Stopping Distance — Sum of the driver reaction distance and the vehicle braking distance.

Traffic Control Zone — Operational zone established on or near a roadway for the rerouting of traffic and protection of civilians and responders; may include a hot, warm, and cold zone depending on the incident.

Training Evolution — Operation of fire and emergency services training covering one or several aspects of fire fighting.

Trunnion — In a hydraulic cylinder, the pivoting end of the piston rod that is connected to the anchor ear by the heel pin.

Turntable — Rotational structural component of the aerial device. Its primary function is to provide continuous rotation on a horizontal plane.

U

Unity of Command — Organizational principle in which workers report to only one supervisor in order to eliminate conflicting orders.

V

Vacuum — In the fire and emergency services, a pressure that is somewhat less than atmospheric pressure; a vacuum is needed to facilitate drafting of water from a static source.

Variable-Flow Demand-Type Balanced-Pressure Proportioner — Foam proportioning system that is used in both fixed and mobile applications; a variable speed mechanism drives the foam pump and automatically monitors the flow of foam to produce an effective foam solution.

Variable-Flow Variable-Rate Direct-Injection System — Apparatus-mounted foam system that injects the correct amount of foam into the pump piping, thereby supplying all discharges with foam. The system automatically monitors the operation of the hoselines and maintains a consistent quality of foam solution.

Vaulted Surfaces — Ground above underground vaults, such as underground parking structures, utility chases, drainage culverts, and basements, that extends under sidewalks or underground transportation systems.

Venturi Effect — Physical law stating that when a fluid, such as water or air, is forced under pressure through a restricted orifice, there is an increase in the velocity of the fluid passing through the orifice and a corresponding decrease in the pressure exerted against the sides of the constriction. Because the surrounding fluid is under greater (atmospheric) pressure, it is forced into the area of lower pressure.

Voltmeter — Device used for measuring existing voltage in an electrical system.

Volute — Spiral, divergent chamber of a centrifugal pump, in which the velocity energy given to water by the impeller blades is converted into pressure.

W

Warm Zone — Area between the hot and cold zones that usually contains the decontamination corridor; typically requires a lesser degree of personal protective equipment than the Hot Zone.

Water Hammer — Force created by the rapid deceleration of water; causes a violent increase in pressure that can be powerful enough to rupture piping or damage fixtures. Generally results from closing a valve or nozzle too quickly.

Water Supply Pumper — Pumper that takes water from a source and sends it to attack pumpers operating at the fire scene.

Water Tower — Aerial device primarily intended for deploying an elevated master stream; not generally intended for climbing operations. Also known as Elevating Master Stream Device.

Wear Rings — Replaceable rings that are attached to the impeller and/or the pump casing to allow a small running clearance between the impeller and pump casing without causing wear of the actual impeller or pump casing material.

Wet-Barrel Hydrant — Fire hydrant that has water all the way up to the discharge outlets; may have separate valves for each discharge or one valve for all the discharges. This type of hydrant is only used in areas where there is no danger of freezing weather conditions.

Wildland/Urban Interface — Line, area, or zone where an undeveloped wildland area meets a human development area.

Wye — Hose appliance with one female inlet and two or more male outlets; the outlets are usually smaller than the inlet and are usually gated.

Index

hard intake hose service test, 74–75
  NFPA® standards, 29–30
  poor maintenance as cause of accidents, 89
  post-maintenance/repair inspection, 48
  systemic maintenance program, 30
  weekly inspections, 72–73
defined, 29, 30
fire suppression equipment, 48–49
  personal protective equipment (PPE), A-19
  poor maintenance as cause of accidents, 89
Manhole, 523
Manifold lines, calculating pressure loss, 217, 234–237, 260–263
Manual (parked) regeneration switch, 94
Manual on Uniform Traffic Control Devices (MUTCD), 151, A-55
Manual shift transmission, 41, 97, 126–127
Manufacturers' tests, 516–517
MAP. *See* Member assistance program (MAP)
Marine Unit, 21
Master intake and discharge gauges, 324–326
Master streams
  appliance, 200
  calculating pressure loss, 217
  foam nozzle, 504
  nozzles, 199–200
  total pressure loss calculations, 237–239, 263–265
Material Safety Data Sheet (MSDS), 489
Mathematical skills, 82
Maximum lift, 404–405
Mechanical blower, 505
Mechanical failure, as cause of accidents, 89
Mechanical foam, 480
Media functions at incidents, A-14
Medical incidents, positioning apparatus, 155
Medical requirements, A-21
Medium diameter hose, 344
Medium-expansion foam generator, 505
Member assistance program (MAP), A-26–A-30
  stress, A-28–A-30
  substance abuse, A-27
  tobacco use/dependence, A-27–A-28
Mercury and water pressure, 173
Metric conversions, 6–8
Midi-pumper, 16
Midship pumps, 309–311
Military specifications (Mil-Specs), 489
Mini-pumper, 16
Mirror adjustment, 96–97
Miscible liquids, 480, 481
Mission of the fire service, A-5–A-6
Misuse of apparatus, as cause of accidents, 88
Mitigation of hazardous materials incidents, A-11
Mobile water supply
  apparatus, 17–19
    functions, 18
    safety and efficiency requirements, 18

water supply capacity, 17
  hard-suction hose for drafting, A-80–A-81
  operations, A-63
  portable water tank deployment, A-82–A-83
Mop-up, 148
MSDS (Material Safety Data Sheet), 489
Multistage centrifugal fire pumps, 301–304
  changeover, 302
  clapper (check) valves, 304, 305
  impellers, 301
  pumping in series (pressure) position, 302
  pumping in the parallel (volume) position, 301–302
  transfer valve, 303
Municipal water supply system, 182–188
  distribution system, 184–188
    average daily consumption (ADC), 188
    defined, 184
    distributors, 185
    grid system, 184–185
    maximum daily consumption (MDC), 188
    peak hourly consumption (PHC), 188
    primary feeders, 184
    secondary feeders, 185
    water main valves, 185–187
    water pipes, 187–188
    water system capacity, 188
  means of moving water, 183–184
    combination system, 183–184
    direct pumping system, 183
    gravity system, 183
  sources of water supply, 182–183
  water processing or treatment facilities, 184
MUTCD (Manual on Uniform Traffic Control Devices), 151, A-55

N

National Fallen Firefighters Foundation (NFFF), A-16
National Fire Academy, A-13
National Fire Protection Association® (NFPA®). *See also specific NFPA standard*
  Critical Incident Stress Debriefing (CISD), A-30
  fire hydrant standards, A-60
National Incident Management System (NIMS)
  apparatus typing, 17
  water shuttle operations, 454–455
National Incident Management System-Incident Command System (NIMS-ICS), 454
  courses, A-15
  functions, A-13
  purpose of, A-13
National Institute for Occupational Safety and Health (NIOSH), 85
  firefighter heart attack at the scene, A-4
  line-of-duty-death (LODD) recommendations, A-4
  study of firefighter risks, A-25
National Wildfire Coordinating Group, apparatus typing, 17
Natural static water supply sources, 410–414

University of Illinois Fire Service Institute (IFSI) study of fire fighting risks, A-25
USFA (United States Fire Administration), 79
Utility companies, A-13

V

Vacuum of water pressure, 175
Vacuum primers, 323
Vacuum test, 523–524, 532
Valves
    ball-type, 316, 317
    bleeder, 318
    butterfly, 317
    bypass, 316
    clapper (check) valves, 304, 305
    fire pump, 316–317
    float, 323
    four-way hydrant valves, A-65, A-66
    gate valves, 317, A-60
    indicating, 186
    intake pressure relief valves, 435–436
    internal intake pressure relief valve test, 526
    nonindicating valves, 186–187
    outside screw and yoke, 186
    pilot, 320
    post indicator valve, 186
    pressure-reducing, 365
    push-pull valve handles, 316
    radiator fill, 329
    relief, 319–321
    transfer valve, 303
    water main, 185–187
Variable-flow demand-type balanced pressure proportioner, 500–501
Variable-flow variable-rate direct injection, 500
Velcro® fasteners, A-45
Velocity pressure, 176
Venturi Effect, 324
Vernier, 327
Vests, A-44
Visual acuity for driver/operators, 82
Visual lead time for stopping, 105
Visual warning devices, 101–102
Voltmeter, 326
Volunteer fire departments
    description, A-10
    driver/operator selection, 80
    funding, A-10
    staffing, A-11
Volunteer fire departments, driver/operator selection, 80
Volunteer firefighters, A-11
Volute of centrifugal pumps, 299

W

Walk-around method of inspection, 36, 52–59
Warm zone (limited access or yellow zone), 154, A-52, A-53
Warning devices, 100–102

audible warning devices, 101
    use during emergencies, 100
    visual warning devices, 101–102
Washing apparatus, 33–34
Water
    advantages as extinguishing agent, 169
    characteristics, 167–168
    density, 167
    disadvantages as extinguishing agent, 169–170
    fire extinguishing ability, 168
    force
        defined, 170
        determination of, 171
    freezing water and water shuttle operations, 454
    friction loss
        applying principles, 179–181
        coefficient of friction, 177
        critical velocity, 181
        defined, 177
        for given velocity, loss is the same, regardless of water pressure, 179
        principles of, 178–179
        reducing, 181
        varies directly with length of hose or pipe, 178
        varies inversely as the fifth power of the hose diameter, 179
        varies with the square of the increase in flow velocity, 178
        water hammer, 181–182
    loss and gain, elevation and altitude, 176
    municipal distribution system, 184–188
        average daily consumption (ADC), 188
        defined, 184
        distributors, 185
        grid system, 184–185
        maximum daily consumption (MDC), 188
        means of moving water, 183–184
        peak hourly consumption (PHC), 188
        primary feeders, 184
        secondary feeders, 185
        water main valves, 185–187
        water pipes, 187–188
        water system capacity, 188
    municipal supply system, 182–188
        combination system, 183–184
        direct pumping system, 183
        gravity system, 183
        means of moving water, 183–184
        sources of water supply, 182–183
        water processing or treatment facilities, 184
    nonpotable, 356
    pressure
        defined, 170
        example, 170, 171
    pressure, types of, 174–176
        atmospheric pressure, 174–175
        flow pressure (velocity pressure), 176

Indexed by Nancy Kopper.

Notes